the THOUSAND & ONE Nights,

VOL. II.

كتاب الف ليلة وليلة

THE THOUSAND AND ONE NIGHTS,

COMMONLY CALLED, IN ENGLAND

The Arabian Nights' Entertainments.

A NEW TRANSLATION FROM THE ARABIC WITH COPIOUS NOTES.

BY

EDWARD WILLIAM LANE,

HON. M.R.S.L., ETC.

AUTHOR OF "THE MODERN EGYPTIANS."

ILLUSTRATED BY MANY HUNDRED ENGRAVINGS ON WOOD,

From Original Designs by William Harvey.

A NEW EDITION,

FROM A COPY ANNOTATED BY THE TRANSLATOR;

EDITED BY HIS NEPHEW,

EDWARD STANLEY POOLE.

IN THREE VOLUMES.—VOL. II.

EAST-WEST PUBLICATIONS, LONDON

AND

LIVRES DE FRANCE, CAIRO

First published in 1838
This edition published in 1859

ISBN 0 85692 043 6

Design and Production Services by Elron Press Ltd., London WC2

Printed and bound in Great Britain at
The Camelot Press Ltd, Southampton

فهرسة

CONTENTS OF THE SECOND VOLUME.

CHAPTER XIX.

LIST OF ILLUSTRATIONS IN VOLUME II.

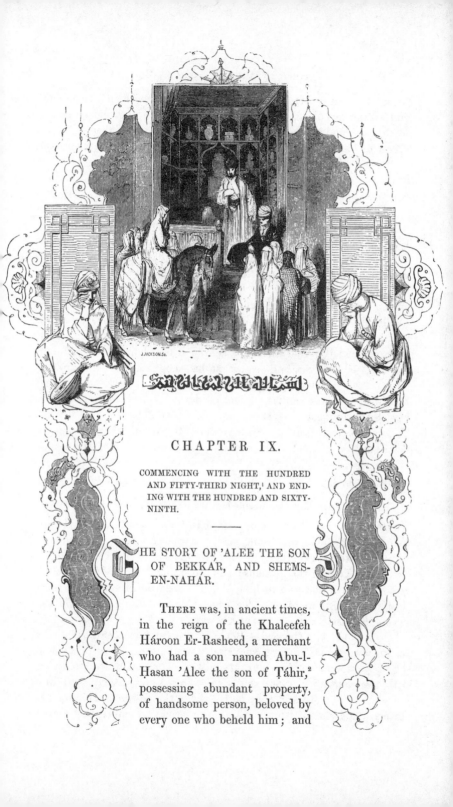

CHAPTER IX.

COMMENCING WITH THE HUNDRED AND FIFTY-THIRD NIGHT,[1] AND ENDING WITH THE HUNDRED AND SIXTY-NINTH.

THE STORY OF 'ALEE THE SON OF BEKKÁR, AND SHEMS-EN-NAHÁR.

There was, in ancient times, in the reign of the Khaleefeh Hároon Er-Rasheed, a merchant who had a son named Abu-l-Ḥasan 'Alee the son of Ṭáhir,[2] possessing abundant property, of handsome person, beloved by every one who beheld him; and he used to enter the palace of the Khaleefeh without permission; and all the concubines of the Khaleefeh, and his other female slaves, loved him; and he used to keep company with the King, and recite verses to him, and relate to him strange anecdotes. But still he sold and bought in the market of the merchants; and there used to sit at his shop a young man of the sons of the Kings of the Persians,[3] called 'Alee the son of Bekkár.[4]

This young man was of handsome stature, of elegant shape, of perfect figure, with rosy cheeks, with joined eyebrows, sweet in speech, with laughing mouth, a lover of merriment and gaiety. And it happened that they were both sitting talking together and laughing, when, lo, there came ten female slaves, like moons, and each of them was endowed with beauty and loveliness, and justness of stature; and among them was a damsel riding upon a mule with an embroidered saddle, the stirrups of which were of gold, and she was covered with an izár of delicate fabric, and round her waist was a girdle of gold-embroidered silk: and when they arrived at the shop of Abu-l-Ḥasan, she alighted, and, seating herself at his shop, saluted him, and he returned her salutation. And when 'Alee the son of Bekkár beheld her, his reason was captivated, and he desired to rise; but she said to him, Sit in thy place. Wherefore wouldst thou depart on our arrival? This is not just conduct.—So he replied, By Allah, O my mistress, I flee from that which I have beheld. And how excellent is the saying of the poet!—

She is the sun: her place is in heaven: comfort then the heart with a becoming patience:
For thou art not able to ascend unto her; nor is she able to descend unto thee.

And when she heard this reply, she smiled, and said to Abu-l-Ḥasan, What is the name of this young man, and whence is he? He answered her, He is a stranger: his name is 'Alee the son of Bekkár, and he is son of the King of the Persians; and the stranger should be honoured. And thereupon she said to him, When my slave-girl cometh to thee, do thou bring him to me. To which Abu-l-Ḥasan replied, On the head. She then rose, and went her way.

Now as to 'Alee the son of Bekkár, he became in such a state that he knew not what to say; and after a while, the slave-girl came to Abu-l-Ḥasan, and said to him, My mistress summoneth thee, together with thy companion. So Abu-l-Ḥasan rose, and taking with him 'Alee the son of Bekkár, they both went to the palace of Hároon Er-Rasheed, and she introduced them into a private chamber, and seated them; and the tables were placed before them, and they ate, and washed their hands. She then brought to them the wine, and they made themselves merry with it; after which, she desired them to rise. They therefore rose and went with her, and she conducted them into another private chamber, raised upon four columns, decked with a variety of furniture, and decorated in the most beautiful manner, as though it were one of the palaces of Paradise, so that they were astonished at the rarities which they beheld. And while they were amusing themselves with the sight of these extraordinary objects, lo, ten female slaves approached with a graceful and conceited gait, resembling moons, dazzling the sight, and confounding the imagination. They stood in ranks, looking like the black-eyed damsels of Paradise; and after them came ten other female slaves, with lutes in their hands, and other instruments of diversion and mirth; and they saluted the two guests, and played upon the lutes, and sang verses; and every one of them was a temptation to the servants of God. After these, came ten more female slaves, like them, high-bosomed and of equal age, with black eyes, and red cheeks, with joined eyebrows, and languishing looks, a temptation to God's servants, and a delight to beholders; and they were clad in various kinds of coloured silks, such as astonished the mind. They stationed themselves at the door; and after them came ten female slaves more beautiful than they, attired in magnificent apparel; and these, also, stationed themselves at the door.

At last there came forth from the door twenty female slaves, and among them was one named Shems-en-Nahár,[5] like the moon among the stars. She was encircled by the exuberant locks of her hair, disposed like necklaces upon her; and wore blue trousers, and an izár of silk embroidered with gold, and round her waist was a girdle adorned with a variety of jewels. She continued advancing with a dignified gait until she seated herself upon the couch; and when 'Alee the son of Bekkár beheld her, he recited these verses:—

Verily this is she who is the source of my malady, and of the protraction of my transport, and prolonging of my passion!
In her presence I find that my soul hath melted, through my eagerness for her and the wasting of my bones.

He then said to Abu-l-Ḥasan, Hadst thou acted well towards me, thou hadst informed me of these things before I came in hither, in order that I might have applied my mind to consider the case, and fortified it by patience to endure the affliction that hath befallen it. And he

wept and groaned and lamented. So Abu-l-Ḥasan said to him, O my brother, I desired nothing for thee but good; but I feared to acquaint thee with this, lest such transport should affect thee as would prevent thy meeting her, and would interpose an obstacle between thee and thy union with her. Be cheerful, then, and happy; for she offereth thee good fortune, and receiveth thee with favour.—And ’Alee the son of Bekkár said, What is the name of this damsel? Abu-l-Ḥasan answered, She is named Shems-en-Nahár, and is one of the concubines of the Prince of the Faithful, Hároon Er-Rasheed, and this place is the palace of the Khaleefeh.

Then Shems-en-Nahár sat contemplating the charms of ’Alee the son of Bekkár, and he gazed at her beauty, and they were engrossed with mutual love; and she ordered the female slaves to seat themselves, each of them in her proper place, upon a couch: so each sat before a window; and she commanded them to sing; whereupon one of them took her lute, and sang thus:—

Repeat the message a second time, and receive the answer aloud.
Unto thee, O prince of the comely, I stand to complain of my case!
O my master! O dear as my heart, and precious to me as my life!
Bestow upon me a kiss, as a gift, or else as a loan.
I will pay it thee back (may thy life be prolonged!) exactly as I took it;
And if thou desire an addition, receive it, and be content.
O thou who clothest me with the garment of sickness, may the garment of health delight thee!

And 'Alee the son of Bekkár was charmed, and said to her, Sing to me some more verses of the same kind. She therefore touched the strings, and sang these lines:—

By excessive distance, O my beloved, thou hast caused mine eyelids long to weep.
O delight of mine eye, and its desire, and goal of my utmost wishes and my worship!
Have pity upon him[6] whose eye is drowned in the tears of the distracted and sorrowful lover!

Shems-en-Nahár then ordered another slave-girl to sing; and after her, another: and 'Alee the son of Bekkár next desired one who was near him to do the same; and when she had finished her song, he sighed, and shed abundant tears; and Shems-en-Nahár, seeing him weeping and groaning and lamenting, burned with transport and passion, and was consumed by excessive love and distraction. So she rose from the couch, and advanced to the door of the chamber; and 'Alee the son of Bekkár rose also, and met her; and they embraced each other, and fell down fainting at the door. The female slaves, therefore, came to them, and, lifting them up, brought them back into the chamber, and sprinkled upon them some rose-water; and when they recovered, they found not Abu-l-Ḥasan; for he had hidden himself by the side of a couch: and the damsel said, Where is Abu-l-Ḥasan? So he came forth to her from the side of the couch; and she saluted him, and said, I beg of God that He will enable me to recompense thee, O thou of kind conduct! Then addressing 'Alee the son of Bekkár, she said, O my master, thy love hath not become extreme without my experiencing the like; and we have no resource but to bear with patience that which hath befallen us.—By Allah, O my mistress, replied 'Alee the son of Bekkár, my union with thee will not content me, nor will the flame that I feel for thee be extinguished, nor the love for thee that hath taken possession of my heart quit me, until my soul departeth! Having said this, he wept, and his tears descended upon his cheek like rain; and when Shems-en-Nahár beheld him thus weeping, she wept with him; whereupon Abu-l-Ḥasan said, By Allah, I am in wonder at your case, and am perplexed by your condition; for your state is wonderful, and your case is extraordinary! If ye weep thus when ye are together, how will it be after ye are separated! This is not a time for lamentation and weeping, but a time for joy and gladness.

So Shems-en-Nahár made a sign to a female slave, who arose and returned with some maids carrying a table, the dishes of which were of silver, containing a variety of viands. The slave-girl then placed the table before them; and Shems-en-Nahár began to eat, and to feed 'Alee the son of Bekkár, until they were satisfied, when the table was removed, and they washed their hands, and the perfuming-vessels were brought with various kinds of aloes-wood, and the sprinkling-bottles with rose-water, and they were perfumed and scented; after which, vessels of graven gold were presented to them, containing varieties of drinks, and fresh and dried fruits, such as the appetite desired, and such as delighted the eyes; and next, a slave-girl brought them a basin of carnelion full of wine. Shems-en-Nahár then chose ten maids, whom she stationed by them, and ten female slaves from among the singing-girls, and, having dismissed all the rest of the slave-girls to their apartments, ordered some of those who remained present to play upon the lute; and they did as she commanded them. One of them sang; and when she had finished her song, Shems-en-Nahár filled a cup, and drank it, and then filled it again and gave it to 'Alee the son of Bekkár, and ordered another slave-girl to sing; after which, 'Alee the son of Bekkár drank his cup, and returned it to Shems-en-Nahár, who filled it, and handed it to Abu-l-Ḥasan. She then took a lute, and said, No one shall sing over my cup but myself:—and, having tightened the strings, she sang these verses:—

The tears fall confusedly upon his cheeks, through transport; the fire of love flaming in his breast.
He weepeth when united, fearing their separation; his tears flowing when they are near, and when distant.

She then sang the following words of the poet:—

Our life be thy ransom, O cup-bearer, whom beauty hath clad from the bright parting of thy hair unto thy feet! [7]
The sun beameth from thy hands, and from thy mouth shine the Pleiades, and the full moon riseth from the upper border of thy vest.[8]
Verily thy cups which have rendered us intoxicated are those which are distributed around by thine eyes.

Is it not wonderful that thou art a full moon, when waning is experienced not by thee, but by thy lovers?
Art thou a deity, that thou killest and reanimatest, by receiving whom thou wilt, and withdrawing from others?
From the model of thy form hath God originated beauty, and the fragrance of the zephyr from thy disposition.
Thou art not of this order of created beings; but thou art an angel sent by thy Maker.

When 'Alee the son of Bekkár, and Abu-l-Ḥasan, and the rest of those who were present, heard these verses sung by Shems-en-Nahár, they almost flew with delight, and they sported and laughed; but while they were thus enjoying themselves, lo, a female slave came, trembling with fear, and said, O my mistress, the Prince of the Faithful hath come, and he is at the door, with 'Afeef[9] and Mesroor and others. And when they heard her words, they nearly died with fright; but Shems-en-Nahár laughed, and said, Fear not. And she said to the female slave, Return them an answer while we remove from this place. She then gave orders to shut the doors of the apartment, and to let down the curtains over them, while they remained in it, and she closed the door of the adjoining saloon, and then went forth into the garden, and, seating herself upon her couch, ordered a slave-girl to rub her feet,[10] commanding the rest of the female slaves to go to their apartments, and desiring the girl who remained with her to leave the gate open, that the Khaleefeh might enter. And Mesroor came in, and those who were with him, twenty in number, with swords in their hands; and they saluted Shems-en-Nahár, and she said to them, Wherefore have ye come? They answered, The Prince of the Faithful saluteth thee: he hath become cheerless through desire of seeing thee, and informeth thee that he hath experienced this day unusual joy and happiness, and wisheth now to complete it by thy presence. Wilt thou, then, come to him, or shall he come to thee?—And she rose, and, kissing the ground, replied, I hear and obey the commands of the Prince of the Faithful. She then gave orders to bring her chief female attendants and the other slaves, and they came in, and she intimated to them that she was going to comply with the commands of the Khaleefeh. The place was completely prepared; but she said to the eunuchs, Go to the Prince of the Faithful, and inform him that I shall soon be waiting for him, when I shall have prepared the place for him with the carpets and other things. So the eunuchs repaired quickly to the Prince of the Faithful, and Shems-en-Nahár arose and went to her beloved 'Alee the son of Bekkár, and pressed him to her bosom, and took leave of him. And he wept violently, and said, O my mistress, prolong to me this leave-taking: perhaps it may help to hasten the termination of my life through my love of thee: but I beg of God that He will bestow upon me patience to endure the passion with which He hath afflicted me.—By Allah, replied Shems-en-Nahár, none will fall into a state of dissolution but myself; for thou wilt go forth into the market-street, and wilt enjoy the company of such as will amuse thee, and thou wilt be preserved from danger, and thy passion will be kept concealed. But as to me, I shall fall into trouble, especially since I have made an appointment with the Khaleefeh; for probably great danger will await me in consequence, on account of my desire and love and passion for thee, and my grief at having parted from thee. With what tongue shall I sing, and with what heart shall I present myself before the Khaleefeh, and with what language shall I converse with the Prince of the Faithful, and with what look shall I behold a place where thou art not, and how shall I be in an assembly in which thou art not included, and with what taste shall I drink wine of which thou art not present to partake? —Abu-l-Ḥasan said to her, Be not perplexed; but be patient; and be not remiss in conversing with the Prince of the Faithful this night, nor shew him any neglect.

And while they were thus talking, a slave-girl came, and said, O my mistress, the pages of the Prince of the Faithful are come. Where-

upon she arose, and said to the slave-girl, Take Abu-l-Ḥasan and his companion, and conduct them to the upper projecting window that overlooketh the garden, and leave them there till it is dark: then contrive means of leading them forth. So the slave-girl took them, and ascended with them to the projecting window, and, having closed the door upon them, went her way; and they remained looking into the garden. And lo, the Khaleefeh arrived, preceded by about a hundred eunuchs with swords in their hands, and around him were twenty female slaves, like moons, clad in the richest apparel, and each having upon her head a crown set with rubies and other jewels, and in her hand a lighted candle. The Khaleefeh walked in the midst of them, while they surrounded him on every side, and Mesroor and 'Afeef and Waṣeef[11] preceded him; and he advanced among them with a graceful carriage.[12] Shems-en-Nahár and all the female slaves who were with her rose to him, and met him at the gate of the garden, and, having kissed the ground before him, preceded him until he seated himself upon the couch, when all the female slaves and the eunuchs who were in the garden stationed themselves around him, and the candles were lighted, and the instruments of music were played upon until he commanded his attendants to disperse, and to seat themselves upon the couches; whereupon Shems-en-Nahár took her seat upon a couch by the side of that of the Khaleefeh, and began to converse with him.—All this time, Abu-l-Ḥasan and 'Alee the son of Bekkár were looking on and hearing; the Khaleefeh not seeing them.—The

Khaleefeh then began to toy with Shems-en-Nahár, and gave orders to open the apartment where she had been sitting; and they opened its door and its windows, and lighted the candles, so that the place, in the hour of darkness, shone like the day; after which, the eunuchs removed thither the drinking-vessels.—At the sight of these things, Abu-l-Ḥasan exclaimed, Verily I have never beheld the like of these vessels and beverages and rarities, nor have I ever heard of anything to be compared with these varieties of jewels! It seemeth to me as though I were dreaming! My reason is confounded, and my heart palpitateth!—But as to 'Alee the son of Bekkár, after Shems-en-Nahár had quitted him, he remained a while stretched upon the floor, through the violence of his passion; and when he recovered, he began to gaze at this unparalleled scene, and said to Abu-l-Ḥasan, O my brother, I fear that the Khaleefeh will see us, or become acquainted with our case; and my fear is chiefly on thine account; for as to myself, I know that I am of the number of those who are about to perish; and the cause of my death is nothing else than my love and desire, and the excess of my transport and distraction; and I beg deliverance of God from the affliction that I suffer.

'Alee the son of Bekkár, and Abu-l-Ḥasan, continued gazing from the projecting window at the Khaleefeh and the scene around him until the feast was entirely prepared before him, when the Khaleefeh looked towards one of the female slaves, and said, Let us hear, O Gharám,[13] some of thy delightful singing:—whereupon, with charming modulations, she sang these verses:—

The transport of a Bedaweeyeh[14] whose family are parted from her, and who yearneth towards the willow of the Ḥejáz, and its laurel,[15]
Whose ardour and tears at beholding a company of travellers are as the fire and the water for their entertainment,
Is not greater than the transport that I feel for my beloved, who regardeth me as guilty of an offence in loving him.

And when Shems-en-Nahár heard this song, she fell down in a swoon from the couch upon which she was sitting, and became unconscious. The female slaves, therefore, arose and lifted her up. And as soon as 'Alee the son of Bekkár beheld her from the window, he also fell down in a fit; and Abu-l-Ḥasan exclaimed, Verily, fate hath divided desire between you with equality! But while they were conversing, lo, the slave-girl who had brought them up to the window came to them, and said, O Abu-l-Ḥasan, arise, thou and thy companion, and descend; for the world hath become narrow unto us, and I fear that our affair will be exposed: arise, therefore, immediately, or we die. Abu-l-Ḥasan replied, How shall this young man arise with me? He hath not strength to raise himself.—So the slave-girl sprinkled rose-water upon his face until he recovered, and Abu-l-Ḥasan and the slave-girl lifted him up, and carried him down from the window, and proceeded a little way, when the slave-girl opened a small door of iron, and placed Abu-l-Ḥasan and 'Alee the son of Bekkár upon a maṣṭabah outside. She then clapped her hands,[16] and there came a boat with a rower in it, and she led them on board of it, and said to the boatman, Land them on the opposite bank. And when they had embarked, and quitted the garden, 'Alee the son of Bekkár looked back towards the apartment and the garden, and bade them farewell in the words of these verses:—

I stretch forth a feeble hand to take leave, with the other upon my burning bosom, beneath my heart.
O let not this be the end of our union; nor let this be the last refreshment that I enjoy!

The slave-girl then said to the boatman, Make haste with them. So he plied his oars to make all haste, and, accompanied by the slave-girl, they crossed over to the opposite bank, when she departed, taking leave of them, as they landed, and saying to them, It had been my desire not to part from you; but I cannot proceed further than this spot. And she returned.

'Alee the son of Bekkár lay prostrate before Abu-l-Ḥasan, unable to rise; so Abu-l-Ḥasan said to him, This is not a place of safety, and we are here in fear for our lives, on account of the robbers and the sons of wickedness. And upon this, 'Alee the son of Bekkár rose, and advanced a little way; but he was unable to walk on. Now Abu-l-Ḥasan had friends in that quarter; and he repaired to one of them in whom he confided, and knocked at his door; upon which the man came forth to him quickly; and when he beheld him and his companion, he welcomed them, and conducted them into his house, and, having seated them, conversed with them, and asked them where they had been. Abu-l-Ḥasan answered, We came forth this evening, obliged to do so by a man with whom I had some pecuniary transactions, it having been told me that he was about to set forth on a journey with my property. So I went out this night and repaired to him, taking, to cheer me, this my companion, 'Alee the son of Bekkár, and we came hoping to see him; but he hid himself from us, and we saw him not. We therefore returned with nothing, and, finding it difficult to get back this night, and seeing no other lodging for us but thine abode, we came unto thee, depending on thy usual kindness.— The man of the house then welcomed them again, and studied to shew them honour; so they remained with him during the rest of the night; and when the morning came, they went forth from him, and proceeded until they arrived at the city, and entered it; and as they passed by the house of Abu-l-Ḥasan, he conjured his companion 'Alee the son of Bekkár to enter, and took him in. They then laid themselves down on beds for a little while, after which they awoke; and Abu-l-Ḥasan ordered his servants to furnish the house handsomely; and they did so; Abu-l-Ḥasan saying within himself, I must cheer this young man, and divert him from his present thoughts; for I know his case.

And when 'Alee the son of Bekkár recovered, he called for water, and they brought it him, and he arose and performed the ablution, and recited the divinely-ordained prayers which he had omitted during the preceding day and night, and began to console himself by conversation. When Abu-l-Ḥasan, therefore, saw him do thus, he approached him and said, O my master 'Alee, it will be most suitable to thy present case that thou remain with me this next night, in order that thy heart may become dilated, and the anguish of desire that thou sufferest be dispelled, and that thou mayest beguile the time with us. He replied, Do what seemeth fit unto thee; for at all events I cannot escape from that which hath befallen me; so do as thou wilt. And Abu-l-Ḥasan arose and summoned his servants and brought his friends, and sent to the singers and instrumental performers, who came; and they remained eating and drinking and making merry during the rest of the day, until the evening, when they lighted the candles, and the wine-cups circulated among them, and the time passed with them pleasantly. Then a female singer took a lute, and thus sang:—

I have been shot at by fortune with the arrow of an eye, which hath struck me down, and I have parted from the beloved.
Fortune hath been hostile to me, and my patience hath failed; but I expected before that this would come to pass.

And when 'Alee the son of Bekkár heard these words, he fell down in a fit, and he remained in it until daybreak; and Abu-l-Ḥasan despaired of him; but when daylight came, he recovered, and desired to return to his house. Abu-l-Ḥasan could not prevent him, fearing what might be the result of his case; and his servants brought him a mule, and mounted him upon it, and Abu-l-Ḥasan accompanied him until he took him into his house; and when he was safe there, Abu-l-Ḥasan praised God for his escape from this calamity, and began to console him; but he had no power over himself, through the violence of his passion. Abu-l-Ḥasan then bade him farewell; and 'Alee the son of Bekkár said to him, O my brother, cease not to impart to me whatever information thou mayest have to give. He replied, I hear and obey.

So Abu-l-Ḥasan arose and departed from him to his shop, and opened it, and sat expecting some tidings from the damsel; but no one brought him any news. He passed the next night in his house, and when the morning came, he arose and proceeded to the house of 'Alee the son of Bekkár, and, going in to him, found him laid upon his bed, with his friends around him, and the physicians with him, each of them prescribing for him something, and feeling his pulse. And when Abu-l-Ḥasan entered, and beheld him, he smiled; and Abu-l-Ḥasan saluted him, and inquired respecting his state; after which, he sat by him until all the rest of the people had gone forth,

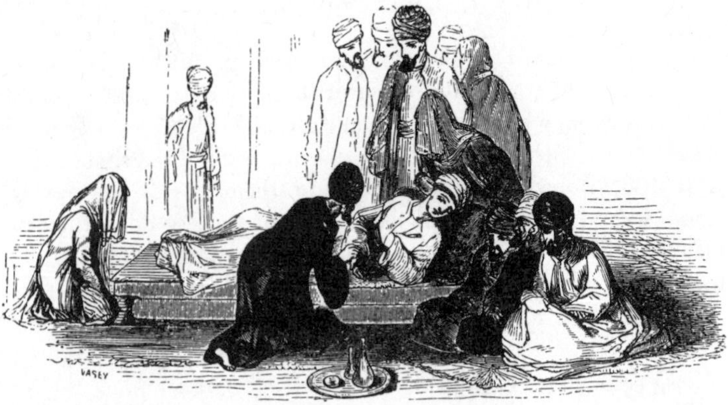

when he said to him, What is this state in which I find thee? 'Alee the son of Bekkár answered, It hath been spread about that I am sick, and my friends have heard this report, and I have no strength to rise and walk that I might give the lie unto him who asserteth me to be ill; so I remain prostrated here as thou seest me, and my friends have come to visit me; but, O my brother, hast thou seen the slave-girl, or heard any news from her? Abu-l-Ḥasan replied, She hath not come to me since she parted from us on the bank of the Tigris:—and he added, O my brother, beware of disgrace, and abstain from this weeping. But 'Alee the son of Bekkár said, O my brother, I have no control over myself:—and he sighed, and recited some verses, and added, I am afflicted by a calamity from which I was lately exempt, and can hope for no greater ease than death. Abu-l-Ḥasan said, Perhaps God will restore thee.

And he went down from him, and repaired to his shop, and opened it; and he had not long sat there when the slave-girl came, and saluted him; and he returned her salutation, and, looking at her, observed that her heart was throbbing, and that she bore an aspect of sadness. He said to her, Thou art welcome! How is Shems-en-Nahár?—She answered, I will presently acquaint thee with her case: —and asked, How is 'Alee the son of Bekkár? Abu-l-Ḥasan, therefore, informed her of everything that he had experienced; and she lamented and sighed, and wondered at his case. She then said, The state of my mistress is more wonderful than that; for when ye went away, I returned with my heart throbbing on your account, scarcely believing in your escape; and on my return, I found my mistress lying prostrate in the chamber, speaking not nor answering any one. The Prince of the Faithful was sitting at her head, finding no one to acquaint him with her case, and not knowing what she suffered; and she continued in her fit until midnight, when she recovered, and the Prince of the Faithful said to her, What hath befallen thee, O Shems-en-Nahár, and what hath happened to thee this night? And when she heard the words of the Khaleefeh, she kissed his feet, and answered him, O Prince of the Faithful, may God make me to be thy ransom! A derangement of the stomach hath given me a head-ache, and excited a heat in my body, so I fell down in a fit from the violence of my suffering, and I know not what happened to me afterwards. The Khaleefeh, therefore, asked her, What hast thou taken this day? And she answered, I breakfasted upon a dish that I had never eaten before. She then feigned that she had recovered strength, and called for some wine, and, having drunk it, begged the Prince of the Faithful to return to his diversion. So he resumed his seat in the chamber; and when I came to her, she asked me respecting thee and thy companion, and I informed her what I had done with you, and acquainted her with the verses which 'Alee the son of Bekkár had recited: whereupon she was silent. The Khaleefeh then sat, and ordered the same female slave to sing; and she sang these two verses:—

There hath been to me no pleasure in my life since your departure; and would that I knew your state since you left me!
It were fit that my tears should be of blood, when ye are weeping on account of my absence.

And when Shems-en-Nahár heard these words, she fell down again in a swoon: and I laid hold of her hand, and sprinkled some rose-water upon her face, and she recovered; upon which I said to her, O my mistress, expose not thyself and those whom thy palace containeth! By the existence of thy beloved I conjure thee to have patience!—But she replied, Can anything worse than death befall me? I desire it; for it will bring me ease.—And while we were thus conversing, a slave-girl sang these words of the poet:—

They said, Perhaps patience may be followed by ease. But I replied, How is patience to be found since his departure?
For he made a settled compact with me, to cut the cords of patience, at the time of his embracing me.

And as soon as she had finished, Shems-en-Nahár again fell down in a fit. The Khaleefeh saw her, and, coming to her quickly, gave orders to remove the wine, and commanded each of the female slaves to return to her apartment. He then sat with her during the remainder of the night, until the morning, when he summoned the physicians, and desired them to employ means for her restoration, not knowing that she was suffering from love and desire. I remained with her till I thought her recovered, and this it was which prevented my coming unto you before. I left with her a number of her special attendants, when she ordered me to repair to you that I might obtain news of 'Alee the son of Bekkár, and return to her.—And when Abu-l-Ḥasan heard her words, he wondered, and said to her, By Allah, I have acquainted thee with his whole case. Return, therefore, to thy mistress, and salute her, and exhort her to have patience, and say to her, Conceal thy secret:—and tell her that I am acquainted with her case, and know it to be one of difficulty, requiring prudent management.—And the slave-girl thanked him, and bade him farewell, and returned to her mistress.

Abu-l-Ḥasan then remained in his shop until the close of the day; and when the day had passed, he arose, and locked up his shop, and went to the house of 'Alee the son of Bekkár, and knocked at the door; upon which there came forth to him one of his servants, who conducted him within.—And when he went in to his friend, the latter smiled, and drew a good omen from his coming, and said to him, O Abu-l-Ḥasan, thou hast made me desolate by thy remaining away from me this day, and my soul is attached to thee for the rest of my life.—Abstain from these words, replied Abu-l-Ḥasan; for, if it were possible to ransom thee, I would give my life as thy ransom. This day the slave-girl of Shems-en-Nahár came, and informed me that she had been prevented from coming before only by the Khaleefeh's sitting with her mistress, and acquainted me with what had happened to her mistress.—And he related to him all that he had heard from the slave-girl; whereupon 'Alee the son of Bekkár lamented violently, and wept, and then, looking towards Abu-l-Ḥasan, said to him, By Allah, I conjure thee to assist me in my affliction, and tell me what plan is to be pursued; and I beg of thy goodness that thou wilt pass the night here with me, in order that I may be cheered by thy conversation. So Abu-l-Ḥasan complied with his desire, replying that he would stay with him that night; and they passed the night conversing together, till 'Alee the son of Bekkár, after weeping, and shedding copious tears, recited some verses, and uttered a great cry, and fell down in a swoon. Abu-l-Ḥasan thought that his soul had quitted his body: and he remained in his fit until daylight came, when he recovered, and conversed again with Abu-l-Ḥasan; and Abu-l-Ḥasan continued sitting with him till near the mid-time between sunrise and noon.

He then departed from him, and repaired to his shop, and opened it; and lo, the slave-girl came and stood before him; and when he looked towards her, she made a sign of salutation to him, and he returned her greeting, and she delivered to him the salutation of her mistress, and said to him, How is 'Alee the son of Bekkár?—O slave-girl, he replied, ask not respecting his state, and the violence of desire that he suffereth; for he sleepeth not by night, nor findeth rest by day; watching hath emaciated him, and anguish hath overcome him, and he is in a condition by no means pleasing to a friend. She then said to him, My mistress saluteth thee and him, and hath written to him a letter, and she is in a state more afflicting than his; she hath intrusted to me the letter, and said, Return not to me without an answer to it, and do as I have commanded thee.—Here is the letter with me. Wilt thou, then, go with me to 'Alee the son of Bekkár, that we may receive the answer from him?—Abu-l-Ḥasan answered her, I hear and obey. And he locked up his shop, and, taking with him the slave-girl, repaired with her by a way different from that by which he had come, and they proceeded until they arrived at the house of 'Alee the son of Bekkár, when he stationed her at the door, and entered the house. And as soon as 'Alee the son of Bekkár beheld him he rejoiced at his coming, and Abu-l-Ḥasan said to him, The cause of my coming is, that such a man hath sent to thee his slave-girl with a note conveying his salutation to thee, and hath mentioned in it that the reason of his failing to visit thee is an event that hath happened to him which excuseth him. The slave-girl is standing at the door. Wilt thou give her permission to enter?—'Alee replied, Bring her in. And Abu-l-Ḥasan made a sign to him that she was the slave-girl of Shems-en-Nahár; and he understood the sign; and when he beheld her, he was moved, and rejoiced, and said to her, with a sign, How is the master? May God grant him restoration and health!—She answered, Well:—and she produced the letter, and gave it to him; and he took it and kissed it and read it, and then handed it to Abu-l-Ḥasan, who found written in it as follows:—

This messenger will acquaint thee with my news: so be content with his tidings instead of beholding me.
Thou hast left a lover in severe affliction on thine account, and his eye is incessantly sleepless.
I suffer the pangs of patience in my trouble; for no creature can ward off the blows of destiny.

To proceed:—I have written to thee a letter without fingers,[17] and spoken to thee without a tongue, and the complete exposition of my state is this,—that I have an eye which sleeplessness never quitteth, and a heart from which solicitudes are never absent; and I am as though I had never known health or happiness, nor beheld a comely countenance, nor passed a pleasant life: I am as if my nature were made up of passion, and of the torment of excessive love and melancholy; and sickness hath become uninterrupted to me; and desire, augmented; and longing expectation, increased.[18] I beg of God to hasten our union, that the trouble of my mind may be dispelled; and I desire that thou send me some words from thee, that I may cheer myself by them; and do thou assume a becoming patience until God give relief. And peace be on thee.

When 'Alee the son of Bekkár had read this letter from beginning to end, he said, With what hand shall I write, and with what tongue shall I complain and lament? He then drew himself up with difficulty, and sat, and took a paper in his hand, and thus wrote:—

In the name of God, the Compassionate, the Merciful.—Thy letter, O my mistress, hath arrived, and given ease to a soul wearied by transport and desire, and conveyed restoration to a wounded heart ulcerated by disease; and thine emaciated slave hath understood all the gracious words contained in it; and by thy head, O my mistress, I am in the state described by the poet:—

The heart is contracted; and solicitude, extended; and the eye, sleepless; and the body, wearied;
And patience, cut short; and disjunction, continued; and reason, deranged; and the heart, snatched away.

And know that complaint extinguisheth not the fire of affliction; but it appeaseth him whom longing desire hath disordered, and whom separation destroyeth; and I will comfort myself by the mention of the word "union:"—and how excellent is the saying of the poet:—

If there were not, in love, displeasure and content, where were the sweetnesses of notes and epistles?

On Abu-l-Ḥasan's reading this letter, it excited painful feelings in him, and its purport wounded his vitals; and he gave it to the slave-girl, and when she had taken it, 'Alee the son of Bekkár said to her, Convey to thy mistress my salutation, and acquaint her with my transport and desire, and how love pervadeth my flesh and my bones; and tell her that I want a person to deliver me from the sea of destruction, and to liberate me from this perplexity. He then wept, and the slave-girl wept with him, and took leave of him, and departed from him.

Abu-l-Ḥasan went forth with her, and bade her farewell, and repaired to his shop; and as he sat there, he found his heart compressed, and his bosom contracted, and he was perplexed at his case. He remained immersed in thought during the rest of the day, and the ensuing night; and on the following day he went to 'Alee the son of Bekkár, and sat with him until the other persons had departed, when he asked him respecting his state; and he began to complain of his desire, and his excessive love and distraction, and recited these words of the poet:—

Persons, before me, have complained of love's torment, and living and dead have been terrified by estrangement;
But an instance of feelings like those in my bosom I have never heard of nor beheld.

And Abu-l-Ḥasan said to him, I have never beheld nor heard of any lover like thee. Wherefore this transport and infirmity and agitation when thou art attached to a complying object of love? How would it be if thou wert attached to one who was adverse and deceitful, and if thy affair were exposed?—And 'Alee the son of Bekkár, says Abu-l-Ḥasan, inclined to my words, and thanked me for them.—Now I had (he continues) a friend who was acquainted with my case, and the case of 'Alee the son of Bekkár, and knew that we were leagued together; but no one else was informed of what passed between us; and he used to come to me and ask me respecting the state of 'Alee the son of Bekkár; and soon after, he questioned me with respect to the damsel. I answered him, She invited him to her, and more than hath already happened between them cannot take place; and this is the last of their case; but I have devised for myself a plan of proceeding which I desire to lay before thee.—His friend asked, What is it? And Abu-l-Ḥasan answered, I am a man known to have extensive dealings with men and women, and I fear that the affair of these two persons may be discovered, and that such an event will be the cause of my destruction, and of the seizure of my property, and the ruin of my family. It is my opinion that I should collect together my property, and fit myself out, and repair to the city of El-Baṣrah, and there remain until I see what will be the result of their case, that no one may know my situation; for love hath gained entire possession of them, and letters have passed between them. Their intermediary is a slave-girl, who at present keepeth their secrets; but I fear that anxiety may overcome her, and she may reveal their case to some one, and so the news of their affair may spread, and occasion my destruction; since I have no excuse to offer to my accusers.—His friend replied, Thou hast acquainted me with a perilous affair, such as the wise and knowing must regard with fear. May God avert from thee the evil that thou apprehendest, and save thee from the result which thou dreadest! This opinion is right.—So Abu-l-Ḥasan departed to his house, and occupied himself in settling his affairs, and preparing himself for the journey to the city of El-Baṣrah, and three days had not passed before he had finished his affairs and set forth to El-Baṣrah.

Three days after this, his friend came to visit him, and, finding him not, asked his neighbours respecting him, and they answered him, He departed three days ago to El-Baṣrah; for he had pecuniary dealings with the merchants of that city, and therefore went to demand the money of his debtors, and he will soon return. And the man was perplexed at his case, and knew not whither to go, saying, Would that I had not parted with Abu-l-Ḥasan! He then devised a stratagem by means of which to obtain access to 'Alee the son of Bekkár; and he repaired to his house, and said to one of his young men, Beg permission for me of thy master that I may enter and salute him. So the servant entered, and acquainted his master with the request, and then returned to him, and gave him permission to enter. He therefore went in to him, and found him reclining upon the cushion, and he saluted him, and 'Alee the son of Bekkár returned his salutation, and welcomed him; whereupon the man apologized to him for having failed to visit him before during the period of his illness, and said to him, O my master, an intimate friendship subsisteth between me and Abu-l-Ḥasan, and I used to intrust to him my secrets, and never relinquish him for an hour; and I was absent on some business with a number of my friends for the space of three days, and then, going to him, found his shop closed; wherefore I asked the neighbours respecting him, and they said, He hath gone to El-Baṣrah. —Now I know no friend of his more true than thou: by Allah, then, acquaint me with his case.—And when 'Alee the son of Bekkár heard his words, his colour changed, and he was agitated, and replied, I have not heard the news of his departure before this day; and if the case be as thou hast said, trouble hath befallen me. He then shed tears, and recited these two verses:—

I was weeping on account of joy that had passed, while my friends were yet unsevered from me;
But now my adverse fortune hath parted us, and I have to weep also for my friends.

And he hung down his head towards the ground, in thought; and after a while, he raised it, and, looking towards a servant belonging to him, said to him, Go to the house of Abu-l-Ḥasan, and ask respecting him, whether he be still there or on a journey; and if they answer, He hath gone on a journey,—ask whither he hath gone. So the servant went, and after a short absence came back to his master, and said, When I inquired respecting Abu-l-Ḥasan, his dependants informed me that he had gone on a journey to El-Baṣrah; but I found a slave-girl waiting at the door, and when she beheld me she knew me; but I knew her not; and she said to me, Art thou the servant of 'Alee the son of Bekkár? And I answered her, Yes. And she said, I have a letter for him, from the dearest of his friends. So she came with me, and she is standing at the door.—Upon this, 'Alee the son of Bekkár said, Bring her in. And the servant went forth to her, and brought her in; and the man who was sitting with the Son of Bekkár looked at the slave-girl, and saw that she was an elegant person. The slave-girl then advanced to the Son of Bekkár, and saluted him, and talked with him in a low voice; and he uttered oaths during the conversation, swearing that he had not mentioned a thing which she spoke of; after which, she bade him farewell, and departed.

Now the man, the friend of Abu-l-Ḥasan, was a jeweller; and when the slave-girl had departed, he found an opportunity to speak, and said to 'Alee the son of Bekkár, There is no doubt whatever but that the palace of the Khaleefeh hath some demand upon thee, or that thou hast dealings with it.[19]—And who, said 'Alee the son of Bekkár, acquainted thee with that? The jeweller answered, My knowledge of it is through this slave-girl; for she is the slave-girl of Shems-en-Nahár; and she came to me some time ago with a note in which was written that she desired a necklace of jewels; so I sent to her a costly necklace. And when 'Alee the son of Bekkár heard his words, he was so agitated that the jeweller feared his dissolution; but presently he recovered himself, and said, O my brother, I conjure thee by Allah to tell me how thou knowest her. The jeweller replied, Abstain from urging the inquiry. But 'Alee the son of Bekkár said to him, I will not desist from pressing thee until thou acquaint me with the truth. So the jeweller said, I will inform thee, provided that no suspicion respecting me enter thy mind, nor any restraint be imposed upon thee by my words, and I will not conceal from thee any secret, but will explain to thee the truth of the affair; on the condition, however, that thou acquaint me with thy true case, and the cause of thy sickness. He therefore told him his story, and then said, By Allah, O my brother, nothing induced me to conceal my affair from others than thyself except my fear that people might remove the veils of protection from others. And the jeweller said to him, I desired not an interview with thee but on account of my great affection for thee, and my zeal for thee, and my compassion for thy heart in consideration of the torment that it suffereth from separation. Perhaps I may be a comforter to thee in the place of my friend Abu-l-Ḥasan during the period of his absence. Be happy, then, and cheerful.—And 'Alee the son of Bekkár thanked him for his speech, and recited these two verses:—

> If I said that I was patient after his estrangement, my tears and the excess of my lamentation would belie me.
> And how can I conceal the tears that are flowing down my cheek in consequence of the separation of my friend?

He then, for a while, remained silent; after which he said to the jeweller, Knowest thou what the slave-girl told me secretly? He answered, No, by Allah, O my master. And 'Alee the son of Bekkár said, She supposed that I had advised Abu-l-Ḥasan to depart to the city of El-Baṣrah, and that I thus devised a stratagem that there might be no more correspondence and intercourse; and I swore to her that such had not been the case; but she believed me not, and departed to her mistress retaining her evil opinion; for she inclined to Abu-l-

Ḥasan. The jeweller replied, O my brother, I understood from the state of the slave-girl this affair; but, if it be the will of God (whose name be exalted!), I will aid thee to attain thy desire.—And how, said 'Alee the son of Bekkár, wilt thou manage with her when she taketh fright like a wild animal of the desert? The jeweller answered, I must employ all my endeavours to assist thee, and my contrivance to obtain acquaintance with her, without making any exposure, or occasioning any mischief. He then begged leave to depart; and 'Alee the son of Bekkár said to him, O my brother, be mindful to conceal the secret. And he looked at him, and wept.

The jeweller bade him farewell, and departed, not knowing what to do in order to promote the affair of 'Alee the son of Bekkár, and he continued on his way meditating upon his case, and beheld a paper lying in the street: so he took it up, and looked at its direction, and lo, it was, From the most humble friend to the most excellent object of affection.—And he opened the paper, and saw written in it as follows:—

The messenger came from thee to give me hopes of union; but I rather imagined that he had misconceived:
I rejoiced not, therefore; but my grief increased, through my knowledge that my messenger had not rightly understood.

To proceed:—Know, O my master, that I am unacquainted with the cause of the interruption of the correspondence between me and thee; but if cruelty have originated from thee, I will requite it with fidelity; and if affection have departed from thee, I will preserve affection during estrangement; for I will act towards thee as saith the poet:—

> Be haughty: I will endure:—and tyrannize: I will be patient:—and be difficult: I will be abject:—and depart: I will approach:—and say: I will hear:—and command: I will obey.

And when he had read it, lo, the slave-girl approached, looking to the right and left, and saw the paper in his hand; so she said to him, O my master, verily this paper dropped from me. But he returned her not an answer, walking on: and the slave-girl followed him until he approached his house; and he entered, and the slave-girl behind him. She then said to him, O my master, return to me this paper; for it dropped from me. And he looked at her, and said, O slave-girl, fear not, nor be grieved, but tell me the story with truth; for I am a concealer of secrets; and I conjure thee by an oath that thou hide from me nothing of the affair of thy mistress: perhaps God may assist me to accomplish her desires, and make easy by my means things that now are difficult. And when the slave-girl heard his words, she replied, O my master, a secret will not be lost when thou art its depositary, nor will an affair be unsuccessful when thou strivest to accomplish it. Know that my heart hath inclined to thee, and I will acquaint thee with the truth of the affair, and do thou give me the letter.—She then told him the whole story, and added, God is witness of the truth of what I say. He replied, Thou hast spoken truth; for I am acquainted with the foundation of the story. And he proceeded to relate to her the case of 'Alee the son of Bekkár, and how he had become acquainted with the state of his mind, telling her the story from first to last. And when she had heard this, she rejoiced; and they agreed together that she should take the paper and give it to 'Alee the son of Bekkár, and of all that should happen she should return and inform him. So he gave her the paper, and she took it and sealed it as it was before, saying, My mistress Shems-en-Nahár gave it to me sealed; and when he hath read it and given me an answer, I will bring it to thee.

The slave-girl then bade him farewell, and repaired to 'Alee the son of Bekkár, whom she found expecting her coming; and she gave him the paper and he read it, and then wrote for her an answer, and gave it to her. She therefore took it, and returned with it to the jeweller, according to the agreement; and he broke open its seal, and read it, and saw written in it,—

> Verily the messenger by whom our correspondence was kept concealed hath failed, having conceived displeasure:[20]
> Choose for me, therefore, a faithful messenger from among you, who approveth truth, and approveth not falsehood.

To proceed:—Verily cruelty hath not originated from me, nor have I abandoned fidelity, nor have I broken a covenant, nor have I cut short affection, nor have I ceased from grief, nor have I found after separation aught but destruction, nor have I had any knowledge of that which ye have mentioned, nor do I love anything but what ye love: by Him who knoweth every secret and hidden action, my wish is only for union with the person whom I love; and my business, the concealment of the desire that I suffer, though disease afflict me in consequence. This is the exposition of my state: and peace be on you.

When the jeweller read this paper, and knew its contents, he wept violently. The slave-girl then said to him, Go not forth from this place until I return to thee; for he hath made an accusation against me; but he is excused; and I desire to effect an interview between thee and my mistress Shems-en-Nahár, by whatever stratagem it may be accomplished. I left her prostrate, waiting for my bringing her the answer.—Then the slave-girl repaired to her mistress, and the jeweller passed the night troubled in heart; and when the morning came, he performed the prayers of that period, and sat expecting her arrival; and lo, she approached, and with joy came in to him, and he said to her, What is the news, O slave-girl? She answered, I went from thee to my mistress, and gave to her the paper which 'Alee the son of Bekkár wrote; and when she had read it and understood its meaning, her mind was perplexed; so I said to her, O my mistress, fear not the frustration of the affair between you in consequence of the absence of Abu-l-Ḥasan; for I have found one who will take his place, and who is better than he, and of higher rank, and one who will keep secrets.—And I related to her what had passed between thee and Abu-l-Ḥasan, and how thou obtainedst his confidence and that of 'Alee the son of Bekkár, and how that note dropped from me and thou foundest it, and I acquainted her with the determination made between me and thee.—And the jeweller wondered extremely.—She then said to him, She desireth to hear thy words, that she may be confirmed by them in her belief of the covenants made between thee and him: make up thy mind, then, immediately to repair with me to her. But when the

jeweller heard these words of the slave-girl, he considered that the visiting her was a momentous affair, and of great peril, not to be undertaken, nor suddenly attempted: so he replied, O my sister, I am of the sons of the common class, and not like Abu-l-Ḥasan; for Abu-l-Ḥasan was of high rank, of known reputation, in the habit of frequenting the palace of the Khaleefeh because its inmates required his merchandise; but as for me, Abu-l-Ḥasan used to converse with me and I trembled before him. If thy mistress, therefore, desireth my conversation with her, it will be requisite that it be in some other place than the palace of the Khaleefeh, distant from the abode of the Prince of the Faithful; for my heart will not consent to that which thou proposest.—So he refused to go with her. She proceeded to tell him that she would be surety for his safety, and said to him, Be not apprehensive nor fearful. But while they were thus talking, lo, his legs shook, and his hands trembled; and the slave-girl therefore said to him, If it will be painful to thee to go to the palace of the Khaleefeh, and thou canst not accompany me, I will persuade her to come to thee: therefore move not from thy place until I return to thee with her. She then departed; but soon returned to the jeweller, and said to him, Take care lest there be with thee a slave-girl or man-servant.

He replied, There is no one with me but a black female slave advanced in age, who serveth me. And the slave-girl arose, and closed the doors between the jeweller's female slave and himself, and sent his young men out from the house.

After this, the slave-girl went forth, and returned with a damsel behind her, and the latter entered the jeweller's abode with her, imparting a sweet odour to the house; and when the jeweller saw her, he rose and stood up, and placed a cushion for her, and seated himself before her. She remained a while without speaking, until she had rested herself, when she uncovered her face, and it appeared to the jeweller as though the sun had risen in his abode. She then said to her slave-girl, Is this the man of whom thou spakest to me? The slave-girl answered, Yes. And she looked towards the jeweller, and said to him, How art thou? He answered, In prosperity:—and prayed for her.[21] And she said to him, Thou hast induced us to come to thee, and to acquaint thee with our secret. And she asked him respecting his family and his children; and he acquainted her with all his circumstances, and said to her, I have a house beside this, which I have devoted to the purpose of assembling there with my friends and brethren, and I have in it nothing but what I have mentioned to thy slave-girl. After this, she asked him how he had become acquainted with the foundation of the story; and he informed her of the particulars which she demanded, from the first of the affair to the last: whereupon she sighed for the separation of Abu-l-Ḥasan, and said, O such a one, know that the souls of mankind accord in their desires, and persons stand in need, one of another; an action is not accomplished without words; nor a wish, without exertion; nor doth ease come unless after fatigue; nor doth success ensue but through the means of the generous. And now I have acquainted thee with our affair, and it is in thy power to expose or protect us; but thy generous disposition requireth nothing to be added; for thou already knowest that this my slave-girl concealeth my secret, and on that account occupieth a high place with me; and I have chosen her for the transaction of my affairs. Let none, then, be more worthy in thy sight than she, and do thou acquaint her with thy proceedings; and be of good heart; for thou art secure from what thou fearest on our account, and no place shall be closed from thee but she shall open it unto thee, and she shall convey to thee my messages for 'Alee the son of Bekkár, and thou shalt be the intermediary in the transmittal of communications between me and him.

Shems-en-Nahár then arose, scarcely able to do so, and departed, and the jeweller walked before her until she arrived at the gate of the palace, after which he returned, and sat in his place, having beheld, of her beauty, what astonished him, and heard, of her words, what confounded his reason, and witnessed, of her elegance and politeness, what amazed him. He remained reflecting upon her endowments until his mind became tranquillized; when he demanded food, and ate as much as would stay his spirit. He then changed his clothes, and went forth from his house, and repaired to 'Alee the son of Bekkár, whose servants came and met him, and walked before him until they introduced him to their master, and he found him laid upon his bed; and when he beheld the jeweller, he said to him, Thou hast been tardy in coming to me, and increased my anxiety. Having thus said, he dismissed his servants, and gave orders to shut his doors, and said to the jeweller, I have not closed my eye since thou quittedst me; for the slave-girl came to me yesterday, bringing a sealed letter from her mistress Shems-en-Nahár.—And he proceeded to relate to him all that had passed between him and her; after which he said, I have become perplexed in my affair, and my patience hath failed; for Abu-l-Ḥasan was a cheering companion unto me, as he knew the slave-girl. And when the jeweller heard his words, he laughed: so 'Alee the son of Bekkár said to him, Wherefore dost thou laugh at my words, when I have augured well of thy coming, and taken thee as a provision against misfortunes. He then wept, and recited these verses:—

Many a one laugheth at my tears on beholding me; but had he suffered as I have, it had made him weep.
None pitieth the afflicted for what he endureth, but one alike anxious, whose affliction hath been protracted.
My transport, yearning, sighing, thought, and distraction, are for a friend whose habitation is in the recesses of my heart:
He hath made his abode there, and never quitteth it; yet seldom can I enjoy an interview with him:
I have no intimate whom I approve in his stead; and I have chosen no friend whatever but him.

And when the jeweller heard these words from him, and understood the verses which he recited, he wept at his weeping, and acquainted him with all that had happened to him with the slave-girl since he had quitted him. 'Alee the son of Bekkár listened to his speech; and at every word of his that he heard, the colour of his face continued to change from yellowness to redness, and his body became at one time stronger, and at another weaker. And when he had ended his account, the Son of Bekkár wept, and said to him, O my brother, I am at all events perishing, and would that my end were near! I beg of thee, in thy kindness, to shew favour to me in all my affairs until God shall please to bring about what seemeth fit unto Him, and I will not oppose thee in word.—The jeweller replied, Nothing will quench this fire in thee except an interview with the person with whom thou art enamoured; but it should be in some other place than this, which is one of danger: it should be in a house of mine next to my own abode. The slave-girl came to me there, together with her mistress, and it is the place that she chose for herself: I desire, therefore, your interview with each other, and there shall ye complain one to another of what ye have suffered.—So 'Alee the son of Bekkár said, Do as thou desirest, and what thou seest fit is right.

I remained with him, says the jeweller, that night, conversing with him until the morning came, when I performed the morning-prayers, and went forth from him, and repaired to my abode. And I had not long remained there when the slave-girl came and saluted me, and I returned her salutation, and acquainted her with the plan decided upon between me and 'Alee the son of Bekkár; whereupon she said, Know that the Khaleefeh hath gone away from us, and that there is no one in our abode, and it is more safe for us, and better. I replied, What thou sayest is true; but it is not like this my house; for this is safer, and more suited to us. The slave-girl therefore said, It shall be as thou seest fit; and I go to my mistress to acquaint her with that which thou hast mentioned, and to propose to her what thou hast said. She then repaired to her mistress, and made the proposal to her, and returned to my house, and said to me, My mistress acquiesceth in that which thou hast said. And she took forth from her pocket a purse containing some pieces of gold, saying to me, My mistress saluteth thee, and saith to thee, Take this, and procure for us with it what we require.—But I swore that I would not expend anything of it. So she took it again, and returned to her mistress, and said to her, He hath not accepted the money; but returned it to me.—And after the slave-girl had gone, I repaired to my other house, and removed thither, of the utensils and furniture, what the case required, and transported thither the vessels of silver and of china-ware, and prepared all that we required of food and drink; and when the slave-girl came again, and beheld what I had done, it pleased her; and she ordered me to bring 'Alee the son of Bekkár; but I replied, None shall bring him but thou.

Accordingly she went to him and brought him, attired in the most perfect manner, and with a brightened aspect; and when he came, I met him and welcomed him, and seated him upon a mattress suitable to his condition, and placed before him some sweet-scented flowers in vessels of china-ware and crystal, and conversed with him about an hour; after which, the slave-girl departed, and was absent until after the sunset-prayers, when she returned, accompanied by Shems-en-Nahár with two maids and none else. As soon as she beheld 'Alee the son of Bekkár and he beheld her, they both fell down fainting upon the floor, and remained so for an hour; and when they recovered, they drew near to each other, and sat conversing tenderly; and after this, they made use of some perfumes, and began to thank me for my conduct to them. I then said to them, Have ye any desire for food? And they answered, Yes. So I brought to them some food, and they ate until they were satisfied, and washed their hands; and I conducted them to another chamber, where I brought them the wine; and they drank it, and became merry: whereupon Shems-en-Nahár said to me, O my master, complete thy kindness, and bring to us a lute or some

other musical instrument, that we may now perfect our enjoyment. I replied, On my head and my eye. And I arose, and brought a lute, and she took it and tuned it, and, placing it in her lap, played upon it in an admirable manner, and sang these two verses:—

I have been so sleepless that it would seem as though I loved sleeplessness; and so emaciated that disease appears to be natural to me;
And my tears have flowed upon my cheek, burning it. Would that I knew if we shall meet after our separation!

She proceeded to sing verses so as to confound the mind, with various modulations and with pleasing allusions, and the hearers almost flew with delight at her admirable singing; and when we had remained seated some time, and the cups circulated among us, the damsel, in charming tones, sang some verses commencing thus:—

The beloved gave me a promise to meet me, and performed it on a night that I shall count as worth many.

After this, I left them in that house, and departed to the house in which I resided, and there passed the night, until the morning. And when the morning came, I performed my divinely-ordained prayers, and drank some wine,[22] and sat thinking of going to them at my other house; and as I was sitting, lo, my neighbour came in to me, terrified, and said to me, O my brother, it was no light matter to me that befell thee this last night in thy other house. So I said to him, O my brother, and what hath happened? Acquaint me with that which hath occurred in my house.—He answered, The robbers who came to our neighbours yesterday, and murdered such a one and took his property, saw thee yesterday removing thy things to thy other house, and came thither in the night, and took what thou hadst there, and murdered thy guests.—I arose, therefore, I and my neighbour, and we went to that house, and found it empty: nothing remained in it; and I was perplexed at my case, and said, As to the things, I care not for their loss; and if I borrowed some of them from my friends and they are lost, there is no harm in that; for they know my excuse in the disappearance of my property and the plundering of my house; but as to 'Alee the son of Bekkár, and the concubine of the Prince of the Faithful, I fear that their affair will be rumoured abroad, and it will be the cause of the loss of my life.—The jeweller then looked towards his companion, and said to him, Thou art my brother and my neighbour, and wilt conceal what I should not expose: what course of conduct, then, dost thou advise me to pursue? The man answered him, That which I advise thee to do is, that thou be on thy guard; for they who entered thy house and took thy property have murdered a most distinguished party from the palace of the Khaleefeh, and have murdered also a party from the house of the chief magistrate of the police, and the guards of the court search for them everywhere, and perhaps they will find them, and thy wish will be attained without any effort of thine. And when the jeweller heard these words, he returned to his house in which he resided, and said within himself, Verily that which hath happened to me is what Abu-l-Ḥasan feared, and on account of which he departed to El-Baṣrah, and I have fallen into it.

The plunder of his house became publicly known among the people, and they came to him from every quarter; and some of them rejoiced at his misfortune, and some participated in his anxiety, while he uttered his complaints to them, and neither ate nor drank. And as he sat repenting, lo, one of his servants came in to him, and said to him, There is a person at the door who asketh for thee, whom I know not. So the jeweller went forth to him and saluted him, and found him to be a man whom he knew not; and the man said, I have something to say to thee. He therefore conducted him into his house, and asked him, What hast thou to say to me? The man answered, Go with me to thy other house. The jeweller said, And dost thou know my other house? And he answered, Thy whole case is known to me, and I know also that by which God will dispel thine anxiety.—So I said within myself (continues the jeweller), I will go with him whither he desireth. I then repaired with him to the house, and when the man saw the house, he said, It is without a door-keeper, and we cannot sit in it: come with me, therefore, to another house. And the man continued going about from place to place, and I with him, until the night overtook us; and I put no question to him. He ceased not on his way, and I with him, till we went forth into the open plain, saying, Follow me. And he hurried on, and I hurried behind him, until we arrived at the river, when he embarked with me in a boat, and the boatmen rowed with us, till we had crossed over to the other bank; whereupon he landed from the boat, and I landed after him, and he took my hand, and conducted me into a street which I had never entered before in the whole course of my life, and I knew not in what quarter it was. He then stopped at the door of a house, and opened it, and entered, taking me in with him, and locked the door with a lock of iron; after which, he led me along its passage till we came into the presence of ten men, who were as though they were one and the same man, and they were brothers.

When we went in to them, the man first mentioned saluted them, and they returned his salutation, and ordered me to sit down. So I seated myself, feeble from excessive fatigue; and they brought me some rose-water, and sprinkled it upon my face, and gave me to drink some wine, and placed before me some food. I therefore said [within myself], If there were anything injurious in the food, they would not eat with me. And when we had washed our hands, each of us returned to his place, and they said, Dost thou know us? I answered, No: nor in my life have I known your abode: nay, I know not him who brought me unto you. They then said, Acquaint us with thy story, and utter no falsehood. So I said, Know that my case is wonderful, and my affair is extraordinary. And are ye, I added, acquainted with aught of my story? They answered, Yes: we are the persons who took thy things last night, and we took thy friend, and her who was singing. And upon this I said, May God let down the curtain of his protection over you! Where are my friend and she who was singing? And they made a sign to me with their hands, pointing to one side, and answered, Here: but by Allah, O our brother, none of us hath learnt their secret, and since we brought them we have had no interview with them, nor asked them respecting their condition, on account of the appearance of dignity and respectability which we have observed in them; and it was this which prevented our killing them. Acquaint us, therefore, with their true history, and thou shalt be secure of thine own safety and of theirs.—When I heard these words, says the jeweller, I almost died with fear and terror, and said to them, Know that, if generosity be lost, it is to be found only with you; and if I have a secret which I fear to reveal, none but your breasts will conceal it. And I proceeded to expatiate in this manner, and found that readiness in making the communication to them would be more advantageous than concealing it; so I acquainted them with all that had befallen me until I arrived at the end of the story. And when they heard my tale, they said, And is this young man 'Alee the son of Bekkár, and this female Shems-en-Nahár? And they excused themselves to both of them, and afterwards said to me, Verily, of that which we took from thy house, part is gone; and this is what hath remained of it. They then restored to me most of the things, and bound themselves to convey them back to their place in my house, promising also that they would restore to me the rest: but they became divided into two parties; one party on my side, and the other against me. After this, we went forth from that house.—Such was my case.

Now as to 'Alee the son of Bekkár, and Shems-en-Nahár, they were at the point of death through fear. I approached them and saluted them, and said to them, What can have happened to the slave-girl and the two maids, and whither have they gone? They answered, We have no knowledge of them. And we continued on our way until we arrived at the place where was the boat, when they put us into it; and it was the boat in which we had crossed over in the preceding evening. The boatman rowed with us until he had conveyed us to the opposite bank, and they landed us. But we had scarcely seated ourselves on the bank, when a troop of horsemen came and surrounded us on every side; whereupon the men who were with us sprang up in haste like eagles, and the boat returned to them, and they embarked in it, and it proceeded with them over the river, while I remained with 'Alee the son of Bekkár, and Shems-en-Nahár, upon the bank of the river, we being unable either to move or to remain at rest. The horsemen said to us, Whence are ye? And we were perplexed for the answer; and I said to them, Verily those whom ye beheld with us we know not; but we saw them here; and as to ourselves, we are singers, and they desired to take us to sing to them, and we escaped not from them save by stratagem and soft words: therefore liberate us on this occasion, since ye have witnessed their conduct. The horsemen, however, looked towards Shems-en-Nahár and 'Alee the son of Bekkár, and said to me, Thou hast not spoken truth: if thou be a person of veracity inform us who ye are, and whence ye are, and in which of the quarters of the city ye reside. And I knew not what to say; but Shems-en-Nahár arose and approached the chief of the horsemen, and

spoke to him privately; whereupon he descended from his horse, and mounted her upon it, and, taking the bridle in his hand, led her along; and in like manner he did to 'Alee the son of Bekkár, and to me also. The chief of the horsemen then proceeded with us to a place on the bank of the river, and called out in his foreign language,[23] upon which there approached him a number of men, and he embarked us on board a boat, his companions embarking in another boat, and they rowed us on until we arrived at the palace of the Khaleefeh, while we suffered death from the excess of our fear. [Shems-en-Nahár having there landed,] we proceeded until we came to the place from which there was a way leading to our quarter, and there we landed, and we walked on, with a party of the horsemen cheering us by their company, till we entered the house [of 'Alee the son of Bekkár], when the horsemen who were with us bade us farewell, and went their way.

As to ourselves, we entered the house, and were unable to move from our place, not knowing morning from evening, and we continued thus until the morning came. And at the close of the day, 'Alee the son of Bekkár fell down in a fit, and the women and the men wept over him, as he lay prostrate and motionless; and some persons of his family came to me, and said, Tell us what hath happened to our son, and acquaint us with the cause of the state in which he is. I replied, O people, hear my words, and do nothing unpleasant to me; but be patient, and he will recover, and will acquaint you himself with his story. I then urged them, and impressed them with the fear of occasioning what would disgrace me with them, and while we were thus talking, lo, 'Alee the son of Bekkár moved in his bed, and his family rejoiced, and the people dispersed from him, and his family forbade me from quitting him. They sprinkled some rose-water upon his face, and when he recovered, and scented the air, they began to ask him respecting his state, and he commenced acquainting them; but his tongue would not return an answer quickly. After this, he made a sign to them that they should give me liberty to repair to my abode.

Accordingly, they suffered me to go, and I went forth, scarcely believing in my escape, and proceeded to my house, between two men, until I arrived and went in to my family; and when they beheld me in that state, they slapped their faces; but I made a sign to them with my hand that they should be silent, and they were silent. Then the two men went their way; and I rolled about in my bed the rest of the night, and awoke not till the mid-hour between sunrise and noon, when I found my family surrounding me, and saying, Who hath brought misfortune upon thee, and by his wickedness smitten thee? And I said to them, Bring me some wine. So they brought it, and I drank of it until I was satisfied, and then said to them, There hath happened what hath happened. And they went their way. And after this, I excused myself to my companions, and inquired of them respecting the things that had gone from my house, asking if any of the property had returned. They answered, A portion hath returned; for a man came and threw it down within the door of the house, and we saw him not. So I comforted myself, and remained in my house two days, unable to rise from my place; after which I fortified myself, and walked to the bath, with my heart troubled respecting the Son of Bekkár, and Shems-en-Nahár, having heard no tidings of them during that period, and having been unable to go to the house of 'Alee the son of Bekkár, and unable to rest in my place through my fear for myself. I then repented before God (whose name be exalted!) of the actions that had been committed by me, and praised Him for my safety.

And after a while, my mind suggested to me to repair to that place, and to return immediately; and when I was about to go, I beheld a woman standing, and looked attentively at her, and lo, she was the slave-girl of Shems-en-Nahár; and when I knew her, I went on, and hastened in my pace; but she followed me, and I was alarmed at her: and every time that I looked at her, fear of her overcame me, while she continued saying, Stop, that I may tell thee something. I, however, paid no regard to her, and stopped not until I came to a mosque in a place where there were no people; whereupon she said to me, Enter this mosque, that I may say a word to thee, and fear nothing. And she conjured me; so I entered the mosque, and she entered after me; and I performed the prayers of two rek'ahs; after which I approached her, sighing, and said to her, What dost thou desire? And she asked me respecting my state, and I told her what had happened to me and to 'Alee the son of Bekkár, and said to her, What is thy story? She answered, Know that when I saw that the men had broken open the door of thy house, and entered, I feared them, apprehending that they were from the Khaleefeh, and that they would take me and my mistress, and we should perish immediately; so I fled over the terraces, together with the two maids, and we cast ourselves down from a high place among a party of people, and fled thence until we arrived at the palace of the Khaleefeh, in a most

ignominious plight. We kept our affair secret, and remained in a state of torture as on hot embers until the next night became dark, when I opened the river-gate, and summoned the boatman who conveyed us away on the former night, and said to him, We know not what is become of my mistress; therefore take me in the boat that I may search for her upon the river: perhaps I may obtain some tidings of her. So he conveyed me in the boat, and proceeded with me along the river until midnight, when I saw a boat approaching the gate, with a man rowing in it, and other men,[24] and a woman lying prostrate among them; and the boatman continued rowing on until he arrived at the shore; and when the woman landed, I looked attentively at her, and lo, she was Shems-en-Nahár. I therefore landed and went to her, stupified with joy at beholding her after I had despaired of seeing her again; and when I came before her, she ordered me to give to the man who had brought her a thousand pieces of gold. Then I and the two maids carried her and laid her upon her bed, and she continued during the rest of that night in a troubled state; and when the morning came, she forbade the female slaves and eunuchs to come in to her or to approach her that day. But on the following day she recovered, and I found her as though she had come forth from a burial-ground; so I sprinkled some rose-water upon her face, and changed her clothes, and washed her hands and her feet, and ceased not to persuade her until I excited in her a desire for some food; and I gave her some wine to drink, though she had no appetite for it.

And when she took the air, and strength returned to her, I said to her, O my mistress, have a regard for thyself, for thou hast suffered difficulties enough, and hast been at the point of destruction. But she replied, O good slave-girl, death were easier to me than that which hath befallen me; for it seemed that I should be killed, and that no stratagem could save me; because the robbers, when they took us from the house of the jeweller, asked us and said, Who art thou, and what is thy condition?—but I answered, I am a singing girl:—and they believed me: then they asked 'Alee the son of Bekkár respecting himself, and said to him, Who art thou, and what is thy condition?—and he answered, I am of the common people. And they took us, and we proceeded with them until they brought us to their abode, and we hastened with them, through the excess of our fear; and when they had rested with us at their dwelling, they looked at me, and, seeing the apparel and necklaces and jewels with which I was decked, they disbelieved my assertion, and said, These necklaces belong not to one of the female singers. They then said to me, Be veracious to us, and tell us the truth. What is thy history?—But I returned them no answer, saying within myself, Now will they kill me for the ornaments and apparel that are upon me:—and I uttered not a word. And they looked towards 'Alee the son of Bekkár, and said to him, And whence art thou; for thine appearance is not that of the common people? But he was silent. We concealed our affair, and wept. And God inclined the hearts of the robbers towards us; and they said to us, Who is the owner of the house in which ye were? We answered them, Its owner is such a one, the jeweller. And one of them said, I know him well, and I know that he is residing in his other house, and I will take upon myself to bring him to you immediately. And they agreed together to put me in a place by myself, and 'Alee the son of Bekkár in a place by himself, and said to us, Rest ye, and fear not

that your affair will be revealed, for ye are secure from us. Then their companion went to the jeweller, and brought him, and he revealed our case to them, and we went in to him; after which, one of the men provided for us a boat, and they placed us in it, and crossed over with us to the opposite bank, and, having landed us there, departed. And a troop of horse, of the patrol, came, and said, Who are ye? So I spoke with the chief of the patrol, and said to him, I am Shems-en-Nahár, the concubine of the Khaleefeh: I made myself merry with wine, and went forth to visit some of my acquaintances among the wives of the wezeers, and the robbers came upon me, and took me, and brought me to this place, and when they beheld you they fled; and I am able to requite thee. And when the chief of the horsemen heard my words, he knew me, and, descending from his horse, mounted me upon it, and in like manner he did to 'Alee the son of Bekkár and to the jeweller; and in my heart now burneth a flame of fire on their account, especially for the jeweller, the companion of the Son of Bekkár: repair, therefore, unto him, and salute him, and inquire of him respecting 'Alee the son of Bekkár.

I blamed her (said the slave-girl) for what she had done, and cautioned her, saying to her, O my mistress, fear for thyself:—but she cried out at me, and was angry at my words. I then arose and departed from her, and came unto thee; but found thee not; and I feared to go to the Son of Bekkár;[25] so I stood looking out for thee, that I might ask thee respecting him, and know in what state he is. And I beg of thy goodness that thou wilt receive from me some money; for probably thou borrowedst some things of thy friends and thou hast lost them, and it is necessary that thou make a compensation to them for such of their things as have been lost in thy house.—So I replied, says the jeweller, I hear and obey. I then walked with her until we came near to my house, when she said to me, Stop here until I return to thee. And she departed, and returned bringing the money, and gave it to me, saying, O my master, in what place shall we meet thee? I answered her, I will go to my house immediately, and will endure hardship for thy sake, and devise some means of procuring thee access to him; for access to him is difficult at the present time.

She then bade me farewell, and departed, and I carried the money to my abode, and, counting it, found it to be five thousand pieces of gold; and I gave some of it to my family, and to every one who had anything in my possession I gave a compensation. After this, I took my young men, and repaired to the house from which the things had been lost, and brought the carpenters and the builders, and they restored it to its former state; and I placed my female slave in it, and forgot what had happened to me. I then went to the house of 'Alee the son of Bekkár, and when I arrived there, his slaves accosted me, and one of them said to me, The slaves of our master have been seeking thee night and day, and he hath promised them that whosoever of them bringeth thee to him he will emancipate him; so they are searching for thee, but know not where thou art. Vigour hath returned to my master; but he recovereth and relapseth frequently; and when he recovereth, he mentioneth thee, and saith, Ye must bring him unto me for a moment, and he shall return and go his way.—So I went with the young man to his master, and found him unable to speak; and when I beheld him, I seated myself at his head, and he opened his eyes, and, seeing me, he wept, and said to me, Thou art welcome. I then raised him, and seated him, and pressed him to my bosom; and he said to me, Know, O my brother, that since I laid myself down I have not sat up until now; and praise be to God for my beholding thee!—I continued raising him, says the jeweller, until I placed him upon his feet, and made him walk some paces, and changed his clothes, and he drank some wine; and when I saw in him signs of vigour, I related to him what had happened with the slave-girl; no one else hearing me; after which I said to him, Brace up thy nerves, for I know what thou sufferest. And he smiled, and I said to him, Thou wilt experience nothing but what will rejoice thee and cure thee. Then 'Alee the son of Bekkár gave orders to bring a repast; and they brought it; and he made a sign to his young men, whereupon they dispersed; and he said to me, O my brother, hast thou seen what hath befallen us? And he excused himself to me, and asked me how I had been during the late period. So I acquainted him with all that had happened to me from first to last; and he wondered, and said to the servants, Bring me such and such things. And they brought him costly furniture, and articles of gold and silver, more than I had lost, and gave to me all of them; and I sent them to my house, and remained with him the next night. And when the morning broke, he said to me, Know that to everything there is an end; and the end of love is death or union; and I am nearer unto death: would that I had died, then, before that which hath happened to me! Had not God been propitious to us, we had been disgraced; and I know not what will effect my deliverance from my present state. Were it not for my fear of God, I would hasten my own destruction. And know, O my brother, that I am like the bird in the cage, and that my life is expiring in consequence of my distresses; but it hath a known period, and a decreed end.—And he poured forth his tears; and I said to him, O my master, know that I purpose repairing to my house; for perhaps the slave-girl will return to me with news. He replied, There will be no harm in thy doing so; but return quickly to acquaint me.

I therefore took leave of him, and departed to my house; and I had scarcely sat down when I beheld the slave-girl approaching, weeping and wailing; and I said to her, What is the cause of this?—O my master, she answered, know that an event hath happened to us from which we are in fear; for when I went away from thee yesterday, I found my mistress incensed against one of the two maids who were with us that night, and she gave orders to beat her; and she feared her mistress, and fled; and one of the officers charged to keep the door met her, and took her, and desired to send her back to her mistress. But she gave him a hint, and he coaxed her, and desired her to make known her case, upon which she acquainted him with our proceedings; and the news reached the Khaleefeh, and immediately he gave orders to remove my mistress Shems-en-Nahár and all her property to his own palace, and appointed twenty eunu̇chs to guard her. I have not yet had an interview with her, nor acquainted her with the cause; but I suspect it is on that account, and therefore am in fear for myself, and am perplexed, O my master, not knowing what stratagem to employ in my affair and hers, and she hath no one more faithful in keeping a secret than myself. Go thou, therefore, O my master, to 'Alee the son of Bekkár, quickly, and acquaint him with this, in order that he may be prepared; and if the affair be exposed, we will contrive some means for our own escape.—Upon this, says the jeweller, excessive anxiety overcame me, and the universe became dark before my face at the words of the slave-girl. She proposed her departure, and I said to her, What is thy advice?—It is my advice, she answered, that thou hasten to 'Alee the son of Bekkár, if he be thy friend, and thou desire his escape: thine be it to communicate this news to him quickly; and be it mine to apply myself to learn further news. She then bade me farewell, and went forth.

And when the slave-girl had gone away, I arose and went forth after her, and repaired to 'Alee the son of Bekkár. I found him holding forth to himself expectations of union, and soothing himself with impossibilities; and when he saw that I had returned to him quickly, he said to me, I see thee to have come back to me immediately. I replied, Cease to indulge thine attachment and to promise thyself success, and abstain from thus busying thy mind; for an event hath occurred that may occasion the loss of thy life and thy property. And when he heard these words, his condition became changed, and he was agitated, and said, O my brother, acquaint me with that which hath happened.—O my master, I replied, know that such and such things have happened, and if thou remain in this thy house till the close of the day, thou wilt inevitably perish. And 'Alee the son of Bekkár was confounded, and his soul almost quitted his body, and he

exclaimed, Verily to God we belong, and verily to Him we return!—and said, What shall I do, O my brother; and what is thy advice? I answered, My advice is, that thou take with thee as much of thy property as thou canst, and of thy young men such as thou confidest in, and that thou repair with us to another country before this day shall have expired. And he said to me, I hear and obey. He then arose, perplexed at his case, now walking, and now falling down, and took what he could, and made an excuse to his family, charging them with such orders as he desired, and, taking with him three loaded camels, mounted his horse. I also had done the same, and we went forth privately, and stopped not in our journey during the rest of the day and the next night, until the close of the night, when we put down our loads, and tied up our camels' feet, and slept; and, being overcome by fatigue, we were neglectful of ourselves; and lo, robbers surrounded us, and took all that we had with us, and slew the young men on their attempting to defend us. They then left us in our place, in a miserable condition, after they had taken away the property; and when we had arisen, we proceeded until morning, and arrived at a town, and, entering it, repaired to its mosque, stripped of our clothing.

We sat in one side of the mosque the remainder of the day, and passed the next night in it, without food or drink; and at daybreak we performed the morning-prayers, and sat down again; and lo, a man entered, and saluted us, and, after performing the prayers of two rek'ahs, looked towards us and said, O men, are ye strangers? We answered, Yes: robbers have intercepted us and stripped us, and we entered this town, but know not in it any one with whom to lodge. So the man said to us, Will ye arise and accompany me to my house. I said, therefore, to 'Alee the son of Bekkár, Arise and let us go with him, and save ourselves from two troubles: the first is, that we fear some one may come in to us who knoweth us in this mosque, and so we may be disgraced; and the second, that we are strangers, and have no place in which to lodge. And 'Alee the son of Bekkár replied, Do what thou wilt. The man then said to us a second time, O poor men, comply with my desire, and come with me to my abode. I therefore replied, We hear and obey. And the man took off, and gave to us, part of his own clothing, and clad us, and spoke kindly to us; and we arose and went with him to his house; and he knocked at the door, and there came forth to us a young eunuch, who opened the door; and the man, the owner of the house, entered, and we entered after him. He then gave orders to bring a wrapper, containing clothes, and

pieces of muslin for turbans, and clad us with two suits, and gave us two pieces of muslin, and we turbaned ourselves, and sat down; and lo, a slave-girl approached us with a table, and placed it before us, and we ate a little; after which, the table was removed, and we remained with him until night.

And 'Alee the son of Bekkár sighed, and said to me, O my brother, know that I am inevitably perishing, and I desire to give thee a charge, which is this: that when thou seest me to have died, thou repair to my mother, and acquaint her, that she may come to this place for the sake of receiving the visits of condolence for me, and be present at the washing of my corpse; and exhort her to bear my loss with patience. He then fell down in a fit; and when he recovered, he heard a damsel singing at a distance, and reciting verses; and he listened to her and heard her voice; one moment becoming insensible; and another, recovering; and another, weeping in his anguish and grief at that which had befallen him: and he heard the damsel sing, with charming modulations, these verses:—

Separation hath quickly intervened between us, after intimate intercourse and friendship and concord.
The vicissitudes of fortune have disunited us. Would that I knew when would be our meeting!
How bitter is separation after union! Would that it never gave pain unto lovers!
The strangulation of death is short, and ceaseth; but the disjunction of the beloved ever tortureth the heart.

And as soon as 'Alee the son of Bekkár had heard her song, he uttered a groan, and his soul quitted his body.

When I saw that he was dead, says the jeweller, I gave a charge respecting him to the master of the house, and said to him, Know that I am going to Baghdád to acquaint his mother and his other relations, that they may come to prepare his funeral. I then repaired to Baghdád, and entered my house, and changed my clothes; after which, I went to the house of 'Alee the son of Bekkár. And when his young men saw me, they came to me and inquired of me respecting him; and I asked them to beg permission for me to have an interview with his mother; and she gave me permission. So I entered and saluted her, and said, Verily, when God decreeth an event, there is no escaping from it; and a soul cannot depart but by the permission of God, according to the decree which prescribeth its term. And from these words, the mother of 'Alee the son of Bekkár inferred that her son had died; and she wept violently, and then said to me, By Allah, I conjure thee to tell me: hath the soul of my son been taken? But I could not return her an answer, through the excess of my grief: and when she saw me in this state, she was suffocated with weeping, and fell upon the floor in a fit; and as soon as she recovered, she said, How did it happen to my son? I replied, May God abundantly compensate thee for his loss!—and then acquainted her with all that had happened to him, from beginning to end. She said, Did he give thee any charge? And I answered her, Yes:—and informed her of that with which he had charged me, and said to her, Hasten to perform his funeral. But on hearing my words, she fell down again in a swoon: and when she recovered, she resolved to do as I had charged her.

I then returned to my house, thinking, on my way, upon the charms of his youth; and while I was thus proceeding, lo, a woman laid hold upon my hand, and, looking at her, I saw her to be the slave-girl who used to come from Shems-en-Nahár. Despondency had overcome her; and when we recognised each other, we wept together until we arrived at the house, when I said to her, Hast thou become acquainted with the case of 'Alee the son of Bekkár? She answered, No, by Allah. And I related to her what had happened to him, and then said to her, And in what state is thy mistress?—The Prince of the Faithful, she answered, would not listen to what any one said against her, in consequence of the violence of his love for her; but regarded all her actions in a favourable light, and said to her, O Shems-en-Nahár, thou art dear in my estimation, and I will endure with thee in spite of thine enemies. He then gave orders to furnish a gilded apartment, and an elegant closet; and she became in high favour with him in consequence of that event. And it happened that he was sitting to take his usual beverage, and the concubines were before him, and he ordered them to sit in their places, and seated Shems-en-Nahár by his side (but her patience had failed, and her disorder had increased); and he then commanded one of the female slaves to sing: so she took the lute and struck its chords and sang thus:—

Many a one hath invited me to love, and I have yielded; and my tears write the tale of my transport upon my cheek;
As if the drops from the eye were acquainted with our case, and revealed what I hid, and hid what I revealed.
Why, then, desire I secrecy, or the concealment of my love, when the violence of my passion for thee sheweth what I feel?
Death hath become pleasant to me since the loss of those I love; but would that I knew what would please them after me!

And when Shems-en-Nahár heard that slave-girl's song, she was unable to keep her seat, and fell down in a fit. The Khaleefeh threw down the cup, and drew her towards him, and cried out, and the female slaves raised a clamour, and the Prince of the Faithful, turning her over, found that she was dead. He lamented for her death, and gave orders to break all the ḳánoons[26] and other instruments of music that were there, and removed her corpse to a closet, where he remained with it for the rest of the night;[27] and when the day broke, he made preparations for her funeral, and commanded to wash and shroud and bury her, and mourned for her greatly, asking no questions respecting her condition, or her past conduct.

The slave-girl then said, I conjure thee by Allah that thou acquaint me with the period when the funeral-procession of 'Alee the son of Bekkár is to set forth, and that thou let me be present at his burial. So I replied, As for myself, in whatsoever place thou desirest, thou shalt find me; but as for thee, who can obtain access to thee in the place where thou residest? She said, however, The Prince of the Faithful, when Shems-en-Nahár died, emancipated her female slaves, on the same day, and I am one of them, and we are staying at her tomb, in such a place.[28] I therefore arose and went with her, and, arriving at the burial-ground, visited the tomb of Shems-en-Nahár, and then went my way, and remained waiting for the funeral-procession of 'Alee the son of Bekkár until it arrived, when the people of Baghdád went forth to join it, and I went with them; and I found the slave-girl among the women, and she was the most violent of them in lamentation; and I never witnessed in Baghdád a greater funeral-procession than this. We pursued our way, densely crowding together, until we came to his tomb, and buried him; and I have not discontinued my visits to his tomb, nor to that of Shems-en-Nahár.

NOTES TO CHAPTER NINTH.

NOTE 1. In the first of the Notes to Chapter viii., I have mentioned that the long story from which the contents of that chapter are extracted terminates with the hundred and forty-fifth Night. It is followed by several moral fables, extending to the end of the hundred and fifty-second Night. Two of these I have translated, and here insert, as I think them at least worthy of a second-rate place in the present collection. The rest are short, and very inferior.

The Fable of the Peacock and Peahen, the Duck, the Young Lion, the Ass, the Horse, the Camel, and the Carpenter, &c.

"There was, in ancient times, a peacock who resorted to the sea-side[1] with his mate. This place abounded with savage beasts, and all other wild animals were there, but it also abounded with trees and rivers; and the peacock with his mate roosted by night in one of those trees, through their fear of the wild beasts, in the morning betaking themselves to seek their sustenance. Thus they continued until, their fear increasing, they sought another place in which to reside; and while they were searching for it, an island appeared before them, with many trees and rivers. So they took up their abode in this island, and ate of its fruits, and drank of its rivers. And as they were thus living, lo, a duck approached them, in a state of great terror, and advanced without stopping until she came to the tree upon which was the peacock with his mate; whereupon she felt secure. The peacock, therefore, doubted not but that this duck had a wonderful story to tell; and he asked her respecting her state, and the reason of her fear. She answered, I am sick with grief, and my fear is of the son of Adam. Beware then, beware of the sons of Adam.—So the peacock said to her, Fear not, now that thou hast come unto us. And the duck replied, Praise be to God who hath dispelled my anxiety and grief by your vicinity! I have come in the desire of gaining your affection. —And when she had uttered these words, the peacock's mate descended to her, and said to her, Welcome to friendship and ease and amplitude! No evil awaiteth thee. And how can the son of Adam obtain access to us when we are in this island in the midst of the sea? From the land he cannot reach us, and from the sea he cannot come

[1] The word which I render "sea" (namely "baḥr") also signifies "a great river."

up against us. Rejoice, therefore, at this announcement, and tell us what hath befallen thee from the son of Adam.

"So the duck said, Know, O peahen, that I have passed all my life in this island in safety, and seen nothing disagreeable, till I slept one night, and beheld in my sleep the figure of a son of Adam, who conversed with me, and I conversed with him. But I heard a speaker say to me, O duck, beware of the son of Adam, and be not deceived by his words, nor by his suggestions to thee; for he aboundeth with stratagems and guile. Beware then, be fully aware, of his craftiness; for he is guileful and crafty as the poet hath said of him,—

With his tongue he will offer thee sweet expressions; but he will elude thee like the fox.

And know that the son of Adam circumventeth the fish, and draweth them out from the waters, and shooteth the birds with an earthen bullet,[2] and entrappeth the elephant by his craftiness. No one is secure from the mischief of the son of Adam, and neither bird nor wild beast can escape from him. Thus I have acquainted thee with that which I have heard respecting the son of Adam.—So I awoke from my sleep fearful and terrified; and to the present time my heart hath not become dilated, through my fear for myself from the son of Adam, lest he surprise me by his artifice, and catch me in his snares. When the close of day overtook me, my strength was impaired and my energy failed.

"I then felt a desire to eat and drink. I therefore went walking forth, with a troubled mind and a contracted heart, and, arriving at yonder mountain, I found, at the entrance of a cave, a young lion, of yellow colour. When this young lion beheld me, he rejoiced exceedingly at my arrival; my colour and my elegant form pleased him, and he called out to me, saying, Draw near to me: and on my approaching him he said to me, What is thy name, and what is thy genus? I therefore answered, My name is duck, and I am of the genus of birds. And I then said to him, What is the reason of thy sojourning until the present time in this place? The young lion answered, The reason of it is, that my father the lion hath been for days cautioning me against the son of Adam; and it happened that I beheld last night in my sleep the figure of a son of Adam. Then the young lion related to me the like of that which I have related unto thee; and when I heard his words I said to him, O lion, I have had recourse unto thee that thou mayest slay the son of Adam, and be resolved upon his slaughter; for I fear for myself extremely from him, and my fear is increased from seeing that thou also fearest the son of Adam although thou art Sulṭán of the wild beasts.—I ceased not, O my sister, to caution the young lion against the son of Adam, and to urge him to slay him, until he rose suddenly from the place where he was, and walked forth, I walking behind him; and he lashed his back with his tail.

"He proceeded, and I behind him, down the road; and we found a dust raised, which subsided, and there appeared in the midst of it a run-away, naked ass, now galloping and running, and now rolling on the ground. When the lion beheld him he called out to him: so the ass came to him submissively: and the lion said to him, O thou animal of infatuated mind, what is thy genus, and what is the reason of thy coming unto this place?—O son of the Sulṭán, answered the ass, as to my genus, I am an ass; and the reason of my coming to this place is my flight from the son of Adam. So the young lion said, And art thou also afraid of the son of Adam that he should kill thee? The ass answered, No, O son of the Sulṭán; but my fear is lest he employ a stratagem against me, and ride me; for he hath a thing called the pad,[3] which he placeth on my back, and a thing called the girth, which he draweth round my belly, and a thing called the crupper, which he inserteth beneath my tail, and a thing called the bit, which he putteth in my mouth; and he maketh for me a goad, and goadeth me with it, and he requireth me to exert myself beyond my ability in running. When

[2] This seems to allude to the cross-bow. [3] A kind of stuffed saddle, for asses and mules.

I stumble, he curseth me; and when I bray, he revileth me.[4] Afterwards, when I have grown old, and can no longer run, he putteth upon me a pack-saddle of wood, and committeth me to the water-sellers (saḳḳàs), who load me with water upon my back from the river, in goat-skins, and in similar things, such as jars; and I cease not to suffer abasement and contempt and fatigue until I die, when they throw me upon the mounds of rubbish to the dogs.[5] What then can be greater than this anxiety that I suffer, and what calamity is greater than these calamities that I endure?—Now when I heard, O peahen, the words of the ass, my flesh quaked with horror of the son of Adam, and I said to the young lion, O my master, the ass is excused, and his words have added to my terror. The young lion then said to the ass, Whither art thou going? The ass answered, I saw the son of Adam before sunrise at a distance, and I fled from him, and now I desire to depart, and to run without stopping, from the violence of my fear of him: perhaps I may find a place that will afford me an asylum from the perfidious son of Adam.

"Now while the ass was conversing with the young lion on this subject, and was desirous of bidding us farewell, and departing, there appeared unto us a cloud of dust; whereupon the ass brayed and cried out, looking in the direction of the dust. And after a while, the dust dispersed, and discovered a black horse, with a white spot on his forehead like a dirhem.[6] This horse, beautiful with the white spot on his forehead, handsomely marked with white next the hoof, with becoming legs, and neighing, stopped not in his course until he came before the young lion. And when the young lion beheld him, he admired him, and said to him, What is thy genus, O majestic wild beast, and what is the reason of thy fleeing away into this wide and extensive desert?—O lord of the wild beasts, answered the horse, I am one of the genus of horses, and the reason of my running away is my flight from the son of Adam. And the young lion wondered at the words of the horse, and replied, Say not thus, for it is disgraceful to thee. Thou art tall and stout; and how then fearest thou the son of Adam, notwithstanding the bulk of thy body, and the swiftness of thy running, when I, with the smallness of my body, have determined to encounter the son of Adam, to attack him, and eat his flesh, and to appease the terror of this poor duck, and establish her securely in her home? Now, on thy coming here, thou hast broken my heart by thy words, and deterred me from that which I desired to do; seeing that the son of Adam hath overcome thee, in spite of thy greatness, and feared not thy height and thy breadth, though, if thou kickedst him with thy hoof, thou wouldst kill him, and he could not prevail against thee; but thou wouldst make him to drink the cup of perdition.—But the horse laughed when he heard the words of the young lion, and said, Far, far is it from my power to overcome him, O son of the King! Let not my height nor breadth nor my bulk deceive thee with respect to the son of Adam, for, in the excess of his

---

[4] The reason of this is, because the ass brays in consequence of his seeing the Devil.—"The last animal that entered with Nooḥ [or Noah, into the ark,] was the ass; and Iblees (whom God curse!) clung to his tail. The ass had just entered the ark, and began to be agitated, and could not enter further into the ark, whereupon Nooḥ said to him, 'Enter, wo to thee!' But the ass was still agitated, and was unable to advance. So Nooḥ said, 'Enter, though the Devil be with thee.' And the ass entered, and Iblees (whom God curse!) entered with him. And Nooḥ said, 'O enemy of God, who introduced thee into the ark?' He answered, 'Thou: thou saidst unto the ass, Enter, though the Devil be with thee.'—So it is said that this is the reason why the ass, when he seeth the Devil, brayeth." (Kitáb el-'Onwán fee Mekáïd en-Niswán.)

[5] See Note 47 to Chapter ii.

[6] That is, round, and like a silver coin.—The Arabs are much influenced in their estimation of horses by what they consider lucky or unlucky colours and marks. The Prophet said, "The best horses are black, with white foreheads, and having a white upper lip: next to these, a black horse with white forehead, and three white legs: next to this, a bay horse with these marks."—"A bay with white forehead, and white fore and hind legs, is best; and a sorrel with white forehead and legs is also good."—"Prosperity is with sorrel horses." —"The Prophet judged shikál [or the having the right hind foot and the left fore foot, or the right fore foot and left hind foot, white,] to be bad in a horse." (Mishkát el-Maṣábeeḥ, vol. ii. pp. 252 and 250.)

artifice and his craftiness he maketh for me a thing called a tethering-rope, and putteth to my four feet two tethering-ropes of cords made of the fibres of the palm-tree, wound round with felt, and attacheth me by my head to a high stake. I remain standing, thus attached, unable to lie down or to sleep. And when he desireth to ride me, he maketh for me a thing of iron into which to put his feet, called the stirrup, and placeth upon my back a thing called the saddle, binding it with two girths under the hollow of my forelegs; and he putteth in my mouth a thing of iron called the bit, affixing to it a strip of leather termed the bridle. Then when he rideth on my back, upon the saddle, he taketh hold of the bridle and guideth me with it, and striketh me on my flanks with the stirrups until he maketh them bleed.[7] Ask not, O son of the Sulṭán, what I suffer from the son of Adam; for when I have grown old and lean, and am unable to run fleetly, he selleth me to the miller, to employ me in turning the mill, and I cease not to do so night and day, until I become infirm from age, when he selleth me to the butcher, who slaughtereth me: he strippeth off my skin and plucketh my tail and selleth them to the sieve-makers, and he melteth down my fat.[8]—And when the young lion heard these words of the horse, he became more enraged and vexed, and said to him, When didst thou part from the son of Adam? He answered, I parted from him at midday, and he is following my tracks.

"And while the young lion was thus talking with the horse, lo, a dust rose, and afterwards dispersed, and there appeared in the midst of it a furious camel, uttering a gurgling noise, and striking the ground with his feet. Thus he continued to do until he came up to us; and when the young lion beheld him, great and stout, he thought that he was the son of Adam, and was about to spring upon him; but I said to him, O son of the Sulṭán, this is not the son of Adam, but he is a camel; and it seemeth that he is fleeing from the son of Adam. And as I was thus engaged, O my sister, in speaking to the young lion, the camel came before the young lion, and saluted him; and he returned his salutation, and said to him, What is the reason of thy coming unto this place? He answered, I have come fleeing from the son of Adam.—And thou, said the young lion, with thy huge make and height and breadth, how fearest thou the son of Adam, when, if thou kickedst him with thy foot, thou wouldst kill him.—O son of the Sulṭán, answered the camel, know that the son of Adam hath subtleties not to be supported, and nothing overcometh him but death; for he putteth in my nose a string called a nose-ring,[9] and upon my head he putteth a halter: then he committeth me to the least of his children, and the little child draweth me along by the string, notwithstanding my great bulk. They load me also with the heaviest burdens, and take me with them on long journeys. They employ me in difficult labours during the hours of the night and the day; and when I have grown old, and have become disabled, my master no longer endureth my society; but selleth me to the butcher, who slaughtereth me, and selleth my skin to the tanners, and my flesh to the cooks. Ask not, therefore, what I suffer from the son of Adam.—The young lion then said to him, At what hour didst thou part from the son of Adam? He answered, I parted from him at the hour of sunset; and I imagine that, coming to my place after my departure, and finding me not, he is on the way to seek me; therefore suffer me, O son of the Sulṭán, to flee into the deserts and wastes. But the young lion replied, Wait a little, O camel, that thou mayest see how I will tear him, and feed thee with his flesh, and break his bones, and drink his blood.—O son of the Sulṭán, rejoined the camel, I fear for thee from the son of Adam; for he is guileful and crafty. And he recited the saying of the poet,—

> When the severe alighteth in the land of a people, there is nothing for its inhabitants but to depart.[10]

---

[7] The shovel-shaped Arab stirrup is used as a spur.

[8] "To make candles." (Note by the sheykh Moḥammad 'Eiyád.)

[9] This is generally done to the light camel (or dromedary) used for riding.

[10] The sheykh Moḥammad 'Eiyád remarks in a marginal note, that "it would have been more

"But as the camel was conversing thus with the young lion, lo, a dust rose, and after a while dispersed from around a short and thin old man. On his shoulder was a basket containing a set of carpenter's tools, upon his head was a branch of a tree, with eight planks, and he was leading by the hand young children, and walking at a brisk pace. He advanced without stopping until he drew near to the young lion; and when I beheld him, O my sister, I fell down from the violence of my fear. But as to the young lion, he arose and walked forward to him and met him; and when he came up to him, the carpenter laughed in his face, and said to him with an eloquent tongue, O glorious King, endowed with liberality, may Allah make thine evening and thine intention prosperous, and increase thy courage and thy power! Protect me from him who hath afflicted me, and by his wickedness smitten me; for I have found none to aid me but thee.—Then the carpenter stood before the lion, and wept and sighed and lamented. And when the young lion heard his weeping and lamenting, he said to him, I will protect thee from the object of thy dread. Who then is he who hath oppressed thee, and what art thou, O thou wild beast, the like of whom I have never in my life beheld, and than whom I have never seen any of more handsome form nor any of more eloquent tongue; and what is thy condition?—So the carpenter answered, O lord of the wild beasts, as to myself, I am a carpenter; and as to him who hath oppressed me, he is a son of Adam, and on the morning after this night he will be with thee in this place. And when the young lion heard these words from the carpenter, the light became converted into darkness before his face: he growled and snorted; his eyes cast forth sparks; and he cried out, saying, By Allah, I will remain awake this night until the morning, and will not return to my father until I accomplish my desire! Then looking towards the carpenter, he said to him, I see thy steps to be short, and I cannot hurt thy feelings; for I am endowed with generosity; and I imagine that thou canst not keep pace in thy walk with the wild beasts: acquaint me, then, whither thou art going. The carpenter replied, Know that I am going to the Wezeer of thy father, to the lynx; for, when it was told him that the son of Adam had trodden this region, he feared for himself greatly, and sent to me a messenger from among the wild beasts, that I might make for him a house in which he might reside, and find an asylum, and that should debar from him his enemy, so that no one of the sons of Adam might obtain access to him. Therefore, when the messenger came to me, I took these planks and set forth to him.

"On hearing these words of the carpenter, the young lion became envious of the lynx, and said to him, By my life, thou must make for me a house with these planks before thou make for the lynx his house; and when thou hast finished my work, go to the lynx, and make for him what he desireth. But when the carpenter heard what the young lion said, he replied, O lord of the wild beasts, I cannot make for thee anything until I have made for the lynx what he desireth: then I will come to serve thee, and make for thee a house that shall protect thee from thine enemy. The young lion, however, said, By Allah, I will not let thee go from this place until thou make for me a house with these planks. He then crept, and sprang upon the carpenter, desiring to jest with him, and struck him with his paw, throwing down the basket from his shoulder. The carpenter fell down in a swoon, and the young lion laughed at him, and said, Wo to thee, O carpenter! Verily thou art weak, and without strength: so thou art excused for thy fearing the son of Adam.—But when the carpenter had fallen down upon his back, he became violently enraged. He however concealed this from the young lion, through his fear of him; and afterwards, he sat and laughed in the face of the young lion, saying to him, Well, I will make for thee the house. So he took the

---

proper to quote here the saying of En-Nábighah [Edh-Dhubyánee]:—

'I have been told that Aboo-Ḳáboos hath threatened me; and there is no resting within the sound of the growling of the lion.'"

"Aboo-Ḳáboos" was the surname of Noạmán Ibn-El-Mundhir Ibn-Imra-el-Ḳeys.

planks that he had with him, and nailed together the house, making it to suit the measure of the young lion, and left its door open; for he made it in the form of a chest. He made for it a large aperture with a cover pierced with numerous holes, and, taking forth some new nails, said to the young lion, Enter this house by this aperture, that I may arch it over thee. The young lion therefore rejoiced at this, and advanced to the aperture; but he saw that it was narrow. The carpenter said to him, Enter, and crouch down upon thy four legs. And the lion accordingly did so, and entered the chest, but his tail remained outside. He then desired to draw back and come forth; but the carpenter said to him, Wait, that I may see if it will admit thy tail with thee. So the young lion complied with his directions; and the carpenter, having folded the young lion's tail, and stuffed it into the chest, placed the cover upon the aperture quickly, and nailed it. The young lion cried out, saying, O carpenter, what is this narrow house that thou hast made for me? Let me come forth from it.—But the carpenter replied, Far, far be it from thee! Repentance for what hath passed will not avail; for thou wilt not come forth from this place.—Then the carpenter laughed, and said to the young lion, Thou hast fallen into the cage, and become the basest of wild beasts.—O my brother, said the young lion, what is this discourse that thou addressest to me?—Know, O dog of the desert, replied the carpenter, that thou hast fallen into the snare that thou fearedst: destiny hath overthrown thee, and caution will not avail thee.—So when the young lion heard his words, O my sister, he knew that he was the son of Adam, against whom his father had cautioned him when he was awake, and the invisible speaker in his sleep; and I was convinced that this was he without doubt or uncertainty. I therefore feared him greatly for myself, and, retiring to a little distance from him, waited to see what he would do with the young lion. And I saw, O my sister, the son of Adam dig a trench in that place, near the chest in which was the young lion; and he threw him into the trench, and threw wood upon him, and burnt him with fire. So my fear, O my sister, increased; and for two days I have been fleeing from the son of Adam, in my fear of him.

"The peahen, when she heard these words from the duck, wondered at them extremely, and said, O my sister, thou art now secure from the son of Adam; for we are in one of the islands of the sea, to which the son of Adam hath no way of access; therefore choose a residence with us until God make easy thy affair and ours. The duck replied, I fear that some nocturnal calamity may befall me; and no fugitive slave can detach himself from fate. But the peahen rejoined, Reside with us, and be like us. And she continued to urge her until she did so; and she said to the peahen, O my sister, thou knowest how little is my patience; and if I had not seen thee here, I had not remained. The peahen replied, If anything be [written] on our forehead, we must experience its accomplishment;[11] and when our predestined end approacheth, who will deliver us? A soul departeth not until it hath enjoyed the whole of its sustenance

[11] This figurative expression has given rise to a common vulgar belief of the Arabs, that the unchangeable destinies of every human being are written upon his skull in what we term the "sutures."

and its decreed period.—And while they were thus conversing, a cloud of dust approached them; whereupon the duck cried out, and descended into the sea, saying, Beware, beware, though there be no refuge from destiny![12] The dust was great; but as it subsided, there appeared in the midst of it an antelope. So the duck and the peahen felt secure; and the latter said to the duck, O my sister, that which thou fearest is an antelope, and see, he hath approached us: no harm will befall us from him; for the antelope eateth the herbs which spring from the earth; and as thou art of the genus of birds, he is of the genus of wild beasts: therefore feel secure, and be not anxious; since anxiety wasteth the body. And the peahen had not finished her words when the antelope came up to them to shade himself beneath the tree; and on beholding the peahen and the duck, he saluted them, and said to them, I have entered this island to-day, and have seen no place more fruitful than it, nor any more pleasant as an abode. He then invited them to keep him company and to treat him with sincere friendship; and when the duck and the peahen saw his affection for them, they addressed him kindly, and became desirous of his society. They swore to be faithful friends, one to another, and they passed the night together, and ate together. Thus they continued in safety, eating and drinking, until there passed by them a vessel that was wandering from its course in the sea. It anchored near them, and the people came forth, and dispersed themselves in the island, and, seeing the antelope and the peahen and the duck together, they approached them. So the antelope fled into the desert, and the peahen soared into the sky; but the duck remained infatuated, and they continued to run after her until they captured her, when she cried out, saying, Caution is of no avail to me against fate and destiny! And they departed with her to their vessel."

The antelope and the peahen mourned incessantly for the loss of the duck, and concluded that her unhappy end was occasioned by her neglecting to repeat the praises of God; for it is the general practice of everything that God hath created to celebrate his praises,[13] and the neglect of doing so causeth its destruction.

The Fable of the Fox and the Wolf.

"A fox and a wolf inhabited the same den, resorting thither together, and thus they remained a long time. But the wolf oppressed the fox; and it so happened that the fox counselled the wolf to assume benignity, and to abandon wickedness, saying to him, If thou persevere in thine arrogance, probably God will give power over thee to a son of Adam; for he is possessed of stratagems, and artifice, and guile: he captureth the birds from the sky, and the fish from the sea, and cutteth the mountains and transporteth them; and all this he accomplisheth through his stratagems. Betake thyself, therefore, to the practice of equity, and relinquish evil and oppression; for it

---

[12] "It is proper to be cautious and to flee: otherwise it would be as if one threw himself into destruction." (Note by the sheykh Moḥammad 'Eiyád.) See Ḳur-án, ch. ii. v. 191.

[13] See Note 30 to the Introduction.

will be more pleasant to thy taste.—The wolf, however, received not his advice; on the contrary, he returned him a rough reply, saying to him, Thou hast no right to speak on matters of magnitude and importance. He then gave the fox such a blow that he fell down senseless; and when he recovered, he smiled in the wolf's face, apologizing for his shameful words, and recited these two verses:—

If I have been faulty in my affection for you, and committed a deed of a shameful nature,
I repent of my offence, and your clemency will extend to the evil-doer who craveth forgiveness.[14]

So the wolf accepted his apology, and ceased from ill-treating him, but said to him, Speak not of that which concerneth thee not, lest thou hear that which will not please thee. The fox replied, I hear and obey. I will abstain from that which pleaseth thee not; for the sage hath said, Offer not information on a subject respecting which thou art not questioned; and reply not to words when thou art not invited; leave what concerneth thee not, to attend to that which *doth* concern thee; and lavish not advice upon the evil, for they will recompense thee for it with evil.—And when the wolf heard these words of the fox, he smiled in his face; but he meditated upon employing some artifice against him, and said, I must strive to effect the destruction of this fox. As to the fox, however, he bore patiently the injurious conduct of the wolf, saying within himself, Verily, insolence and calumny occasion destruction, and betray one into perplexity; for it hath been said, He who is insolent suffereth injury, and he who is ignorant repenteth, and he who feareth is safe: moderation is one of the qualities of the noble, and good manners are the noblest gain. It is advisable to behave with dissimulation towards this tyrant, and he will inevitably be overthrown.—He then said to the wolf, Verily the Lord pardoneth and becometh propitious unto his servant when he hath sinned; and I am a weak slave, and have committed a transgression in offering thee advice. Had I foreknown the pain that I have suffered from thy blow, I had known that the elephant could not withstand nor endure it; but I will not complain of the pain of that blow, on account of the happiness that hath resulted unto me from it; for, if it had a severe effect upon me, its result was happiness; and the sage hath said, The beating inflicted by the preceptor is at first extremely grievous; but in the end it is sweeter than clarified honey.—So the wolf said, I forgive thine offence, and cancel thy fault; but beware of my power, and confess thyself my slave; for thou hast experienced my severity unto him who sheweth me hostility. The fox, therefore, prostrated himself before him, saying to him, May God prolong thy life, and mayest thou not cease to subdue him who opposeth thee! And he continued to fear the wolf, and to dissemble towards him.

"After this, the fox went one day to a vineyard, and saw in its wall a breach; but he suspected it, saying within himself, There must be some cause for this breach; and it hath been said, Whoso seeth a hole in the ground, and doth not shun it, and be cautious of advancing to it boldly, exposeth himself to danger and destruction. It is well known that some men make a figure of the fox in the vineyard, and even put before it grapes in plates, in order that a fox may see it, and advance to it, and fall into destruction. Verily I regard this breach as a snare; and it hath been said, Caution is the half of cleverness. Caution requireth me to examine this breach, and to see if I can find there anything that may lead to perdition. Covetousness doth not induce me to throw myself into destruction.—He then approached it, and, going round about examining it warily, beheld it; and lo, there was a deep pit, which the owner of the vineyard had dug to catch in it the wild beasts that despoiled the vines; and he observed over it a slight covering. So he drew back from it, and said, Praise be to God that I regarded it with caution! I hope that my enemy, the wolf, who hath made my life miserable, may fall into it; so that I alone may enjoy absolute power over the vine-

---

[14] This couplet, slightly varied, occurs again, in the story of the Prince Ḳamar-ez-Zemán and the Princess Budoor.

yard, and live in it securely! Then, shaking his head, and uttering a loud laugh, he merrily sang these verses:—

Would that I beheld at the present moment, in this well, a wolf
Who hath long afflicted my heart, and made me drink bitterness perforce!
Would that my life may be spared, and that the wolf may meet his death!
Then the vineyard will be free from his presence, and I shall find in it my spoil.

Having finished his song, he hurried away until he came to the wolf, when he said to him, Verily God hath smoothed for thee the way to the vineyard without fatigue. This hath happened through thy good fortune. Mayest thou enjoy, therefore, that to which God hath granted thee access, in smoothing thy way to that plunder and that abundant sustenance without any difficulty!—So the wolf said to the fox, What is the proof of that which thou hast declared? The fox answered, I went to the vineyard, and found that its owner had died; and I entered the garden, and beheld the fruits shining upon the trees.

"So the wolf doubted not the words of the fox, and in his eagerness he arose, and went to the breach. His cupidity had deceived him with vain hopes, and the fox stopped and fell down behind him as one dead, applying this verse as a proverb suited to the case:—

Dost thou covet an interview with Leylà?[15] It is covetousness that causeth the loss of men's heads.

And when the wolf came to the breach, the fox said to him, Enter the vineyard; for thou art spared the trouble of breaking down the wall of the garden, and it remaineth

for God to complete the benefit. So the wolf walked forward, desiring to enter the vineyard, and when he came to the middle of the covering of the hole, he fell into it; whereupon the fox was violently excited by happiness and joy; his anxiety and grief ceased, and, in merry tones, he sang these verses:—

Fortune hath compassionated my case, and felt pity for the length of my torment,
And granted me what I desired, and removed that which I dreaded.
I will therefore forgive its offences committed in former times;
Even the injustice it hath shewn in the turning of my hair gray.
There is no escape for the wolf from utter annihilation;
And the vineyard is for me alone, and I have no stupid partner.

He then looked into the pit, and beheld the wolf weeping in his repentance and sorrow for himself, and the fox wept with him. So the wolf raised his head towards him, and said, Is it from thy compassion for me that thou hast wept, O Abu-l-Ḥoṣeyn?[16]—No,

---

15 "Leylà" is a common proper-name of women.

16 "Abu-l-Ḥoṣeyn" is a surname commonly given to the fox; and in some parts, an appellation always given to that animal instead of "thaạlab," which is in those parts applied to the jackal; but I believe that these two animals are often mistaken, one for the other. It signifies "Father (i. e. occupant) of the little fortress."

answered the fox; by Him who cast thee into this pit; but I wept for the length of thy past life, and in my regret at thy not having fallen into this pit before the present day. Hadst thou fallen into it before I met with thee, I had experienced refreshment and ease. But thou hast been spared to the expiration of thy decreed term and known period.—The wolf, however, said to him, Go, O evil-doer, to my mother, and acquaint her with that which hath happened to me: perhaps she will contrive some means for my deliverance. But the fox replied, The excess of thy covetousness and eager desire have entrapped thee into destruction, since thou hast fallen into a pit from which thou wilt never be saved. Knowest thou not, O ignorant wolf, that the author of the proverb saith, He who thinketh not of results will not be secure from perils?—O Abu-l-Ḥoseyn, rejoined the wolf, thou wast wont to manifest an affection for me, and to desire my friendship, and fear the greatness of my power. Be not, then, rancorous towards me for that which I have done unto thee; for he who hath one in his power and yet forgiveth will receive a recompense from God; and the poet hath said,—

Sow good, even on an unworthy soil; for it will not be fruitless wherever it is sown.
Verily, good, though it remain long buried, none will reap but he who sowed it.[17]

—O most ignorant of the beasts of prey, said the fox, and most stupid of the wild beasts of the regions of the earth, hast thou forgotten thy haughtiness and insolence and pride, and thy disregarding the rights of companionship, and thy refusing to be advised by the saying of the poet?—

Tyrannize not, if thou hast the power to do so; for the tyrannical is in danger of revenges.
Thine eye will sleep while the oppressed, wakeful, will call down curses on thee, and God's eye sleepeth not.[18]

—O Abu-l-Ḥoseyn, exclaimed the wolf, be not angry with me for my former offences; for forgiveness is required of the generous, and kind conduct is among the best means of enriching oneself. How excellent is the saying of the poet!—

Haste to do good when thou art able; for at every season thou hast not the power.

"He continued to abase himself to the fox, and said to him, Perhaps thou canst find some means of delivering me from destruction. But the fox replied, O artful, guileful, treacherous wolf, hope not for deliverance; for this is the recompense of thy base conduct, and a just retaliation. Then shaking his jaws with laughing, he recited these two verses:—

No longer attempt to beguile me; for thou wilt not attain thine object.
What thou seekest from me is impossible. Thou hast sown, and reap then, vexation.

—O gentle one among the beasts of prey, resumed the wolf, thou art in my estimation more faithful than to leave me in this pit! He then shed tears, and repeated this couplet:—

O thou whose favours to me have been many, and whose gifts have been more than can be numbered!
No misfortune hath ever yet befallen me but I have found thee ready to aid me in it.

The fox replied, O stupid enemy, how art thou reduced to humility and submissiveness, and abjection and obsequiousness, after thy disdain and pride, and tyranny and haughtiness! I kept company with thee through fear of thine oppression, and flattered thee without a hope of conciliating thy kindness; but now, terror hath affected thee, and punishment hath overtaken thee.—And he recited these two verses:—

O thou who seekest to beguile, thou hast fallen in thy base intention.
Taste, then, the pain of shameful calamity, and be with other wolves cut off.

—The wolf still entreated him, saying, O gentle one, speak not with the tongue of

---

[17] The first verse of this couplet occurs in p. 50 of Vol. I: and four of the verses next preceding occur again, in the story of Ḥasan of El-Baṣrah.

[18] This couplet, slightly varied, occurs in Vol. I. p. 240. I do not note *every* repetition of this kind, because all the verses are *quotations*.

enmity, nor look with its eye; but fulfil the covenant of fellowship with me before the time for discovering a remedy shall have passed. Arise and procure for me a rope, and tie one end of it to a tree, and let down to me its other end, that I may lay hold of it. Perhaps I may so escape from my present predicament, and I will give thee all the treasures that I possess.—The fox, however, replied, Thou hast prolonged a conversation that will not procure thy liberation. Hope not, therefore, for thine escape through my means; but reflect upon thy former wicked conduct, and the perfidy and artifice which thou thoughtest to employ against me, and how near thou art to being stoned. Know that thy soul is about to quit the world, and to perish and depart from it: then wilt thou be reduced to destruction; and an evil abode is it to which thou goest!—O Abu-l-Ḥoseyn, rejoined the wolf, be ready in returning to friendship, and be not so rancorous. Know that he who delivereth a soul from destruction hath saved it alive, and he who saveth a soul alive is as if he had saved the lives of all mankind.[19] Follow not a course of evil; for the wise abhor it; and there is no evil more manifest than my being in this pit, drinking the suffocating pains of death, and looking upon destruction, when thou art able to deliver me from the misery into which I have fallen.—But the fox exclaimed, O thou barbarous, hard-hearted wretch! I compare thee, with respect to the fairness of thy professions and the baseness of thine intention, to the falcon with the partridge. —And what, asked the wolf, is the story of the falcon and the partridge?

"The fox answered, I entered a vineyard one day to eat of its grapes, and while I was there, I beheld a falcon pounce upon a partridge; but when he had captured him, the partridge escaped from him and entered his nest, and concealed himself in it; whereupon the falcon followed him, calling out to him, O idiot, I saw thee in the desert hungry, and, feeling compassion for thee, I gathered for thee some grain, and took hold of thee that thou mightest eat; but thou fleddest from me, and I see no reason for thy flight unless it be to mortify. Shew thyself, then, and take the grain that I have brought thee, and eat it, and may it be light and wholesome to thee.—So when the partridge heard these words of the falcon, he believed him and came forth to him; and the falcon stuck his talons into him, and got possession of him. The partridge, therefore, said to him, Is this that of which thou saidst that thou hadst brought it for me from the desert, and of which thou saidst to me, Eat it, and may it be light and wholesome to thee? Thou hast lied unto me; and may God make that which thou eatest of my flesh to be a mortal poison in thy stomach.—And when he had eaten it, his feathers fell off, and his strength failed, and he forthwith died.

"The fox then continued, Know, O wolf, that he who diggeth a pit for his brother soon falleth into it himself; and thou behavedst with perfidy to me first.—Cease, replied the wolf, from addressing me with this discourse, and propounding fables, and mention not unto me my former base actions. It is enough for me to be in this miserable state, since I have fallen into a calamity for which the enemy would pity me; much more the true friend. Consider some stratagem by means of which I may save myself, and so assist me. If the doing this occasion thee trouble, thou knowest that

[19] These words, "and he who saveth," &c., are from the Ḳur-án, ch. v. v. 35.

the true friend endureth for his own true friend the severest labour, and will suffer destruction in obtaining the means of his deliverance; and it hath been said, An affectionate friend is better than an own brother. If thou procure means for my escape, I will collect for thee such things as shall be a store for thee against the time of want, and then I will teach thee extraordinary stratagems by which thou shalt make the plenteous vineyards accessible, and shalt strip the fruitful trees: so be happy and cheerful.—But the fox said, laughing as he spoke, How excellent is that which the learned have said of him who is excessively ignorant like thee.—And what have the learned said? asked the wolf. The fox answered, The learned have observed, that the rude in body and in disposition is far from intelligence, and nigh unto ignorance; for thine assertion, O perfidious idiot, that the true friend undergoeth trouble for the deliverance of his own true friend, is just, as thou hast said; but acquaint me with thine ignorance, and thy paucity of sense, how I should bear sincere friendship towards thee with thy treachery. Hast thou considered me a true friend unto thee, when I am an enemy who rejoiceth in thy misfortune? These words are more severe than the piercing of arrows, if thou understand. And as to thy saying that thou wilt give me such things as will be a store for me against the time of want, and wilt teach me stratagems by which I shall obtain access to the plenteous vineyards, and strip the fruitful trees—how is it, O guileful traitor, that thou knowest not a stratagem by means of which to save thyself from destruction? How far, then, art thou from profiting thyself, and how far am I from receiving thine advice! If thou know of stratagems, employ them to save thyself from this predicament, from which I pray God to make thine escape far distant. See then, O idiot, if thou know any stratagem, and save thyself by its means from slaughter, before thou lavish instruction upon another. But thou art like a man whom a disease attacked, and to whom there came a man suffering from the same disease to cure him, saying to him, Shall I cure thee of thy disease? The first man therefore said to the other, Why hast thou not begun by curing thyself? So he left him and went his way.—And thou, O wolf, art in the same case. Remain then in thy place, and endure that which hath befallen thee.

"Now when the wolf heard these words of the fox, he knew that he had no kindly feeling for him; so he wept for himself, and said, I have been careless of myself; but if God deliver me from this affliction, I will assuredly repent of my overbearing conduct unto him who is weaker than I; and I will certainly wear wool,[20] and ascend the mountains, commemorating the praises of God (whose name be exalted!), and fearing his punishment; and I will separate myself from all the other wild beasts; and verily I will feed the warriours in defence of the religion, and the poor.—Then he wept and lamented. And thereupon the heart of the fox was moved with tenderness for him. On hearing his humble expressions, and the words which indicated his repenting of arrogance and pride, he was affected with compassion for him, and, leaping with joy, placed himself at the brink of the pit, and sat upon his hind legs, and hung down his tail into the cavity. And upon this, the wolf arose, and stretched forth his paw towards the fox's tail, and pulled him down to him: so the fox was with him in the pit. The wolf then said to him, O fox of little compassion, wherefore didst thou rejoice in my misfortune? Now thou hast become my companion, and in my power. Thou hast fallen into the pit with me, and punishment hath quickly overtaken thee. The sages have said, If any one of you reproach his brother for deriving his nourishment from miserable means, he shall experience the same necessity:—and how excellent is the saying of the poet!—

When Fortune throweth itself heavily upon some, and encampeth by the side of others,
Say to those who rejoice over us, Awake: the rejoicers over us shall suffer as *we* have done.

---

[20] I will wear wool, which is the distinguishing costume of the Ṣoofees and Welees. (Marginal note by the sheykh Moḥammad 'Eiyád.) It is a common custom of the religious devotees among the Muslims to wear woollen garments.

I must now, he continued, hasten thy slaughter, before thou behold mine.—So the fox said within himself, I have fallen into the snare with this tyrant, and my present case requireth the employment of artifice and frauds. It hath been said, that the woman maketh her ornaments for the day of festivity; and, in a proverb, I have not reserved thee, O my tear, but for the time of my difficulty:—and if I employ not some stratagem in the affair of this tyrannical wild beast, I perish inevitably. How good is the saying of the poet!—

Support thyself by guile; for thou livest in an age whose sons are like the lions of a forest;
And brandish around the spear of artifice, that the mill of subsistence may revolve;
And pluck the fruits; or if they be beyond thy reach, then content thyself with herbage.

"He then said to the wolf, Hasten not to kill me, lest thou repent, O courageous wild beast, endowed with might and excessive fortitude. If thou delay, and consider what I am about to tell thee, thou wilt know the desire that I formed; and if thou hasten to kill me, there will be no profit to thee in thy doing so; but we shall die here together.—So the wolf said, O thou wily deceiver, how is it that thou hopest to effect my safety and thine own, that thou askest me to give thee a delay? Acquaint me with the desire that thou formedst.—The fox replied, As to the desire that I formed, it was such as requireth thee to recompense me for it well; since, when I heard thy promises, and thy confession of thy past conduct, and thy regret at not having before repented, and done good, and when I heard thy vows to abstain from injurious conduct to thy companions and others, and to relinquish the eating of the grapes and all other fruits, and to impose upon thyself the obligation of humility, and clipping thy claws, and breaking thy dog-teeth, and to wear wool, and offer sacrifice to God (whose name be exalted!), if He delivered thee from thy present state, I was affected with compassion for thee, though I was before longing for thy destruction. So when I heard thy profession of repentance, and what thou vowedst to do if God delivered thee, I felt constrained to save thee from thy present predicament. I therefore hung down my tail that thou mightest catch hold of it and make thine escape. But thou wouldst not relinquish thy habit of severity and violence, nor desire escape and safety for thyself by gentleness. On the contrary, thou pulledst me in such a manner that I thought my soul had departed: so I became a companion with thee in the abode of destruction and death; and nothing will effect the escape of myself and thee but one plan. If thou approve of this plan that I have to propose, we shall both save ourselves; and after that, it will be incumbent on thee to fulfil that which thou hast vowed to do, and I will be thy companion.—So the wolf said, And what is thy proposal that I am to accept? The fox answered, That thou raise thyself upright; then I will place myself upon thy head, that I may approach the surface of the earth, and when I am upon its surface I will go forth and bring thee something of which to take hold, and after that thou wilt deliver thyself. But the wolf replied, I put no confidence in thy words; for the sages have said, He who confideth when he should hate, is in error:—and it hath been said, He who confideth in the faithless is deceived, and he who maketh trial of the trier will repent, and he who distinguisheth not between circumstances, and attributeth to each its proper success, but regardeth all circumstances alike, his fortune will be small, and his calamities will be many. How excellent also is the saying of the poet!—

Let not your opinion be otherwise than evil; for ill opinion is among the strongest of intellectual qualities.
Nothing casteth a man into a place of danger like the practice of good, and a fair opinion.

And the saying of another:—

Always hold an evil opinion, and so be safe. Whoso liveth vigilantly, his calamities will be few.
Meet the enemy with a smiling and an open face; but raise for him an army in the heart to combat him.

And that of another:[21]—

> The most bitter of thine enemies is the nearest whom thou trustest in: beware then of men, and associate with them wilily.
> Thy favourable opinion of fortune is a weakness: think evil of it, therefore, and regard it with apprehension.

—Verily, rejoined the fox, an evil opinion is not commendable in every case; but a fair opinion is among the characteristics of excellence, and its result is escape from terrors. It is befitting, O wolf, that thou employ some stratagem for thine escape from thy present predicament; and it will be better for us both to escape than to die. Relinquish, therefore, thine evil opinion and thy malevolence; for if thou think favourably of me, I shall not fail to do one of two things: either I shall bring thee something of which to lay hold, and thou wilt escape from thy present situation, or I shall act perfidiously towards thee, and save myself and leave thee; but this is a thing that cannot be; for I am not secure from meeting with some such affliction as that which thou hast met with, and that would be the punishment of perfidy. It hath been said in a proverb, Fidelity is good, and perfidy is base. It is fit, then, that thou trust in me; for I have not been ignorant of misfortunes. Delay not, therefore, to contrive our escape; for the affair is too strait for thee to prolong thy discourse upon it.

"The wolf then said, Verily, notwithstanding my little confidence in thy fidelity, I knew what was in thy heart, that thou desiredst my deliverance when thou wast convinced of my repentance; and I said within myself, If he be veracious in that which he asserteth, he hath made amends for his wickedness; and if he be false, he will be recompensed by his Lord. So now I accept thy proposal to me; and if thou act perfidiously towards me, thy perfidy will be the means of thy destruction.—Then the wolf raised himself upright in the pit, and took the fox upon his shoulders, so that his head reached the surface of the ground. The fox thereupon sprang from the wolf's shoulders, and found himself upon the face of the earth, when he fell down senseless. The wolf now said to him, O my friend, forget not my case, nor delay my deliverance.

"The fox, however, uttered a loud laugh, and replied, O thou deceived; it was nothing but my jesting with thee and deriding thee that entrapped me into thy power; for when I heard thy profession of repentance, joy excited me, and I was moved with delight, and danced, and my tail hung down into the pit; so thou pulledst me, and I fell down to thee. Then God (whose name be exalted!) delivered me from thy hand. Wherefore, then, should I not aid in thy destruction, when thou art of the associates of the Devil? Know that I dreamt yesterday that I was dancing at thy wedding, and I related the dream to an interpreter, who said to me, Thou wilt fall into a frightful danger, and escape from it. So I knew that my falling into thy power and my escape was the interpretation of my dream. Thou too knowest, O deceived idiot, that I am thine enemy. How then dost thou hope, with thy little sense and thine ignorance, that I will deliver thee, when thou hast heard what rude language I used? And how shall I endeavour to deliver thee, when the learned have said, that by the death of the sinner are produced ease to mankind and purgation of the earth. Did I not fear that I should suffer, by fidelity to thee, such affliction as would be greater than that which may result from perfidy, I would consider upon means for thy deliverance.—So when the wolf heard the words of the fox, he bit his paw in repentance.[22] He then spoke softly to him; but obtained nothing thereby. With a low voice he said to him, Verily, you tribe of foxes are the sweetest of people in tongue, and the most pleasant in jesting; and this is jesting in thee; but every time is not convenient for sport and joking.—O

---

[21] Eṭ-Ṭughráee, the author of the "Lámeeyet el-'Ajam." (Marginal note by the sheykh Moḥammad 'Eiyád.)

[22] "Biting one's hand" is a common expression of the Arabs, similar to ours of "biting one's lip." The action denoted by the former expression I have witnessed on more than one occasion. A friend of mine in Cairo had a frequent habit of doing thus in jest.

idiot, replied the fox, jesting hath a limit which its employer transgresseth not. Think not that God will give thee possession of me after He hath delivered me from thy power.—The wolf then said to him, Thou art one in whom it is proper to desire my liberation, on account of the former brotherhood and friendship that subsisted between us; and if thou deliver me, I will certainly recompense thee well. But the fox replied, The sages have said, Take not as thy brother the ignorant and wicked; for he will disgrace thee, and not honour thee: and take not as thy brother the liar; for if good proceed from thee he will hide it, and if evil proceed from thee he will publish it. And the sages have said, For everything there is a stratagem, except death; and everything may be rectified, except the corruption of the very essence; and everything may be repelled, except destiny. And as to the recompense that thou assertest I deserve of thee, I compare thee, in thy recompensing, to the serpent fleeing from the Ḥáwee,[23] when a man saw her in a state of terror, and said to her, What is the matter with thee, O serpent? She answered, I have fled from the Ḥáwee; for he seeketh me; and if thou deliver me from him, and conceal me with thee, I will recompense thee well and do thee every kindness. So the man took her, to obtain the reward, and eager for the recompense, and put her into his pocket; and when the Ḥáwee had passed and gone his way, and what she feared had quitted her, the man said to her, Where is the recompense? for I have saved thee from that which thou fearedst and dreadedst. But the serpent answered him, Tell me in what member I shall bite thee; for thou knowest that we exceed not this recompense. She then inflicted upon him a bite from which he died.—And thee, O idiot, continued the fox, I compare to that serpent with that man. Hast thou not heard the saying of the poet?—

> Trust not a person in whose heart thou hast made anger to dwell; nor think his anger hath ceased.
>
> Verily, the vipers, which are smooth to the touch, and shew graceful motions, hide mortal poison.

—O eloquent and comely-faced animal, rejoined the wolf, be not ignorant of my condition, and of the fear with which mankind regard me. Thou knowest that I assault the strong places, and strip the vines. Do, therefore, what I have commanded thee, and attend to me as the slave attendeth to his master.—O ignorant idiot, who seekest what is vain, exclaimed the fox, verily I wonder at thy stupidity, and at the roughness of thy manner, in thine ordering me to serve thee and to stand before thee as though I were thy slave. But thou shalt soon see what will befall thee, by the splitting of thy head with stones, and the breaking of thy treacherous dog-teeth.

"The fox then stationed himself upon a mound overlooking the vineyard, and cried out incessantly to the people of the vineyard until they perceived him and came quickly to him. He remained steady before them until they drew near unto him and unto the pit in which was the wolf, and then he fled. So the owners of the vineyard looked into the pit, and when they beheld the wolf in it, they instantly pelted him with heavy stones, and continued throwing stones and pieces of wood upon him, and piercing him with the points of spears, until they killed him, when they departed. Then the fox returned to the pit, and, standing over the place of the wolf's slaughter, saw him dead; whereupon he shook his head in the excess of his joy, and recited these verses:—

> Fate removed the wolf's soul, and it was snatched away. Far distant [from happiness] be his soul that hath perished!
>
> How long hast thou striven, Aboo-Sirḥán,[24] to destroy me! But now have burning calamities befallen thee.
>
> Thou hast fallen into a pit into which none shall descend without finding in it the blasts of death.

---

[23] The Ḥáwee is a performer of sleight-of-hand tricks, and various feats with serpents, &c., which I have described in my work on the Modern Egyptians, vol. ii. ch. vii.

[24] This is an appellation of the wolf.

—After this, the fox remained in the vineyard, alone and in security, fearing no mischief."

NOTE 2. In several copies, and perhaps in most, this person is called an "'Aṭṭár," which appellation is generally given not merely to a seller of essences, but to a druggist and perfumer.

NOTE 3. The word which I here render "Persians" (namely "'Ajam") is applied to any and all people who are not Arabs; but often to the Persians in particular; and this seems to be here required by the subsequent expression of *the* King of the 'Ajam. Here I may also remark, that the phrase "of the *sons* of the Kings," &c., is often used to signify "of the *descendants* of the Kings," &c.; and that it would have been more consistent to have employed this phrase, as applied to 'Alee the son of Bekkár, in a later passage, instead of "son of the King;" for he is not distinguished in the story as a Prince.

NOTE 4.—*On the Custom of frequenting Shops for the sake of Amusement.* It is perfectly consistent with Arab manners and customs, as existing in the present day and as exhibited in histories, to describe Abu-l-Ḥasan as keeping company with the Khaleefeh, and 'Alee the son of Bekkár as being in the habit of sitting at Abu-l-Ḥasan's shop. Among the Muslims in general, trade is far more honourable than it is in the estimation of a large proportion of the independent classes in this country; so much so, that it is regarded by the former as disgraceful in a man, however high his rank, or great his wealth, not to be able, by some occupation, as the profession of arms or of literature or science, or by some trade or art, to procure his subsistence in case of necessity: therefore the pursuit of trade excludes no man of good breeding among them from the society of his superiors in rank. But the free intercourse of different ranks of Muslims is further and very greatly promoted by the law of the separation of the sexes; persons being thus enabled to associate with each other, regardless of difference of wealth or station, without the risk of occasioning unequal matrimonial connections: so this law, being felt by neither sex as oppressive, is regarded by them as productive of results which constitute the Muslim's chief enjoyments,—the highest degree of domestic comfort, and the most free and extensive society with his fellow-men. Thus it is with both sexes; and neither would give up the pleasure that they hence derive for a different system of society, somewhat extending their domestic intercourse, but often destroying the pleasures of home, and contracting into a compass comparatively narrow the fellowship which they enjoy abroad.

The Arabs in general seldom give entertainments except on particular occasions, such as that of a marriage, or a circumcision; and hence, as well as for the reasons above stated, a shop is often frequented for the purpose of passing time in agreeable conversation. For women to do this, in the present day, is not considered decent; but they have their places of resort as well as the other sex: with them, a visit to the bath is a much longer and more social affair than it is with the men: and there they indulge in free conversation with strangers of their own sex. In their visits to their friends and relations, also, they have an advantage over the men; for not only are these visits frequent, but all the female inmates of a house generally accompany the mistress, the stay is often prolonged from an early hour until near sunset, and the guests are liberally and merrily entertained.—But I must return to the shop.—Much of the pleasure and much of the profit that I derived while living in Cairo was obtained at the shops of persons with whom I was acquainted, and at those of strangers. The reader of the present work has a sufficient notion of the general construction of Arab shops to see that a person seated on the maṣṭabah may enjoy at the same time conversation with the owner, and perhaps with other visiters, and a close and unobstructed view of whatever is passing in the street. I regret that I did not often adopt the proper means of preserving a complete recollection of what I heard and witnessed at places of this kind: had I done so, I might here offer to the reader something more entertaining than the following extract from a journal in which I sometimes, when in an idle mood, wrote the occurrences of the day, during my second visit to Egypt.

Oct. 27th (1834).—I generally pay a visit to the shop of the Báshà's booksellers (two persons employed to sell the books which are printed at the government-press) on the mornings of Monday and Thursday, when auction-markets are held in the street where the shop is situate, and in the neighbouring mart called Khán El-Khaleelee[25] (the chief Turkish bázár), occasioning the street to be much crowded, and to present an amusing scene; but I am often more amused with the persons who frequent the shop where I take my seat. I found there, to-day, an old man, a celebrated character, whose name I must not mention: he had been possessed of large property; but the greater part of it had been confiscated; he, however, had contrived to hide much of his wealth, and has since employed friends to trade with it privately; so that he has still a large income; one-third of which he always gives to the poor!—The elder of the two booksellers was relating his having just purchased a house. There lived next door to him, he said, a fiḳee,[26] a member of the Azhar, and of some repute, to whom belonged fourteen ḳeeráṭs (or twenty-fourth parts) of the house in which he (the fiḳee) lodged: the other ten ḳeeráṭs of this house were the property of a tailor. The bookseller's house was entered, from the roof, and plundered, three times, of wheat, butter, &c.; and the fiḳee was accused by him of having committed these thefts, and confessed that he had; urging, in palliation, that he had only taken his food. The bookseller caused him to be imprisoned in the citadel; and, after he had been confined there many days, offered to procure his liberation if he would sell to him his share of the house. This was done: it was sold for six purses and a half.[27] The bookseller then desired to possess himself of the tailor's share, and proposed to him to repair or separate or sell; for the house was in a very dilapidated state; but he refused to comply with any one of these requisitions: he was therefore summoned to the court of the Ḳáḍee, and compelled to sell his share; for which he demanded five purses. Having received this sum of money, he met, on his way home, a friend, whom he told what he had done. "O fool!" said the friend: "thou mightest have asked ten purses, and it would have been given." And the tailor no sooner heard these words than he threw down the bag in the middle of the street, kicked off his shoes, and for several minutes continued slapping his face, and crying out, like a woman, "O my sorrow!" He then snatched up the bag, and ran away with it, crying in the same manner all the way, and leaving his friend to follow

25 El-Maḳreezee says that this Khán was built by El-Khaleelee in the latter half of the eighth century of the Flight, on the site of the burial-ground of the Fáṭimee Khaleefehs, whose bones were thrown upon the mounds of rubbish outside the city. This and other interesting facts of the same kind relating to Cairo and the history of Egypt under Muslim domination have been given in the "Englishwoman in Egypt," a work to which I ought to have referred the reader in an earlier page, as it presents a series of remarkably-faithful pictures of Arab and Turkish female society.—Ed.

26 This is the common appellation of a person of the inferior class of professors of religion and law.

27 A purse is the sum of five hundred piasters: it was then equivalent exactly to five pounds sterling.

him with his shoes.—Soon after the bookseller had told this story, there joined us a Persian darweesh, whom I had often met there before, and a fat, merry-looking, red-faced man, loaded with ragged clothing, shewing the edge of a curly head of hair below his turban, and carrying a long staff. Everybody at the shop, except myself, kissed his hand: he offered his hand to me, and, after taking it, I kissed my own; and he did the like. I was informed that he was a celebrated welee, or saint. He took snuff, smoked from my pipe, and had a constant smile upon his countenance; though he seldom spoke: almost the only words that he uttered were a warm commendation of an answer which I gave to the Persian: on his (the Persian's) asking me why I had not already departed from Cairo, as I had intended, I said that the servant of God was passive, and not elective; and this sentiment, though common, seemed much to please the welee: he repeated it with emphasis.—There next joined us a man of a very respectable and intelligent appearance, applying for a copy of the sheykh Rifá'ah's account of his visit to France, lately printed at Booláḳ. Asking what were the general contents of this book, a person present answered him, that the author relates his voyage from Alexandria to Marseilles; how he got drunk on board the ship, and was tied to the mast and flogged; that he ate pork in the land of infidelity and obstinacy, and that it is a most excellent meat; how he was delighted with the French girls, and how superior they are in charms to the women of Egypt; and, having qualified himself, by every accomplishment, for an eminent place in Hell, returned to his native country. This was an ironical quizz on the sheykh Rifá'ah, for his strict, conscientious adherence to the precepts of El-Islám during his voyage, and his residence in France. The applicant for this book had a cataract in each of his eyes; and I advised him to seek relief from the French surgeon Clot Bey; but he said that he was afraid to go to the hospital; for he had heard that many patients there were killed and boiled, to make skeletons: he afterwards, however, on my assuring him that his fears were groundless, promised to go.—While I was talking with him, there began to pass by the shop a long funeral-train, consisting of numerous fiḳees, and many of the eminent 'Ulamà. On my asking whose funeral it was, I was answered, "The Sheykh El-Menzeláwee," Sheykh of the Saạdeeyeh darweeshes. I was surprised, having seen him a few days before in apparently good health. Presently I saw him walking in the funeral-procession: so I asked again; but was answered as before. "Why," said I, "praise be to God, the Sheykh is walking with you, in good health." I was then told that the deceased was his wife. Some Saạdeeyeh in the procession were performing a zikr as they passed along; repeating the word "Alláh!" When the bier came in view, I heard the women who followed uttering their zagháreeṭ, or cries of joy, instead of lamenting; for the deceased was a famous saint. She was the sister of the late Sheykh of the Saạdeeyeh; and it is believed that her husband, the present Sheykh, derives his miraculous powers from her. It is said that she prophesied, yesterday, the exact hour of her death this day. The women began to lament when the corpse left the house; and, as is usually the case when this is done at the funeral of a saint, the bearers declared that they could not move it: as soon as the lamentations were changed to the cries of joy, the bearers pretended to find their work quite easy.

Note 5. "Shems-en-Nahár" signifies "the Sun of Day."

Note 6. The masculine seems to be here used for the feminine gender. See Note 36 to Chapter viii.

Note 7. See Note 25 to Chapter vi., on the modern custom of shaving the head.

Note 8. In this verse, the wine-cup is compared to the sun, the teeth of the cup-bearer are likened to the Pleiades, and his face is compared to the full moon.

Note 9. "'Afeef" signifies "Chaste," and "Abstinent."

NOTE 10. This order was given to make the messengers suppose that she had been sleeping. See Note 55 to Chapter iii.

NOTE 11. Waṣeef," here used as a proper name, signifies "a young man-servant."

NOTE 12. A procession similar to that here described is seen in the streets of Cairo, when a bridegroom returns to his house, from the mosque, where he has performed the prayers of nightfall previously to his first visit to the bride. He and his friends and other attendants proceed in the form of an oblong ring, all facing the interior of the ring (so that the foremost walk backwards), and each bearing in his hand one or more wax candles, and sometimes a sprig of ḥennà or some other flower, except the bridegroom and the friend on either side of him. These three form the latter part of the ring, which generally consists of twenty or more persons. The procession is headed by musicians, by persons carrying mesh'als (or cresset-lights), and by others bearing lamps.

NOTE 13. "Gharám" signifies "Desire," "Vehemence of Desire," or "Passion," &c.

NOTE 14. I use the modern term "Bedaweeyeh" (signifying an Arab female of the Desert) for the old appellation "Aạrábeeyeh."

NOTE 15. The word which I render "laurel," namely "rend," is also applied to the myrtle, and to aloes-wood. The willow (which is of the kind called Oriental) and the rend are here to be understood as emblems of the object of the Bedaweeyeh's love.

NOTE 16. Clapping the hands (striking the palm of the left hand with the fingers of the right) is the usual mode of summoning a servant.

NOTE 17. This, I suppose, is meant to imply that the disorder of her mind incapacitated her from using the pen.—The substitution of the masculine gender for the feminine (as in the verses preceding) is not uncommon.

NOTE 18. There is an omission here in the Cairo edition, and it appears, from the edition of Breslau, that what is given in the former as the contents of Shems-en-Nahár's letter consists partly of her letter and partly of 'Alee's answer. I supply the omission (ending with the words, "and by thy head, O my mistress,") from the Calcutta edition of the first two hundred nights, to avoid the necessity of using my own judgment in correcting the blunders which here, as usual, occur in the Breslau edition, though the latter differs less in its context, than the former, from my standard copy,

NOTE 19. The meaning of this is, "Thou hast dealings with the *women* of the palace."—"How is thy house?" is a phrase often used as a delicate mode of inquiring respecting the health of a man's wife or ḥareem.

NOTE 20. My sheykh remarks, that this relates to the departure of Abu-l-Ḥasan; but, from what follows, I think it rather applies to the slave-girl.

NOTE 21. By his praying for her, is merely meant his uttering some such words as "God keep thee!" or "God bless thee!"

NOTE 22. The word which I render "wine" is "ḳahweh," which is the term now applied to "coffee." I believe coffee to be here meant by it; but probably it is an error or interpolation of a copyist.

NOTE 23. El-Moạtaṣim, the son, and third successor, of Hároon Er-Rasheed, is said to have been the first Khaleefeh who formed a military corps of foreigners (in this case, Turkish slaves); and from his time, the natives of the greater part of the Arabian Empire gradually became subject to the military despotism of Turkish and other foreign guards and governors. Thus it was in Egypt and Syria under the Memlook Sulṭáns, who originated in the corps formed by Eṣ-Ṣáliḥ Eiyoob, the last of the dynasty of Ṣaláḥ-ed-Deen; and thus it continued after the conquest of those countries by the 'Osmánlee Turks under the Sulṭán Seleem, until Moḥammad 'Alee, after he had exterminated or expelled the Memlook forces, organized his Egyptian troops, and almost entirely displaced the Turkish soldiery.

Note 24. I have substituted "other men" for "another man."

Note 25. I have remarked in my work on the Modern Egyptians, that it is almost impossible for a woman to have a private interview with a man who has a ḥareem in his own house; or to enter the house of a man who is neither married nor has a concubine-slave, without attracting the notice of the neighbours, and causing their immediate interference. This remark applies to those cases in which the two parties are not very nearly related.

During my second residence in Egypt, the wives of my servants often came to my house in Cairo, yet they never ventured to enter it. A maid-servant, about nine years of age, frequently brought messages to me from her master, and came up into my sitting-room when I was alone; but this caused no scandal. On one occasion, however, my character was called in question: I was accused of admitting a woman into my room, and had some difficulty to satisfy my neighbours and others. I had purchased some female ornaments and attire of the head, and, having a friend with me, a man between forty and fifty years of age, I induced him to put them on in the place of his turban, that I might the better judge of them; then seating him in a projecting window next the street, for the sake of a foolish joke I suddenly opened a small casement at his side, and thrust forth his head. But little did I expect the result. A bean-seller, sitting at his shop in the street, nearly opposite, saw the apparition, and pointed it out to two or three other persons, and soon there collected before the house a little crowd, whom the bean-seller began to harangue, expressing his astonishment that an Efendee like myself, one who had always appeared to him to have conducted himself most respectably, should have been guilty of so foul an action as that of introducing a woman into his house, having no ḥareem: that a person devoted to study, and one whom sheykhs of the Azhar [28] frequented, and who delighted in attending the religious festivals, should act in so shameless a manner! I began to be uneasy at witnessing and hearing what passed; and the people were consulting as to the course they should pursue, when I compelled my friend, who had quickly withdrawn his head, to shew it again, and exhibit his beard; whereupon the bean-seller was still more amazed, at recognising the well-known countenance of a respected sheykh, one connected with the Azhar too, who had a hundred times saluted him in approaching my door. But this did not satisfy his audience nor himself: it was suspected that the sheykh was a party to my offence; and it was only by constraining the latter to go down into the street and explain the whole affair, that tranquillity was restored. My character, eventually, did not suffer even from the imputation of a culpable deviation from general custom; as practical jokes are not uncommon among the Arabs in the best society.

Note 26. The ḳánoon is a kind of dulcimer, of which I have given engravings and a description in my work on the Modern Egyptians (vol. ii. ch. v.).[29] Its name is from the Greek κανὼν, or from the same origin; and has the same signification; that is, "rule," "law," "custom." It is laid upon the knees of the performer, and played with two plectra, attached to the fore fingers; each plectrum being placed between the finger and a ring, or thimble. There are three chords (of lamb's gut) to each note, and generally, altogether, twenty-four treble chords.

Note 27.—*On the State of the Soul between Death and the Judgment.* It is believed that the soul remains with the body until the expiration of the first night after the burial, when it departs to the place appointed for the abode of good souls until the last

[28] The great collegiate mosque of Cairo.

[29] A female playing on the ḳánoon is the subject of the tail-piece to these notes.

day, or to the appointed prison in which wicked souls await their final doom; but with respect to the state of souls in the interval between death and judgment, there are various opinions, which Sale thus states.[30] As to the souls of the good, he says, "1st. Some say that they stay near the sepulchres; with liberty, however, of going wherever they please; which they confirm from Moḥammad's manner of saluting them at their graves, and his affirming that the dead heard those salutations as well as the living, though they could not answer. Whence perhaps proceeded the custom of visiting the tombs of relations, so common among the Mohammadans. 2ndly. Others imagine they are with Adam, in the lowest heaven; and also support their opinion by the authority of their prophet, who gave out that in his return from the upper heavens in his pretended night-journey, he saw there the souls of those who were destined to paradise on the right hand of Adam, and those who were condemned to hell on his left. 3rdly. Others fancy the souls of believers remain in the well Zemzem, and those of infidels in a certain well in the province of Ḥaḍramót, called Barahoot;[31] but this opinion is branded as heretical. [On this subject, however, see the next paragraph.] 4thly. Others say they stay near the graves for seven days; but that whither they go afterwards is uncertain. 5thly. Others, that they are all in the trumpet, whose sound is to raise the dead. And 6thly. Others, that the souls of the good dwell in the forms of white birds, under the throne of God. As to the condition of the souls of the wicked, besides the opinions that have been already mentioned, the more orthodox hold that they are offered by the angels to heaven, from whence being repulsed as stinking and filthy, they are offered to the earth, and being also refused a place there, are carried down to the seventh earth, and thrown into a dungeon, which they call Sijjeen, under a green rock, or according to a tradition of Moḥammad, under the devil's jaw, to be there tormented till they are called up to be joined again to their bodies."—But the souls of prophets are believed to be admitted immediately into paradise, and those of martyrs are said to rest in the crops of green birds which eat of the fruits of paradise and drink of its rivers.

Of the opinions above mentioned, with respect to the souls of the faithful, I believe the first to be that which is most prevalent. It is generally said, that these souls visit their respective graves every Friday; and according to some, they return to their bodies on that day, after the period of the afternoon prayers, and on Saturday and Monday; or on Thursday, Friday, and Saturday; and remain until sunrise.[32]—I believe also, from having heard frequent allusions made to it, as a thing not to be doubted, that the opinion respecting the Well of Barahoot commonly prevails in the present day. El-Ḳazweenee says of it, "It is a well *near* Ḥaḍramót; and the Prophet (God bless and save him!) said, 'In it are the souls of the infidels and hypocrites.' It is an 'Ádite well, [i. e. ancient, as though made by the ancient tribe of 'Ád,] in a dry desert, and a gloomy valley; and it is related of 'Alee (may God be well pleased with him!), that he said, 'The most hateful of districts unto God (whose name be exalted!) is the Valley of Barahoot, in which is a well whose water is black and fetid, where the souls of the infidels make their abode.' El-Aṣma'ee hath related of a man of Ḥaḍramót, that he said, 'We find near Barahoot an extremely-disgusting and fetid smell, and then news is brought to us of the death of a great man of the chiefs of the infidels.' It is related also, that a man who passed a night in the Valley of Barahoot said, 'I heard all the night [exclamations of] O Roomeh! O Roomeh!—and I mentioned this to a learned man, and he told me that it was the name of the angel commissioned to keep guard over the souls of the infidels.'"[33]

---

[30] Preliminary Discourse, sect. iv.

[31] So in the Ḳámoos, and in my MS. of the Ajáïb el-Makhlooḳát of El-Ḳazweenee; but by Sale written "Borhût."

[32] Murshid ez-Zoowár ilà Ḳuboor el-Abrár (the Director of the Visiters to the Tombs of the Just) by 'Abd-Er-Raḥmán El-Khazrejee El-Anṣáree: MS. in my possession.

[33] 'Ajáïb el-Makhlooḳát.

NOTE 28. The emancipation of slaves on the occasion of a death is a custom often observed. Sometimes this is done in accordance with the will of the deceased: at other times, by the free will of the heirs; but in the latter cases, the merit of the act is transferred to the soul of the deceased; its object being, to increase his happiness in the future world.

CHAPTER X.

COMMENCING WITH THE HUNDRED AND SEVENTIETH NIGHT, AND ENDING WITH PART OF THE TWO HUNDRED AND FORTY-NINTH.

THE STORY OF THE PRINCE KAMAR-EZ-ZEMÁN AND THE PRINCESS BUDOOR.[1]

There was, in ancient times, a King named Sháh-Zemán,[2] possessing numerous troops and attendants and guards. He dwelt in the Islands of Khálidán,[3] which are adjacent to the country of the Persians;[4] and had married four daughters of Kings, besides whom he had among his female slaves sixty concubines. His age, however, was advanced, and his bones were wasted, and he had not been blessed with a son: so he meditated in his mind, and mourned and was disquieted, and complained of this to one of his wezeers, saying, I fear that, when I die, my kingdom will be lost; for I have no son to succeed to it after me. But the Wezeer replied, Perhaps God will yet bring to pass some event: therefore place thy reliance upon God, O King, and perform the ablution, and recite the prayers of two rek'ahs.[5] It is also my advice that thou give a banquet, and invite to it the poor and the needy, and let them eat of it and pray to God (whose name be exalted!) that He may bless thee with a son: perchance there may be among them a pure soul, whose prayer, being righteous, will be answered.[6] After that thou wilt probably obtain thy desire.—The King complied with his advice, and his wife conceived, and when she had completed her months she gave birth to a male child like the unclouded full moon in the dark night: so he named him Ḳamar-ez-Zemán.[7] He rejoiced at his birth with the utmost joy, and they decorated the city for seven days; the drums were beaten, and the messengers imparted the glad tidings; the nurses and the midwives carried him, and he was reared with magnificence and fondness until he attained the age of fifteen years.

He was of surpassing beauty and comeliness, and justness of stature and form, and his father loved him so that he could not be absent from him by night nor by day; and the King Sháh-Zemán complained to one of his wezeers of the excess of his love for his son, saying, O Wezeer, I fear for my son Ḳamar-ez-Zemán from the calamities and accidents of fortune, and desire to marry him during my life. The Wezeer therefore replied, Know, O King, that marriage is laudable, and there will be no harm in thy marrying thy son during thy life. So upon this the King Sháh-Zemán said, Bring hither to me my son Ḳamar-ez-Zemán. And he came, and hung down his head towards the ground in modesty before his father. His father then said to him, O Ḳamar-ez-Zemán, know that I desire to marry thee and to rejoice in thee during my life. But he replied, Know, O my father, that I have no need of marriage, and my soul inclineth not to women; for I have found books with narratives of their fraudulence, and miracles have been occasioned by their cunning. The poet hath said,—

> If ye ask my opinion of women, I will tell you that I am a physician acquainted with their affairs:
> When the head of a man hath become gray, or his wealth is diminished, he hath no share of their affection.

And another hath said,—

> Oppose women; for so wilt thou obey [God] becomingly; since the youth will not prosper who giveth them his rein:
> They will hinder him from attaining perfection in his excellencies though he pass a thousand years in the study of science.

—After reciting these verses he added, O my father, marriage is a thing that I will never do, though I be made to drink the cup of perdition. And when the King Sháh-Zemán heard these words of his son, the light became darkness before his face, and he was grieved excessively at the want of obedience which his son Ḳamar-ez-Zemán manifested towards him: yet, from the love that he bore him, he repeated not what he had said, nor provoked him to anger: on the contrary, he shewed favour and regard towards him, and treated him with every kind of fondness that could draw affection to the heart.

Meanwhile, Ḳamar-ez-Zemán increased every day in beauty and comeliness, and in elegance and tenderness of manner. The King Sháh-Zemán bore with him patiently for a whole year, until he became perfect in eloquence and grace: mankind were ravished by his beauty, and every zephyr that blew wafted the praises of his loveliness: he became a temptation unto lovers, and as a paradise to the desirous; sweet in his speech; his face put to shame the full moon; he was endowed with justness of stature and form, and with graceful and engaging manners, resembling a twig of the Oriental willow or an Indian cane, and his cheek supplied the place of the anemone, as his

figure did that of the willow-branch. He was graceful as the poet hath said in thus describing him:—

> He appeared, and they said, Blessed be Allah! Glory be to Him who moulded and perfected him!
> He is King of the comely universally; for all of them have become subjects unto him.
> The moisture of his mouth is like melted honey; and his teeth are like pearls joined together.
> All charms are united in him alone, and all mankind are confounded at his loveliness.
> Beauty hath written upon his cheek, I acknowledge that no one is comely but he.

Now when he had completed another year, his father called him and said to him, O my son, wilt thou not listen to my words? And upon this Ḳamar-ez-Zemán fell down upon the floor before his father, through awe and shame, and said to him, O my father, how should I refuse to attend to thy words, when God hath commanded me to obey thee, and to abstain from opposing thee? So the King Sháh-Zemán continued, Know, O my son, that I desire to marry thee and to rejoice in thee during my life, and to make thee Sulṭán over my dominions before my death. But when Ḳamar-ez-Zemán heard these words of his father, he hung down his head for a while; after which he raised it, and replied, O my father, this is a thing that I will never do, though I be made to drink the cup of perdition. I know that God hath imposed on me the obligation of yielding obedience unto thee; but by his claims upon thee I conjure thee that thou constrain me not to marry: and think not that I will marry during the whole course of my life; for I have perused the books of the former and the later generations, and known all the calamities and misfortunes that have happened to them through the disturbances occasioned by women, and their endless artifice, and the disasters that have proceeded from them. How excellent is the saying of the poet:—

> He whom shameless women have entrapped will never see deliverance,
> Though he build a thousand castles encrusted over with lead;
> For their construction will not avail: the fortresses will not profit.
> Verily women are treacherous to every one near and distant:
> With their fingers dyed with ḥennà; with their hair arranged in plaits;
> With their eyelids painted with koḥl; they make one to drink of sorrows.[8]

—And when the King Sháh-Zemán heard these words from his son Ḳamar-ez-Zemán, and understood the verses that he quoted, he returned him not an answer, from the excess of his affection for him; but treated him with increased favours and consideration.

The assembly broke up immediately; and after it was dissolved, the King Sháh-Zemán summoned his Wezeer, and in private said to him, O Wezeer, tell me what I shall do in the affair of my son Ḳamar-ez-Zemán; for I consulted thee on the subject of marrying him as preparatory to making him Sulṭán, and thou advisedst me to do so, and to mention the matter of marriage to him: so I proposed it to him, and he disobeyed me: acquaint me, therefore, now, with that which thou seest to be best. The Wezeer replied, That which I advise thee to do, O King, is, that thou have patience with him for another year; and when thou desirest to speak to him after that on the subject of marriage, speak not to him privately, but address him on a judgment-day, when all the emeers and wezeers are present, and all the troops are standing before thee. Then, when all these are assembled, send to thy son Ḳamar-ez-Zemán, and summon him to thy presence; and when he hath come, address him on the subject of marriage in the presence of all the emeers and wezeers, and the chamberlains and lieutenants, and other lords of the empire, and the soldiers and the impetuous warriours; for he will be bashful before them, and will not be able to oppose thee in their presence.—And when the King Sháh-Zemán heard these words of his Wezeer, he rejoiced exceedingly; he approved of the Wezeer's advice, and bestowed upon him a magnificent robe of honour.[9]

The King Sháh-Zemán had patience with his son Ḳamar-ez-Zemán another year; and every day that passed over him, the latter increased in beauty and loveliness, and in elegance and consummate grace, until he had nearly attained the age of twenty years. God clad him with the apparel of comeliness, and crowned him with the crown of perfection: his eye was more enchanting then Hároot;[10] and the play of his glance, more seductive than Eṭ-Ṭághoot:[11] his cheeks shone with redness; and his eye-lashes scorned the sharp, piercing sword:[12] the whiteness of his forehead resembled the shining moon; and the blackness of his hair was like the dark night.—The King Sháh-Zemán, having attended to the words of the Wezeer, waited another year until a festival-day, when the King's court was attended by all the emeers and wezeers, and the chamberlains and other lords of the empire, and the soldiers and impetuous warriours. He then sent for his son Ḳamar-ez-Zemán, who, when he came, kissed the ground before him three times, and stood before his father with his hands placed together behind his back.[13] And his father said to him, Know, O my son, that I have summoned thee on this occasion before the

present assembly, with all the troops before me, for the purpose of giving thee a command, and do not thou oppose me in that which I say. It is, that thou marry; for I desire to marry thee to a daughter of one of the Kings, and to rejoice in thee before my death.—But when Ḳamar-ez-Zemán heard these words of his father, he hung down his head for a while towards the ground; and afterwards, raising it towards his father, the madness of youth affected him, and the ignorance of a stripling's age, and he replied, As to myself, I will never marry, though I be made to drink the cups of perdition: and as to thee, thou art a man of great age and of little sense. Hast thou not asked me before this day, twice before the present occasion, on the subject of marriage, and I would not consent to the proposal?[1]—Then Ḳamar-ez-Zemán unclasped his hands from behind his back, and tucked up his sleeves from his arms, before his father, in his anger.

His father was abashed and ashamed, because this had happened before the lords of his empire, and the soldiers who were present at the festival: but presently the royal energy returned to him, and he cried out at his son, and terrified him; and, calling to the memlooks, commanded them to seize him. They therefore laid hold upon him; and he ordered them to bind his hands behind him, and they did so, and led him forward before his father. He hung down his head in fear and timidity, his face and his forehead were bespangled with moisture, and his shame and confusion were excessive, while his father abused him and reviled him, saying to him, Wo to thee, O baseborn, and nursling of impurity![15] How couldst thou presume to make me this reply before my soldiers and armies? But hitherto no one hath chastised thee. Knowest thou not that this which thou hast done, had it proceeded from any one of the common people, it had been disgraceful in him?—He then commanded the memlooks to loose the cords that bound his hands behind him, and to imprison him in one of the towers of the castle. The farráshes,[16] therefore, immediately went into the saloon that was in the tower, and swept it, and wiped its pavement; and they placed in it a couch for Ḳamar-ez-Zemán, upon which they spread a mattress and a leathern covering; and they put for him a cushion, and a large lantern and a candle; for the place was dark in the day-time. Then the memlooks conducted Ḳamar-ez-Zemán into this saloon, and stationed a eunuch at its door. And when they had done this, Ḳamar-ez-Zemán ascended the couch, with broken spirit and mourning heart. He had already blamed himself, and repented of his injurious conduct to his father, when repentance availed him not, and he exclaimed, Malediction upon marriage and girls and deceitful women! Would that I had attended to my father's command and married; for if I had done so, it had been better for me than being in this prison!—Thus did it befall Ḳamar-ez-Zemán.

Now as to his father, he remained upon his throne during the rest of the day, until sunset, when he retired with the Wezeer, and said to him, Know, O Wezeer, that thou hast been the cause of all this which hath happened between me and my son, by the advice that thou gavest me; and what dost thou counsel me to do now?—O King, answered the Wezeer, leave thy son in the prison for a period of fifteen days: then summon him before thee, and command him to marry; for he will never oppose thee again. And the King received this advice of the Wezeer, and slept that night with a heart troubled on account of his son; for he loved him excessively, because he had no son beside him. The King Sháh-Zemán used to remain without sleep every night until he put his arm under the neck of Ḳamar-ez-Zemán, and then he slept. So he passed that night with a heart disordered on his account, and remained turning over from side to side as though he were lying upon the burning embers of Hell: uneasiness overcame him, and sleep visited him not all that night: his eyes poured forth tears, and he repeated the words of the poet:—

> My night is tedious, while the slanderers sleep. It is enough that thy heart is terrified by separation.
> I exclaimed, while my night was prolonged by anxiety, O light of the morning, wilt thou not return?

But as to Ḳamar-ez-Zemán, when night came, the eunuch placed before him the lantern, and lighted the candle, which he placed in a candlestick; and after this, he brought him some food. So he ate a little, and sat expostulating with himself for his ill manners towards his father the King Sháh-Zemán, saying, Knowest thou not that the son of Adam is a dependant of his tongue, and that the tongue of a man is that which betrayeth him into perils? Thus he continued to expostulate with himself, and to blame himself, until tears overcame him; his aching heart was tortured, and he repented extremely of that which his tongue had uttered against his father. And when he had finished his repast, he demanded water to wash his hands, and cleansed them of what adhered to them from the food. He then performed the ablution preparatory to prayer, and recited the prayers of sunset and nightfall; after which he sat upon the couch, reciting the Ḳur-án.[17] He recited the Chapters of "The Cow" and "The Family of 'Emrán" and "Yá-Seen" and "The Compassionate" and "Blessed be He in whose hand is the Kingdom" and the "Two Preventives," and finished by supplication, and seeking refuge with God.[18] Having done this, he laid himself on the couch, upon a mattress covered with Maạdinee satin,[19] with two facings, and stuffed with ostrich-feathers; and when he desired to sleep, he took off his outer clothes, and slept in a shirt of delicate waxed stuff, having upon his head a blue kerchief of the fabric of Marw,[20] and appearing like the moon in its fourteenth night. He then covered himself with a sheet of silk, and slept, with the lighted lantern at his feet, and the lighted candle at his head; and he continued asleep until the first third of the night had expired, not knowing the hidden event that awaited him, and what God, who knoweth all secrets, had decreed to befall him.

Now the saloon and the tower were ancient, and had been deserted for many years; and in the tower[21] was a Roman[22] well, inhabited by a Jinneeyeh of the posterity of Iblees the Accursed. The name of that Jinneeyeh was Meymooneh[23] the daughter of Ed-Dimiryáṭ, one of the celebrated Kings of the Jánn.[24] And when Ḳamar-ez-Zemán had remained asleep until the first third of the night had passed, this 'Efreeteh ascended from the Roman well to repair towards heaven for the purpose of listening by stealth;[25] and on reaching the upper part of the well, she saw a light shining in the tower, contrary to what was usual. She had resided in that place for a long period of years, and said within herself, I have never witnessed anything like this before. And she wondered at this thing extremely, inferring that some strange cause had occasioned it. She then proceeded in the direction of the light, and found that it issued from the saloon: so she entered it, and saw the eunuch sleeping at its door; and when she entered the saloon,[26] she found a couch placed there, with the form of a man sleeping upon it, and a lighted candle at his head, and a lighted lantern at his feet;

and the 'Efreeteh wondered at this light. She advanced towards it by little and little, and, relaxing her wings, stood over the couch, and removed the sheet from his face, and looked at him. She remained for an hour in a state of astonishment at his beauty and loveliness, and found that the light of his face surpassed that of the candle: it gleamed with splendour: his eyes had been wantoning like those of the gazelle, and were intensely black; his cheeks were brilliantly red, and his eyelids were languishing; his eyebrows were arched; and his odour diffused itself like fragrant musk. At the sight of him, Meymooneh the daughter of Ed-Dimiryáṭ extolled the perfection of God, and exclaimed, Blessed be Allah, the best of creators!—for this 'Efreeteh was of the believing Jinn. So she continued a while gazing at the face of Ḳamar-ez-Zemán, exclaiming, There is no deity but God!—and wishing, but without envy, that she were like him in beauty and loveliness. She said within herself, By Allah, I will not injure him, nor suffer any one to hurt him, but from every evil I will ransom him; for this comely face deserveth nothing save that people should gaze at it and extol the perfection of God: but how could his family leave him neglected in this ruinous place! If any of our Márids came up unto him now they would destroy him!—The 'Efreeteh then bent over him, and kissed him between his eyes; after which she let down the sheet over his face, and covered him with it.

Having done this, she spread her wings, and soared aloft towards heaven. She rose from the precincts of the saloon, and continued her upward flight through the sky until she drew near to the lowest heaven, when she heard the flapping of wings flying through the air. So she proceeded in the direction of their sound, and when she approached the being to whom they belonged, she found him to be an 'Efreet, named Dahnash, whereupon she pounced upon him like a hawk. When Dahnash, therefore, perceived her, and knew that she was Meymooneh, the daughter of the King of the Jinn, he feared her; the muscles of his side quivered, and he implored her favour, saying to her, I conjure thee by the Most Great Name, and by the most noble talisman,[27] engraved upon the seal of Suleymán, that thou treat me with benevolence, and hurt me not! And when Meymooneh heard these words of Dahnash, her heart was moved with tenderness towards him, and she said to him, Thou hast conjured me by a mighty oath; but I will not liberate thee until thou hast informed me whence thou art now come.—O mistress, he replied, know that I come from the further extremity of the country of China, and from among the

islands, and I will acquaint thee with a wonder that I have beheld this night; and if thou find my words to be true, do thou suffer me to go my way, and write me a document in thine own hand declaring that I am thine emancipated slave, so that no one of the bands of the Jinn, either of the upper who fly or of the lower or those who dive,[28] may oppose me. Meymooneh said to him, And what hast thou seen this night, O Dahnash? Acquaint me, and tell me no falsehood, desiring by thy lie to escape from my hand; for I swear by the inscription engraved upon the stone of the seal of Suleymán the son of Dáood (on both of whom be peace!), that, if thy words be not true, I will pluck out thy feathers with my hand, and tear thy skin, and break thy bones.—Then the 'Efreet Dahnash the son of Shemhoorish[29] the Flyer said to her, If my words be not true, do with me what thou wilt, O my mistress. And he proceeded thus.

I came forth this night from the Interior Islands in the region of China,[30] which are the dominions of the King El-Ghayoor,[31] the monarch of the Islands and the Seas and the Seven Palaces, and have seen a daughter of that King, than whom God hath created none in her age more beautiful. I know not how to describe her to thee; for my tongue would fail to do so; but I will mention to thee some of her characteristics as nearly as I can.—As to her hair, it is like the nights of emigration and separation; and as to her face, it is like the days of union. Well hath the poet said in describing her,—

> She spread forth three locks of her hair one night, and exhibited four nights together;
> And she turned up her face towards the moon of heaven, and shewed me two moons in the same instant.

She hath a nose like the edge of the polished sword, and cheeks like deep-red wine, or like anemones; her lips resemble coral and carnelion, and the moisture of her mouth is more delicious than the best wine, and would quench the fire of the inflamed; her tongue is put in motion by ample intelligence and a ready reply; she hath a bosom that is a temptation to him who beholdeth it—extolled be the perfection of Him who created and finished it!—by the side of which are two smooth and round arms; and, as the poet hath said,—

> She hath hips, connected with a slender waist, which tyrannize both over me and her:
> They confound me when I think upon them, and weigh her down when she would rise.

Her other charms, the describer cannot reckon; but all that I have mentioned, two delicate feet, the work of the protecting and recompensing Creator, support; and I wondered how they could sustain what was above them.[32] Other particulars I omit; for language would fail to describe them, and no sign would convey a just idea of them.

The father of this damsel (continued Dahnash) is a mighty King, an impetuous horseman, who crosseth the seas of the surrounding regions by night and day, dreading not death, nor fearing the escape of his foe, for he is a despotic tyrant, and an oppressive conqueror; he is lord of numerous armies and regions and islands and cities and habitations. His name is the King El-Ghayoor, and he is monarch of the Islands and the Seas and the Seven Palaces. He loved this

his daughter, whom I have described unto thee, with exceeding love, so that he collected the treasures of all the other Kings, and with them built for her seven palaces,[33] each of a particular kind. The first palace is of crystal; the second, of marble; the third, of the iron of China; the fourth, of onyx and other precious stones; the fifth, of silver; the sixth, of gold; and the seventh, of jewels. He filled the seven palaces with varieties of magnificent furniture, and vessels of gold and silver, and utensils of every kind that Kings could require, and commanded his daughter to reside in each palace for a certain period of the year, and then to remove to another of them. Her name is the Queen Budoor.[34] When her beauty became celebrated, and her fame spread throughout the surrounding countries, all the Kings sent to her father to request her of him in marriage; and he mentioned the subject of marriage to her; but she disliked it, and said to her father, O my father, I have no wish at all to marry; for I am a princess and a queen, ruling over men, and I desire not a man to rule over me. Yet the more she shewed reluctance to marry, so much the more did her suitors increase in eagerness to possess her. All the Kings of the Interior Islands of China sent presents and rarities to her father with

letters requesting her as a wife, and he repeated the proposals to her many times; but she opposed his wish, and was angry with him, and said to him, If thou mention the subject of marriage to me again, I will take a sword, and put its hilt upon the floor and its point to my bosom, and lean upon it until it protrude from my back, and thus kill myself. So when her father heard these words from her, the light became darkness before his face, and his heart was tortured excessively on her account; for he feared that she would kill herself. He was perplexed respecting both her and the Kings who sought her in marriage from him, and said to her, If thou art determined not to marry, abstain from going out and coming in. He then conveyed her into an apartment, and there confined her, commissioning ten old women, ḳahramánehs,[35] to guard her, and forbidding her to behold the seven palaces; after which, he made it appear that he was incensed against her, and sent letters to all the Kings, informing them that she was afflicted with insanity, and that she had been confined for a year.

The 'Efreet Dahnash, having related these facts to the 'Efreeteh, said, I go to her, O my mistress, every night, and gaze at her, and enjoy for a long time the sight of her face, and kiss her between her eyes while she lieth asleep; but from my love for her I do her no injury; for her loveliness is surpassing: every one who seeth her is jealous of her with respect to his own self. I conjure thee, O my mistress, that thou come with me and behold her beauty and loveliness, and justness of form and proportion; and afterwards, if thou desire to chastise me or to enslave me, do it; for it is thine to command, and thine to forbid.—Then the 'Efreet Dahnash hung down his head towards the earth, and lowered his wings. But the 'Efreeteh Meymooneh, after laughing at his words, and spitting in his face, said to him, What is this damsel of whom thou speakest? She is of no more value than a fragment of base pottery! What wouldst thou say if thou sawest my beloved? By Allah, I thought thou hadst some wonderful tale, or extraordinary story, O accursed! I have seen a man this night, such that if thou beheldest him even in a dream, thou wouldst be paralyzed with astonishment at him.—And what, said Dahnash, is the story of this young man? She answered, Know, O Dahnash, that this young man hath experienced the like of that which hath happened to thy beloved, whom thou hast mentioned.[36] His father commanded him many times to marry; but he refused; and his father, when he had thus opposed him, was incensed against him, and imprisoned him in the tower in which I reside; and as I came forth this night, I beheld him.—O my mistress, replied Dahnash, shew me this young man, that I may see whether he be more beautiful than my beloved, the Queen Budoor, or not; for I do not imagine that there existeth in this age the like of my beloved.—Thou liest, rejoined the 'Efreeteh, O accursed! O most unlucky of Márids, and most contemptible of devils! for I am certain that there existeth not the equal of my beloved in these countries. Art thou mad, then, that thou comparest thy beloved unto mine?—I conjure thee by Allah, O my mistress, resumed Dahnash, that thou come with me to see my beloved, and I will return with thee and behold thine.—It must be so, O accursed, said Meymooneh; for thou art a knavish devil; but I will not accompany thee, nor shalt thou go with me, except on the condition of a bet: if thy beloved, whom thou holdest to be superior, prove more beautiful than mine, whom I regard as superior, the bet shall be thine and against me; but if my beloved prove to be the more beautiful, the bet shall be mine and against thee. The 'Efreet Dahnash replied, O my mistress, I consent to this condition willingly: come then with me to the islands. But Meymooneh said, The place of my beloved is nearer than that of thine: here it is beneath us: so descend with me to see my beloved; and after that, we will repair to thine. And Dahnash replied, I hear and obey.

They then descended, and alighted within the precincts of the saloon in the tower, and Meymooneh, having stationed Dahnash by the side of the couch, put forth her hand, and raised the sheet from the face of Ḳamar-ez-Zemán, the son of the King Sháh-Zemán; whereupon his face beamed and shone, and glistened and glittered. Meymooneh beheld him, and then, turning her eyes immediately towards Dahnash, said to him, Look, O accursed, and be not the basest of fools: for I am a maiden, and am fascinated by him. So Dahnash looked towards him, and remained a while contemplating him; after which, he shook his head, and said to Meymooneh, By Allah, O my mistress, thou art excused; but it remaineth to be shewn that the female is different from the male: yet, by Allah, this thy beloved is, of all men, he who beareth the nearest resemblance to my beloved, in beauty and loveliness and elegance and all perfection: both of them have been formed alike in the mould of beauty. But when Meymooneh heard these words of Dahnash, the light became darkness before her eyes, and she struck him with her wing upon his head with such force that he almost experienced his

predestined end from the violence of the blow; and she said to him, I swear by the brightness of his glorious aspect that thou shalt go, O accursed, this instant, and lift up thy beloved, and bring her quickly unto this place, that we may put them together, and see them both while they lie asleep side by side: then it will be manifest unto us which of them is the more beautiful. If thou do not what I have commanded thee forthwith, O accursed, I will burn thee with my fire,[37] and dart at thee my destructive sparks, and scatter thee, torn in pieces, over the deserts, making thee an example to the stationary and the night-traveller.—So Dahnash replied, O my mistress, thy command shall be obeyed; but I know that my beloved is more beautiful, and sweeter.

Then the 'Efreet Dahnash flew away immediately, and Meymooneh flew with him to guard him; and after they had been absent an hour, they returned conveying the damsel, who was clad in a shirt of delicate Venetian stuff, with two borders of gold embroidered in the most admirable manner, presenting the following verses worked upon the extremity of each sleeve:—

Three things have prevented her from paying us a visit, through fear of the spy and the angry envier;
The light of her forehead, and the sound of her ornaments, and the constant scent of ambergris inherent in her.
Suppose she hide her forehead with the end of her sleeve, and pull off her jewels; how can she divest her of her odour?[38]

The 'Efreet and 'Efreeteh descended with this damsel, and, having extended her by the side of the young man, uncovered the faces of both, and they bore the strongest resemblance to each other, as though they were twins, or an only brother and sister: they were a temptation to the abstinent. Dahnash and Meymooneh began to gaze upon them, and the former said, Verily my beloved is the more beautiful.—Nay, replied Meymooneh, my beloved is the more beautiful. Woe to thee, O Dahnash! Art thou blind? Dost thou not behold his beauty and loveliness, and justness of stature and form? But hear what I say of my beloved, and if thou be a true lover of her with whom thou art enamoured, say of her as I shall say of my beloved.—She then kissed Ḳamar-ez-Zemán several times, and recited an ode in his praise. And when Dahnash heard it, he was extremely delighted, and full of admiration; but he said, Thou hast recited these tender verses on thy beloved with thy mind engrossed by him: I will now endeavour to recite some, the best that I can think of. So he approached his beloved, Budoor, and, having kissed her between the eyes, looked towards the 'Efreeteh Meymooneh, and towards his beloved, and recited an ode; but with a wandering mind. And when he had finished, the 'Efreeteh said, Thou has done well, O Dahnash: but which of these two is the more beautiful? He answered, My beloved, Budoor, is more beautiful than thine.—Thou liest, O accursed! she replied; for my beloved is more beautiful than thine.

Thus they continued contradicting each other, until Meymooneh cried out at Dahnash, and would have laid violent hands upon him; but he abased himself before her, and, softening his speech, said to her, Let not the truth be grievous unto thee: annul thy assertion and mine; for we each pronounce in favour of our beloved: let each of us, therefore, reject both the opinions, and let us seek one to judge between us with equity, and by his sentence we will abide. Meymooneh replied, So shall it be. She then struck the floor with her foot, and there arose from it an 'Efreet, blind of one eye, and with a diseased skin; his eyes were slit upwards in his face; upon his head were seven horns, and he had four locks of hair hanging down to the ground; his hands were like those of the Ḳuṭrub,[39] with claws like the claws of the lion; and his feet were like the elephant's, with hoofs like those of the ass. As soon as this 'Efreet arose, and beheld Meymooneh, he kissed the ground before her, and, placing his hands together behind his back, said to her, What dost thou require, O my mistress, O daughter of the King? She answered, O Ḳashḳash, I desire that thou judge between me and this accursed Dahnash. She then acquainted him with the case from first to last; and upon this, the 'Efreet Ḳashḳash looked upon the face of the young man, and upon that of the damsel, and beheld them embracing each other as they lay asleep, the arm of each being under the neck of the other, resembling each other in beauty and loveliness, and equal in charms. The Márid Ḳashḳash gazed, and wondered at their beauty, and, after he had long kept his eyes upon them, looked towards Meymooneh and Dahnash, and recited some amatory verses, and then added, By Allah, neither of them is more or less beautiful than the other; but they bear the strongest resemblance to each other in beauty and loveliness, and elegance and perfection; and they are not to be pronounced different from each other in these respects because they are of different sexes. I have to propose, however, another mode of determining the question; and it is this: that we wake each of them without the knowledge of the other; and the one who shall be most inflamed with love for the other shall be confessed to be the inferior in beauty and loveliness.—Excellent, said Meymooneh, is this advice that thou hast given, and I approve of it.—And I also, said Dahnash, approve of it.

Upon this, therefore, Dahnash transformed himself into a flea, and bit Ḳamar-ez-Zemán upon his neck, in a soft place: so Ḳamar-ez-Zemán put his hand to his neck, and scratched the place of the bite, on account of the violence of the smarting that it occasioned, and, moving sideways, found something lying by him, from which proceeded a breath more fragrant than musk, with a body softer than butter. Ḳamar-ez-Zemán wondered at this exceedingly, and immediately raised himself. Looking at this person lying by his side, he found it to be a damsel like a precious pearl, or like a shining sun,[40] with a form like the letter Alif,[41] of quinary[42] stature, high-bosomed, and with red cheeks. And when Ḳamar-ez-Zemán thus beheld the lady Budoor, the daughter of the King El-Ghayoor, and observed her beauty and loveliness as she lay asleep by his side, he saw upon her body a shirt of Venetian stuff, and upon her head a koofeeyeh of cloth of gold adorned with jewels, and on her neck a long necklace of precious gems such as none of the Kings could procure. His reason was confounded at the sight, and he said within himself, What God desireth will come to pass, and what He desireth not will not happen! He then turned her over with his hand, and attempted to rouse her; but she awoke not; for Dahnash had made her sleep heavy: so Ḳamar-ez-Zemán squeezed her with his hand, and shook her, saying, O my beloved, awake, and see whom I am; for I am Ḳamar-ez-Zemán. But she awoke not, nor moved her head. And he remained for an hour reflecting upon her case, and said within himself, If my conjecture be true, this damsel is she to whom my father desireth to marry me, and for three years I have refused to do it: but, please God, when morning cometh, I will say to my father, Marry me to her:—and I will not suffer mid-day to pass before I possess her and delight myself with her beauty and loveliness.—He then inclined towards Budoor to kiss her: whereupon Meymooneh the Jinneeyeh trembled and was confounded: but as to the 'Efreet Dahnash, he leaped for joy. When

Ḳamar-ez-Zemán, however, was about to kiss her upon the mouth, he feared God, and turned away his face, saying within himself, I will have patience; for perhaps my father, when he was incensed against me, and imprisoned me in this place, brought unto me this bride, and commanded her to sleep by my side, to prove me by her, and charged her not to appear awake on my attempting to rouse her, and said to her, Whatsoever Ḳamar-ez-Zemán do to thee, acquaint me with it. And probably my father is standing concealed in some place to observe me, while I see him not, and he will witness all that I do with this damsel, and in the morning will reproach me, and say to me, How dost thou say, I have no need of marriage,—and kiss that damsel, and embrace her! So I will withhold myself from her, lest I be exposed before my father. I will not touch this damsel from the present moment, nor look towards her; but will only take from her something that may be a token in my keeping and a memorial of her, that there may be a sign between me and her.—Then Ḳamar-ez-Zemán raised the hand of the damsel, and took her ring from her little finger. It was worth a large sum of money; for its stone was a precious jewel; and around it were engraved these verses:—

Think not that I have forgotten your promises, notwithstanding the length of your alienation.
O my lord, be generous and propitious towards me! Perhaps I may kiss your mouth and your cheeks.
By Allah, I will never relinquish you, though you should transgress the bounds of love.

So Ḳamar-ez-Zemán took off this ring from the little finger of the Queen Budoor, and, having put it on his own little finger, turned his back towards her, and slept.

The Jinneeyeh Meymooneh, when she saw this, rejoiced, and said to Dahnash and Ḳashḳash, Have ye seen my beloved, Ḳamar-ez-Zemán, how he hath abstained from this damsel? This is the result of the perfection of his excellencies. Consider how he beheld this damsel and her beauty and loveliness, and yet embraced her not, nor passed his hand over her; but turned his back to her, and slept.—They answered her, We have witnessed his perfect conduct.

Meymooneh then transformed herself into a flea, and, entering beneath the clothes of Budoor, the beloved of Dahnash, bit her; whereupon she opened her eyes, and sat up, and beheld a young man sleeping by her side, and snoring in his sleep, with cheeks like anemones, and eyes that put to shame the beautiful Ḥooreeyehs, and a mouth like the seal of Suleymán.[43] When she beheld him, distraction and ecstasy and desire overcame her, and she said within herself, O my disgrace! This young man is a stranger: I know him not; and wherefore is he lying by my side in the same bed?—Then looking at him again, and contemplating his elegance and his amorous aspect, and his beauty and loveliness, she said, By Allah, he is a youth comely as the moon, and my heart is almost rent by ecstasy of love for him, and by the violence of passion excited by his beauty and loveliness! But how am I disgraced by his means! By Allah, if I had known that this handsome youth was the person who demanded me in marriage of my father, I had not rejected him, but had married him, and delighted myself with his loveliness.—Then the Queen Budoor immediately looked in the face of Ḳamar-ez-Zemán, and said to him, O my lord, and beloved of my heart, and light of mine eye, awake from thy sleep! And she shook him with her hand. But Meymooneh the Jinneeyeh immersed him in sleep, and pressed down his head with her wing: so he awoke not. The Queen Budoor shook him again with her hand, and said to him, By my life I conjure thee to comply with my desire and awake from thy sleep! Arise, O my master, and recline upon the cushion, and sleep not!—But Ḳamar-ez-Zemán returned her no reply, nor addressed her with a word; still snoring in his sleep. So the Queen Budoor said, Wherefore art thou so proud, with thy beauty and loveliness and elegance and amorous aspect? As thou art comely, so am I also. Why then dost thou act thus? Have they instructed thee to manifest aversion towards me, or hath my father, that ill-omened old man, forbidden thee to speak to me this night?—Ḳamar-ez-Zemán then opened his eyes; whereupon her love for him increased. God instilled into her heart a passion for him, and she cast at him a glance which occasioned her a thousand sighs; her heart throbbed, and she said to Ḳamar-ez-Zemán, O my master, speak to me! O my beloved, converse with me! O object of my passion, return me a reply, and tell me what is thy name; for thou hast captivated my reason!—But all this while, Ḳamar-ez-Zemán remained immersed in sleep, and replied not a word. And the Queen Budoor sighed, and said, Wherefore art thou so self-satisfied? Then she shook him again, and turned over his hand, and seeing her ring upon his little finger, she uttered a cry of astonishment, and said with an amorous manner, Alas! Alas! By Allah, thou art my beloved, and thou lovest me; but thou seemest to affect an aversion towards me, though thou camest to me while I was asleep, and I know not what thou hast done unto me; yet I will not pull off my ring from thy

little finger.—And she searched for something to take from him, and, taking off his ring from his finger, put it on hers, instead of her own ring; after which she kissed his mouth and his hands, and placed one of her hands beneath his neck, and the other under his arm, and fell asleep again by his side.

When Meymooneh beheld this, she rejoiced exceedingly, and said to Dahnash, Hast thou seen, O accursed, how thy beloved hath acted in the distraction of her passion for my beloved, and how he hath acted in his pride and dissimulation? There is no doubt, then, that my beloved is more beautiful than thine: but I pardon thee.—She then wrote for him a paper of manumission, and, looking towards Ḳashḳash, said to him, Do thou insinuate thyself with him beneath his beloved, and assist him to convey her back to her place; for the night is gone, and the opportunity for the accomplishment of my intention is past. So Dahnash and Ḳashḳash advanced towards the Queen Budoor, and insinuated themselves beneath her, and, having flown away with her and conveyed her back to her place, restored her to her bed, while Meymooneh remained alone, gazing at Ḳamar-ez-Zemán as he lay asleep, until but little of the night remained, when she went her way.

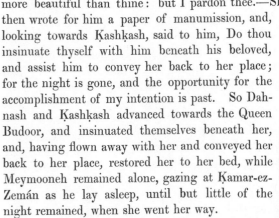

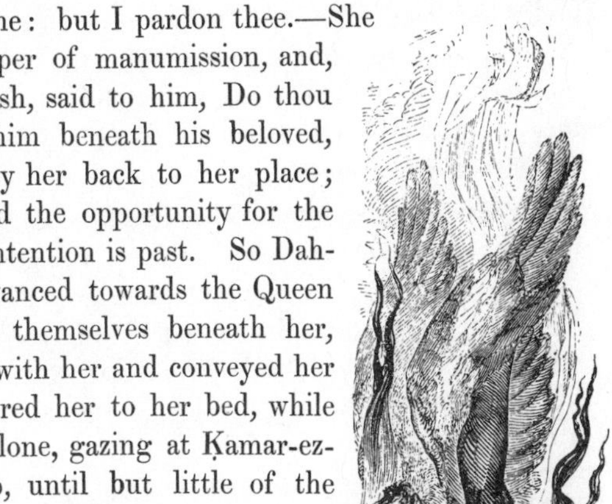

Now when daybreak came, Ḳamar-ez-Zemán awoke from his sleep, and looked to the right and left; but found not the damsel with him. So he said within himself, What meaneth this affair? It seemeth that my father would excite in me a desire to marry the damsel who was with me, and, having done this, hath taken her away secretly, that my desire for her may increase.—He then called out to the eunuch who was sleeping at the door, and said to him, Wo to thee, O accursed! Rise!—The eunuch, therefore, rose, his reason wandering from sleep, and brought to him the basin and ewer. And Ḳamar-ez-Zemán rose, and performed the ablution, recited the morning-prayers, and sat repeating the praises of God.[44] Then looking towards the eunuch, he saw him standing in attendance before him, and he said to him, Wo to thee, O Ṣawáb! Who hath come hither, and taken away the damsel from my side while I was asleep?—The eunuch said, O my master, what damsel?—The damsel who was sleeping with me this night, answered Ḳamar-ez-Zemán. And the eunuch was disturbed at his words, and replied, There was no damsel with thee, nor any one else: and how could a damsel come in when I was sleeping behind the door and it was locked? By Allah, O my master, neither male nor female came in to thee.—But Ḳamar-ez-Zemán exclaimed, Thou liest, O ill-omened slave! Art thou also of sufficient rank to presume to deceive me, and wilt thou not acquaint me whither hath gone the damsel who was sleeping with me this night, nor inform me who took her away from me?—The eunuch, agitated by what he said, answered, By Allah, O my master, I have neither seen a young woman nor a young man. And Ḳamar-ez-Zemán was enraged at the words of the eunuch, and said to him, They have taught thee deceit, O accursed! Come hither then to me.

So the eunuch approached him, and Ḳamar-ez-Zemán took him by the collar, and threw him down upon the floor, and then, kneeling upon him, kicked him and squeezed his throat until he became insensible; after which, he tied him to the well-rope, and lowered him into the well till he reached the water, and let him down into it; and it was in the cold season of a severe winter. He plunged the eunuch in the water, and then drew him up, and let him down again; and thus he continued to do. The eunuch all the while cried for help, and shrieked and called; but Ḳamar-ez-Zemán replied, By Allah, O accursed, I will not draw thee out from this well until thou acquaint me with the story of that damsel and tell me who took her away while I slept. So the eunuch said, Deliver me from the well, O my master, and I will acquaint thee with the truth. Ḳamar-ez-Zemán, therefore, drew him up from the well, and took him out, stupified with what he had suffered from the dipping and plunging and cold and beating and torture. He trembled like the reed in the tempestuous wind, his teeth were locked together, and his clothes were dripping. And when he found himself upon the floor he said, Suffer me, O my master, to go and take off my clothes, and wring them, and spread them in the

sun, and put on others: then I will return to thee quickly, and acquaint thee with the affair of that damsel, and relate to thee her story.—By Allah, O ill-omened slave, replied Ḳamar-ez-Zemán, if thou hadst not experienced the pains of death, thou hadst not confessed the truth! Go out then to do what thou desirest, and return to me quickly and relate to me the story of the damsel.

The eunuch, upon this, went forth, scarcely believing in his escape, and ran without stopping until he went in to the King Sháh-Zemán, the father of Ḳamar-ez-Zemán, when he found the Wezeer by his side, and they were conversing on the affair of Ḳamar-ez-Zemán. He heard the King say to the Wezeer, Verily I have not slept this last night from the trouble of my heart respecting Ḳamar-ez-Zemán, and I fear that some evil will befall him from his confinement in that ancient tower: it was not at all fit to imprison him. But the Wezeer replied, Fear not for him: by Allah, no harm will happen unto him. Leave him imprisoned for a month, that his temper may become softened.—And while they were thus talking, the eunuch came in to them, in the condition above described, and said to the King, O our lord the Sulṭán, insanity hath befallen thy son, and thus hath he done unto me; and he said to me, A damsel passed this night with me, and went away secretly: acquaint me, therefore, with her history.—But I know not the affair of this damsel.—And when the Sulṭán Sháh-Zemán heard these words respecting his son Ḳamar-ez-Zemán, he cried out, saying, Oh, my son!—and was violently enraged against the Wezeer who had been the cause of these events, and said to him, Arise, and ascertain for me the state of my son.

The Wezeer, therefore, went, treading upon the skirts of his dress through his fear of the King, and proceeded with the eunuch to the tower. The sun had risen, and the Wezeer went in to Ḳamar-ez-Zemán, and found him sitting upon the couch, reciting the Ḳur-án; and he saluted him, and, seating himself by his side, said to him, O my master, this ill-omened slave hath brought us information that hath troubled and agitated us, and the King was incensed at it. So Ḳamar-ez-Zemán said, O Wezeer, and what hath he told you concerning me to trouble my father? In truth he hath troubled none but me.—The Wezeer answered, He came to us in a miserable plight, and told us a thing—God forbid that it should be true of thee!—he uttered a lie respecting thee such as is not proper to be mentioned. Allah preserve thy youth,[45] and thy sound reason and thine eloquent tongue, and far be it from thee that anything base should proceed from thee!—Ķamar-ez-Zemán, therefore, said to him, O Wezeer, and what hath this ill-omened slave said?—He informed us, answered the Wezeer, that thou hadst become mad, and hadst said to him, There was a damsel with me last night.—Didst thou then say to the eunuch these words.—And when Ķamar-ez-Zemán heard this, he was violently enraged, and said to the Wezeer, It is evident to me that ye taught the eunuch to act as he did, and forbade him to acquaint me with the affair of the damsel who was sleeping with me this last night: but thou, O Wezeer, art more sensible than the eunuch; tell me therefore immediately whither is gone the beautiful damsel who was sleeping in my bosom last night; for ye are they who sent her to me and commanded her to pass the night in my bosom; and I slept with her until the morning, when I awoke, and found her not. Where, therefore, is she now?—O my master Ķamar-ez-Zemán, replied the Wezeer, may the name of Allah encompass thee![46] By Allah, we sent not any one to thee this last night, and thou sleepedst alone, with the door locked upon thee, and the eunuch sleeping behind it; and neither damsel nor any one else came to thee. Return then to thy reason, O my master, and no longer trouble thy heart.—But Ķamar-ez-Zemán, enraged at his words, said to him, O Wezeer, that damsel is my beloved, and she is the beautiful creature with the black eyes and the red cheeks whom I embraced last night. And the Wezeer wondered at his words, and asked him, Didst thou see that damsel this night with thine eye and awake, or in sleep?—O ill-omened old man, said Ķamar-ez-Zemán, dost thou imagine that I saw her with my ear? Nay, I saw her with my eyes, and awake, and turned her over with my hand, and remained awake by her half of the entire night, enjoying the contemplation of her beauty and loveliness, and elegance and amorous aspect: but ye charged her that she should not speak to me; so she pretended to be asleep, and I slept by her side until the morning, when I awoke from my sleep and found her not.—The Wezeer replied, O my master Ķamar-ez-Zemán, perhaps thou sawest this in thy sleep, and it is the result of confused dreams or vain fancies occasioned by eating a mixture of different kinds of food, or an idea inspired by the wicked devils.—O ill-omened old man, ex-

claimed Ḳamar-ez-Zemán, wherefore dost thou too make a jest of me, and tell me that perhaps this is a result of confused dreams, when the eunuch hath confessed to me that the damsel was here, and said to me, I will immediately return to thee and relate to thee her story?

He then instantly arose, and, drawing near to the Wezeer, grasped his beard in his hand. It was a long beard, and Ḳamar-ez-Zemán took it and twisted it round his hand, and pulled him by it so that he threw him down from the couch upon the floor; and the Wezeer felt as if his soul had departed, from the violence with which his beard was pulled. Ḳamar-ez-Zemán then continued kicking the Wezeer with his feet, and beating him upon the back of his neck with his hands, until he had almost put an end to him. So the Wezeer said within himself, If the slave, the eunuch, saved himself from this mad youth by his lie, it is more fit that I also should save myself by a lie; else he will destroy me: therefore now will I lie, and save my life from him; for he is mad: of his madness there is no doubt. Accordingly, he looked towards Ḳamar-ez-Zemán and said to him, O my master, be not angry with me; for thy father charged me to conceal from thee the affair of this damsel; but now I am weak and wearied by the beating; for I am become an old man, and have not strength to endure blows: grant me then a short delay, that I may relate to thee the story of the damsel.—Upon this, therefore, he ceased from beating him, and said to him, Why wouldst thou not acquaint me with her history until after beating and disgrace? Arise now, O ill-omened old man, and tell me her story.—The Wezeer then said to him, Dost thou ask respecting the damsel with the beautiful face and consummate form?—Yes, said Ḳamar-ez-Zemán: inform me, O Wezeer, who brought her to me and put her to sleep with me, and where she is now, that I may myself go to her. And if my father, the King Sháh-Zemán, hath done thus unto me to prove me by that beautiful damsel, with the view of my marrying her, I consent to do so. He did all this to me, and inflamed my heart with love for that damsel, and afterwards separated her from me, only because of my refusal to marry. But now I consent to marry. I say again, I consent to marry. So acquaint my father with this, O Wezeer, and advise him to marry me to that damsel; for I desire none but her, and my heart hath loved none other. Arise then, and hasten to my father, and advise him to be quick in marrying me: then return to me soon—immediately.

The Wezeer believed not in his escape from Ḳamar-ez-Zemán until he had gone forth from the tower, and he ran on until he came into the presence of the King Sháh-Zemán; when the King said to him, O Wezeer, wherefore do I behold thee in a state of confusion, and who hath by his wickedness injured thee, so that thou hast come in terror? He answered, I have brought thee news.[47]—And what is it? asked the King.—Know, answered the Wezeer, that madness hath befallen thy son Ḳamar-ez-Zemán.—And when the King heard these words, the light became darkness before his face, and he said, O Wezeer, explain to me the nature of the madness of my son. The Wezeer replied, I hear and obey:—and he acquainted him with that which his son had done: whereupon the King said to him, Be informed, O Wezeer, that I will grant thee, in return for the news which thou hast brought me of the madness of my son, the striking off of thy head, and the cessation of my favours to thee, O most ill-omened of Wezeers, and basest of Emeers! For I know that thou hast been the cause of the madness of my son by the wicked advice which thou gavest me first and last. By Allah, if any mischief or madness have befallen my son, I will nail thee upon the ḳubbeh,[48] and make thee to taste affliction.

The King then rose upon his feet, and, taking the Wezeer with him, entered the tower in which was Ḳamar-ez-Zemán; and when they came to him, he stood up to his father, descending quickly from the couch upon which he was sitting; and, having kissed his father's hands, drew backwards, and hung down his head towards the ground, and stood before his father with his hands joined behind his back.

Thus he remained a while; after which, he raised his head towards his father, and, with tears flowing from his eyes down his cheeks, recited the words of the poet:—

> If I have been guilty of a fault against you, and committed a deed of a shameful nature,
> I repent of my offence, and your clemency will extend to the evil-doer who craveth forgiveness.

And upon this, the King arose, and embraced his son Ḳamar-ez-Zemán, kissing him between the eyes, and seated him by his side upon the couch. Then looking towards the Wezeer with the eye of anger, he said to him, O dog of Wezeers, wherefore dost thou say of my son such and such things, and terrify my heart on his account? And he turned towards his son, and said to him, O my son, what is the name of this day?—O my father, he answered, to-day is Saturday, and to-morrow is Sunday, and next after it is Monday, then Tuesday, then Wednesday, then Thursday, and then Friday. And the King said to him, O my son, O Ḳamar-ez-Zemán, praise be to God for thy safety! What is the name of this month, in Arabic?—Its name, he answered, is Zu-l-Ḳaạdeh, and it is followed by Zu-l-Ḥejjeh, and Moḥarram, and Ṣafar, and Rabeeạ el-Owwal, and Rabeeạ eth-Thánee, and Jumáda-l-Oolà, and Jumada-th-Thániyeh, and Rejeb, and Shaạbán, and Ramaḍán, and Showwál.[49] So the King rejoiced at this answer exceedingly, and spat in the face of the Wezeer, and said to him, O wicked old man, how dost thou assert that my son Ḳamar-ez-Zemán hath become insane, when the case is that none hath become insane but thyself? The Wezeer shook his head, and was about to speak; but it occurred to his mind that he should rather wait a little, to see what would happen.

The King then said to his son, O my son, what were those words that thou spakest to the eunuch and the Wezeer, when thou saidst to them, I was sleeping with a beautiful damsel this last night? And what is the affair of this damsel whom thou hast mentioned?—And Ḳamar-ez-Zemán laughed at the words of his father, and answered him, O my father, know that I have not strength to endure jesting; therefore add not to me another word of it; for my temper is straitened by that which ye have done unto me. Know, O my father, that I consent to marriage; but on the condition that thou marry me to that damsel who was sleeping with me this last night; for I am certain that it was thou who sentest her to me and causedst me to be enamoured of her, and that thou sentest to her before the morning, and tookest her away from me.—At this the King exclaimed, The name of Allah encompass thee, O my son! Allah preserve thy reason from derangement! What is this damsel of whom thou assertest that I sent her to thee this last night and then sent to take her away from thee before the morning? By Allah, O my son, I have no knowledge of this affair. I conjure thee, then, to inform me: is not this a confused dream, or a fancy resulting from food? For thou passedst this last night with a heart troubled on the subject of marriage, and inspired with fancies by the mention of that subject. Malediction upon marriage and its hour, and upon him who advised me on that matter! There is no doubt but that thy temperament is disturbed on that account, so that thou hast dreamt that a beautiful damsel was embracing thee, and thou believest in thine own mind that thou sawest this awake, when all this, O my son, was a confused dream.—But Ḳamar-ez-Zemán replied, Abstain from these words, and swear to me by Allah, the Creator, the Omniscient, the Destroyer of the mighty, and the Annihilator of the Kisràs,[50] that thou hast had no knowledge of the damsel or her abode. So the King said, By Allah the Great, the God of Moosà and Ibráheem, I have had no knowledge of that which thou mentionest, and probably it was a confused dream that thou sawest in sleep.

Then Ḳamar-ez-Zemán said, I will propose to thee a parable, to prove to thee that this happened when I was awake, by asking thee if it have ever happened that any person dreamt that he was fighting, and, after a severe contest, awoke from his sleep and found in his hand a sword stained with blood? His father answered, No, by Allah, O my son: such a thing hath never occurred. Then, said Ḳamar-ez-Zemán, I will acquaint thee with that which hath happened unto me; and it was this: I seemed as though I awoke this last night from my sleep at midnight, and found a damsel sleeping by my side, whose figure and form were as mine, and I embraced her, and touched her with my hand, and took her ring, which I put on my finger, and she pulled off my ring and put it on her finger. But I regarded her with reserve, from a feeling of bashfulness towards thee; for I imagined that thou hadst sent her, and hadst concealed thyself in some place to observe my actions. So I was ashamed to kiss her upon her mouth on thy account, as it occurred to my mind that thou desiredst to tempt me by her, to excite me to marry. Afterwards I awoke from my sleep at the commencement of the dawn, and found no trace of the damsel, nor obtained any tidings of her; and what happened between me and the eunuch and the Wezeer was in consequence of this. Now how could this affair be as thou supposest, when the incident of the ring is true? Were it not for the ring I should imagine that it was a dream; but this is her ring which is upon my little finger at the present moment. See, O King, what is its value.

Ḳamar-ez-Zemán then handed the ring to his father, who, having taken it, and turned it round, looked towards his son, and said to him, Verily some great and important revelation dependeth upon this ring, and that which happened to thee last night with this damsel is a mysterious affair. I know not how this visiter came in among us, and no one was the cause of all this but the Wezeer. I conjure thee, however, by Allah, O my son, that thou be patient; for probably God will dispel this affliction from thee, and send thee complete relief; as the poet hath said,—

Probably Fortune will turn its rein, and bring prosperity; for Fortune is changeable.
My desires may be blest, and my wants performed, and happy events may follow adverse.

O my son, he continued, I have now convinced myself that thou art not insane; but no one can clear up thy affair save God.—Ḳamar-ez-Zemán replied, By Allah, O my father, search after this damsel for me, and hasten her coming; else I shall die of anguish. Then, with an expression of transport, he looked towards his father, and recited these two verses:—

If your promise of an actual interview be false, grant the lover an interview or a visit in sleep.
But how, they replied, can the phantom present itself to the eye of a youth from whom sleep is banished?

O my father, he added,[51] I have not patience to wait for her even an hour. And upon this, the King smote his hands together, and exclaimed, There is no strength nor power but in God, the High, the Great! No stratagem will avail in this affair!—He then took the hand of his son, and led him to the palace, where Ḳamar-ez-Zemán laid himself upon the bed of sickness, and his father seated himself at his head, mourning and weeping for his son, and leaving him neither by night nor day.

At length the Wezeer said to the King, O King of the age, how long wilt thou remain shut up from the troops with thy son Ḳamar-ez-Zemán. Probably the order of the realm may be corrupted by thy estrangement from the lords of thy empire. It is incumbent on the wise, when various diseases afflict his body, to apply himself to restoratives for his bones; and it is my advice that thou remove thy son from this place to the pavilion in the palace overlooking the sea, and pass thy time in retirement there with thy son, appointing two days in every week, namely, Thursday and Monday, for the procession of state and for holding the court. So, on those two days, the emeers and wezeers, and chamberlains and lieutenants, and other lords of the empire and chief men of the state, and the impetuous warriours and the rest of the soldiers and subjects, shall come in unto thee and submit to thee their cases, and thou shalt perform their wants and judge between them, and take from them and give to them, and command and forbid; and the rest of the week thou shalt pass with thy son Ķamar-ez-Zemán. Thus thou shalt continue to do until God dispel thy grief and his: and be not confident, O King, of thy safety from the vicissitudes of fortune and the calamities of time; for the wise is always cautious.—And when the Sulṭán heard these words of the Wezeer, he approved his advice, and saw that it was suitable to his case: it made an impression upon him, and he feared that the order of his realm would be disturbed around him; so he arose immediately, and gave orders to remove his son from that place to the pavilion in the palace overlooking the sea. The access to it was over a causeway in the midst of the sea, the width of which was twenty cubits. Around the pavilion were windows overlooking the sea, its floor was paved with coloured marbles, and its ceiling was painted with the finest pigments of every colour and decorated with gold and ultramarine; and they spread in it for Ķamar-ez-Zemán silken carpets, hung its walls with brocade, and suspended in it curtains adorned with jewels. Ķamar-ez-Zemán entered it, and from the excess of his passion he became extremely restless, his heart was troubled, his complexion became pallid, and his body wasted. His father sat at his head mourning for him; and every Thursday and Monday the King gave permission to every one of the emeers and wezeers, and chamberlains and lieutenants, and other lords of the empire, and all the soldiers and subjects who desired, to come in to him in that pavilion. So they entered, and performed their several services, and remained with him until the close of the day, when they dispersed and went their way; after which, the King went in to his son Ķamar-ez-Zemán in that place, and left him not night nor day; and thus he continued to do for many days and nights. Thus did it happen unto Ķamar-ez-Zemán.

Now I must relate what took place with the Queen Budoor, the daughter of the King El-Ghayoor, the lord of the Islands and the Seven Palaces.—When the Jinn had carried her back and laid her again in her bed, there remained of the night no more than three hours; and when daybreak came she awoke from her sleep, and sat up, and looked to the right and left; but saw not her beloved who had been lying in her bosom. Upon this, her heart was agitated, her reason quitted her, and she uttered a great cry. So all her female slaves and nurses and ḳahramánehs awoke and came in to her, and the chief of them, advancing towards her, said to her, O my mistress, what hath befallen thee?—O ill-omened old woman, said the lady Budoor, where is my beloved, the beautiful youth who was sleeping this night in my bosom? Inform me whither he hath gone.—And when the ḳahramáneh heard these words, the light became darkness before her face, and, fearing greatly from her power, she said, O my mistress Budoor, what mean these disgraceful words? But the lady Budoor exclaimed, Wo to thee, O ill-omened old woman! Where is my beloved, the beautiful youth with the lovely face and the black eyes and the joined eyebrows who was with me from nightfall until near daybreak?—By Allah, answered the old woman, I have seen neither a young man nor any other person, and I conjure thee by Allah, O my mistress, that thou jest not in this unreasonable manner, lest our lives be lost; for perhaps this jest may come to the knowledge of thy father, and who will deliver us from his hand? The Queen Budoor said to her, There was a young man passing this last night with me, in countenance the most comely of men.—Heaven preserve thy reason! exclaimed the ḳahramáneh: there was no one passing the night with thee. And upon this, Budoor looked at her hand, and found the ring of Ḳamar-ez-Zemán upon her finger, and found not her own ring. So she said to the ḳahramáneh, Wo to thee, O deceitful! Dost thou tell a lie, and say to me, There was no one passing the night with thee,—and swear to me by Allah falsely?—By Allah, replied the ḳahramáneh,

I have not told thee a lie, nor sworn falsely. And the lady Budoor was enraged at her; and, drawing a sword that was by her, struck the ḳahramáneh, and would have killed her.[52] But the eunuch and the female slaves cried out at her, and went and acquainted her father with her state.

The King, therefore, came immediately to his daughter, the lady Budoor, and said to her, O my daughter, what is the matter with thee?—O my father, said she, where is the young man who was sleeping by my side this last night?—Her reason fled from her head, and she began to look to the right and left, and then rent her vest to its skirt. So when her father saw her do thus, he ordered the female slaves and eunuchs to seize her; and they laid hold upon her, and bound her, and put a chain of iron upon her neck, and attached her to a window of the palace.[53] Now as to her father, the world became strait unto him; for he loved her, and her state was grievous to him. He therefore summoned the astrologers and sages, and those skilled in [magic] characters, and said to them, Whosoever cureth my daughter of her present disorder, I will marry him to her, and will give him half of my kingdom; and whoso faileth to cure her, I will strike off his head, and hang it over the palace-gate. And so he continued to do until he had cut off, on her account, forty heads. He sought all the sages; but all the people held back from attempting her cure, and all the sages were unable to restore her; her case perplexed the men of science, and those skilled in [magic] characters.

The lady Budoor remained in the same state for three years.—Now she had a foster-brother named Marzawán, who had travelled to the most remote countries and been absent from her during all that period. He loved her with an excessive love, greater than the love of brothers; and when he came back, he went in to his mother, and inquired of her respecting his sister, the lady Budoor. So she said to him, O my son, insanity hath befallen thy sister; she hath been in this state for three years, with a chain of iron upon her neck, and the physicians have been unable to cure her. And when Marzawán heard these words, he said, I must visit her: perhaps I may discover her ailment, and be able to cure her. His mother, therefore, when she heard him say this, replied, Thou must visit her; but wait until to-morrow, that I may devise some stratagem to forward thy purpose. She then walked to the palace of the lady Budoor, and, accosting the eunuch who was charged to keep the door, gave him a present, and said, I have a daughter who was brought up with the lady Budoor,

and I have married her; and in consequence of that which happened to thy mistress, her heart became greatly concerned for her state. I therefore beg of thy goodness that my daughter may pay her a short visit, to see her, and then return by the way that she came without any person's knowing of her visit.—The eunuch replied, That will be impossible, except at night: so after the Sulṭán shall have come to see his daughter, and gone forth, enter thou with thy daughter.

The old woman then kissed the hand of the eunuch, and went forth to her house; and at the commencement of the next night she arose immediately, and taking her son Marzawán, clad him in a suit of women's attire, after which she placed his hand in her own, and conducted him into the palace. She advanced with him until she brought him to the eunuch, after the departure of the Sulṭán from his daughter, and when the eunuch saw her, he arose, and said to her, Enter; but prolong not thy stay. So when the old woman entered with her son Marzawán, he saw the lady Budoor in the state already described, and he saluted her, after his mother had taken off his women's apparel. Marzawán then took forth his books that he had brought with him, and lighted his candle. But the lady Budoor, looking at him, recognised him, and said to him, O my brother, thou hast been travelling, and tidings of thee have been suspended.—True, he replied; but God hath restored me in safety, and I desired to travel again, and nothing prevented me from doing so except this news that I have heard respecting thee; in consequence of which my heart hath been tormented on thine account; wherefore I have come to thee in the hope that I may discover thy disorder and be able to cure thee.—But she said, O my brother, dost thou imagine it to be madness that hath befallen me? Then, making a sign to him, she recited these two verses:—

They said, Thou ravest upon him whom thou lovest. And I replied, The sweets of life are only for the mad.
Well: I am mad: then bring me him upon whom I rave; and if he cure my madness, do not blame me.

So Marzawán perceived that she was in love; and he said to her, Acquaint me with thy story, and with all that hath happened to thee: perhaps God may discover to me that which may bring thee deliverance. The lady Budoor therefore replied, O my brother, hear my story. It is this:—I awoke from my sleep one night, in the last third of the night, and, sitting up, beheld by my side a young man, the most beautiful of youths, such as the tongue cannot describe, like a twig of the Oriental willow, or an Indian cane. So I thought that my father had ordered him to act thus, to tempt me by him; for he had required me to marry, when the Kings demanded me of him to wife, and I refused; and this idea prevented my rousing him. I feared that, if I embraced him, he would perhaps acquaint my father with it. And when I awoke in the morning, I found his ring in the place of my own. This is my story; and, O my brother, my heart hath been devoted to him ever since I beheld him; from the excess of my passion and desire I taste not the savour of sleep, and have no occupation but that of pouring forth floods of tears, and reciting verses, night and day. See, then, O my brother, how thou canst assist me in my affliction.—Upon this, Marzawán hung down his head towards the ground for a while, wondering, and knowing not what to do. He then raised his head, and said to her, All that hath occurred to thee is true; and verily the story of this young man hath wearied my imagination; but I will travel about through all the countries, and search for the means of thy restoration. Perhaps God will accomplish it by my hand. Have patience, therefore, and be not disquieted.—Having thus said, he bade her farewell, praying that she might be endowed with patience, and departed from her.

He returned to the house of his mother, and slept that night, and

when the morning came he prepared for travelling. So he went forth, and continued journeying from city to city and from island to island for the space of a whole month, after which he entered a city called Eṭ-Ṭarf,[54] and inquired the news of the people, hoping to find the remedy of the Queen Budoor. Whenever he had entered a city or passed by it, he had heard it said that the Queen Budoor, the daughter of the King El-Ghayoor, had been afflicted by insanity; and he ceased not to inquire the news until he arrived at the city of Eṭ-Ṭarf, when he heard that Ḳamar-ez-Zemán, the son of the King Sháh-Zemán, was sick, and that distraction and insanity had afflicted him. When Marzawán, therefore, heard his story, he asked some of the people of that city respecting his country and capital; and they answered him, The Islands of Khálidán; and between us and them is a voyage of a whole month by sea; but by land, the journey is six months.

So Marzawán embarked in a ship bound for the Islands of Khálidán. The ship was fitted for the voyage, and the wind was favourable to her for the space of a month, when the city appeared before them; but when they had come in sight of it, and had almost gained the shore, there arose against them a tempestuous wind, which carried away the yard, and the sails fell into the sea, and the vessel was capsized with all that it contained. Every one sought his own safety; but as to Marzawán, the force of the current bore him along until it conveyed him beneath the King's pavilion, in which was Ḳamar-ez-Zemán. It happened, in accordance with destiny, that the emeers and wezeers had assembled in attendance upon him, and the King Sháh-Zemán was sitting with the head of his son Ḳamar-ez-Zemán in his lap, and a eunuch was whisking the flies from him. Ḳamar-ez-Zemán for two days had neither eaten nor drunk, nor had he spoken; and the Wezeer, standing at his feet, near the window looking over the sea, raised his eyes, and beheld Marzawán about to be destroyed by the current, and at his last gasp: whereupon his heart was moved with pity for him, and, approaching the Sulṭán, he stretched forth his head towards him, and said, I beg thy permission that I may descend to the court of the pavilion and open its gate, that I may save a man who is at the point of drowning in the sea, and turn his anguish into joy. Perhaps God, on that account, may deliver thy son from his present affliction.—The Sulṭán replied, All that hath befallen my son hath been caused by thee, and probably if thou deliver this drowning man, he will discover our affairs, and behold my son in this state, and exult over me. But I swear by Allah, that if this drowning man come up and see my son and then go forth and divulge any of our secrets, I will assuredly strike off thy head before his; for thou, O Wezeer, art the cause of all that hath befallen us, first and last. Then do as thou desirest.

The Wezeer accordingly arose, and, opening the door of the court, went down upon the causeway, and proceeded twenty steps until he came to the sea, when he beheld Marzawán at the point of death. He therefore stretched forth his hand to him, and seized him by the hair of his head, and drew him up; and Marzawán came forth from the sea in a state of insensibility, with his stomach filled with water, and his eyes protruding. The Wezeer waited until his spirit returned to him, and then took off from him his clothes, and clad him with others, putting on his head one of the turbans of his young men; after which he said to him, Know that I have been the means of thy

deliverance from drowning, and be not thou the means of my death and of thine own.—How so? said Marzawán. The Wezeer answered, Because thou wilt now come up and pass among emeers and wezeers, all of them silent, speaking not, on account of Ḳamar-ez-Zemán, the son of the Sulṭán. And when Marzawán heard the mention of Ḳamar-ez-Zemán, he knew him, having heard his story in the countries whence he had come; but he said, Who is Ḳamar-ez-Zemán? The Wezeer answered, He is the son of the Sulṭán Sháh-Zemán, and is sick, laid upon his bed, without rest, knowing not night from day. He hath almost parted with life, from the wasting of his body, and become numbered among the dead; he passeth the day in burning, and the night in torment, and we have despaired of his life, and made sure of his dissolution. Beware of looking at him, or at any place but that whereon thou puttest thy foot; else thy life and mine will be sacrificed.—Marzawán then said, I conjure thee by

Allah to inform me respecting this youth whom thou hast described to me, and to tell me what is the cause of this state in which he is. So the Wezeer replied, I know no cause of it, save that his father, three years ago, required him to marry, and he refused; and he awoke in the morning and asserted that he had been sleeping and saw by his side a damsel of surpassing beauty, such as confounded the reason and baffled description, and he told us that he had taken off her ring from her finger and put it on his own finger, and put his ring on her finger; and we know not the mystery of this affair. By Allah, then, O my son, come up with me into the pavilion, and look not at the King's son. After that, go thy way. For the heart of the Sulṭán is filled with rage against me.—So Marzawán said within himself, By Allah, this is what I sought! He then followed the Wezeer until he came to the pavilion; and the Wezeer seated himself at the feet of Ḳamar-ez-Zemán. But as to Marzawán, he forthwith advanced until he stationed himself before Ḳamar-ez-Zemán, and looked at him; whereupon the Wezeer became as one dead, and, looking at Marzawán, made signs to him that he should go his way; but Marzawán feigned to take no notice. He continued gazing at Ḳamar-ez-Zemán, and, knowing that he was the object of his search, said, Extolled be the perfection of Him who hath made his stature like hers, and his complexion like hers, and his cheek like hers! So Ḳamar-ez-Zemán opened his eyes, and listened; and when Marzawán saw that he was listening to his words, he recited these verses :—

I see thee full of ecstasy and anxiety and melody, delighting in describing the charms of beauty.
Art thou smitten by love, or struck by arrows? For this is the habit of none but the wounded.
Give me cups of wine then to drink, and sing to me the praises of Suleymà and Er-Rabáb and Ten'om.[55]
I am jealous of the garments upon her sides, when she covereth with them her delicate body;
And I envy the cups that touch her mouth, when she putteth them upon the kissing-place.
Think me not killed by a keen-edged sword; for I have been wounded with the arrows of eyes.
When we met each other I found her fingers dyed red as though stained with the juice of 'andam;[56]
And she said, while she kindled a flame in my vitals, speaking as one who concealeth not love,
Have patience: this is not a dye that I have used;[57] and do not accuse me of falsehood and deceit;
But when I had seen thee lying asleep, with my hand and my arm and my wrist uncovered,

I shed tears of blood at parting, and wiped them with my hand; so my fingers
were stained with the blood.

Had *I* wept before *her*, in my passion for her, I had eased my soul before
repentance came;

But *she* wept before *me:* her tears drew mine; and I said, The merit belongs to
the precedent.[58]

Blame me not for loving her; for I swear by love that I am full of torment on
her account.

I weep for one whose face beauty hath adorned, and like whom there is none
among the Arabs or foreigners:

She hath Luḳmán's wisdom, and Yoosuf's form, and Dáood's sweet voice, and
Maryam's chastity;

While *I* have Yaaḳoob's grief, and Yoonus's regret, and Eiyoob's affliction, and
Adam's condition.[59]

Yet kill her not, though I die of my passion for her; but ask her why she held my
blood as lawful to her.

When Marzawán recited these verses, the words descended upon
the heart of Ḳamar-ez-Zemán as coolness and health, and, turning his
tongue in his mouth, he made a sign to the Sulṭán with his hand, as
though he would say, Let this young man sit by my side. And when
the Sulṭán conceived these words of his son Ḳamar-ez-Zemán, after he
had been enraged against the young man, and determined to strike
off his head, he rejoiced exceedingly. He arose, and seated Marzawán
by the side of his son, and, accosting him with kindness, said to
him, From what country art thou? He answered, From the Interior
Islands, from the dominions of the King El-Ghayoor, the lord of the
Islands and Seas, and of the Seven Palaces. And the King Sháh-
Zemán said, Perhaps relief may come to my son Ḳamar-ez-Zemán
through thy means. Then Marzawán addressed Ḳamar-ez-Zemán,
and said to him in his ear, Strengthen thy heart, and be cheerful and
happy; for as to her on whose account thou hast been reduced to this
condition, ask not respecting her state.[60] Thou hast concealed thy
affair,[61] and fallen sick; but she made known her feelings, and became
distracted, and is now imprisoned in the most miserable condition,
with a collar of iron upon her neck. But, if it be the will of God,
the restoration of you both shall be effected by my means.—And
when Ḳamar-ez-Zemán heard these words, his soul returned to him,
and he recovered his senses, and made a sign to the King his father
that he should raise him in a sitting posture. So the King rejoiced
excessively, and seated his son. He then dismissed all the wezeers
and emeers, and Ḳamar-ez-Zemán sat reclining between two cushions.
The King gave orders to perfume the pavilion with saffron, and to
decorate the city, and said to Marzawán, By Allah, O my son, this

is an auspicious event. He treated him with the utmost favour, and called for food for him. So they placed it before him, and he ate, and Ḳamar-ez-Zemán ate with him. He passed the next night with him, and the King also remained with them both that night, in the excess of his joy at the restoration of his son.

On the following morning, Marzawán began to tell his story to Ḳamar-ez-Zemán, saying to him, Know that I am acquainted with her in whose company thou wast, and her name is the lady Budoor, the daughter of the King El-Ghayoor. He then related to him all that had happened to the lady Budoor, from beginning to end, and acquainted him with the excess of her love for him.—All that hath happened unto thee with thy father, said he, hath happened to her with her father: thou art without doubt her lover, and she is thine: so strengthen thy heart and thy resolution; for I will conduct thee unto her, and unite you both, and act with you as saith one of the poets:—

If the object of love be adverse to its sufferer, and persist in shewing excessive aversion,
Yet will I effect the union of their persons, as though I were the pivot of a pair of scissors.

He continued to encourage Ḳamar-ez-Zemán until he ate and drank and his soul returned to him and he recovered from his disorder; and he ceased not to converse with him and cheer and amuse him, and recite to him verses, until he entered the bath, when his father gave orders again to decorate the city, in his joy at this event, and bestowed robes of honour, and gave alms, and liberated those who were confined in the prisons.

Marzawán then said to Ḳamar-ez-Zemán, Know that I came not from the lady Budoor but for this purpose: it was the object of my journey to deliver her from her present sufferings; and it only remaineth for us to devise some stratagem that we may go to her; for thy father cannot endure the idea of thy separation. But to-morrow do thou ask him to permit thee to go forth to hunt in the desert, and take with thee a pair of saddle-bags full of money, mount upon a swift horse, and take with thee a spare horse. I also will do the like; and say thou to thy father, I desire to amuse myself in the desert, and to hunt, and see the open country, and to pass there one night: therefore trouble not thy heart at all on my account.—And Ḳamar-ez-Zemán rejoiced at the words of Marzawán, and, going in to his father, asked his permission to go forth to hunt, saying as Marza-

wán desired him. And his father granted him permission, but said to him, Pass no more than one night away, and on the morrow be with me again; for thou knowest that life hath no pleasure unto me without thee, and that I do not believe thee to have entirely recovered from thy disorder. Then the King Sháh-Zemán recited to his son these two verses:—

> If I found myself possessed of every delight, and the world were mine with the empire of the Kisràs,[62]
> It were less unto me than the wing of a gnat if mine eye did not also behold thy form.

Having thus said, he equipped Ḳamar-ez-Zemán, together with Marzawán, giving orders that they should be furnished with six horses, and a dromedary to carry the money, and a camel to carry the water and food; and Ḳamar-ez-Zemán forbade that any one should go forth with him to attend upon him. So his father bade him farewell, and pressed him to his bosom, saying to him, I request thee, by Allah, do not be absent from me more than one night; and during that night, sleep will be forbidden unto me.

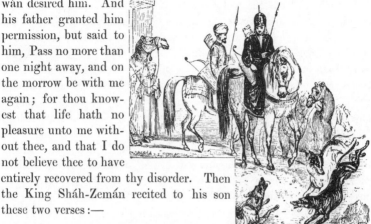

Ḳamar-ez-Zemán and Marzawán then went forth, and mounted two horses, having with them the dromedary bearing the money, and the camel laden with the water and the food, and, turning their faces towards the open country, proceeded the first day until evening, when they alighted and ate and drank, and fed their beasts and rested a while. After this they mounted again and journeyed on, and continued on their way for the space of three days; and on the fourth day they came to a spacious tract in which was a forest, where they alighted. Marzawán then took the camel and one of the horses, and slaughtered them, cut off their flesh, and stripped their bones, and, taking from Ḳamar-ez-Zemán his shirt and drawers, rent them in pieces, and daubed them with the blood of the horse. He also took Ḳamar-ez-Zemán's melwaṭah, and tore it, and daubed it with the blood, and threw it in a spot where the road divided; after which, they ate and drank and proceeded. So Ḳamar-ez-Zemán asked Marzawán the reason of this which he had done; and Marzawán answered, Know that thy father, the King Sháh-Zemán, after thou hast been absent from him one night and not returned to him on the second, will mount, and follow our track until he cometh to this blood which I have spilled, when he will see thy clothes torn and bloody, and will imagine that some accident hath befallen thee from robbers who obstruct the roads, or from a wild beast of the desert; whereupon he will abandon all hope of thee, and return to the city; and by this stratagem we shall attain our desire.—Ḳamar-ez-Zemán therefore replied, Excellently hast thou done.—They continued their journey days and nights, Ḳamar-ez-Zemán weeping all the while, until he rejoiced at drawing near to the country which they sought, when he recited these verses:—

Wilt thou tyrannise over a lover who hath never been unmindful of thee, and be indifferent to him after thy desiring him?
May I forfeit thy consent if in love I have deceived thee, and be recompensed by abandonment if I have been false!
I have been guilty of no fault to deserve harsh conduct; or if I have offended, I come repentant.
Thine abandonment of me is a wonderful misfortune; but fortune is always giving rise to wonders.

When he had finished reciting these verses, the Islands of the King El-Ghayoor appeared before him, and Ḳamar-ez-Zemán rejoiced exceedingly, and thanked Marzawán for what he had done. They entered the city, and Marzawán lodged Ḳamar-ez-Zemán in a Khán, where they rested three days from the fatigues of the journey. After this, Marzawán conducted Ḳamar-ez-Zemán into the bath, and clad him in the attire of a merchant, and made for him a geomantic tablet of gold,[63] with a set of instruments, and an astrolabe of gold. He then said to him, Arise, O my lord; station thyself beneath the King's

palace, and call out, I am the calculator, the writer, the astrologer! Where then is he who desireth to consult me?—For the King, as soon as he heareth thee, will send for thee, and introduce thee to his daughter, thy beloved; and when she beholdeth thee, the madness that she suffereth will cease; and her father, rejoicing in her safety, will marry her to thee, and divide his kingdom with thee; for he hath imposed this condition on himself.

So Ḳamar-ez-Zemán took the advice of Marzawán, and went forth from the Khán, wearing the dress, and having with him the set of instruments which we have described, and walked on until he stationed himself beneath the palace of the King El-Ghayoor, when he called out, I am the writer, the calculator, the astrologer! I perform the ceremonies of marriage-contracts,[64] and write sure charms, and make calculations, and write the geomantic characters by which the hidden treasures are discovered! Where then is the seeker?—And when the people of the city heard these words, as they had not for a long time seen a calculator or an astrologer, they stood around him and gazed at him, and, wondering at the beauty of his form and the elegance of his youth, they said to him, We conjure thee by Allah, O our lord, expose not thyself in this manner through thine ambition to marry the daughter of the King El-Ghayoor; but turn thine eyes towards these heads that are hung up; for their owners have all of them been killed on this account, and their ambition led them to perdition.—But Ḳamar-ez-Zemán regarded not their words. On the contrary, he raised his voice, and cried again, I am the writer, the calculator! I bring near the hidden treasures to the seeker!—The people still besought and forbade him; but instead of hearing their words, he again raised his voice, and cried as before. Whereupon they were all angry with him, and said to him, Thou art none other than a proud and foolish young man. Have compassion upon thy youth and tender years, and thy beauty and loveliness.—But he cried out, and said, I am the astrologer, the calculator! Is there, then, any seeker?

And while the people were attempting to dissuade him from doing thus, the King El-Ghayoor heard the crying, and the clamour of the people, and said to the Wezeer, Bring to us this astrologer. So the Wezeer descended, and took Ḳamar-ez-Zemán, who, when he went in unto the King, kissed the ground before him, and recited these two verses:—

Eight glorious qualities are united in thee;—by their means may fortune continue thy servant;—
Sure knowledge, and piety, and nobility, and munificence, and fluency, and eloquence, and preeminence, and conquest.

And when the King El-Ghayoor beheld him, he seated him by his side, and accosted him graciously, saying, O my son, by Allah call not thyself an astrologer, nor comply with my condition; for I have bound myself, that, whosoever visiteth my daughter and doth not cure her of that which hath befallen her, I will strike off his head; and that, whosoever cureth her, I will marry her to him. Let not then thy beauty and loveliness and justness of form deceive thee. By Allah! by Allah! if thou cure her not, I will strike off thy head!—Ḳamar-ez-Zemán replied, I agree to this condition. So the King El-Ghayoor desired the ḳáḍees to bear witness against him, and delivered him to the eunuch, saying to him, Conduct this person to the lady Budoor.

The eunuch, therefore, took him by the hand, and proceeded with him along the passage; but Ḳamar-ez-Zemán went on before him; and the eunuch began to say to him, Wo to thee! Hasten not to thine own destruction. By Allah, I never knew any astrologer but thee hasten to his own destruction! But thou knowest not the calamities that are before thee.—The eunuch then stationed Ḳamar-ez-Zemán behind the curtain which was over the door; and Ḳamar-ez-Zemán said to him, Which of the two modes will be more agreeable to thee: my treating and curing thy mistress here, or my going in to her, and curing her within the curtain? And the eunuch wondered at his words, and answered him, If thou cure her here, it will be a greater proof of thy excellent skill. Upon this, therefore, Ḳamar-ez-Zemán seated himself behind the curtain, and, taking forth the inkhorn and pen, wrote upon a paper these words:—

He whom estrangement hath afflicted is to be cured by the performance of the engagement of his beloved: but misery is the lot of him who hath despaired of his life, and made sure of his dissolution; for whose sorrowful heart there is no supporter or helper, and for whose sleepless eye there is no reliever from anxiety; who passeth his day in burning, and his night in torture; whose body hath suffered continual wasting; and to whom no messenger hath come from his beloved.—He then wrote these verses:—

I write with a heart devoted to thinking of thee, and with a wounded eyelid shedding tears of blood,
And a body clad by ardent longing and grief with the garment of leanness, and brought into subjection.
I complain unto thee of the torment of my love, and the utter exhaustion of my patience.
Be favourable, then, and merciful and indulgent; for my heart is breaking through the violence of my passion.

And beneath these verses he wrote:—The restoration of the heart is effected by union with the beloved; and God is the only physician who can cure him whom the object of his affection hath oppressed. If you or we have been deceitful, may the deceiver be disappointed. There is nothing more charming than a lover who is faithful to an unfeeling object of affection.—Then, at the foot of his letter, he wrote thus:—From the distracted and distressed, the passionate and perplexed, whom longing and ardent desire have disquieted, the captive of transport and distraction, Ḳamar-ez-Zemán, the son of Sháh-Zemán, to the peerless one of her age, and the preeminent among the beautiful Ḥooreeyehs, the lady Budoor, the daughter of the King El-Ghayoor:

—Know that I pass my night in sleeplessness, and my day in perplexity, suffering from excessive wasting and sickness, and love and desire, uttering abundant sighs, and pouring forth torrents of tears, the slave of love, the victim of passion, persecuted by desire, the companion of disease. I am that restless one whose eye never sleepeth; the slave of love whose tears are never interrupted: the fire of my heart is never extinguished; and the flame of my desire never disappeareth.—After this, he wrote upon the margin of the letter this admired verse:—

> Peace from the treasuries of the grace of my Lord be on her who possesseth my soul and my heart.

And he added:—

> Grant me some words of your conversation, that you may shew me pity, or that my heart may be at rest.
> From the excess of my love for you, and my transport, I make light of that which rendereth me abject.
> God guard a people whose abode was distant from me, and whose secret I kept in every situation!
> But now fortune, in its kindness, hath favoured me, and brought me to the threshold of the beloved.
> I beheld Budoor in the bed by my side; and by her sun, the moon of my fortune was brightened.

Then, having sealed the letter, he wrote these verses in the place of the address:—

> Inquire of my letter what my pen hath written, and the characters will acquaint thee with my transport and anguish.
> My hand is writing while my tears are flowing, and my desire complaineth of my disorder to the paper.
> My tears cease not to pour upon the paper. If they stopped, I would cause them to be followed by my blood.

And he added this other line:—

> I have sent thy ring which I took in exchange when we were together: then send me mine.

(For he had enclosed the ring of the lady Budoor in the letter.)

He then handed the letter to the eunuch, who took it and went in with it to the lady Budoor; and she received it from his hand, and found in it her ring. And when she read it, and understood its object, she knew that her beloved was Ḳamar-ez-Zemán, and that it was he who was standing outside the curtain; whereupon her reason fled, through the joy that she experienced. She arose immediately, and, pressing her feet against the wall, strained with all her might against the iron collar, and broke it from her neck, together with the chains, and went forth, and threw herself upon Ḳamar-ez-Zemán, kissing his mouth like a pigeon feeding its young. She embraced him in the violence of her passion, and said to him, O my master, do I see this awake or in sleep; and hath God indeed graciously granted us our reunion? She then praised God, and thanked Him, for reuniting her after her despair. And when the eunuch saw her in this state, he went running to the King El-Ghayoor, and, kissing the ground before him, said to him, O my lord, know that this astrologer is the wisest of all the astrologers; for he cured thy daughter while he stood behind the curtain, and went not in to her.—Is this news true? said the King.—O my lord, answered the eunuch, arise and see her, how she hath broken the chains of iron and come forth to the astrologer, kissing and embracing him.

So the King El-Ghayoor arose and went in to his daughter; and when she beheld him, she arose, and covered her head. The King, rejoicing at her restoration, kissed her between her eyes; for he loved her excessively; and then graciously addressed Ḳamar-ez-Zemán, asking him respecting his condition, and saying, From what country art thou? Therefore Ḳamar-ez-Zemán acquainted him with his rank, and informed him that his father was the King Sháh-Zemán, relating to him the whole story from beginning to end, and acquainting him with all that had happened to him with the lady Budoor, and how he had taken her ring from her finger and she had put on his ring. At this the King El-Ghayoor wondered, and said, Your story must be recorded in books, and read after you, age after age. Then immediately he summoned the ḳáḍees and witnesses, and performed the lady Budoor's contract of marriage to Ḳamar-ez-Zemán, and gave orders to decorate the city for seven days. A banquet was prepared, the city was decorated, and the people praised God for his having caused the lady Budoor to fall in love with a handsome young man of the sons of the Kings. The women displayed her before him, and the marriage was concluded; and on the following day the King made a feast, to which all [who desired], of the inhabitants of the Interior and Exterior Islands, were admitted, and the feast was continued during a whole month.

After this, Ḳamar-ez-Zemán thought upon his father, and dreamt that he saw him, and that he heard him say, O my son, dost thou act thus towards me? He therefore awoke sorrowful, and acquainted his wife with the dream. So she went in with him to her father, and, having informed him of this, they begged his permission to set forth on the journey; and he gave permission to Ḳamar-ez-Zemán; but the lady

Budoor said, O my father, I cannot endure his separation. Wherefore he replied, Journey thou with him. He granted her permission to remain with Ķamar-ez-Zemán a whole year, and desired her after that to pay him, her father, an annual visit; whereupon she kissed her father's hand, and Ķamar-ez-Zemán did the same. The King El-Ghayoor then fitted out his daughter and her husband: he prepared for them the furniture for the journey, sent forth for them the horses and dromedaries, together with a litter for his daughter, loaded for them the mules and dromedaries, and provided them with all that they required for the journey. And on the day of departure, he bade farewell to Ķamar-ez-Zemán, and bestowed upon him a magnificent dress of gold stuff adorned with jewels, presenting him also with a treasure of wealth, and giving him a charge respecting his daughter Budoor. After which he went forth with them both to the limits of the Islands, where he bade farewell again to Ķamar-ez-Zemán, and, going in to his daughter Budoor as she reposed in the litter, embraced her, and wept. Then coming out

from her, he went to her husband, and again bade him farewell, and kissed him; and having done this, he parted from them, and returned to his islands with his troops, after he had ordered Ḳamar-ez-Zemán and his wife to continue their journey.

So Ḳamar-ez-Zemán and the lady Budoor proceeded with their attendants the first day and the second and the third and the fourth, and continued for the space of a month. They then alighted in a spacious meadow, abounding with herbage; and in it they pitched their tents, and ate and drank and rested. And when the lady Budoor slept, Ḳamar-ez-Zemán went in and found her asleep, clad in a silken shirt of apricot-colour, and with a koofeeyeh of gold stuff adorned with jewels upon her head; and he observed a precious stone, red like 'andam,[65] tied to the band of her trowsers, with two lines of writing, in characters not to be read, engraved upon it.[66] Ḳamar-ez-Zemán, wondering at this, said within himself, If this precious stone were not a thing of great importance to her she would not have tied it thus upon the band of her trowsers, and so concealed it, that she might not suffer it to be away from her. What then can she do with this; and what can be the secret property that it possesseth?—He then took it and went forth with it from the tent, to look at it in the light; but as he was examining it, lo, a bird pounced upon it, and, having seized it from his hand, flew away with it, and then alighted with it upon the ground.[67]

Ḳamar-ez-Zemán, fearing to lose the precious stone, ran after the bird; but the bird proceeded at the same rate as Ḳamar-ez-Zemán, who continued running after it from valley to valley and from hill to hill until night came and darkness commenced, when the bird went to roost upon a high tree, while Ḳamar-ez-Zemán stood beneath it, confounded, and faint with hunger and fatigue. He thought himself lost, and desired to return; but knew not the place from which he had come; and, night overtaking him, he exclaimed, There is no strength nor power but in God, the High, the Great! He then slept beneath the tree upon which the bird was roosting until the morning, when he awoke from his sleep, and found that the bird had just risen and flown from the tree. So he walked after it; and the bird continued flying by little and little at the same rate as that at which

Ḳamar-ez-Zemán walked; upon seeing which, he smiled, and said, Allah! it is wonderful that this bird yesterday flew at the same rate as I ran, and to-day, knowing that I am tired, and cannot run, flieth at the same rate as I walk! Verily this is wonderful! But I must follow this bird, and it will lead me either to the preservation of my life or to my death. So I will follow it whither it goeth; for at all events it will not stay but in an inhabited country.—He then continued following the bird, which passed every night upon a tree; and he followed it for the space of ten days, feeding upon the plants of the earth, and drinking of the rivers; after which he came in sight of a city, and the bird darted into this city as rapidly as a glance, and disappeared from Ḳamar-ez-Zemán, who knew not whither it had gone. Upon this he wondered, and exclaimed, Praise be to God who hath preserved me, so that I have arrived at this city! Then seating himself by some water, he washed his hands and feet and face, and rested a while, reflecting upon his former life of ease, and considering his present state of distance from his country and his friends, and of hunger and weariness.

Having thus rested, he entered the gate of the city, not knowing whither to go, and walked through the whole of the city. He had entered by the land-gate, and he walked on till he went forth from the sea-gate, without meeting any one of its inhabitants. The city was on the shore of the sea; and when he had gone forth from the sea-gate, he walked on until he came to the gardens of the city; and he entered among the trees, and went and stood by the gate of one of the gardens; whereupon the gardener came forth to him and welcomed him, saying to him, Praise be to God that thou hast escaped the people of this city! Enter then this garden quickly, before any one of its inhabitants shall see thee.—So, upon this, Ḳamar-ez-Zemán entered the garden, with a wandering mind, and said to the gardener, What is the history of the inhabitants of this city? The gardener answered, Know that the people of this city are all of them Magians; and I conjure thee by Allah to tell me how thou camest to this place, and what was the reason of thy entering our country.[68] Ḳamar-ez-Zemán, therefore, acquainted him with all that had happened to him; and the gardener wondered at it extremely, and said to him, Know, O my son, that the countries of El-Islám[69] are distant from hence: between them and this place is a distance of four months' voyage by sea; and by land, a journey of a whole year. We have a ship that saileth every year with merchandise to the nearest of the countries of El-Islám, proceeding hence to the Sea of the Ebony Islands,[70] and thence to the Islands of Khálidán, whose King is the Sulṭán Sháh-Zemán.—And upon this, Ḳamar-ez-Zemán meditated within himself a while, and knew that there was no plan more suitable for him than that of his remaining there with the gardener, and becoming his assistant for a fourth of the produce.[71] So he said to him, Wilt thou take me as thy assistant on the condition of my receiving the fourth of the produce of this garden? And the gardener answered, I hear and obey. He then instructed him in the conducting of the water among the trees;[72] and Ḳamar-ez-Zemán occupied himself in doing this, and in hoeing up the grass: the gardener clad him with a blue vest reaching to his knees; and he betook himself to watering the trees, pouring forth floods of tears and reciting verses by night and day on the subject of his beloved Budoor.

But as to his wife, the lady Budoor, she awoke from her sleep and asked for her husband, Ḳamar-ez-Zemán; but found him not; and feeling the knot of the band of her trowsers, she found that it was untied, and that the precious stone was lost; whereupon she said within herself, O Allah! this is wonderful! Where is my beloved? It seemeth that he hath taken the stone, and gone, and knoweth not the secret virtue that it possesseth. Whither can he have gone? Some wonderful event must have occasioned his departure; for he cannot willingly part from me for an hour. Accursed be the stone, and the hour when it brought this mischief!—She then reflected, and said within herself, If I go forth to the attendants and acquaint them with the loss of my husband, they will covet me: I must therefore have recourse to stratagem. So she put on some clothes of Ḳamar-ez-Zemán, and a turban like his, and, having thrown a lithám[73] over part of her face, put into her litter a slave-girl; after which she went forth from her tent, and called out to the young men, who immediately brought her the horse, and she mounted, giving orders to bind on the burdens. They accordingly did this, and proceeded; and she concealed her case; for she resembled Ḳamar-ez-Zemán, so that no one doubted her to be really him. She continued her journey, together with her attendants, days and nights, until she came in sight of a city overlooking the sea, and by it she alighted, and there she pitched her tents, for the sake of taking rest. She then asked the name of this city, and was answered, This is the City of Ebony, and its King is the King Armánoos, who hath a daughter named Ḥayát-en-Nufoos.[74]

Now when the lady Budoor had alighted here to rest, the King Armánoos sent a messenger from his palace to learn for him the tidings of this (supposed) King who had encamped outside the city. So the messenger, on coming to the party, inquired of them, and they informed him that this was a King's son who had wandered from his way, and who was journeying to the Islands of Khálidán, to the King Sháh-Zemán. The messenger, therefore, returned to the King Armánoos, and acquainted him with the news; and as soon as the King heard it, he descended with the lords of his empire to visit the stranger. As he approached the tents, the lady Budoor advanced towards him on foot, and the King Armánoos alighted, and they saluted each other. He then took her and conducted her into the city, and went up with her into his palace, where he gave orders to prepare a banquet, and to convey her to the mansion of entertainment; and there she remained three days.

After this, it happened that the lady Budoor had entered the bath, and she displayed a face shining like the full moon, so that all who beheld her were filled with admiration of her beauty, and she was clad in a vest of silk embroidered with gold, and adorned with jewels. The King Armánoos then accosted her graciously, and said to her, Know, O my son, that I am now a very old man, and in my life I have never been blest with a child, except a daughter, who resembleth thee in form and stature, and in beauty and loveliness. I am unable any longer to fulfil the duties of a King. Wilt thou, then, O my son, reside in my land, and dwell in my country? If so, I will marry thee to my daughter, and give thee my kingdom.—Upon this, the lady Budoor hung down her head, and her forehead became moistened by bashfulness. She said within herself, What can be done, seeing that I am a woman? If I disobey his command, and depart, probably he will send after me an army, and kill me; and if I obey him, probably I shall be disgraced: I have lost my beloved Ḳamar-ez-Zemán, and know not what is become of him; and I have no means of preserving myself, unless by assenting to his desire, and residing with him until God accomplish what must come to pass.—She then raised her head, and paid submission to the King by saying, I hear and obey:—whereupon the King rejoiced, and gave orders to proclaim throughout the Ebony Islands that rejoicings should be celebrated and the houses decorated. He assembled the chamberlains and lieutenants, and emeers and wezeers, and the other lords of his empire, and the ḳáḍees of his city, and, having abdicated the throne, appointed the lady Budoor Sulṭán in his stead, and clad her with the royal vestments. All the emeers presented themselves before her, complaining not of her youth; and every one of them who looked at her was astonished at her extreme beauty and loveliness.

So when the lady Budoor had been created Sulṭán, and the drums had been beaten to announce the joyful event, the King Armánoos prepared his daughter Ḥayát-en-Nufoos for her marriage; and after a few days, they introduced the lady Budoor to the lady Ḥayát-en-Nufoos. They resembled two full moons by the side of each other, or two suns that had risen together; and when the attendants had closed the doors upon them, and let down the curtains, after they had lighted the candles for them, and spread the bed, the lady Budoor sat with the lady Ḥayát-en-Nufoos, and, reflecting upon her beloved Ḳamar-ez-Zemán, her grief became violent, and she poured forth tears, and recited some verses commencing thus:—

O ye who have quitted me, with my heart full of trouble, your absence hath left no life in my body!

Then sitting by the side of the lady Ḥayát-en-Nufoos, she kissed her upon the mouth, and, arising abruptly, performed the ablution, and continued praying until the lady Ḥayát-en-Nufoos had fallen asleep, when she entered the bed, and turned her back to her till the morning. And when the morning arrived, the old King and his wife came in to their daughter, and asked her how she was. So she acquainted them with what had happened, and with the verses that she had heard.

But the Queen Budoor, having gone forth, seated herself on the throne, and the emeers and other lords of the empire, and all the chiefs and soldiers, went up to her, and congratulated her on her accession to the throne, kissed the ground before her, and prayed for her, while she accosted them with smiles, bestowed upon them robes of honour, and increased the fiefs of the emeers. So all the soldiers and people loved her, and prayed for the continuance of her reign, having no doubt that she was a man; and she commanded and forbade, and dispensed justice and equity, liberated the persons who were confined in the prisons, and remitted the custom-taxes. She continued sitting in the hall of judgment until night, and then, entering the chamber that was prepared for her, found the lady Ḥayát-en-Nufoos sitting there. She therefore seated herself by her side, and patted her on the back, caressed her, and kissed her between the eyes, and then, as before, recited some verses deploring the absence of her husband; after which, she rose upon her feet, and, having wiped away her tears, performed the ablution, and prayed, and continued praying until sleep overcame the lady Ḥayát-en-Nufoos. The Queen Budoor then laid herself by her side, and so remained until the morning; when she rose, and performed the morning-prayers, seated herself upon the throne, commanded and forbade, and administered justice and equity. In the meantime, the King Armánoos went in to his daughter, and she informed him of all that had happened to her, repeating to him the verses which the Queen Budoor had recited, and said to him, O my father, I have never beheld any one more sensible or more bashful than my husband; but he only weepeth and sigheth. Her father, therefore, replied, O my daughter, have patience with him yet this third night only; and if he treat thee not with the respect that is due to thee, we shall know what course to pursue with him: I will divest him of the regal authority, and banish him from our country.—Thus he agreed with his daughter to do, and thus he resolved in his mind.

Now when the next night came, the Queen Budoor arose from the throne, and, returning to the chamber prepared for her in the palace, saw the candles lighted, and the lady Ḥayát-en-Nufoos sitting there; whereupon she thought of her husband, and of the events that had happened to herself and him during the last few days; and she wept, and continued groaning, and again recited some verses expressive of her unhappy state. She then desired to arise to prayer; but Ḥayát-en-Nufoos clung to her skirts, and said to her, O my master, art thou not ashamed to act thus towards my father who hath treated thee with so much kindness, and to regard me with this protracted indifference? And when the Queen Budoor heard this, she sat down, and replied, O my beloved, what sayest thou?—What I say, rejoined Ḥayát-en-Nufoos, is this; that I have beheld no one so self-satisfied as thou. Is then every one who is lovely thus selfish? But I say not this on my own account: I do so only in my fear for thee from the King Armánoos; for he hath resolved, if thou pay me not proper respect, to depose thee from the sovereignty to-morrow, and to banish thee from his country; and probably his rage may so increase that he may kill thee. I therefore am moved with compassion for thee, and have given thee good advice; and it is thine to decide how thou wilt act.—On hearing these words, the Queen Budoor hung down her head towards the ground, and was perplexed at her case, saying within herself, If I oppose his wish, I perish; and if I obey him, I am disgraced; but I am now Queen of all the Ebony Islands, and they are under my rule, and I cannot meet again with Ḳamar-ez-Zemán unless in this place; for there is no way by which he can return to his country but by the Ebony Islands. I will therefore commit my case unto God, who is the Best Director.—She then said to Ḥayát-en-Nufoos, O my beloved, my neglect of thee hath been involuntary. And she related to her all that had befallen her from beginning to end, adding, I conjure thee by Allah to conceal my case and to keep my secret until God reunite me with my beloved Ḳamar-ez-Zemán, and after that we shall see what will happen.—Upon this, Ḥayát-en-Nufoos was filled with the utmost wonder, and, being moved with pity for her, prayed for her reunion with her beloved, and said to her, O my sister, fear not nor be alarmed; but have patience until God accomplish that which must come to pass. The bosoms of the ingenuous are the sepulchres of secrets; and thy secret I will not reveal.—Then they toyed together, and embraced each other, and slept until near the call to morning-prayers, when the mother of Ḥayát-en-Nufoos came in to her, and was satisfied with her report. The Queen Budoor, after performing the morning-prayers, repaired to the hall of judgment, and there, seated upon the throne, judged the people; and the King Armánoos was rejoiced at what he heard; his bosom expanded, and he gave banquets; and thus they continued for a length of time.—Such were the adventures of Ḳamar-ez-Zemán and the Queen Budoor.

But as to the King Sháh-Zemán,—after the departure of his son to the chase, accompanied by Marzawán, as already related, he waited until the second night; and when his son came not, his reason was perplexed, and he slept not that night. He became in a state of the utmost disquiet, his excitement was excessive, and he burned with anxiety; and scarcely had the day broke when he rose. He sat expecting his son until midday; but he came not; and his heart became impressed with a dread of separation, and he burned with fears for his son. He wept until he wetted his clothes with his tears, and then, wiping away the tears, he issued a proclamation commanding his forces to march, and urging them to undertake a long expedition. So all the troops mounted, and the Sulṭán went forth, with a heart tortured for his son, and full of grief. He disposed his army in six divisions, on the right and left, and before and behind, and said to them, To-morrow ye shall meet at the parting of the road. The troops, therefore, being thus divided, the horsemen set forth, and proceeded the rest of that day until the hour of darkness; and they continued on their way the whole of the night, and the next day till noon, when they arrived at a spot where the road divided into four branches; so that they knew not which way to go. But here they beheld torn clothes, and mangled flesh, and they looked at the traces of the blood, and observed every piece of the clothes. So when the King Sháh-Zemán saw this, he uttered a great cry from the bottom of his bosom, and exclaimed, Oh, my son! He slapped his face, and plucked his beard, and rent his clothes, feeling convinced of the death of his son. His weeping and wailing were excessive, and the troops wept with him, all of them regarding as certain the destruction of Ḳamar-ez-Zemán: they threw dust upon their heads, and the night overtook them while they wept and wailed so that they were at the point of death. The King Sháh-Zemán then returned with his troops to his city, convinced of the death of his son, and concluding that either a wild beast or a robber had attacked him and torn him in pieces. He issued a proclamation throughout the Islands of Khálidán that the people should wear black in token of mourning for his son Ḳamar-ez-Zemán, and built for himself an edifice which he named the House of Lamentations; and every Thursday and Monday he decided the affairs of his troops and people; passing the rest of the week in the House of Lamentations, mourning for his son, and bewailing him with elegies.

Meanwhile, the Queen Budoor remained monarch of the Land of Ebony, the people pointing at her with the finger, and saying, This is the son-in-law of the King Armánoos; and every night she slept with the lady Ḥayát-en-Nufoos, complaining of the absence of her husband Ḳamar-ez-Zemán, and describing to her his beauty and loveliness, desiring an interview with him were it only in her sleep.

Now Ḳamar-ez-Zemán continued residing in the garden, with its owner, for a length of time, weeping night and day, and sighing, and lamenting in verses the past times of enjoyment and happiness, while the gardener, to console him, told him that the ship would sail at the end of the year to the countries of the Muslims. Thus he remained until, one day, he saw the people assembling together, at which he wondered; and the gardener came in to him, and said to him, O my son, cease from work this day, and water not the trees; for this day is a festival of the people, whereon they visit one another. Therefore rest, and only keep thine eye upon the garden; for I desire to look out for the vessel for thee, since there remaineth but a short time, and to send thee to the country of the Muslims.—The gardener then went forth; and Ḳamar-ez-Zemán remained alone in the garden. His heart was broken, his tears flowed, and he continued weeping until he fell down in a swoon; and when he recovered, he rose, and walked about the garden reflecting upon his misfortunes and upon his protracted estrangement and separation. His reason being thus disturbed, he stumbled, and fell upon his face, and his forehead struck against the root of a tree with such violence that his blood flowed, and mingled with his tears. He, however, wiped away the blood, and dried up his tears, and, having bound his forehead with a piece of rag, arose, and continued his walk about the garden. And he turned up his eyes towards a tree upon which were two birds contending together; and one of them overcame the other; it pecked at its neck, and severed its head from its body, and, taking the head, flew away with it. The body of the bird thus killed then fell upon the ground

before Ḳamar-ez-Zemán, and as it lay there, lo, two great birds pounced down upon it, and, one of them placing itself at its upper extremity and the other at its tail, they depressed their wings over it, and stretched forth their necks towards it, and moaned. So Ḳamar-ez-Zemán wept for his separation from his wife when he beheld the two birds moaning over their companion. After this, he saw the two birds make a hollow, and bury in it the slaughtered bird; and having done so, they soared aloft into the sky; but after they had been absent a while, they returned bringing with them the bird that had committed the murder. They alighted with it upon the grave of the slaughtered bird, and there crouched upon it and killed it: they rent open its body, tore out its bowels, and poured its blood upon the grave of the slaughtered bird: then they strewed about its flesh, and tore its skin, and, pulling out all that was within it, they scattered it in different places.

All this took place while Ḳamar-ez-Zemán looked on in wonder; and as he happened to cast a glance towards the place where the two great birds had killed the other, he observed something shining. So he approached it, and saw it to be the bird's crop: and he took it and opened it, and found in it the stone that had been the cause of his separation from his wife. As soon as he beheld it he knew it, and fell upon the ground in a fit, through his joy; and when he recovered he said within himself, This is a good sign, and an omen of my reunion with my beloved! He then examined it, drew it over his eye,[75] and tied it upon his arm, anticipating from it a happy result; after which he rose and walked about, waiting for the gardener. He continued searching for him until night; but he came not. So Ḳamar-ez-Zemán slept in his usual place until the morning, when he arose to his work.

Having girded himself with a rope of the fibres of the palm-tree, he took the hoe and the basket, and went into the midst of the garden till he came to a locust-tree, and he struck at its root with the hoe, whereupon the blow loudly resounded. So he removed the earth from its place; and having done this, he discovered a trap-door, on opening which he found an aperture; and he descended into it, and beheld an old saloon, of the age of Thamood and 'Ád,[76] spacious, and [containing a number of jars] filled with red gold; upon which he said within himself, Fatigue is past, and joy and happiness have come! He then ascended from this place into the garden, and, having replaced the trap-door, resumed his occupation of conducting the water to the trees in the garden.

Thus he continued to busy himself until the close of the day, when the gardener came to him, and said, O my son, receive glad tidings of thy speedy return to thy native land; for the merchants have prepared for the voyage, and the ship after three days is to set sail for the City of Ebony, which is the first of the cities of the Muslims; and when thou hast arrived there, thou wilt travel by land six months to the Islands of Khálidán and the King Sháh-Zemán. So Ḳamar-ez-Zemán rejoiced at this, and, kissing the hand of the gardener, said to him, O my father, like as thou hast given me good tidings, I too give good tidings unto thee. And he acquainted him with the affair of the saloon; whereat the gardener also rejoiced, and replied, I have been eighty years in this garden without finding anything, and thou hast been with me less than a year and hast discovered this: it is therefore thy prize, and a means of terminating thy grief;

and will assist thee to accomplish thy return to thy family and thy reunion with thy beloved. But Ḳamar-ez-Zemán said, It must positively be divided between me and thee. He then took the gardener and conducted him into that saloon, and shewed him the gold, which was in twenty jars: so he took ten and the gardener took ten. And the gardener said to him, O my son, fill for thyself large jars[77] with the 'aṣáfeeree olives[78] which are in this garden; for they exist not in any country but ours, and the merchants export them to all other parts; and place thou the gold in the jars, and the olives over the gold: then close them and take them to the ship. So Ḳamar-ez-Zemán arose immediately, and filled fifty large jars, putting the gold in them, and closing each after he had put the olives over the gold;[79] and the precious stone he put into one of the jars: after which he sat conversing with the gardener, and felt confident of his speedy reunion with his family, saying within himself, When I have arrived at the Ebony Island, I will journey thence to the country of my father, and inquire for my beloved Budoor: but I wonder whether she have returned to her own country, or journeyed on to the country of my father, or whether any accident have happened to her on the way.

He then sat waiting for the expiration of the days, and related to the gardener the story of the birds, and of what passed between them, whereat the gardener wondered. After this, both of them slept until the morning, and the gardener awoke ill, and remained so two days: and on the third day his illness so increased that they despaired of his life. Ḳamar-ez-Zemán, therefore, grieved for the gardener; and while he was in this state, lo, the master of the ship, with the sailors, came and inquired for the gardener: so he acquainted them with his illness. They then said, Where is the young man who desireth to go with us to the Island of Ebony? And Ḳamar-ez-Zemán answered, He is the memlook who is before you.[80] And he desired them to transport the jars to the ship. They therefore removed them to the ship,

and said to Ḳamar-ez-Zemán, Hasten; for the wind hath become fair. And he replied, I hear and obey. He then conveyed his provisions to the ship, and returned to the gardener to bid him farewell; but he found him in the agonies of death: so he seated himself at his head till he died; and he closed his eyes, and prepared his body for burial, and interred it.

Having done this, he repaired to the ship. He found, however, that it had spread its sails and departed; and it continued cleaving the sea until it disappeared from before his eyes. He was confounded and perplexed, and he returned to the garden anxious and sorrowful, and threw dust upon his head. He hired the garden from its proprietor, and employed a man to assist him in watering the trees; and, going to the trap-door, he descended into the saloon, and stowed the remaining gold in fifty other large jars, putting olives over it.[81] He then made inquiries respecting the ship, and the people answered him, That it sailed not more than once in every year. His trouble of mind increased, and he mourned for that which had befallen him, especially for the loss of the precious stone of the lady Budoor. He passed night and day in weeping, and reciting verses.

In the mean time, the wind was favourable to the ship, and it arrived at the Island of Ebony. And it happened in accordance with destiny, that the Queen Budoor was sitting at a window, and beheld the vessel when it cast anchor by the shore. Her heart throbbed at the sight, and she mounted with the emeers and chamberlains, and, repairing to the shore, stopped near the ship as the crew were transporting the merchandise to the magazines. She forthwith summoned the master of the vessel, and asked him what he had brought; and he answered her, O King, I have, in this vessel, aromatics and medicinal powders, and collyriums and plasters and ointments, and wealth and magnificent stuffs and costly merchandise, such as camels and mules cannot carry; among which are various kinds of essences and spices and aloes-wood, and tamarind[82] and 'aṣáfeeree olives, such as are scarcely to be found in this country. On hearing this, she felt a desire for the olives, and said to the owner of the ship, What is the quantity of the olives that thou hast brought? He answered, I have fifty large jars full; but their owner came not with us; and the King shall take of them what he desireth. So she said, Land them, that I may look at them. And the master called out to his crew, whereupon they brought out the fifty jars; and she opened one, and, having looked at the olives, said, I will take these fifty jars and give you their price, whatever it be. The master of the ship replied, These have no value in our country: but their owner remained behind us, and he is a poor man. But she said, What is their price? And he answered, A thousand pieces of silver.—I will take them, replied she, for a thousand pieces of silver.

She then commanded that they should be conveyed to the palace; and when night came, she gave orders to bring to her one of the jars; and she opened it. There was no one in the chamber but herself and Ḥayát-en-Nufoos; and she placed a dish before her, and on her pouring into it some of the contents of the jar, there fell into the dish a heap of red gold; whereupon she said to the lady Ḥayát-en-Nufoos, This is nothing but gold! She therefore examined the whole, and found that all the jars contained gold, and that the olives altogether would not fill one of the jars; and searching among the gold, she discovered the precious stone with it. So she took it and examined it, and found that it was the stone which was attached to the band of her trousers, and which Ḳamar-ez-Zemán had taken. As soon as she recognised it, she cried out in her joy, and fell down in a swoon: and when she recovered, she said within herself, This precious stone was the cause of the separation of my beloved Ḳamar-ez-Zemán; but it is an omen of good fortune! She then told the lady Ḥayát-en-Nufoos that its recovery was a prognostic of her reunion. And when the morning came, she seated herself upon the throne, and summoned the master of the ship, who, when he came, kissed the ground before her; and she said to him, Where did ye leave the owner of these olives? He answered, O King of the age, we left him in the country of the Magians; and he is a gardener. And she said, If thou bring him not, thou knowest not the misfortune that will happen unto thee and to thy ship. She immediately gave orders to affix seals upon the magazines of the merchants, and said to them, The owner of these olives is an offender against me, and is my debtor; and if he come not, I will assuredly slay you all, and seize your merchandise. So they applied to the master of the ship, promising to pay him the hire of the vessel if he would return, and said to him, Deliver us from this tyrant.

The master therefore embarked, and loosed the sails, and God decreed him safety, so that he arrived at the Island of the Magians; and, landing by night, he went up to the garden. The night had become tedious to Ḳamar-ez-Zemán, and he was thinking upon his beloved, as he sat in the garden weeping for the misfortunes that had befallen him; and the master of the ship knocked at the gate of his garden. He therefore opened the gate and went forth to him, and immediately the sailors carried him off, and, embarking with him, loosed the sails, and departed. They continued their voyage days and nights, while Ḳamar-ez-Zemán knew not the occasion of this conduct. He asked them the cause, and they answered him, Thou art an offender against the King of the Ebony Islands, the son of the King Armánoos, and hast stolen his wealth, O thou unlucky! But he replied, By Allah, in my life I never entered that country, nor do I know it.

They continued their voyage with him until they came in sight of the Ebony Islands, and took him up to the lady Budoor, who, as soon as she saw him, knew him, and said, Commit him to the eunuchs, that they may conduct him into the bath. She then dispelled the

fears of the merchants, and bestowed upon the master of the ship a robe of honour worth ten thousand pieces of gold: after which, she went in to the lady Ḥayát-en-Nufoos, and acquainted her with the event, saying to her, Conceal the news until I have attained my desire, and done a deed which shall be recorded, and read after us to Kings and subjects. And when she gave orders to conduct Ḳamar-ez-Zemán into the bath, they did so, and clad him in the apparel of Kings; and when he came forth from the bath, he appeared like a branch of the Oriental willow, or a planet at whose appearance the sun and moon were abashed; and his soul returned to him. He then repaired to her, and entered the palace; but when she beheld him, she restrained her heart, that her purpose might be accomplished. She bestowed upon him memlooks and servants, and camels and mules, gave him a treasury of wealth, and ceased not to promote him from grade to grade until she made him treasurer, delivering all the treasures to his care. She admitted him into high favour, and acquainted the emeers with his station, and they all loved him. Every day the Queen Budoor increased his appointments, and Ḳamar-ez-Zemán knew not the cause of her thus honouring him. From the abundance of his wealth he gave liberal presents; and he served the King Armánoos with such zeal that he loved him, as did the emeers and other great men, and the common people, so that they swore by his life.[83]

But all this time Ḳamar-ez-Zemán wondered at the honours which the Queen Budoor shewed him, and said within himself, By Allah, this love must have some cause; or perhaps this King thus favoureth me from some evil intention: I must therefore ask his permission to depart from his country. Accordingly, he went to the Queen Budoor, and said to her, O King, thou hast bestowed on me great favours, and thy favours will be complete if thou permit me to depart, and take from me all that thou hast bestowed upon me. And the Queen Budoor smiled, and said, What induceth thee to desire to travel, and to rush headlong into perils, when thou art enjoying the highest favour, and extraordinary beneficence?—O King, answered Ḳamar-ez-Zemán, if this favour be without cause, it is most wonderful, especially as thou hast conferred upon me dignities such as are proper for the aged, when I am but a child. The Queen Budoor then took him into a private apartment, and made herself known to him: and he discovered that she was his wife, the Queen Budoor, the daughter of the King El-Ghayoor, lord of the Islands and the Seas; whereupon they embraced and kissed each other. She related to him all that had happened to her from first to last; and he in like manner acquainted her with all that had befallen him.

And when the next morning came, and diffused its light, the Queen Budoor sent to the King Armánoos, and informed him of the truth of her case, that she was the wife of Ḳamar-ez-Zemán, relating to him their story and the cause of their separation; and the King Armánoos, on hearing her tale, wondered at it extremely. He gave orders to write it in letters of gold, and then, looking towards Ḳamar-ez-Zemán, said to him, O son of the King, wilt thou form an alliance with me by marrying my daughter Ḥayát-en-Nufoos? He answered, I must consult the Queen Budoor; for I owe her unlimited gratitude. But when he consulted her, she replied, Excellent is this proposal! Marry her, therefore, and I will be a handmaid to her; for I owe her a debt of kindness and beneficence, and favour and obligation, especially as we are in her abode, and since we have been loaded with the benefits of her father.[84]—So when Ḳamar-ez-Zemán saw that the Queen Budoor inclined to this, and was not jealous of Ḥayát-en-Nufoos, he agreed with her on this subject, and acquainted the King Armánoos with that which the Queen Budoor had said, that she approved of the marriage, and would be a handmaid to Ḥayát-en-Nufoos. And on hearing these words from Ḳamar-ez-Zemán, the King Armánoos rejoiced exceedingly. He went forth immediately, and seated himself upon his throne, and, having summoned all the emeers and wezeers and chamberlains, and the other lords of the empire, acquainted them with the story of Ḳamar-ez-Zemán and his wife the Queen Budoor from first to last, telling them that he desired to marry his daughter Ḥayát-en-Nufoos to Ḳamar-ez-Zemán, and to appoint him Sulṭán over them in the place of his wife the Queen Budoor. Upon which all of them said, Since Ḳamar-ez-Zemán is the husband of the Queen Budoor, who was our sovereign before him when we thought her the son-in-law of our King Armánoos, we are all content to have him as our Sulṭán, and we will be servants unto him, and never swerve from our allegiance to him.

The King Armánoos, therefore, rejoiced at this exceedingly: he summoned the ḳáḍees and witnesses, and the chief officers of the empire, and performed Ḳamar-ez-Zemán's contract of marriage to his daughter, the Queen Ḥayát-en-Nufoos. He celebrated festivities, gave sumptuous banquets, conferred costly robes of honour upon all the emeers and chiefs and soldiers, bestowed alms upon the poor and the needy, and liberated all the prisoners; and the people rejoiced at the accession of the King Ḳamar-ez-Zemán, praying for the continuance of his glory and prosperity, and felicity and honour. As soon as he had become Sulṭán over them, Ḳamar-ez-Zemán remitted the custom-taxes; he conducted himself in a praiseworthy manner towards his people, and resided with his wives in enjoyment and happiness, and fidelity and cheerfulness, behaving towards both of them with impartiality. Thus he remained for a length of time; his anxieties and sorrows were obliterated; and he forgot his father, the King Sháh-Zemán, and the glory and power that he had enjoyed under him.

THE STORY OF THE TWO PRINCES EL-AMJAD AND EL-AS'AD.

After this, God (whose name be exalted!) blessed Ḳamar-ez-Zemán with two male children by his two wives. They were like two shining moons: the elder of them was the son of the Queen Budoor, and his name was the Prince El-Amjad;[85] and the younger was the son of Ḥayát-en-Nufoos, and his name was the Prince El-As'ad;[86] and El-As'ad was more lovely than his brother El-Amjad. They were reared with magnificence and tenderness, and instructed in polite arts and accomplishments: they learned caligraphy and general science, and the arts of government and horsemanship, until they attained the utmost perfection, and became distinguished by consummate beauty and loveliness, so that the women were ravished by their charms. They grew up to the age of seventeen years, always in each other's company, eating and drinking together, and never separated; and all the people envied them on this account. And when they had attained to manhood, and were both endowed with every accomplishment, their father, whenever he made a journey, seated them by turns in the hall of judgment, and each of them judged the people for one day at a time.

Now it happened, in accordance with confirmed destiny and determined fate, that two ladies in the King's palace,[87] on whom he had set his affections, became enamoured of the two princes, El-Amjad and El-As'ad. Each of these two women used to toy with the object of her love, and kiss him, and press him to her bosom; and when his mother beheld this, she imagined that it was only an affection like that of a parent. Love took entire possession of the hearts of the two women, and when they had waited long without finding any way of accomplishing their union, they abstained from drink and food, and relinquished the delight of sleep.

The King then went forth to the chase, and ordered his two sons to sit in his place to administer justice, each of them for one day at a time, according to their custom. So on the first day, El-Amjad, the son of the Queen Budoor, sat for judgment, and commanded and forbade, and invested and deposed, and gave and denied. And his enamoured wrote him a letter, endeavouring to conciliate his affection, and declaring that she was wholly devoted to him, and transported with love for him, exposing her whole case to him, and telling him that she desired to be united to him. She took a paper, and wrote in it these words:—

From the poor, the love-sick female; the mourning, the estranged; whose youth is consumed by love for thee, and whose torment on thine account hath been protracted.—If I described to thee the extent of my sorrow, and the sadness that I suffer, and the violent love that is in my heart, and how I weep and moan, and how my mourning heart is cut in pieces, and my constant griefs, and continual anxieties, and the pain that I endure from separation, and from sadness and ardent desire, the exposition of my case would be too long for a letter, and none could calculate its extent. The earth and heaven have become strait unto me, and I have no hope nor trust but in thee; for I have arrived at the point of death, and suffered the horrors of destruction. My ardour hath become excessive, with my disjunction and estrangement, and if I described the longing desire that I feel, papers would be insufficient for it.—And after this, she wrote these two verses:—

If I would explain the burnings I experience, and the sickness, and ecstasy of love, and agitation,
Neither paper nor pen would remain upon the earth, nor ink, nor a scrap upon which to write.

She then wrapped up the letter in a piece of costly silk, richly perfumed with musk and ambergris, and put with it the silk strings of her hair,[88] for the price of which, treasures would be consumed; after which, she wrapped the whole in a handkerchief, and gave it to a eunuch, commanding him to convey it to the Prince El-Amjad.

So the eunuch went, not knowing the secret destiny that awaited him (for He who is acquainted with all the secrets of futurity ordereth events as He willeth); and when he went in to the Prince El-Amjad, he kissed the ground before him, and handed to him the kerchief with the letter. The Prince El-Amjad, therefore, took the handkerchief from him, and, unfolding it, saw the letter, and opened and read it; and when he understood its meaning, he perceived that the woman contemplated deceit, and had acted disloyally towards his father, the King Ḳamar-ez-Zemán. And upon this he was violently enraged, and abused womankind for their conduct, exclaiming, Execration upon treacherous women, deficient in sense and religion! He then drew his sword, and said to the eunuch, Wo to thee, O wicked slave! Dost thou bear a letter expressive of disloyalty from a woman belonging to thy master? By Allah, there is no good in thee, O thou of black complexion! O detestable in aspect, and irresolute in character! —And he struck him with the sword upon his neck, severing his head from his body: after which, he folded up the handkerchief upon its contents, and, having put it into his pocket, went in to his mother, and acquainted her with what had happened, abusing and reviling her also, and saying, Every one of you is worse [in some respect] than another. By Allah the Great, he added, did I not fear to commit a breach of good manners, injurious to my father Ḳamar-ez-Zemán, I would go in to her and strike off her head, as I struck off the head of the eunuch. —Then he went forth from his mother, the Queen Budoor, in a state of excessive rage. And when the news of what he had done to the eunuch reached his enamoured, she reviled him and cursed him, and devised a malicious stratagem against him. The Prince El-Amjad passed the next night enfeebled by rage and indignation, and trouble of mind, and neither food nor drink was pleasant to him, nor was sleep.

And on the following morning, his brother, the Prince El-As'ad, went forth and seated himself in the place of his father, the King Ḳamar-ez-Zemán, to judge the people; and he judged, and administered justice, and invested and deposed, and commanded and forbade, and gave and bestowed; and he continued sitting in the judgment-hall until near the time of afternoon-prayers. Then his enamoured sent to a deceitful old woman, and, having revealed to her the feelings of her heart, took a paper to write upon it a letter to the Prince El-As'ad, and to complain to him of the excess of her affection, and of the ecstasy of her love for him. And she wrote to him these words:—

From her who is perishing through the ecstasy of love and desire, to the most charming of mankind in disposition and in form, the self-complacent with his loveliness, the haughty with his amorous aspect, who turneth with aversion from the desirer of union with him, who is reluctant to shew favour unto the submissive and abject,—to the cruel and disdainful, the Prince El-As'ad, who is endowed with surpassing beauty, and with admirable loveliness, with the brilliant countenance, and the splendid forehead, and overpowering brightness. This is my letter unto him the love of whom hath dissolved my body, and mangled my skin and my bones.—Know that my patience hath failed, and I am perplexed in my case: desire and sleeplessness have disquieted me, and patience and sleep have denied themselves to me: mourning and watching have been inseparable from me, and violent love and desire have afflicted me, together with disease and infirmity. But may my life be a ransom for thee; and if the slaughter of the love-smitten please thee, may Allah prolong thy life, and from every evil preserve thee!—And she added these verses:—

Fortune hath decreed that I should be thy lover, O thou whose charms shine like the full moon!
Thou possessest consummate comeliness and eloquence; and surpassest all the creation in elegance.
I am willing for thee to be my tormentor. Wilt thou, then, bestow upon me one glance?
Happy is the person who dieth for love of thee. Worthless is the one who doth not like and love thee.

Then she richly perfumed the letter with strong-scented musk, and wound it round with the silken strings of her hair, which were of

the silk of El-'Erák, having oblong emeralds for pendants, adorned with pearls and jewels.[89] Having done this, she delivered it to the old woman, and ordered her to give it to the Prince El-As'ad.

The old woman therefore departed in order to please her, and immediately went in to the Prince El-As'ad, who was alone when she entered; and she handed him the paper, with what was enclosed with it, and waited a long time for the answer. Meanwhile, the Prince El-As'ad read the paper, and understood its contents; and, having wrapped it up again in the silk strings, he put it in his pocket. He was enraged to the utmost degree, and cursed deceitful women: then rising, he drew his sword from its scabbard, and, striking the neck of the old woman, severed her head from her body; after which, he arose and proceeded until he went in to his mother, and he reviled her too, in his anger with the sex. He then went forth from her, and repaired to his brother, the Prince El-Amjad, to whom he related all that had happened to him, telling him that he had killed the old woman who had brought him the letter. And the Prince El-Amjad replied, By Allah, O my brother, yesterday, while I was sitting on the throne, the like of that which hath happened to thee this day happened to me also. And he acquainted him with the whole occurrence. They remained conversing together that night, and cursing deceitful women, and charged each other to conceal this affair, lest their father, the King, should hear of it, and kill the two women. So they passed the night in incessant grief until the morning.

And when the next morning came, the King arrived with his troops from the chase, and went up to his palace; and having dismissed the emeers, he arose, and entered the palace, whereupon he beheld the two women who had acted thus towards his sons, lying on their bed, in a state of extreme weakness. They had contrived a plot against the two Princes, and agreed to destroy them; for they had disgraced themselves in their eyes, and dreaded the consequence of their being so known to have offended. When the King, therefore, saw them in this condition, he said to them, What is the matter with you? And they rose to him, and kissed his hands, and, reversing the true state of the case, answered him, Know, O King, that thy two sons, who have been reared in the enjoyment of thy beneficence, have acted disloyally towards thee by their conduct to us, and have dishonoured thee. And when Ḳamar-ez-Zemán heard these words, the light became darkness before his face, and he was violently incensed, so that his reason fled through the excess of his rage, and he said, Explain to me this occurrence. So each of them told the story that she had framed, and both of them wept violently before the King.

When the King, therefore, witnessed their weeping, and heard their words, he felt convinced of their truth; and, being enraged to the utmost degree, he arose with the desire of falling upon his two sons and killing them. But his father-in-law, the King Armánoos, met him. He was just then entering to salute him, having heard of his return from the chase; and he beheld him with the drawn sword in his hand, and with blood dropping from his nostrils, by reason of the violence of his rage. So he asked him what troubled him, and Ḳamar-ez-Zemán acquainted him with all that had been done (as he supposed) by his sons El-Amjad and El-As'ad, and said to him, I am now going in to them to kill them in a most ignominious manner, and make them a most shameful example. His father-in-law, the King Armánoos, being alike incensed against them, said to him, And excellent would be the deed that thou wouldst do, O my son; and may God grant no blessing unto them, nor to any sons who commit such actions against the honour of their father: but, O my son, the author of the proverb saith, He who looketh not to results, fortune will not attend him:—and they are at all events thy sons. It will be proper that thou kill them not with thine own hand; for in doing so thou wouldst drink of their anguish,[90] and repent afterwards of having

put them to death, when repentance would not avail. But send them with one of the memlooks, that he may kill them in the desert, when they are absent from thine eye.

So when the King Ḳamar-ez-Zemán heard these words of his father-in-law, the King Armánoos, he saw them to be just. He therefore sheathed his sword, and, returning, seated himself upon his throne, and summoned his Treasurer,[91] who was a very old man, experienced in the management of affairs, and the vicissitudes of fortune. And he said to him, Go in to my two sons El-Amjad and El-As'ad, bind their hands firmly behind them, and put them in two chests, and place them upon a mule: then mount thou, and go forth with them into the midst of the desert, and slaughter them; after which, fill for me two glass bottles with their blood, and bring them to me quickly.

The Treasurer answered, I hear and obey. He then arose immediately, and, repairing to El-Amjad and El-As'ad, met them on the way, coming forth from the vestibule of the palace. They had clad themselves in the richest of their apparel for the purpose of visiting their father, to salute him, and compliment him on his safe arrival from his hunting-expedition. And when the Treasurer saw them, he laid hold upon them, saying, O my two sons, know that I am a slave under command, and your father hath given me an order: will ye then obey his command? They answered, Yes. And upon this, the Treasurer bound their hands behind them, put them in two chests, and, having placed them on the back of a mule, went forth with them from the city. He proceeded with them over the desert until near noon, when he halted with them in a waste and desolate place, and, alighting from his horse, put down the two chests from the back of the mule, and opened them, and took forth from them El-Amjad and

El-As'ad. When he looked at them, he wept violently on contemplating their beauty and loveliness, and afterwards drew his sword, and said to them, By Allah, O my lords, it is painful to me to do an abominable deed unto you; but I am excusable in this case; for I am a slave under command, and your father the King Ḳamar-ez-Zemán hath ordered me to strike off your heads. And they replied, O Emeer, do what the King hath commanded thee; for we patiently submit to that which God (to whom be ascribed all might and glory!) hath decreed to befall us; and thou art absolved of the guilt of shedding our blood.

They then embraced each other, and bade each other farewell; and El-As'ad said to the Treasurer, By Allah I conjure thee, O uncle, that thou make me not to drink the anguish of my brother, nor his sighing; but kill me before him, that so my fate may be more easy to me. El-Amjad also said to the Treasurer as El-As'ad had said, and made use of blandishment to him that he might kill him before his brother, saying to him, My brother is younger than I; therefore make me not to taste his affliction. Then each of them wept most violently, and the Treasurer wept also at witnessing their lamentation; and the two brothers again embraced each other, and bade each other farewell, one of them saying to the other, Verily all this is owing to the artifice of those two deceitful women; and there is no strength nor power but in God, the High, the Great! Verily to God we belong, and verily unto Him we return!—And El-As'ad, embracing his brother, uttered groans, and afterwards recited these verses:—

> O Refuge of the complainer, and Asylum of the fearful![92] Thou art ready to attend to every request!
> I have no resource but to knock at thy door; and if I be rejected, at whose door shall I knock?
> O Thou whose treasures of bounty are imparted by the word Be,[93] shew favour; for all good is in Thee!

And when El-Amjad heard the weeping of his brother, he likewise wept, and pressed him to his bosom, reciting these two verses:—

> O Thou whose favours to me have been many, and whose gifts have been more than can be numbered!
> No misfortune hath ever yet befallen me but I have found Thee ready to help me in it!

Then El-Amjad said to the Treasurer, I implore thee by the One, the Omnipotent, the King, the Protector, that thou kill me before my brother El-As'ad: perhaps the fire of my heart may so be assuaged; and let it not burn more. But El-As'ad, weeping, said, None shall be killed first but myself. So El-Amjad said, The best plan will be this, that thou embrace me, and I embrace thee, so that the sword may fall upon us and kill us with one blow.

And when they both embraced, face to face, and clung together, the Treasurer bound them, and tied them with ropes, weeping while he did so. He then drew his sword, and said, By Allah, O my lords, it is indeed hard to me to kill you. Have ye any want? If so, I will perform it. Or any commission? If so, I will execute it. Or any message? If so, I will convey it.—And El-Amjad answered, We have no want to be performed; but as to commission, I charge thee to place my brother El-As'ad beneath, and myself above, that the blow may fall upon me first; and when thou hast killed us, and returned unto the King, and he saith to thee, What didst thou hear from them before their death?—that thou answer him, Verily thy two sons send thee their salutation, and say to thee, Thou knowest not whether they were innocent or guilty, and thou hast killed them, and not assured thyself of their guilt, nor considered their case.—Then recite to him these two verses:—

> Verily women are devils created for us. I seek refuge with God from the artifice of the devils.
> They are the source of all the misfortunes that have appeared among mankind in the affairs of the world and of religion.

Then said El-Amjad, We desire of thee nothing but that thou repeat to him these two verses which thou hast heard, and also, I beseech thee by Allah that thou have patience with us while I repeat to my brother these two other verses.—And, weeping violently, he said,—

> We have examples in the Kings who have gone before us.
> How many, great and small, have travelled in this road!

And when the Treasurer heard these words of El-Amjad, he wept violently, so that he wetted his beard; and as to El-As'ad, his eyes filled with tears, and he recited these verses:[94]—

> Fortune is disposed, by its very constitution, to guile, and is full of fraudulence and of stratagems.
> The saráb [95] of the desert is to her like shining teeth; and the horror of darkness, like the black-edged eyelid.
> My offence against her (hateful is her nature) is as that of the sword when the warriour draweth back.

When El-As'ad had finished reciting his verses, he embraced his brother El-Amjad, so that they appeared together like a single person, and the Treasurer drew his sword, and was about to strike them. But, lo, his horse started away in fright over the desert. He was worth a thousand pieces of gold, and upon him was a magnificent saddle, worth a great sum of money. So the Treasurer threw the sword from his hand, and went after his horse. His heart was inflamed, and he continued running after the horse, to take him, until he entered a forest; and he entered after him; but the horse pursued his way into the midst of the forest, striking the ground with his hoofs, and the dust rose high, while the horse snorted and neighed in his fury. Now there was in that forest a formidable lion, of hideous aspect, his eyes casting forth sparks; his face was grim, and his form struck the soul with terror: and the Treasurer, looking towards him, beheld this lion approaching him, and he found no way of escape from him, not having with him a sword. So he said within himself, There is no strength nor power but in God, the High, the Great! This calamity hath not befallen me but on account of the crime committed against El-Amjad and El-As'ad, and verily this journey hath been unfortunate from its commencement!

Meanwhile, the heat became intense to El-Amjad and El-As'ad,

and they were affected with a violent thirst, so that their tongues hung out; and they prayed for relief from the thirst. But none relieved them; and they said, Would that we were killed and were at ease from this; but we know not whither the horse hath run away, that the Treasurer hath gone after it and left us bound. Had he come to us and killed us, it had been easier to us than our enduring this torment.—But afterwards El-As'ad said, O my brother, have patience, and the relief of God (whose perfection be extolled, and whose name be exalted!) will come to us; for the horse ran not away but because God is propitious towards us, and nothing afflicteth us but this thirst. He then shook himself, and struggled to the right and left; whereupon his bonds became loosed; and he arose, and loosed the bonds of his brother; after which he took the Emeer's sword, and said to his brother, By Allah, we will not depart hence until we investigate his case, and know what hath happened to him. So they began to follow the footsteps, and they led them to the forest. Therefore one of them said to the other, Verily the horse and the Treasurer have not passed beyond this forest. And El-As'ad said to his brother, Stay here while I enter the forest and examine it. But El-Amjad replied, I will not suffer thee to enter it alone, and we will not enter unless together; so if we escape we shall escape together, and if we perish we shall perish together. Accordingly they both entered, and they found that the lion had sprung upon the Treasurer, who was lying beneath him like a sparrow, but supplicating God, and making a sign towards heaven. So when El-Amjad saw him, he took the sword, and, rushing upon the lion, struck him with the sword between his eyes, and killed him.

The lion fell down prostrate upon the ground, and the Emeer arose, wondering at the event, and saw El-Amjad and El-As'ad, the sons of his lord, standing there; and he threw himself upon their feet, saying to them, By Allah, O my lords, it were not just that I should act so extravagantly with you as to kill you. May he who would kill you cease to exist! With my soul I will ransom you.—Then rising immediately, he embraced them, and inquired of them the cause of the loosing of their bonds, and of their coming to him. They therefore informed him that they had thirsted, and that the bonds of one of them became loosed, so that he loosed the other, because of the purity of their intentions; after which they followed the footsteps until they came to him. And when he heard their words, he thanked them for that which they had done, and went out from the forest with them;

and when they were without the forest they said to him, O uncle, do what our father hath commanded thee. But he replied, Allah forbid that I should attempt any injury to you! Know, however, that I desire to take off your clothes, and to clothe you with mine, and to fill two glass bottles with the blood of the lion. After which, I will go to the King, and tell him that I have killed you. Then do ye travel into other countries; for God's earth is wide. And know, O my lords, that your separation from me will be painful to me.—Having said this, he and the two young men all wept. The latter pulled off their clothes, and the Treasurer clad them with his own, and went to the King.

He had taken the things, and tied up the linen of each of the youths in a wrapper that he had with him, and filled the two glass bottles with the blood of the lion; and he put the two wrappers before him on the back of the horse. Then he bade the youths farewell, and, departing towards the city, proceeded until he went in to the

King, and he kissed the ground before him. And the King saw him with a changed countenance (for this change was occasioned by what he had suffered from his adventure with the lion), and he imagined that it was the consequence of the slaughter of his sons: so he was glad, and said to him, Hast thou accomplished the business? The Treasurer answered, Yes, O our lord. And he handed to him the two wrappers containing the clothes, and the two glass bottles filled with the blood. And the King said to him, What didst thou observe in their conduct, and have they charged thee with aught? He answered, I found them patient, contented to endure their fate, and they said to me, Verily our father is excusable; so convey to him our salutations, and say to him, Thou art absolved of the guilt of our slaughter and of our blood:—but we charge thee to repeat to him these two verses:—

> Verily women are devils created for us. We seek refuge with God from the artifice of the devils.
> They are the source of all the misfortunes that have appeared among mankind in the affairs of the world and of religion.

And when the King heard these words from the Treasurer, he hung down his head towards the ground for a long time, and knew that these words of his two sons indicated that they had been killed unjustly. Then reflecting upon the fraudulence of women, and the calamities occasioned by them, he took the two wrappers and opened them, and began to turn over the clothes of his sons, and to weep. And when he opened the clothes of his son El-As'ad, he found in his pocket a paper written in the hand of the woman who had accused him, together with the silk strings of her hair. So he unfolded the paper and read it, and understood its meaning, and knew that his son El-As'ad had been an object of injustice. And when he turned over the clothes of El-Amjad, he found in his pocket a paper written in the hand of the other woman, his accuser, with the silk strings of her hair enclosed in it; and he opened this paper and read it, and knew that he, also, had been an object of injustice. He struck his hands together, and exclaimed, There is no strength nor power but in God, the High, the Great! I have slain my sons unjustly!—Then he began to slap his face, exclaiming, Oh, my sons! Oh, the length of my grief!—And he gave orders to build two tombs in a house, which he named the House of Lamentations, and inscribed upon the two tombs the names of his two sons; and he threw himself upon the tomb of El-Amjad, weeping and sighing and lamenting, and reciting verses; and then in like manner upon that of El-As'ad. He relinquished the society of his friends and intimates, secluding himself in the House of Lamentations, weeping for his sons, and forsook his women and associates and familiar acquaintances.—Such was his case.

Now as to El-Amjad and El-As'ad, they proceeded over the desert, eating of the herbs of the earth, and drinking of the remains of the rain. At night, one slept while the other watched, till midnight: then the latter slept and the former watched.[96] Thus they continued for the space of a whole month, until their course brought them to a mountain of black flint, the further extremity of which was unknown. At this mountain the road divided into two: one road passed through the midst of it, and the other ascended to its summit. And they pursued the way to the summit of the mountain, and continued ascending it five days; but saw no end to it. Fatigue had overcome them; for they were not accustomed to walking upon the mountains nor elsewhere; and when they despaired of reaching its end, they returned, and pursued the way through the midst of the mountain. Along this they proceeded the whole of the same day, until night; but El-As'ad was fatigued with the length of his journeying, and he said to his brother, O my brother, I can walk no further; for I am reduced to excessive weakness. El-Amjad, however, replied, O my brother, brace up thy nerves: perhaps God may dispel our affliction. They then proceeded for an hour of the night; but El-As'ad was in a state of the utmost fatigue, and he said, O my brother, I am tired and weary with walking. And he fell upon the ground, and wept. His

brother El-Amjad, therefore, carried him and walked on with him, walking a while, and sitting a while to rest, until daybreak gleamed. Thus he ascended the mountain with him, and they found a spring gushing forth, with a stream running from it; and by it was a pomegranate-tree, and a niche for prayer;[97] and they scarcely believed the sight. They then seated themselves by this fountain, and, having drunk of its water, and eaten of the pomegranates of that tree, slept there until the sun rose; when they sat and washed themselves at the spring, and ate again of the pomegranates on the tree, and slept until the time of afternoon-prayers. After this they desired to continue their journey; but El-As'ad was unable to proceed: his feet were swollen. So they remained there three days, until he had rested himself, when they proceeded, and continued many days their journey over the mountain, wearied with thirst, until a city appeared before them at a distance.

Upon this they rejoiced; and they advanced towards it; and when they drew near to it, they offered up thanks to God, whose name be exalted! El-Amjad then said to El-As'ad, O my brother, sit here while I go to this city and see what kind of place it is and inquire respecting its affairs, that we may know where we are in God's wide earth, and know what countries we have traversed in crossing this mountain-range. Had we not journeyed through the midst of it, we had not arrived at this city in a whole year. Praise be to God, then, for our safety!—But El-As'ad replied, By Allah, O my brother, none shall go to the city but myself; and may I be thy ransom; for if thou leave me and descend and be absent from me, thou wilt drown me in anxious thoughts respecting thee, and I have not strength to endure thine absence from me. So El-Amjad said to him, Go, and loiter not.

El-As'ad, therefore, descended from the mountain, taking with him some pieces of gold; and left his brother to wait for his return. He went, and walked on without stopping, at the foot of the mountain, until he entered the city; and as he passed through its streets, there met him in his way an old man, far advanced in age; his beard descended over his breast, and was parted in twain, in his hand was a walking-staff, he was clad in rich garments, and on his head was a large red turban.[98] So when El-As'ad saw him, he wondered at his dress and his appearance; and, advancing towards him, he saluted him, and said to him, Which is the way to the market, O my master? The old man, on hearing his words, smiled in his face, and said to him, O my son, thou seemest to be a stranger. El-As'ad therefore replied, Yes, I am a stranger, O uncle. And the old man said, Thou hast cheered our country by thy presence, O my son, and thou hast made the country of thy family desolate by thine absence. And what dost thou desire from the market?—O uncle, answered El-As'ad, I have a brother whom I have left on the mountain, and we are journeying from a distant country. We have been on the way a period of three months, and arrived in sight of this city: so I came hither to buy some food and to return with it to my brother that we may nourish ourselves with it.—And the old man replied, O my son, receive tidings of every happiness, and know that I have made a banquet, and have with me many guests, and have prepared for it a collection of the best and the most agreeable of dishes, such as the appetite desireth. Wilt thou, then, accompany me to my abode? If so I will give thee what thou requirest, and will not take from thee any money for it. I will also acquaint thee with the affairs of this city. And praise be to God, O my son, that I have met with thee, and that none but myself hath met with thee!

So El-As'ad said, Do as thou art disposed, and hasten; for my brother is waiting for me, and his heart is intent upon me. The old man, therefore, took the hand of El-As'ad, and returned with him to a narrow by-street, smiling in his face, and saying to him, Extolled be the perfection of Him who hath saved thee from the people of this city! He walked on with him until he entered a spacious house, in which was a saloon, and in this saloon were sitting forty old men, far advanced in age, arranged in a ring, with a lighted fire in the midst of them. The old men were sitting around it worshipping it and prostrating themselves to it. And when El-As'ad saw this, his flesh quaked, though he knew not their history. Then the old man first mentioned said to this company, O sheykhs of the Fire, how blessed a day is this! And he called out, saying, O Ghaḍbán![99] Whereupon there came forth to him a black slave, of a most grim visage, flat-nosed, of bending figure, and horrible shape. And the old man made a sign to this slave; upon which he bound El-As'ad; and after he had done so, the old man said to him, Take him down into the subterranean chamber, and there leave him, and say to the slave-girl, such-a-one, Undertake the office of torturing him by night and day,[100] and give him to eat a cake of bread by night and a cake of bread by day, until the period of the voyage to the Blue Sea and the Mountain of Fire, when we will slaughter him upon the mountain as a sacrifice.[101]

Accordingly the slave took him down into that chamber, and delivered him to the girl, who entered upon her office of torturing him, and giving him one cake of bread at the commencement of the day, and one at the commencement of the night, with a mug of salt water between daybreak and sunrise, and the same between sunset and nightfall. Then the old men said, one to another, When the period of the Festival of the Fire arriveth, we will sacrifice him upon the mountain, and by offering him propitiate the Fire. The slave-girl went down to him, and inflicted upon him a painful beating, so that the blood flowed from his limbs, and he fainted; after which, she placed at his head a cake of bread and a mug of salt water, and went away and left him. And El-As'ad recovered his senses at midnight, when he found himself chained, and the beating tortured him. So he wept violently, and, reflecting upon his former state of grandeur and prosperity, and dominion and lordship, he lamented and groaned, and recited these verses:—

Pause at the ruins of the house and inquire respecting us, and think not we are there as formerly.
Fortune, the separator, hath disunited us; yet the hearts of our foes are not appeased by our fate.
A base female is employed to torture me with whips, and her breast is filled with hatred against me.
Yet still, perhaps, God may reunite us, and, by punishing them, repel from us our enemies.

Then extending his hand towards his head, he found a cake of bread, and a mug of salt water. So he ate a morsel to stay his departing spirit, and drank a little of the water, and remained sleepless until the morning, from the abundance of bugs and other vermin.

And when the morning arrived, the slave-girl came down to him again, and pulled off his clothes. They were covered with blood, and stuck to his skin, so that the skin came off with the shirt; and he shrieked, and cried Ah!—and said, O my Lord, if Thou approve of this, increase it upon me;[102] for Thou art not unmindful of him who hath oppressed me! Avenge me, therefore, upon him!—Then he groaned, and recited these verses:—

Be disregardful of thine affairs, and commit them to the course of fate;
For often a thing that enrages thee may eventually be to thee pleasing;
And sometimes what is strait may expand; and what is open, become contracted.
God will do whatsoever He willeth: therefore be not thou repugnant;
But rejoice at the prospect of speedy good that shall make thee forget what hath passed.

And as soon as he had finished reciting these verses, the slave-girl betook herself to beating him until he fainted, when she threw to him a cake of bread, and put a mug of salt water; after which she went up from him and left him in solitude, with the blood flowing from his limbs; and he lay chained, far from his friends, thinking of his brother, and of the glory in which he was before living; yearning and lamenting, sighing and complaining, pouring forth tears, and reciting verses.

Meanwhile, his brother El-Amjad remained expecting him till mid-day; and when he returned not, his heart palpitated, the pain of separation became intense in him, and he shed copious tears, crying out, Oh, my grief! How fearful I was of separation!—Then descending from the mountain, with his tears flowing over his cheeks, he entered the city, and walked on in it until he arrived at the market, when he inquired of some of the people respecting the name of the city, and respecting its inhabitants; and they answered him, This is called the City of the Magians, and its inhabitants [mostly] worship fire, instead of the Almighty King. He then asked them respecting the City of Ebony, and they said, The distance between us and it, by land, is a journey of a year; and by sea, a voyage of four months:[103] its King is called Armánoos, and he hath taken a King as his son-in-law, and put him in his place, and this King is called Ḳamar-ez-Zemán: he is a person of equity and beneficence, and liberality and peace. And when El-Amjad heard the mention of his father, he yearned and wept, and sighed and lamented; and he knew not whither to repair. He had bought and taken with him something to eat, and he went to a place to conceal himself there,[104] and sat down to eat; but, remembering his brother, he wept, and ate no more than enough to stay his departing spirit; after which he arose, and walked through the city, to obtain tidings of his brother. And he found a Muslim,[105] a tailor, in his shop; so he seated himself by him, and related to him his story; and the tailor said to him, If he have fallen into the hand of any of the Magians, thou wilt not see him again without difficulty; but perhaps God will reunite thee with him. Then he added, Wilt thou, O my brother, lodge with me? He answered, Yes. And the tailor rejoiced at this. El-Amjad remained with him many days, and the tailor consoled him, and exhorted him to be patient, and taught him the art of sewing so that he became an adept.

After this, he went forth one day to the shore of the sea, and washed his clothes. He then entered the bath, and, having put on clean clothes, went forth from the bath to amuse himself in the city. And he met in his way a woman endowed with beauty and loveliness, and justness of stature, unequalled in beauty, who, when she beheld him, raised the veil from her face, and made signs to him with her eyebrows and her eyes, and ogled him, and recited these verses:—

I beheld thee approaching, and cast down my eyes, as though, O slender-formed, thou wert the beaming sun;
For thou art the handsomest person that hath appeared, and more handsome to-day than thou wert yesterday.[106]

If beauty were divided, a fifth part of it, or part of a fifth, would belong to Yoosuf;[107]
And the rest would be thine exclusively. May every soul, then, be sacrificed for thine!

And when El-Amjad heard her words, his heart was gladdened by her, and moved with affection for her; the hands of love sported with him, and, making a sign to her, he recited these verses in reply:—

Above the rose of the cheeks are the thorns of lances.[108] Who then will propose to himself to gather?
Extend not the hands towards it; for long have those lances spread wars because of our directing looks at it.
Say to her who hath tyrannised and been a temptation, and who had been more tempting had she acted equitably,
Thy face would increase our perplexity were it veiled, and I see exposure best guardeth beauty such as thine;
As the sun's bare face thou canst not look upon; but when it is veiled by a thin mist thou mayest.
The niggardly female is protected by her niggardness: then ask the guards of the tribe why they would prevent us:
If they wish my slaughter, let them put an end to all their animosity, and leave us at liberty;
For if they attack, they are not more murderous than the eye of her with the mole, when she encountereth us.

She then begged to have some conversation with him: so he said to her, Wilt thou pay me a visit, or shall I repair to thine abode? Whereupon she hung down her head in bashfulness towards the ground, and repeated the words of Him whose name be exalted,—Men shall have the preëminence over women, because of the advantages which God hath given to the one of them over the other.[109]

So El-Amjad understood her intimation, and knew that she desired to accompany him whither he was going. He was therefore obliged to find the place for her; and, being ashamed to take her to the house of the tailor with whom he lodged, he walked on before her. She followed him, and he continued walking on with her from by-street to by-street, and from place to place, until the damsel was tired, and she said to him, O my master, where is thy house? He answered, Before us, and there remaineth but a short distance to it. Then he turned aside with her into a handsome by-street, and continued walking along it, she following him, until he arrived at the end of it, when he found that it was not a thoroughfare. So he said, There is no strength nor power but in God, the High, the Great! And looking towards the upper end of the street, he saw there a great door with two maṣṭabahs; but it was locked. El-Amjad therefore seated himself upon one maṣṭabah, and the damsel seated herself on the other, and said to him, O my master, for what art thou waiting? Upon this, he hung down his head for a long time towards the ground; after which he raised it, and answered her, I am waiting for my memlook; for he hath the key, and I said to him, Prepare for us the food and beverage, and the flowers[110] for the wine, by the time that I come forth from the bath.—He then said within himself, Probably the time will become tedious to her, and so she will go her way and leave me here.

But when the time seemed long to her, she said to him, O my master, thy memlook hath been slow in returning to us, while we have been sitting in the street. And she rose and approached the wooden lock[111] with a stone. So El-Amjad said to her, Hasten not; but be patient until the memlook cometh. Paying no attention, however, to his words, she struck the wooden lock with the stone, and split it in two; so that the door opened. He therefore said to her, What possesseth thee, that thou didst thus?—O my master, said she, what hath happened? Is it not thy house?—He answered, Yes: but there was no necessity for breaking the lock. The damsel then entered the house; and El-Amjad was perplexed in his mind, fearing the people of the house, and knew not what to do. The damsel said to him, Wherefore dost thou not enter, O my master, O light of mine eye, and vital spirit of my heart? He answered her, I hear and obey: but the memlook hath been slow in returning to me, and I know not whether he have done anything of what I ordered him, or not. He then entered with her, in a state of the utmost anxiety, fearing the people of the house. And when he entered the house, he found in it a handsome saloon, with four leewáns,[112] facing one another, and with closets and sidillehs[113] furnished with stuffs of silk and brocade, and in the midst of it was a fountain of costly construction, by which were arranged dishes set with jewels and filled with fruits and sweet-scented flowers; by the side of it were the drinking-vessels, and there was a candlestick with a candle stuck in it. The place was full of precious stuffs; in it were chests, and chairs were set in it, and on each chair was a wrapper of clothes,[114] and upon each of these was a purse full of pieces of gold. The house attested the prosperity of its owner; for its floor was paved with marble.

When El-Amjad beheld this, he was perplexed at his case, and said within himself, My life is lost! Verily to God we belong, and verily unto Him we return!—But as to the damsel, when she saw this place, she was filled with the utmost joy, and said, By Allah, O my master, thy memlook hath not failed in the performance of his task; for he hath swept the place, and cooked the food, and prepared the fruit; and I have come at the best of times. El-Amjad, however, looked not towards her; his mind being engrossed by fear of the people of the house. So she said, O my master, why art thou standing thus? Then heaving a loud sigh, she gave El-Amjad a kiss that sounded like the cracking of a walnut, and said to him, O my master, if thou have made an appointment with some other than myself, I will exert my skill to serve her. At this, El-Amjad laughed from a bosom filled with rage; and advanced and seated himself, panting, and saying within himself, O the ignominious slaughter that I shall suffer when the master of the house cometh!—The damsel had seated herself by his side, and began to sport and laugh, while El-Amjad, anxious and frowning, revolved a thousand things in his mind, saying within himself, The owner of this saloon will certainly come; and what shall I say to him? He will kill me without doubt!—The damsel then rose, tucked up her sleeves, and, taking a table, put upon it the sufreh,[115] and ate, saying to El-Amjad, Eat, O my master. So he advanced to eat; but the doing so gave him no pleasure: on the contrary, he sat looking in the direction of the door until the damsel had eaten and satisfied herself, and removed the table, and brought the dessert; whereupon she commenced eating of the dried fruits. Then she brought forward the beverage, and opened the amphora, and filled a cup, which she handed to El-Amjad; and he took it from her, saying within himself, Ah! Ah! What shall I experience from the owner of this house when he cometh and seeth me?

His eyes were directed towards the vestibule, and the cup was in his hand, and while he was in this state, lo, the owner of the house came. He was a memlook, one of the grandees of the city: for he was the King's Chief Equerry; and he had fitted up that saloon for his pleasure, that his bosom might expand in it, and that he might there enjoy in private the society of such as he desired; and on that day he had sent to a favourite to come to him, and had prepared the apartment for him. The name of this memlook was Bahádir.[116] He was liberal-handed, a person of generosity and beneficence, and charity and obligingness. When he drew near to the saloon, he found the door open: so he entered by little and little, and, looking with stretched-forth head, beheld El-Amjad and the damsel, with the dish of fruit before them, and the wine-service. At that moment, El-Amjad was holding the wine-cup, with his eye directed towards the door; and as soon as his eye met that of the owner of the house, his countenance turned sallow, and the muscles of his side quivered. But when Bahádir saw that his countenance turned sallow, and his condition became changed, he made a sign to him with his finger upon his mouth, as though he would say to him, Be silent, and come hither to me. So El-Amjad put down the cup from his hand, and arose to go to him. The damsel said to him, Whither goest thou? And he shook his head, and made a sign to her that he would be absent but a minute. He then went forth to the vestibule, barefooted:[117] and when he saw Bahádir, he knew that he was the master of the house. He therefore hastened to him, and, having kissed his hand, said to him, I conjure thee by Allah, O my master, before thou do me any injury, that thou hear my words. Then he told him his story from beginning to end, acquainting him with the cause of his having left his country and royal state, and assuring him that he had not entered the saloon by his own choice, but that the damsel was the person who had broken the wooden lock and opened the door and done all these deeds.

When Bahádir, therefore, heard his words, and knew that he was the son of a king, he was moved with sympathy for him, and pitied him, and said, Hear, O Amjad, my words, and obey me, and I will guarantee thy safety from that which thou fearest; but if thou disobey me, I will kill thee. So El-Amjad replied, Command me whatsoever thou wilt, and I will never disobey thee; for I owe my deliverance to thy humanity. And Bahádir said to him, Enter this saloon again, and seat thyself in the place where thou wast, and be at peace. I will presently come in to thee. My name is Bahádir. And when I have come in to thee, abuse me and revile me, and say to me, What is the cause of thy remaining away until this hour? And accept no excuse from me; but arise and beat me; and if thou shew pity for me, I will take away thy life. Enter, then, and enjoy thyself; and whatsoever thou desirest of me, thou wilt find it ready before thee immediately. So pass this night as thou wilt, and to-morrow go thy way. Thus I do to shew respect to thee as being a stranger; for I love the stranger, and to respect him is incumbent on me.—El-Amjad, therefore, kissed his hand, and entered again. His face was now clothed with red and white; and as soon as he entered, he said to the damsel, O my mistress, thou hast gladdened by thy company the place of thy visitation, and this is a blessed night. The damsel replied, Verily this is wonderful from thee,—thy now displaying this sociableness to me. So he said, By Allah, O my mistress, I believed that my memlook

Bahádir had taken from me some necklaces of jewels, each of which was worth ten thousand pieces of gold: wherefore, I went out just now, reflecting upon this, and searched for them, and found them in their place; but I know not why the memlook hath remained away until this hour, and I must punish him. And the damsel became appeased by these words of El-Amjad, and they sported together, and drank, and enjoyed themselves, and continued making merry until near sunset.

Bahádir then came in to them. He had changed his clothes, girded himself, and put on his feet a pair of shoes of the kind worn by memlooks; and, having saluted, and kissed the ground, he placed his hands across, and hung down his head towards the ground, as one acknowledging his guilt. So El-Amjad looked at him with the eye of anger, and said to him, What is the reason of thy delay, O most ill-omened of memlooks?—O my master, he answered, I was busied in washing my clothes, and knew not that thou wast here; for my appointed time, and thine, is nightfall, and not in the day-time. And upon this, El-Amjad cried out at him, and said to him, Thou liest, O most ill-omened of memlooks! By Allah, I must beat thee!—Then rising, he extended Bahádir upon the floor, and took a stick, and beat him gently. But the damsel arose, and, having taken the stick from his hand, inflicted upon Bahádir so severe a beating that his tears flowed;

and he prayed for relief, and locked his teeth together. El-Amjad called out to her, Do not thus! But she replied, Let me satisfy my anger with him. Then El-Amjad snatched the stick from her, and pushed her away. So Bahádir arose, and wiped away the tears from his face, and stood a while waiting upon them: after which he swept the saloon, and lighted the lamps. Meanwhile, the damsel, every time that Bahádir came in or went out, reviled and cursed him; and El-Amjad was angry with her, and said to her, By Allah (whose name be exalted!), leave my memlook; for he is not accustomed to this.

They continued eating and drinking, and Bahádir remained waiting upon them until midnight, when he became fatigued with waiting, and by the beating he had suffered, and slept in the middle of the saloon, and snored. The damsel then, having become intoxicated, said to El-Amjad, Arise; take this sword that is hung up here, and strike off the head of this memlook. If thou do it not, I will employ means for thine own destruction.—What hath possessed thee, said El-Amjad, that thou wouldst kill my memlook? She answered, The pleasure will not be complete without putting him to death; and if thou arise not, I will myself arise and kill him. So El-Amjad said, By Allah I conjure thee that thou do it not. But she replied, I must do it. And she took the sword and drew it, and was determined to kill him. El-Amjad, therefore, said within himself, This is a man who hath acted kindly to us, and protected us, and treated us with beneficence, and hath made himself as a memlook to me. How should we recompense him by slaughter? Never shall that be done!—He then said to the damsel, If the killing of my memlook is indispensable, I am more fit to kill him than thou. And, having taken the sword from her, he raised his hand, and struck the damsel on her neck, severing her head from her body; and her head fell upon the owner of the house: so he awoke and sat up, and opened his eyes, and found El-Amjad standing with the blood-stained sword in his hand. Then looking towards the damsel, he found her slain. He therefore inquired of him respecting her case; and El-Amjad repeated her words, and said to him, She refused to do anything but to kill thee; and this is her recompense. Upon this, Bahádir arose, and, kissing the head of El-Amjad, said to him, O my master, would that thou hadst pardoned her! It now remaineth only to take her forth immediately, before morning.

Bahádir then girded himself, and took the damsel, wrapped her in a cloak, put her in a large basket of palm-leaves, and carried her away, saying to El-Amjad, Thou art a stranger, and knowest not any one;

therefore sit in thy place, and expect me back at sunrise. If I return to thee, I must do thee great favours, and strive to obtain intelligence of thy brother; but if the sun rise and I have not returned to thee, know that God's decree hath been executed upon me: and peace be on thee; and this house shall be thine, with the wealth and stuffs that it containeth.—Having said this, he carried away the basket, and, going forth from the saloon, passed with it through the market-streets, and went with it by the way that led to the sea. But when he had nearly arrived at the sea, he looked aside, and saw that the Wálee and his chief officers had surrounded him. On their recognising him they wondered; and they opened the basket, and found in it a murdered woman. So they seized him, and put him in chains for the rest of the night, until the morning, when they went up with him, taking with them the basket, to the King, and acquainted him with the case. And when the King knew it, he was violently enraged, and said to him, Wo to thee! Thus dost thou ever! Thou killest persons and throwest them into the sea, and takest all their property! How many murders hast thou committed before this?—But Bahádir hung down his head towards the ground before the King. And the King cried out at him, and said to him, Wo to thee! Who killed this damsel?—O my lord, answered Bahádir, I killed her, and there is no strength nor power but in God, the High, the Great! And the King was enraged, and gave orders to hang him. So the executioner descended with him at the King's command, and the Wálee went down with a crier, who proclaimed through the streets of the city that the people should come to behold the spectacle of Bahádir, the King's Chief Equerry; and he conducted him about through the by-streets and market-streets.

But as to El-Amjad, when daylight came and the sun had risen and Bahádir had not returned to him, he exclaimed, There is no strength nor power but in God, the High, the Great! I wonder what hath happened to him!—And while he was thus meditating, lo, the crier proclaimed that the people should come to behold the spectacle of Bahádir; for they were to hang him at mid-day. So when El-Amjad heard this, he wept, and exclaimed, Verily to God we belong, and verily unto Him we return! He hath desired his own destruction on my account, when I am the person that killed her! By Allah, never shall this be!—He then went forth from the saloon, and closed it, and passed through the midst of the city until he came to Bahádir; whereupon, standing before the Wálee, he said to him, O my lord, slay not Bahádir; for he is innocent. By Allah, none killed her but myself.

When the Wálee, therefore, heard his words, he took him, together with Bahádir, and, going up with them both to the King, acquainted him with that which he had heard from El-Amjad. So the King looked at El-Amjad, and said to him, Didst thou kill the damsel? He answered, Yes. And the King said to him, Tell me the cause of thy killing her, and inform me truly. He replied, O King, a wonderful event and an extraordinary occurrence hath happened unto me: if it were engraved on the understanding, it would be a lesson to him who would be admonished. He then related to the King his story, acquainting him with all that had happened to him and his brother from beginning to end. And the King was filled with the utmost wonder at hearing it, and said to him, I know thee now to be excusable. But, O young man, he added, wilt thou be to me a Wezeer? He answered him, I hear and obey. And the King bestowed upon him and upon Bahádir magnificent robes of honour, and gave to El-Amjad a handsome mansion, with servants and officers, conferred upon him all that he required, appointed him pensions and supplies, and ordered him to search for his brother El-As'ad. So El-Amjad took his seat as Wezeer, and exercised authority and administered equity, and invested and deposed, and took and gave. He also sent the crier through the streets of the city to cry his brother; and for many days the crier repeated his proclamation in the great thoroughfare-streets and market-streets; but heard no tidings of him, nor discovered any trace of him.—Such was the case of El-Amjad.

As to El-As'ad, the Magians continued to torture him night and day, and evening and morning, for the space of a whole year, until the Festival of the Magians drew near. Then Bahrám[118] the Magian, [the old man who had inveigled El-As'ad into his house,][119] prepared himself for his voyage, and fitted out for himself a ship, and, having put El-As'ad into a chest, and locked it upon him, transported him to the vessel. It happened, at the time of his conveying the chest to the ship, that El-Amjad, in accordance with fate and destiny, was standing amusing himself by gazing at the sea; and he looked at the things as the men were transporting them to the ship. His heart throbbed at the sight, and he ordered his young men to bring him his horse, and, mounting in the midst of a company of his attendants, repaired to the sea. There stopping by the ship of the Magian, he commanded those who were with him to go on board of it and to search it. So they went on board, and searched the whole of the vessel; but found in it nothing; and they landed from it, and told this to El-Amjad. He therefore mounted again, and returned to his abode; and when he arrived there, and entered the palace, his heart was contracted, and, turning his eyes towards a part of the mansion, he saw two lines inscribed upon a wall; and they were these two verses:—

O my friends, if ye are absent from mine eye, from my heart and my mind ye are not.
But ye have left me in severe affliction, and have banished repose from mine eyelid, while ye sleep.

And when El-Amjad read them, he thought upon his brother, and wept.

Bahrâm the Magian went on board the ship, and called out to the seamen, ordering them to make haste in loosing the sails. So they loosed the sails and departed. They continued their voyage days and nights, every two days taking forth El-As'ad, and giving him a scanty supply of food and a little water, until they drew near to the Mountain of Fire. But a storm of wind then arose against them, and the sea became boisterous to them, so that the vessel wandered from her

course, and, pursuing a wrong direction, they came to a city built upon the sea-shore, having a castle with windows looking over the sea: The ruler of this city was a woman, called the Queen Marjáneh.[120] And the captain of the ship said to Bahrám, O my master, we have wandered from our course, and we must enter the port of this city to take rest, and after that, let God do what He willeth. Bahrám replied, Excellent is thy counsel, and according to it I will act. Then the captain said to him, If the Queen send to put questions to us, what shall be our answer? The Queen Marjáneh is a faithful Muslimeh; and if she know that we are Magians, she will seize our vessel and kill us all.[121]—Bahrám answered, I have this Muslim with us: so we will clothe him in the attire of memlooks, and take him forth with us; and if the Queen see him, she will imagine him to be a memlook; and I will say to her, I am an importer of memlooks, a seller and buyer of them; and I had with me many memlooks; but I have sold them, and this one only remaineth.—And the captain replied, This proposal is good.

They then arrived at the city, and slackened the sails, and cast the anchors; and when the vessel had stayed, lo, the Queen Marjáneh came down to them, attended by her troops, and, halting by the ship, called out to the captain. He therefore went on shore to her, and kissed the ground before her, and she said to him, What is in this thy vessel, and who is with thee?—O Queen of the age, he answered, I have with me a merchant who selleth memlooks. And she said to him, Bring him hither to me. And lo, Bahrám came forth, with El-As'ad walking behind him in the garb of a memlook; and when Bahrám came up to her, he kissed the ground before her. She said to him, What is thy business? And he answered her, I am a slave-merchant. She then looked at El-As'ad, imagining him to be a memlook, and said to him, What is thy name? And, almost suffocated with weeping, he said,[122] My name now, or that which I had formerly? —Then hast thou two names? she asked. He answered, Yes: formerly, my name was El-As'ad; but now, my name is El-Moṭarr.[123] And her heart was moved with affection for him, and she said to him, Art thou able to write? He answered, Yes. So she handed him an inkhorn and a pen and paper, saying to him, Write something, that I may see it. Accordingly, he wrote these two verses:—

What resource hath God's servant when destiny pursueth him under every circumstance, O thou judger;
When God casteth him into the deep, hand-bound, and saith to him, Beware, beware, that thou be not wetted.[124]

And when she saw the paper, she had compassion upon him, and said to Bahrám, Sell to me this memlook. He replied, O my mistress, I cannot sell him; for I have sold all my memlooks except this one. But the Queen Marjáneh said, I will positively take him from thee, either by sale or as a gift. He said to her, I will not sell him nor give him. She, however, seized him and took him, and, having gone up with him to the castle, sent to Bahrám, saying to him, If thou do not set sail this night from our city, I will take all thy property, and destroy thy ship. When the message, therefore, was brought to him, he was grieved excessively, and said, Verily this voyage hath been unfortunate! He then arose, and prepared himself, and, having taken all that he desired, waited for the night, to proceed on his voyage, and said to the seamen, Take your things, and fill your water-skins with water, and set sail with us at the close of the night. So the seamen betook themselves to perform their business.

Meanwhile, the Queen Marjáneh, when she had taken El-As'ad and conducted him into the castle, opened the windows looking over the sea, and ordered the female slaves to bring the food. They therefore brought it to her and El-As'ad, and they both ate. She then ordered them to bring the wine; and they brought it, and she drank with El-As'ad. And God (whose perfection be extolled, and whose name be exalted!) inspired her with love for El-As'ad; and she began to fill the cup and to give it to him to drink until his reason quitted him. After this, he arose, and descended from the saloon, and, seeing a door open, he went through it and walked on till he came to a great garden in which were all kinds of fruits and flowers; and he approached a fountain that was in the garden, and, laying himself down there upon his back, he slept, and night overcame him.—Bahrám, in the mean time, when the night arrived, called out to the sailors of the vessel, saying to them, Loose your sails, and proceed with us on our voyage. They replied, We hear and obey: but wait until we have filled our water-skins, and then we will loose. The seamen then landed with the water-skins, and went round about the castle, and finding nothing but the walls of the garden, they climbed over them, and descended into the garden, and followed the track that led to the fountain; and on their arriving at it, they found El-As'ad lying on his back. They immediately recognised him, and rejoiced at finding him. So they carried him away, after they had filled their water-skins, and leaped down from the wall, and conveyed him quickly to Bahrám the Magian, saying to him, Receive glad

tidings of the accomplishment of thy desire, and of the satisfaction of thy heart: thy drum hath been beaten, and thy pipe hath been sounded;[125] for thy captive, whom the Queen Marjáneh took from thee by force, we have found and brought with us. They then threw him down before him. And when Bahrám beheld him, his heart leaped with joy, and his bosom expanded. He bestowed dresses upon them, and ordered them to loose the sails quickly. They therefore loosed them, and proceeded on their voyage to the Mountain of Fire, and continued their course until the morning.

Now as to the Queen Marjáneh, after El-As'ad had gone down from her, she remained a while expecting his return; and when he came not back to her, she arose and searched for him; but found him not. So she lighted the candles, and ordered the female slaves to seek for him. Then she herself descended, and, seeing the garden open, she knew that he must have entered it. She therefore went into it, and found his shoes by the side of the fountain; and she proceeded to search for him throughout the whole of the garden; but saw nothing of him. She continued to search for him about the borders of the garden until the morning, when she inquired respecting the ship, and they told her that it had set sail in the first third of the night. So she knew that the crew had taken him with them, and the event grieved her; she was violently enraged, and gave orders to fit out immediately ten great ships. She prepared herself, also, for war, and embarked in one of the ten ships; her troops embarking with her, equipped with magnificent accoutrements and weapons of war. They loosed the sails; and she said to the captains of the ships, When ye have overtaken the ship of the Magian, ye shall receive from me robes of honour, and wealth; or, if ye overtake her not, I will kill you every one. The seamen, therefore, were inspired with great fear and hope. They proceeded in the ships that day and the next night, and the second day and the third; and on the fourth day, the vessel of Bahrám the Magian appeared to them; and that day passed not until the Queen's ships had surrounded the ship of the Magian. Bahrám had just then taken forth El-As'ad, and beaten him, and was tormenting him, while El-As'ad cried for relief and deliverance. But he found no creature to relieve or deliver him, and the violent beating tortured him. And the Magian, while he was tormenting him, looked aside, and found that the Queen's ships had surrounded his vessel, and encompassed her as the white of the eye surrounds its black. He made sure of his destruction, and sighed, and exclaimed, Wo to thee, O As'ad! All this hath been occasioned by thee!—Then taking him by his hand, he ordered the sailors to throw him into the sea, saying, By Allah, I will kill thee before mine own death!

Accordingly, the sailors took him up by his hands and feet, and threw him into the midst of the sea. But God (whose perfection be extolled, and whose name be exalted!), desiring his safety and the prolongation of his term of life, permitted that he should sink, and then rise again; and he beat about with his hands and feet until God smoothed his difficulties. Relief came to him, and the waves, striking him, bore him to a distance from the ship of the Magian, and he reached the shore. So he landed, scarcely believing in his escape, and when he was upon the shore he took off his clothes and wrung them, and, having spread them out to dry, sat down naked, weeping for the calamities and captivity that had befallen him, and recited these two verses:—

O Allah, my patience and resources have failed, and my bosom is contracted and my means are cut off!
To whom shall the wretched complain of his case unless unto his Lord, O thou Lord of lords?

After this he arose, and put on his clothes; but knew not whither to go. He ate of the herbs of the earth and of the fruits of the trees, and drank of the water of the rivers, journeying by night and day, until he came in sight of a city. And upon this he rejoiced, and quickened his pace towards the city; but when he arrived at it, the evening had overtaken him, and its gate was shut. It was the same city in which he had been a captive, and to whose King his brother was Wezeer. And when El-As'ad saw that its gate was closed, he

returned towards the burial-grounds, where, on arriving, he found a tomb without a door. So he entered it, and laid himself down to sleep in it, putting his face into his bosom.[126]

Now Bahrám the Magian, when the Queen Marjáneh with her ships overtook him, defeated her by his artifice and subtlety. He returned in safety towards his city, and proceeded thither forthwith, full of joy. And passing by the burial-grounds, he landed from the ship, in accordance with fate and destiny, and walked through the burial-grounds, and saw that the tomb in which El-As'ad was lying was open. So he wondered, and said, I must look into this tomb. And when he looked into it, he saw El-As'ad sleeping there, with his head in his bosom. He therefore looked in his face, and recognised him, whereupon he said to him, Art thou still living? Then he took him up, and conveyed him to his house. He had in his house a subterranean cell, [before mentioned,] prepared for the torture of Muslims, and he had a daughter named Bustán;[127] and he put heavy irons upon the feet of El-As'ad, and put him down into that cell, commissioning his daughter to torture him night and day until he should die. Having done this, he inflicted upon him a painful beating, and closed the cell upon him, and gave the keys to his daughter.

So his daughter Bustán went down to beat him; but finding him to be an elegant young man, of sweet countenance, with arched eyebrows and black eyes, affection for him entered her heart, and she said to him, What is thy name? He answered her, My name is El-As'ad. And she said to him, Mayest thou be fortunate, and may thy days be fortunate![128] Thou art not deserving of torment, and I know that thou hast been treated unjustly.—And she proceeded to cheer him by conversation, and unfastened his irons. Then she asked him respecting the religion of El-Islám. And he informed her that it was the true and right religion, and that our lord Moḥammad was the author of surpassing miracles and manifest signs, and that [the worship of] Fire injured, instead of benefiting: he acquainted her also with the fundamentals of El-Islám; and she yielded to his words. The love of the faith entered her heart, and God (whose name be exalted!) infused into her bosom an affection for El-As'ad; so she pronounced the two professions of the faith,[129] and became one among the people of felicity. She occupied herself in giving him food and drink, conversed and prayed with him, and prepared for him pottages of fowls, until he gained strength, and his disorders ceased, and he was restored to his former health.

After this, the daughter of Bahrám went forth from El-As'ad, and stood at the door; and lo, the crier proclaimed and said, Whosoever hath with him a handsome young man, of such and such a description, and produceth him, he shall have whatever he demandeth of wealth; and whosoever hath him in his keeping and denieth it, he shall be hanged at the door of his house, and his property shall be plundered, and his dwelling shall be demolished. Now El-As'ad had acquainted Bustán the daughter of Bahrám with all that had happened unto him: so when she heard this, she knew that he was the person sought. She therefore went in to him, and related to him the news; and he came forth and repaired to the mansion of the Wezeer; and as soon as he saw the Wezeer, he exclaimed, By Allah, verily this Wezeer is my brother El-Amjad! He went up with the damsel behind him to the palace; and on seeing his brother El-Amjad, he threw himself upon him; whereupon El-Amjad recognised him, and in like manner threw himself upon him, and they embraced each other. The memlooks came around them, and El-As'ad and El-Amjad were, for a while, senseless; and when they recovered from their fit, El-Amjad took his brother and went up with him to the Sulṭán, and related to him his story; upon which, the Sulṭán ordered him to plunder the house of Bahrám. So the Wezeer sent a company of men to do this; and they repaired to Bahrám's house, and plundered it, and brought up his daughter to the Wezeer, who received her with honour. El-As'ad then described to his brother all the torture that he had suffered, and the acts of kindness that the daughter of Bahrám had done him. El-Amjad, therefore, treated her with increased honour. And after this he related to El-As'ad all that had happened to him with the damsel, and how he had escaped from being hanged, and had become Wezeer. And each of them then complained to the other of the distress that he had suffered from the separation of his brother.

The Sulṭán next caused the Magian to be brought, and commanded to strike off his head. Bahrám said, O most excellent King, hast thou determined to kill me? He answered, Yes. Then said Bahrám, Have patience with me a little, O King. And he hung down his head towards the ground, and presently, raising it, made profession of the faith, and vowed himself a Muslim to the Sulṭán. So they rejoiced at his embracing El-Islám. Then El-Amjad and El-As'ad related to him all that had happened to them; and he said to them, O my lords, prepare yourselves to journey, and I will journey with you. And they rejoiced at this, as they did also at his conversion to El-Islám; but they wept violently. Bahrám, therefore, said to them, O my lords, weep not; for ye shall eventually be united [with your family], as Neạmeh and Noạm were united.—And what, they asked him, happened to Neạmeh and Noạm? He replied as follows:—

THE STORY OF NEẠMEH AND NOẠM.[130]

Persons have related (but God is all-knowing), that there was, in the city of El-Koofeh,[131] a man who was one of the chiefs of its inhabitants, called Er-Rabeeạ the son of Ḥátim. He was a man of great wealth, and of prosperous circumstances, and had been blessed with a son whom he named Neạmet-Allah.[132] And while he was one day at the mart of the slave-brokers, he beheld a female slave offered for sale, with a little girl of surprising beauty and loveliness on her arm. So Er-Rabeea made a sign to the slave-broker, and said to him, For how much are this female slave and her daughter to be sold? He answered, For fifty pieces of gold. And Er-Rabeea said, Write the contract, and receive the money, and deliver it to her master. He then paid to the slave-broker the price of the slave, and gave him his brokerage; and, having received the female slave and her daughter, went home with them. And when his uncle's daughter [who was his wife] beheld the female slave, she said to him, O son of my uncle, what is this female slave? He answered, I bought her from a desire of possessing this little-one that is on her arm; and know thou that, when she hath grown up, there will be none like her in the countries of the Arabs or foreigners, and none more lovely than she. And the daughter of his uncle said to her, What is thy name, O slave-girl? She answered, O my mistress, my name is Towfeek.[133]—And what, she asked, is the name of thy daughter? She answered, Saad.[134] And she replied, Thou hast spoken truly. Thou art fortunate, and fortunate is he who hath purchased thee.—She then said, O son of my uncle, what name wilt thou give her?—What thou choosest, he answered. She replied, We will name her Noam.[135] And Er-Rabeea said, There will be no harm in so naming her.

The little Noam was brought up with Neameh[136] the son of Er-Rabeea in one cradle, and in the same manner they were reared until they attained the age of ten years; and each of them was more beautiful than the other.[137] The boy used to say to her, O my sister. And she used to say to him, O my brother. Then Er-Rabeea addressed his son Neameh, when they had attained to this age, and said to him, O my son, Noam is not thy sister; but she is thy slave; and I bought her for thee when thou wast in the cradle: so call her not thy sister from this day.—Then if it is so, replied Neameh to his father, I will marry her. He then went in to his mother, and acquainted her with this; and she said, O my son, she is thy slave. Therefore Neameh the son of Er-Rabeea took her as a wife, and loved her. Four[138] years passed over them while they thus lived, and there was not in El-Koofeh a maid more beautiful than Noam, nor any sweeter or more elegant. She had grown up, and read the Kur-án and works of science, and become skilled in various modes of playing upon sundry instruments: she was distinguished by perfection both in singing and in instrumental music, so that she surpassed all the people of her age. And while she was sitting one day with her husband Neạmeh the son of Er-Rabeeạ in the drinking-chamber, she took the lute, and tightened its chords, and sang these two verses:—

> While thou art my lord, on whose bounty I live, and a sword by which I may annihilate adversities,
> I shall never need recourse to Zeyd nor to 'Amr,[139] nor any but thee, if my ways become strait to me.

And Neạmeh was greatly delighted. He desired her to sing again; and when she had done so, the youth exclaimed, Divinely art thou gifted, O Noạm.

But while they were passing the most agreeable life, El-Ḥajjáj,[140] in his viceregal mansion, was saying, I must contrive to take away this damsel whose name is Noạm, and send her to the Prince of the Faithful, 'Abd-El-Melik the son of Marwán; for there existeth not in his palace her equal, nor is sweeter singing than hers there heard. He then called for an old woman, a ḳahramáneh, and said to her, Go to the house of Er-Rabeeạ, and obtain an interview with the damsel Noạm, and contrive means to take her away; for there existeth not upon the face of the earth her equal.

The old woman assented to the words of El-Ḥajjáj; and when she arose on the following morning, she put on her apparel of wool,[141] hung to her neck a rosary of thousands of beads,[142] and, taking in her hand a walking-staff, and a leathern water-bottle of the manufacture of El-Yemen, proceeded thither, exclaiming, as she went, Extolled be the perfection of God, and praise be to God, and there is no deity but God, and God is most Great, and there is no strength nor power but in God, the High, the Great! She ceased not her ejaculations in praise of God, and her supplications, while her heart was full of artifice and fraud, until she arrived at the house of Neạmeh the son of Er-Rabeeạ at the time of noon-prayers; and she knocked at the door; whereupon the doorkeeper opened to her, and said to her, What dost thou desire? She answered, I am a poor woman, one of those who devote themselves to the service of God, and the time of noon-prayer hath overtaken me: I desire, therefore, to pray in this blessed place. The doorkeeper replied, O old woman, this is the house of Neạmeh the son of Er-Rabeeạ, and it is not a congregational mosque nor a place of worship.—I know, she rejoined, that there is not a congregational mosque nor a place of worship like the house of Neạmeh the son of Er-Rabeeạ, and I am a ḳahramáneh from the palace of the Prince of the Faithful, who have come forth to worship and to travel.

The doorkeeper, however, said to her, It is impossible for thee to enter. Many words passed between them, till the old woman clung to him, and said to him, Shall such a person as myself be forbidden to enter the house of Neạmeh the son of Er-Rabeeạ, when I go to the houses of the emeers and grandees? And Neạmeh came forth, and, hearing their words, laughed, and ordered her to come in after him.

So Neạmeh entered, and the old woman followed him until he went in with her to Noạm; whereupon the old woman saluted her with the best salutation. And when she beheld Noạm, she wondered at her excessive loveliness, and said to her, O my mistress, I commend thee to the protection of God, who hath made thee and thy lord to agree in beauty and loveliness. Then the old woman placed herself at the niche,[143] and betook herself to inclination and prostration and supplication until the day had passed and the night had come with its thick darkness, when the damsel said, O my mother, give rest to thy feet a while. But the old woman replied, O my mistress, whoso seeketh the world to come wearieth himself in the present world; and whoso wearieth not himself in the present world will not attain to the mansions of the just in the world to come. Then Noạm brought the food to the old woman, and said to her, Eat of my food, and beg propitiousness and mercy for me. The old woman, however, replied,

Verily I am fasting; but as to thee, thou art a young woman, and eating and drinking and mirth are suitable to thee. God be propitious to thee! God (whose name be exalted!) hath said, Except him who shall repent, and believe, and shall work a righteous work.[144]—The damsel continued sitting a while with the old woman, conversing with her; after which she said to her master, O my master, conjure this old woman to lodge with us for some time; for the impress of devotion is on her countenance. So he replied, Appropriate to her alone a chamber for devotion, and let not any one go in to her; and perhaps God (whose perfection be extolled, and whose name be exalted!) may grant us benefit from the blessing that attendeth her, and not separate us. And the old woman passed that night praying, and reciting [the Ḳur-án], until the morning, when she came to Neạmeh and Noạm, and, having wished them good morning, said to them, I commend you both to the care of God. But Noạm said to her, Whither goest thou, O my mother? My master hath ordered me to appropriate to thee alone a chamber in which thou mayest seclude thyself for devotion.—The old woman replied, May God preserve him, and continue his favours to you both: but I desire of you that ye charge the door-keeper not to prevent my ingress to you; and if it be the will of God (whose name be exalted!), I will go about to the holy places, and supplicate for both of you at the close of my prayer and devotion every day and night. She then went forth from the house, while the damsel Noạm wept for her separation, not knowing the reason for which she had come to her.

The old woman repaired to El-Ḥajjáj; and he said to her, What hast thou done? She answered him, Verily I have beheld the damsel, and seen her to be such that women have not given birth to any more beautiful in her age. And El-Ḥajjáj said to her, If thou accomplish that which I have commanded thee, abundant good fortune will result to thee from me. She replied, I desire of thee a delay of a whole month. And he said to her, I grant thee a month's delay.—The old woman then accustomed herself to frequent the house of Neạmeh and Noạm, who treated her with increased respect. She continued to pass the morning and evening with them, every one in the house welcoming her, until, one day, being with the damsel alone, she said, O my mistress, by Allah, when I visit the holy places, I will pray for thee; and I wish that thou wouldst accompany me, that thou mightest see the sheykhs[145] that come thither, and they would pray for any blessing for thee that thou desirest. And the damsel Noạm replied, By Allah,

O my mother, take me with thee. So the old woman said to her, Ask leave of thy mother-in-law, and I will take thee with me. The damsel, therefore, said to her mother-in-law, the mother of Neạmeh, O my mistress, ask my master to let me and thee go one day with my mother, the old woman, to prayer and supplication with the poor devotees in the holy places. And when Neạmeh came, and sat down, the old woman went to him and kissed his hand; but he forbade her doing so: and she prayed for him, and went forth from the house. And on the following day she came again, when Neạmeh was not in the house, and, accosting the damsel Noạm, said to her, We prayed for you yesterday; but arise now and amuse thyself, and return before thy master cometh. So the damsel said to her mother-in-law, I conjure thee by Allah that thou give me permission to go out with this just woman to enjoy the sight of the saints of God in the holy places, and I will return quickly, before my master cometh. The mother of Neạmeh replied, I fear lest thy master know of it. But the old woman said, By Allah, I will not let her seat herself upon the ground; but she shall look while she standeth upon her feet, and shall not loiter.

She then took the damsel, by this stratagem, and repaired with her to the palace of El-Ḥajjáj, and acquainted him with her arrival, after she had put her in a private apartment. So El-Ḥajjáj came and looked at her, and saw her to be the most lovely of the people of her age, and such as he had never seen equalled: but when Noạm beheld him, she covered her face. He left her not until he had summoned his chamberlain; and he mounted with him fifty horsemen, and commanded him to take the damsel upon an excellent and swift dromedary, to repair with her to Damascus, and to deliver her to the Prince of the Faithful, 'Abd-El-Melik the son of Marwán, to whom he wrote a letter. And he said to the chamberlain, Give him this letter, and bring from him an answer, and make haste in returning. The chamberlain, therefore, went, and took the damsel upon a dromedary, and journeyed with her, she remaining all the while with tearful eye on account of the separation of her master, until they arrived at Damascus. He begged permission to present himself to the Prince of the Faithful, who gave him permission, and he went in to him, and acquainted him with the affair of the damsel; whereupon the Khaleefeh appropriated to her exclusively a private apartment.

The Khaleefeh then went into his Ḥareem, and, seeing his wife, he said to her, El-Ḥajjáj hath purchased for me a slave-girl from among the daughters of the Kings of El-Koofeh,[146] for ten thousand pieces of gold, and hath sent to me this letter, and her with the letter. His wife replied, May God increase to thee his bounty! And after this, the sister of the Khaleefeh went in to the damsel; and when she beheld her, she said, By Allah, he is not disappointed in whose abode thou art, were thy price a hundred thousand pieces of gold! And the damsel Noạm said to her, O lovely-faced, to whom among the Kings belongeth this palace, and what city is this? She answered her, This is the city of Damascus, and this is the palace of my brother, the Prince of the Faithful, 'Abd-El-Melik the son of Marwán. Then she said to the damsel, It seemeth that thou knewest not this.—By Allah, O my mistress, replied Noạm, I had no knowledge of it. The sister of the Khaleefeh said, And did not he who sold thee and took thy price inform thee that the Khaleefeh had bought thee? And when the damsel heard these words, her tears flowed, and she lamented, and said within herself, The stratagem hath been accomplished against me. Then she said within herself, If I speak, no one will believe me: so I will be silent and be patient; for I know that the relief of God is near at hand. And she hung down her head in bashfulness, and her cheeks were reddened by her late travelling and by the sun. The sister of the Khaleefeh left her that day, and came to her on the following day with linen and with necklaces of jewels, and attired her.

After this, the Prince of the Faithful came in to her, and seated himself by her side, and his sister said to him, Look at this damsel in whom God hath united every charm of beauty and loveliness. So the Khaleefeh said to Noạm, Remove the veil from thy face. But she removed it not, and he saw not her face. He beheld, however, her wrists, and love for her penetrated into his heart, and he said to his sister, I will not visit her again until after three days, that she may in the mean time be cheered by thy conversation. He then arose and went forth from her. And the damsel remained reflecting upon her case, and sighing for her separation from her master Neạmeh. And when the next night came, she fell sick of a fever, and ate not nor drank, and her countenance and her charms became changed. So they acquainted the Khaleefeh with this, and her case distressed him, and he brought in to her the physicians and men of penetration; but no one could discover a remedy for her.

Meanwhile, her master Neạmeh came to his house, and, seating himself upon his bed, called out, O Noạm! But she answered him not. So he arose quickly, and called out again; but no one came in to him; for every female slave in the house hid herself, in her fear of him. He therefore went to his mother, and found her sitting with her hand upon her cheek; and he said to her, O my mother, where is Noạm?—O my son, she answered, with one who is more trustworthy than myself respecting her; namely, the just old woman; for she went forth with her to visit the poor devotees, and to return.—And when, said he, was she accustomed to do this? And at what hour did she go forth?—She answered, She went forth early in the morning.—And how didst thou give her permission to do so? he asked.—O my son, she answered, it was she who persuaded me to it. And Neạmeh exclaimed, There is no strength nor power but in God, the High, the Great! He then went forth from his house, in a state of distraction, and, repairing to the chief of the police, said to him, Dost thou employ stratagems against me, and take my slave-girl from my house? I will assuredly journey and complain against thee to the Prince of the Faithful.—So the chief of the police said, And who took her? He answered, An old woman, of such and such a description, clad in garments of wool, and having in her hand a rosary, the beads of which were thousands in number. And the chief of the police replied, Acquaint me with the old woman, and I will deliver to thee thy slave-girl.—And who knoweth the old woman? said Neạmeh.—And who, said the chief of the police, knoweth what is hidden from the senses, except God, whose perfection be extolled, and whose name be exalted? But he knew that she was an artful woman employed by El-Ḥajjáj. Neạmeh then said to him, I look for my slave-girl

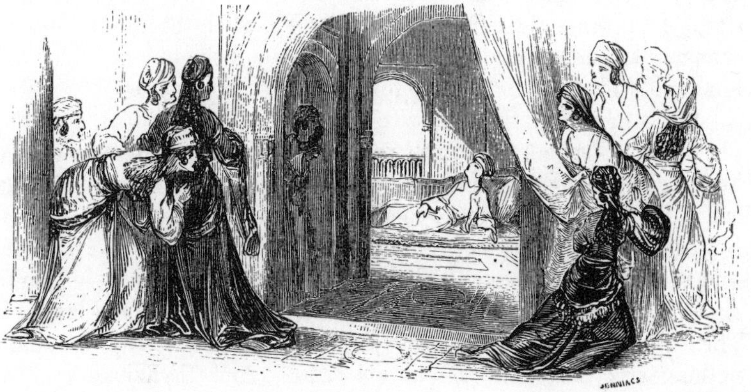

from none but thee, and El-Ḥajjáj shall decide between me and thee. And he replied, Go unto whom thou wilt.

So Neạmeh went to the palace of El-Ḥajjáj. His father was one of the chief people of El-Koofeh: therefore when he arrived at the residence of El-Ḥajjáj, the chamberlain went in and informed him of the case, and El-Ḥajjáj said, Bring him in unto me. And when he stood before him, El-Ḥajjáj said to him, What is thy business? Neạmeh answered him, Such and such things have happened unto me. And El-Ḥajjáj said, Bring ye to me the chief of the police, and we will order him to search for the old woman. Accordingly, when the chief of the police came, he said to him, I desire of thee that thou search for the slave-girl of Neạmeh the son of Er-Rabeeạ. The chief of the police replied, None knoweth what is hidden from the senses, except God, whose name be exalted! But El-Ḥajjáj said to him, Thou must take with thee horsemen, and seek for the damsel in the roads, and look in the towns. Then looking towards Neạmeh, he said to him, If thy slave-girl return not, I will give to thee ten slave-girls from my own mansion, and ten from the mansion of the chief of the police. And he said to the chief of the police, Go forth to search for the damsel. So he went forth.

Neạmeh was full of grief, and despaired of life. He had attained the age of fourteen years, and there was no hair upon the sides of his face. He wept and lamented, and separated himself from his house, and ceased not to weep until the morning. And his father came and said to him, O my son, verily El-Ḥajjáj hath employed a stratagem against the damsel, and taken her; but from hour to hour God giveth relief. Still anxieties increased upon Neạmeh, and he knew not what to say, nor recognised any who came in to him. He remained in a state of infirmity three months, so that his whole condition became changed, and his father despaired of him; and the physicians visited him, and said, There is no cure for him except the damsel.

But while his father was sitting one day, he heard of a skilful physician, a Persian, whom the people described as possessing a sure knowledge of medicine and astrology and geomancy. So Er-Rabeeạ called for him; and when he came, he seated him by his side, treated him with honour, and said to him, See the state of my son. And he said to Neạmeh, Give me thy hand. He therefore gave him his hand, and the physician felt his joints, and looked in his face, and laughed. Then turning his eyes towards his father, he said, Thy son hath nothing else than a disease in his heart. And Er-Rabeeạ replied,

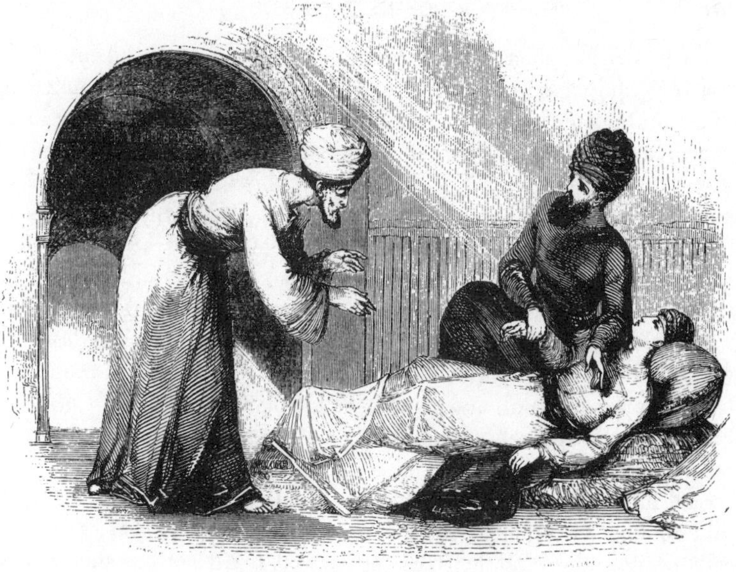

Thou hast spoken truly, O sage: consider, then, the case of my son with thy science, and acquaint me with all his circumstances, and hide from me nothing of his case. So the Persian said, He is engrossed by love for a damsel, and this damsel is in El-Baṣrah or in Damascus, and there is no cure for thy son but his union with her. And Er-Rabeeạ said, If thou bring them together, thou shalt receive from me what will make thee happy, and shalt live all thy life in wealth and delight.—Verily, replied the Persian, this affair is soon managed, and easy. Then looking towards Neạmeh, he said to him, No harm will befall thee; therefore be of good heart and cheerful eye. And he said to Er-Rabeeạ, Take forth from thy property four thousand pieces of gold. He therefore took them forth, and delivered them to the Persian, who said to him, I desire that thy son journey with me to Damascus, and, if it be the will of God (whose name be exalted!), I will not return but with the damsel. Then he looked towards the youth, and said to him, What is thy name? He answered, Neạmeh. And he said, O Neạmeh, sit, and be in the care of God (whose name be exalted!): God hath united thee with the damsel. And upon this he sat up. And the Persian said to him, Fortify thy heart; for we will set forth on our journey as on this day: eat, therefore, and drink, and enjoy thyself, that thou mayest acquire strength for the journey.

The Persian then applied himself to the accomplishment of all that he required, and received from the father of Neạmeh as much as made up the sum of ten thousand pieces of gold, with the horses and camels and other beasts that he required to carry the burdens on the way. After this, Neạmeh bade farewell to his father and his mother, and journeyed with the sage to Aleppo. But he learnt no tidings of the damsel. Then they arrived at Damascus; and after they had remained there three days, the Persian took a shop, and stocked its shelves with precious China-ware and covers, decorated the shelves with gold and costly materials, placed before him glass bottles containing all kinds of ointments and all kinds of sirups, put round the bottles cups of crystal, and placed the astrolabe before him. He clad himself in the apparel of sages and physicians, and stationed Neạmeh before him, having clad him in a shirt and a melwaṭah of silk, and girded him with a silken kerchief embroidered with gold. He then said to him, O Neạmeh, thou art from this day my son; therefore call me not otherwise than thy father, and I will not call thee but as son. So Neạmeh replied, I hear and obey. The people of Damascus now assembled before the shop of the Persian, gazing at the beauty of Neạmeh and at the beauty of the shop and the goods that it contained; and the Persian conversed with Neạmeh in the Persian language; Neạmeh doing the same with him; for he knew that language, as was usually the case with the sons of the great. The Persian became celebrated among the people of Damascus, and they began to describe to him their pains, and he gave them the remedies. He continued to perform the wants of the people, and the inhabitants of Damascus flocked to him, his fame spreading through the city and into the houses of the great.

And while he was sitting one day, lo, an old woman approached him, riding upon an ass with a stuffed saddle of brocade adorned with jewels; and she stopped at the Persian's shop, and, pulling the ass's bridle, made a sign to the Persian, and said to him, Hold my hand. So he took her hand, and she alighted from the ass, and said, Art thou the Persian physician who camest from El-'Erâḳ? He answered, Yes. And she said, Know that I have a daughter, and she is suffering from a disease. She then acquainted him with the symptoms, and he said to her, O my mistress, what is the name of this damsel, that I may calculate her star,[147] and know at what hour the drinking of the medicine will be suitable to her.—O brother of the Persians,[148] she answered, her name is Noạm. And when the Persian heard the name

of Noạm, he began to calculate, and to write upon his hand; [149] and
said to her, O my mistress, I will not prescribe for her a remedy until
I know from what country she is, on account of the difference of air :
acquaint me, therefore, in what country she was brought up, and how
many years is her age. So the old woman replied, Her age is fourteen
years, and the place where she was reared is in the province of El-
Koofeh, in El-'Erák.—And how many months, said the Persian, hath
she been in this country ? The old woman answered him, She hath
resided in this country but a few months. And when Neạmeh heard
the words of the old woman, and the name of his slave-girl, his heart
palpitated. The Persian then said to her, Such and such remedies
will be suitable to her. The old woman, therefore, said to him, Give
me what thou hast prescribed, and may the blessing of God (whose
name be exalted!) attend it. And she threw to him ten pieces of gold
upon the seat of the shop. So the sage looked towards Neạmeh, and
ordered him to prepare for her the drugs of which the remedy was to
be composed; and the old woman began to look at Neạmeh, and to
say, I invoke God's protection for thee, O my son! Verily her form
is like thine!—Then she said to the Persian, O brother of the Persians,
is this thy memlook or thy son? He answered her, He is my son.
Neạmeh then put the things for her into a small box, and, taking a
paper, wrote upon it these two verses :—

> If Noạm bestow on me a glance I care not if Soạdà grant favours, or Juml[150]
>   confer benefits.
> They said to me, Relinquish her, and receive twenty like her. But there is none
>   like her, and I will not relinquish her.

He put the paper into the little box, and sealed it, and wrote upon
its cover, in the Koofee character,[151] I am Neạmeh the son of Er-
Rabeeạ of El-Koofeh. Then he placed the little box before the old
woman.

She therefore took it, and, having bidden them farewell, departed
to the palace of the Khaleefeh. And when she went up with the
things to the damsel, she placed the little box of medicine before her,
saying to her, O my mistress, know that there hath come unto our
city a Persian physician, than whom I have not seen one more
acquainted with matters relating to diseases. And I mentioned to
him thy name, after I had informed him of the symptoms of thy
complaint; whereupon he knew thy disease, and prescribed the
remedy. Then he gave orders to his son, who packed up for thee
this medicine. And there is not in Damascus any one more lovely or

more elegant than his son, nor any more comely than he in apparel. Nor hath any one a shop like his shop.—So she took the little box, and saw, written upon its cover, the name of her master and the name of his father. And when she saw this, her complexion changed, and she said, There is no doubt but that the owner of the shop hath come on my account. Then she said to the old woman, Describe to me this young man. And she replied, His name is Neạmeh, and upon his right eyebrow is a scar; he is clad in costly apparel, and is endowed with consummate beauty. The damsel then said, Hand me the medicine, and may it be attended with the blessing of God (whose name be exalted!), and his aid. And she took the medicine, and swallowed it, laughing, and said to the old woman, Verily it is blessed medicine. And after this, she searched in the little box, and saw the paper. She therefore opened it and read it; and when she understood its meaning, she felt assured that the writer was her master: so her soul was cheered, and she rejoiced; and when the old woman saw that she laughed, she said to her, Verily this is a blessed day. Noạm then said, O ḳahramáneh, I desire food and beverage. And the old woman said to the female slaves, Bring the tables and the dainty viands to your mistress. Accordingly they brought to her the viands, and she sat to eat. And lo, 'Abd-El-Melik the son of Marwán came in to them, and, seeing the damsel sitting and eating the repast, he rejoiced. And the ḳahramáneh said, O Prince of the Faithful, may the health of thy slave-girl Noạm rejoice thee: for there hath arrived at this city a physician, than whom I have seen none more acquainted with diseases and their remedies; and I brought her some medicine from him, and after she had taken of it once, health returned to her, O Prince of the Faithful. Upon this, the Prince of the Faithful said, Take a thousand pieces of gold, and apply thyself to means for her complete restoration.

He then went forth, rejoicing at the damsel's recovery, and the old woman repaired to the shop of the Persian with the thousand pieces of gold, and gave them to him, telling him that she was a female slave of the Khaleefeh. And she handed to him a paper which Noạm had written. So the Persian took it, and handed it to Neạmeh, who, as soon as he saw it, knew her handwriting, and fell down in a swoon; and when he recovered, he opened the paper, and found written in it,—

From the slave-girl despoiled of her happiness, the infatuated in her mind, the separated from the beloved of her heart.—To proceed. Your letter hath reached me, and expanded the bosom, and rejoiced the heart; and it was as the poet hath said,—

The letter arrived, and may the fingers that wrote it be spared to me till they are made to drip with sweet scents.
It was as when Moosà was restored to his mother; or when the garment of Yoosuf was brought to Yaạḳoob.[152]

When Neạmeh read this couplet, his eyes poured forth tears. So the ḳahramáneh said to him, What maketh thee weep, O my son? May God never make thine eye to shed tears!—And the Persian said, O my mistress, how can my son refrain from weeping, when he is the master of this slave-girl, Neạmeh the son of Er-Rabeeạ of El-Koofeh, and when the health of this damsel dependeth upon seeing him, and she hath no disease but the love that she beareth him? Take thou then, O my mistress (he continued), these thousand pieces of gold for thyself, and thou shalt receive from me more than that; and look upon us with the eye of mercy; for we know not any means of rectifying this affair but through thee.—So she said to Neạmeh, Art thou her master? He answered, Yes. And she said, Thou hast spoken truth; for she ceaseth not to mention thee. Neạmeh therefore acquainted her with what had happened to him from first to last; and the old woman said, O youth, thou canst not obtain an interview with her but through my means.

She then mounted, and returned immediately, and, going in to the damsel, looked in her face, and laughed, and said to her, It becometh thee, O my daughter, to weep and to fall sick on account of the separation of thy master, Neạmeh the son of Er-Rabeeạ of El-Koofeh. So Noạm said, The veil hath been removed unto thee, and the truth hath been revealed to thee. And the old woman replied, Let thy soul be happy and thy bosom dilate; for, by Allah, I will unite you both, though the loss of my life be the consequence of it.

Then returning to Neạmeh, she said to him, I went back to the damsel, and had an interview with her, and found her to have a longing desire for thee, greater than that which thou feelest for her; for the Prince of the Faithful desireth to visit her, and she refuseth to receive him. Now if thou have a firm heart, and strength of mind, I will bring you together, and expose myself to peril in your cause, and contrive a stratagem and employ an artifice by which to introduce thee into the palace of the Prince of the Faithful, that thou mayest have an interview with the damsel; for she cannot go forth.—So Neạmeh replied, May Allah recompense thee well! Then she bade him farewell, and repaired to the damsel, and said to her, Verily the soul of thy master departeth by reason of his love for thee, and he desireth an interview with thee. What, then, sayest thou on this matter?—Noạm answered, And I am in the same state: my soul departeth, and I desire an interview with him. Upon this, therefore, the old woman took a wrapper containing female ornaments and a suit of women's apparel, and, repairing again to Neạmeh, said to him, Come into some place with me alone. So he went with her into an apartment behind the shop; and she dyed the ends of his fingers with ḥennà, decked his wrists [with bracelets], decorated his hair [with the ornamented strings of silk],[153] and clad him in the apparel of a slave-girl, adorning him with the best of the things with which female slaves are decked, so that he appeared like one of the black-eyed virgins of Paradise. And when the ḳahramáneh beheld him in this state, she exclaimed, Blessed be Allah, the best of Creators! By Allah, thou art handsomer than the damsel!—She then said to him, Walk, and incline the left shoulder forward, and the right backward, and move thy hips from side to side.[154] So he walked before her as she directed him; and when she saw that he knew the gait of women, she said to him, Wait until I come to thee next night, if it be the will of God (whose name be exalted!), and then I will take thee and conduct thee into the palace; and when thou seest the chamberlains and servants, be bold, and stoop thy head, and speak not with any one. I will prevent their speaking to thee; and in God I trust for success.

Accordingly, when the following morning came, the ḳahramáneh returned to him, and took him and went up with him to the palace. She entered before him, and he followed her steps; but the chamberlain would have prevented his entering; so she said to him, O most ill-omened of slaves, she is the slave-girl of Noạm, the concubine of the Prince of the Faithful, and how dost thou presume to prevent her entering? She then said, Enter, O slave-girl. He therefore entered with the old woman; and they proceeded without stopping to the door which opened into the court of the palace, when the old woman said to him, O Neạmeh, strengthen thyself and fortify thy heart, and enter the palace; then turn to thy left, and count five doors, and enter the sixth door; for that is the door of the place prepared for thee; and fear not if any one address thee; but do not speak with him. And she proceeded with him until they arrived at the doors, when the chamberlain who was commissioned to guard those doors accosted her and said to her, Who is this slave-girl? The old woman answered him, Our mistress desireth to purchase her. The eunuch replied, No one entereth without the permission of the Prince of the Faithful: return with her, therefore; for I will not suffer her to enter, as I have been commanded to do thus.—O great chamberlain, rejoined the kahramáneh, where is thy reason? Verily Noạm, the Khaleefeh's slave-girl, to whom his heart is devoted, hath recovered her health, and the Prince of the Faithful scarce believeth her recovery, and she desireth to purchase this damsel; therefore prevent not her entering, lest it be told her that thou hast done so, and she be enraged against thee; for if she be incensed against thee she will cause thy head to be struck off.—Then she said, Enter, O slave-girl, and attend not to his words, and inform not thy mistress that the chamberlain opposed thine entering.

So Neạmeh stooped his head, and entered, and designed to turn to his left; but he mistook, and turned to his right; and he meant to count five doors, and to enter the sixth; but he counted six, and entered the seventh. And when he had entered this door, he saw a place furnished with brocade; its walls were hung with curtains of silk worked with gold; and in it were perfuming-vessels with aloes-wood and ambergris and strong-scented musk; and he saw a couch at the upper end, furnished with brocade. Neạmeh, therefore, seated himself upon it, not knowing what was decreed him in the secret purpose of God; and as he was sitting reflecting upon his case, lo, the sister of the Prince of the Faithful came in to him, attended by her maid. Seeing the youth sitting there, she imagined him to be a slave-girl: so she advanced to him and said to him, Who art thou, O slave-girl, and what is thy story, and what is the reason of thine entering this place? But Neạmeh spoke not, nor returned her any answer. She then said, O slave-girl, if thou be one of the concubines of my brother, and he hath been incensed against thee, I will conciliate his favour towards thee. But Neạmeh still returned her no answer. And upon this she said to her maid, Stand at the door of the chamber, and suffer no one to enter. Then she approached him, and, observing his loveliness, said, O damsel, inform me who thou art, and what is thy name, and what is the reason of thine entering hither; for I have never before seen thee in our palace. Neạmeh, however, returned her no answer. And thereupon the sister of the King was angry, and put her hand upon Neạmeh's bosom; and, finding that it was not formed like that of a female, she was about to take off his outer clothes, that she might discover who he was. So Neạmeh said to her, O my mistress, I am a memlook, and do thou purchase me: I implore thy protection; then grant it me. And she said, No harm

shall befall thee. Who, then, art thou, and who admitted thee into this my chamber?—Neạmeh answered her, I, O Queen, am known by the name of Neạmeh the son of Er-Rabeeạ of El-Koofeh, and I have exposed my life to peril for the sake of my slave-girl Noạm, whom El-Ḥajjáj, having employed a stratagem against her, hath taken and sent hither. And she said to him again, No harm shall befall thee. Then calling to her maid, she said to her, Go to the private chamber of Noạm.

Now the ḳahramáneh had gone to the chamber of Noạm, and said to her, Hath thy master come to thee? She answered, No, by Allah. So the ḳahramáneh said, Probably he hath made a mistake, and entered some other chamber than thine, and missed his way to thine apartment. And Noạm exclaimed, There is no strength nor power but in God, the High, the Great! Our appointed term hath expired, and we perish!—They then sat together reflecting, and while they were in this state, lo, the maid of the Khaleefeh's sister came in to them, and, having saluted Noạm, said to her, My mistress summoneth thee to her entertainment. Noạm therefore replied, I hear and obey. And the ḳahramáneh said, Perhaps thy master is with the sister of the Khaleefeh, and the veil hath been removed. So Noạm rose immediately, and proceeded until she went in to the Khaleefeh's sister, whereupon the latter said to her, This is thy master who is sitting with me, and it seemeth that he hath mistaken the place; but thou hast nothing to fear, nor hath he, if it be the will of God, whose name be exalted! And when Noạm heard these words from the sister of the Khaleefeh, her soul became tranquillized. She advanced to her master, Neạmeh, and when he beheld her he rose to her. Each of them pressed the other to the bosom, and they both fell down senseless. And when they recovered, the sister of the Khaleefeh said to them, Seat yourselves, that we may contrive means of deliverance from this predicament into which we have fallen. So they both replied, We hear and obey; and it is thine to command. And she said, By Allah, no evil shall ever befall you from us. Then she said to her maid, Bring the repast and the beverage. She therefore brought them. And they ate as much as sufficed them; after which, they sat drinking. The cups circulated among them, and their sorrows quitted them; but Neạmeh said, Would that I knew what will happen after this! The sister of the Khaleefeh then said to him, O Neạmeh, dost thou love thy slave-girl Noạm? He answered her, O my mistress, verily it is the love of her that hath placed me in the state of peril of my life in which I now am. And she said to Noạm, O Noạm, dost thou love thy master Neạmeh?—O my mistress, she answered, verily it is the love of him that hath wasted my body and changed my whole condition. And the Khaleefeh's sister replied, By Allah, ye love each other, and may the person who would separate you cease to exist! Let your eyes, then, be cheerful, and your souls be happy!—So at this they rejoiced.

Then Noạm demanded a lute, and they brought it to her, and she took it and tuned it, and, delighting her hearers with the sounds that she produced, she sang these verses:—

When the slanderers were not content with aught but our separation, though neither of us owed a debt of blood to them,
And they poured upon our ears all the din of war, and my protectors and helpers at the time failed,
I fought them with thine eyes and my tears and my breath,—with the sword and with the torrent and with fire.

And she handed the lute to her master Neạmeh, saying to him, Sing to us some verses. So he took the lute and tuned it, and, having struck some joy-exciting notes, sang these verses:—

The full moon would resemble thee, were it not freckled; and the sun would be like thee, were it not eclipsed.
Verily I wonder—but how full is love of wonders: accompanied by anxieties and ardour and passion!—
That I see the way short when I go to the beloved, and long when I journey away from her.

And when he had finished his song, Noạm filled for him a cup, and handed it to him. He therefore took it and drank it; and then filled another cup, which he handed to the sister of the Khaleefeh, who drank it, and took the lute, and, having tuned its strings, sang this couplet:—

Sorrow and mourning reside in my heart, and violent ardour frequenteth my bosom:
The wasting of my body hath become conspicuous, and my frame is rendered infirm by desire.

She then handed the lute to Neạmeh the son of Er-Rabeeạ, who took it and tuned its strings, and sang this other couplet:—

O thou to whom I gave my soul, and who hast tortured it, and from whom I would liberate it, but could not!
Grant the lover a remedy to save him from destruction, before he dieth; for this is his last breath!

They continued singing verses, and drinking to the melodious sounds of the chords, full of delight and cheerfulness, and joy and happiness; and while they were in this state, lo, the Prince of the Faithful came in to them. As soon as they beheld him, they rose to him, and kissed the ground before him; and he looked at Noạm, who had the lute in her hand, and said, O Noạm, praise be to God who hath dispelled from thee thy affliction and pain! Then looking towards Neạmeh, who was still in the state already described, he said [to his sister], O my sister, who is this damsel that is by the side of Noạm? His sister answered him, O Prince of the Faithful, thou hast a female slave among those designed for thy concubines, who is a cheering companion, and Noạm doth not eat nor drink unless she is with her. And she recited the saying of the poet:—

They are two opposites, and together display different charms; and the beauty of one opposite appears from contrast with the other.

—By Allah, the Great, said the Khaleefeh, verily she is comely as Noạm, and to-morrow I will appoint her a separate apartment by the side of Noạm's, and send forth for her the furniture and linen, and I will send to her everything that is suitable to her, in honour to Noạm. And the sister of the Khaleefeh demanded the food, and she placed it before her brother, who ate, and remained sitting in their company. He then filled a cup, and made a sign to Noạm that she should sing him some verses; whereupon she took the lute, after she had drunk two cups, and sang this couplet:—

When my cup-companion hath given me to drink again and again, three fermenting cups,
I drag my skirts all the night in pride, as though I were thy prince, O Prince of the Faithful.

And the Prince of the Faithful was delighted, and he filled another cup, and handed it to Noạm, commanding her to sing again. Accordingly, after she had drunk the cup, she touched the strings, and sang these verses:—

O most noble of men in the present age, of whom none can boast that he is the equal!
O matchless in dignity and liberality! O Chief and King, in everything renowned!
O Sovereign of all the Kings of the earth, who givest largely, yet imposest not obligation nor pain!
May my Lord preserve thee, mortifying thine enemies, and success and victory brighten thy fortune!

And when the Khaleefeh heard these verses from Noạm, he said to her, Divinely art thou gifted, O Noạm! How eloquent is thy tongue, and how manifest is the perspicuity of thy language!

They thus passed their time in joy and happiness until midnight, when the sister of the Khaleefeh said, Hear, O Prince of the Faithful. I have seen, in books, a story of a certain person of rank.—And what is that story? said the Khaleefeh. His sister answered him, Know, O Prince of the Faithful, that there was, in the city of El-Koofeh, a youth named Neạmeh the son of Er-Rabeeạ; and he had a slave-girl whom he loved, and who loved him. She had been brought up with him in the same bed; and when they both grew up, and mutual love took possession of them, fortune smote them with its adversities, and afflicted them with its calamities, and decreed their separation. The slanderers employed a stratagem against her, until she came forth from his house, and they took her by stealth from the place of his residence. Then the person who stole her sold her to one of the Kings for ten thousand pieces of gold. Now the slave-girl had the same love for her master as he had for her: so he quitted his family and his house, and journeyed to seek for her, and devised means for obtaining a meeting with her. He continued separated from his family and his home, and exposed himself to peril, devoting his soul to the cause, until he obtained an interview with his slave-girl.[155] But when he had come to her, they had scarcely sat down, when the King who had purchased her from the person who stole her came in to them, and hastily ordered that they should be put to death; not acting equitably, nor granting them any delay in his sentence. What, then, sayest thou, O Prince of the Faithful, respecting the want of equity in this King?—The Prince of the Faithful answered, Verily this was a wonderful thing, and it was fit that this King should pardon when he was able to punish; for it was incumbent on him to regard, in his conduct to them, three things: the first, that they were bound by mutual love; and the second, that they were in his abode, and in his power; and the third, that it becometh the King to be deliberate in judging other people; and how much more so, then, in the case in which he is himself concerned? This King, therefore, did a deed not like the actions of Kings.—Then his sister said to him, O my brother, by the King of the heavens and the earth, I beg that thou order Noạm to sing, and that thou listen to that which she shall sing. So he said, O Noạm, sing to me. And, with charming modulations, she sang these verses:—

Fortune was treacherous, and ever hath it been so, smiting down hearts, and kindling solicitudes,
And separating lovers after their union, so that thou seest the tears flow in torrents down their cheeks.
They were, and I was with them, and my life was delightful, and fortune frequently brought us together.
I will therefore pour forth blood with my tears in my grief for thy loss nights and days.

And when the Prince of the Faithful heard these verses, he was moved with excessive delight.

His sister then said to him, O my brother, he who passeth a sentence upon himself must fulfil it, and act as he hath said; and thou hast passed a sentence upon thyself by this decision. And she said, O Neạmeh, stand upon thy feet; and so stand thou, O Noạm. So they both stood up. And the sister of the Khaleefeh said, O Prince of the Faithful, this person who is standing here is the stolen Noạm, whom El-Ḥajjáj the son of Yoosuf Eth-Thaḳafee stole, and sent to thee, lying in that which he asserted in his letter; namely, that he had purchased her for ten thousand pieces of gold. And this

person standing here is Neạmeh the son of Er-Rabeeạ, her master. And I beseech thee by the honour of thy pure forefathers that thou forgive them, and restore them to each other, that thou mayest acquire a recompense on their account; for they are in thy power, and have eaten of thy food and drunk of thy beverage. I am the intercessor for them, and beg of thee the gift of their lives.

And upon this the Khaleefeh said, Thou hast spoken truly: I passed that sentence, and I pass not a sentence and revoke it. He then said, O Noạm, is this thy master? She answered him, Yes, O Prince of the Faithful. And he said, No harm shall befall either of you; for I yield you up to each other. Then he said, O Neạmeh, and how knewest thou her situation, and who described to thee this place?—O Prince of the Faithful, he answered, hear my story, and listen to my tale; for by thy pure forefathers I will not conceal from thee anything. And he related to him the whole of his affair, telling him how the Persian sage had acted with him, and what the ḳahramáneh had done, and how she had brought him into the palace, and he had mistaken the doors. And the Khaleefeh wondered at this extremely. He then said, Bring hither to me the Persian. So they brought him before him; and he appointed him to be one of his chief officers, bestowed upon him robes of honour, and commanded that a handsome present should be given to him, saying, Him who hath thus managed, it is incumbent on us to make one of our chief officers. The Khaleefeh also treated with beneficence Neạmeh and Noạm, bestowing favours upon them and upon the ḳahramáneh; and Neạmeh and Noạm remained with him seven days in happiness and delight, living a most pleasant life. Then Neạmeh begged permission of him to depart with his slave-girl, and he gave them permission to depart to El-Koofeh. Accordingly they set forth on their journey, and Neạmeh was united again with his father and his mother, and they enjoyed the most happy life, until they were visited by the terminator of delights and the separator of companions.

CONCLUSION OF THE STORY OF EL-AMJAD AND EL-AS'AD, &c.

When El-Amjad and El-As'ad heard this story from Bahrám, they wondered at it extremely. They passed the next night, and when the following morning came, they mounted, and desired to go to the King. So they asked permission to enter, and he gave it them:

and when they went in, he received them with honour, and they sat conversing.

But while they were thus sitting, lo, the people of the city cried out, and vociferated one to another, calling for help; and the chamberlain came in to the King, and said to him, Some King hath alighted with his troops before our city, and they are with drawn swords, and we know not what is their purpose. The King therefore acquainted his Wezeer El-Amjad and his brother El-As'ad with that which he had heard from the chamberlain, and El-Amjad said, I will go forth to him, and ascertain the cause of his coming. So El-Amjad went out from the city, and found the King attended by numerous troops and mounted memlooks. And when they saw him, they knew that he was an envoy from the King of the city. They therefore took him and brought him before the Sulṭán; and when he came into his presence, he kissed the ground before him; and lo, the [supposed] King was a woman, with her face covered with a lithám. And she said, Know that I have nothing to demand of you in this city but a beardless memlook, and if I find him with you, no harm shall befall you; but if I find him not, a fierce slaughter shall ensue between me and you; for I have come for no other purpose than to seek him. El-Amjad therefore said, O Queen, what is the description of this memlook, and what is his story, and what is his name? She answered, His name is El-As'ad, and my name is Marjáneh; and this memlook came to me in the company of Bahrám the Magian, who refused to sell him: so I took him from him by force; but he fell upon him and took him away from me in the night by stealth; and as to the description of his person, it is of such and such kind. And when El-Amjad heard this, he knew that he was his brother El-As'ad. He therefore said to her, O Queen of the age, praise be to God who hath brought us relief! Verily this memlook is my brother.—He then related to her his story, and told her what had happened to them in the land of exile, acquainting her also with the cause of their departure from the Ebony Islands; whereat the Queen Marjáneh wondered; and she rejoiced at finding El-As'ad, and bestowed a robe of honour upon his brother El-Amjad. After this, El-Amjad returned to the King, and informed him of what had occurred: whereupon they all rejoiced. The King then descended with El-Amjad and El-As'ad, to repair to the Queen; and when they went in to her they sat and conversed.

And as they were so engaged, lo, the dust rose until it covered the surrounding tracts, and after a while it subsided, and discovered numerous forces, like the swelling sea, equipped with accoutrements and arms; and they approached the city, and then surrounded it as the ring surrounds the little-finger, and drew their swords. Upon this, El-Amjad and El-As'ad said, Verily unto God we belong, and verily unto Him we return! What is this great army? Doubtless it is an enemy; and if we make not an alliance with this Queen Marjáneh to contend with them, they take the city from us and slay us; and we have no resource but to go forth to them and ascertain wherefore they have come.—Then El-Amjad arose, and passed from the gate of the city by the army of the Queen Marjáneh; and when he came to the second army, he found it to be that of his grandfather the King El-Ghayoor, the father of his mother the Queen Budoor. So when he entered into his presence, he kissed the ground before him, and delivered to him the message; whereupon the King said, My name is the King El-Ghayoor, and I have come journeying forth, fortune having afflicted me by the loss of my daughter Budoor; for she quitted me, and returned not to me, and I have heard no tidings of her, nor of her husband Ḳamar-ez-Zemán. Have ye, then, any tidings of them?—And El-Amjad, on hearing this, hung down his head for a while towards the ground, reflecting, until he felt convinced that this was his grandfather, the father of his mother. Then raising his head, he kissed the ground before him, and informed him that he was the son of his daughter Budoor. And as soon as the King heard that he was the son of his daughter, he threw himself upon him, and they both began to weep. The King El-Ghayoor exclaimed, Praise be to God, O my son, that He hath preserved thee, and that I have met with thee! And El-Amjad informed him that his daughter Budoor was well, and also his own father Ḳamar-ez-Zemán, telling him that they were in a city called the City of the Ebony Island. He informed him, also, that Ḳamar-ez-Zemán, his father, had been incensed against him and his brother, and had given orders to slay them, and that the Treasurer had been moved with pity for them, and left them without putting them to death. And upon this, the King El-Ghayoor said, I will return with thee and thy brother to thy father, and reconcile you, and remain with you. So El-Amjad kissed the ground before him. Then the King El-Ghayoor bestowed a robe of honour upon El-Amjad, his daughter's son; and he returned smiling to the King of the city, and acquainted him with the affair of the King El-Ghayoor. And he wondered at this extremely. He sent to the King El-Ghayoor the

offerings of hospitality, horses and camels and sheep and provender and other things; and the like he sent forth to the Queen Marjáneh, informing her of what had happened: whereupon she said, I will accompany you with my troops, and will endeavour to maintain peace.

And while they were thus circumstanced, lo, again a dust rose until it overspread the surrounding tracts, and the day became black from it. They heard beneath it cries and vociferations, and the neighing of horses, and beheld swords glittering, and lances uplifted. And when this army approached the city, and saw the two other armies, they beat the drums. At the sight of this, the King of the city exclaimed, This is none other than a blessed day! Praise be to God who hath caused us to make peace with these two armies; and if it be the will of God, He will give us peace with this other army also. —He then said, O Amjad, go forth, thou and thy brother El-As'ad, and learn ye for us the occasion of the coming of these troops; for they are a vast army: I have never seen any more so. Accordingly

El-Amjad and his brother El-As'ad went forth. The King having closed the gate of the city, in his fear of the troops that surrounded it, they opened it, and the two brothers proceeded until they arrived at the army that had just come, when they found it to be the army of the King of the Ebony Islands, and with it was their father Ḳamar-ez-Zemán. [For he had been informed that they had not been put to death.] As soon as they saw him, they kissed the ground before him, and wept; and when Ḳamar-ez-Zemán beheld them, he threw himself upon them, weeping violently, and excused himself to them, and pressed them to his bosom. He then acquainted them with the terrible desolation that he had suffered from their separation; and El-Amjad and El-As'ad informed him that the King El-Ghayoor had come to them. So Ḳamar-ez-Zemán mounted with his chief officers, and, taking his two sons with him, they proceeded until they came near to the army of the King El-Ghayoor; when one of them went forward to that King, and informed him that Ḳamar-ez-Zemán had arrived. He therefore came forth to receive him, and they met, and wondered at these events, how they had met in that place. The people of the city prepared for them banquets, with varieties of viands and sweetmeats, and presented to them the horses and camels and other offerings of hospitality, together with the provender, and whatever else the troops required.

And again, while they were thus occupied, a dust rose until it overspread the surrounding tracts, and the earth shook under the horses; the drums sounded like stormy winds, and the whole army was equipped with weapons and coats of mail: all the soldiers were clad in black, and in the midst of them was a very old man, whose chin was depressed to his bosom, and who was attired in black clothing. When the people of the city beheld these prodigious forces, the sovereign of the city said to the other Kings, Praise be to God that ye assembled, by the permission of God (whose name be exalted!), in one day, and proved to be all friends! What is this numerous army that hath covered the tracts before us?—The other Kings replied, Fear it not; for we are three monarchs, and each of us hath numerous troops: so, if they be enemies, we will unite with thee and engage them; and so would we if they were augmented by three times as many as they are. And while they were thus conversing, lo, an envoy from those forces approached on his way to the city. So they brought him before Ḳamar-ez-Zemán and the King El-Ghayoor and the Queen Marjáneh and the King of the city; and he kissed the ground, and said, This King is from the regions of El-'Ajam: he hath lost his son for a period of years, and is searching about for him in the countries: if, then, he find him among you, no harm shall befall you; but if he find him not, war ensueth between him and you, and he layeth waste your city. Ḳamar-ez-Zemán replied, He will not attain to this object. But what, he asked, is he called in the regions of El-'Ajam? The envoy answered, He is called the King Sháh-Zemán, the lord of the Islands of Khálidán; and he hath collected this army in the tracts through which he hath passed in searching about for his son. And when Ḳamar-ez-Zemán heard the words of the envoy, he uttered a loud cry, and fell down in a swoon, and he remained a long time in his fit. Then recovering, he wept violently, and said to El-Amjad and El-As'ad and their chief officers, Go, my sons, with the envoy, and salute your grandfather, my father the King Sháh-Zemán, and give him the glad tidings of my being here; for he is mourning for my loss, and to the present time wearing black raiment for my sake. He then related to the Kings who were present all that had happened to him in the days of his youth; and they all wondered at it. After this, they went down with Ḳamar-ez-Zemán, and repaired to his father. Ḳamar-ez-Zemán saluted his father, and they embraced each other, and fell down senseless from the excess of their joy; and when they recovered, the King Sháh-Zemán related to his son all that had happened to him. Then the other Kings saluted him.

They restored Marjáneh to her country, after they had married her to El-As'ad, and charged her that she should not cease to correspond with them. They married El-Amjad to Bustán the daughter of Bahrám; and all of them journeyed to the City of Ebony, where Ḳamar-ez-Zemán had a private interview with his father-in-law [Armánoos], and acquainted him with all that had happened to him, and how he had met with his sons; at which he rejoiced, and congratulated him on his safety. Then the King El-Ghayoor, the father of the Queen Budoor, went in to his daughter, and saluted her, and quenched the ardour of his longing desire by her society, and they remained in the City of Ebony a whole month; after which, the King El-Ghayoor journeyed with his daughter and attendants to his own country, taking El-Amjad with them. And when he had become settled again in his kingdom, he seated El-Amjad to govern in the place of his grandfather. As to Ḳamar-ez-Zemán, he seated his son El-As'ad to govern in his stead in the city of his grandfather Armánoos; his grandfather approving it.[156] Then Ḳamar-ez-Zemán prepared himself, and journeyed with his father the King Sháh-Zemán until he arrived at the Islands of Khálidán. The city was decorated for him, and the drums continued to beat for a whole month in celebration of the happy event, and Ḳamar-ez-Zemán sat governing in the place of his father, until they were visited by the terminator of delights and the separator of companions.—And God is all-knowing.[157]

When Shahrazád had finished this tale, the King Shahriyár exclaimed, O Shahrazád, verily this story is exceedingly wonderful!—O King, she replied, it is not more wonderful than the story of 'Alá-ed-Deen Abu-sh-Shámát. The King said, And what is that story? And she related it thus:—

NOTES TO CHAPTER TENTH.

Note 1. The scenes in which the principal events described in this tale are laid, though I cannot recognise them in the works of any geographer, have led me to search for traces of a Persian origin; but no indication of such an origin have I been able to discover; and as the character of the tale is altogether Arab, I regard it as an Arab composition. Every one who is moderately acquainted with the Arabs and their literature will see that the tale exhibits throughout, in its present state, the life and manners, and the notions, of that people. One of its chief merits, however, consists in its construction; and this, again, is mainly compatible only with the notions of the same people. I think that this tale offers some of the strongest reasons for considering the Thousand and One Nights, in the state in which it is known to us, as almost entirely an Arab work, though framed after the model of one much older; and I have much satisfaction in remarking that my opinion of this tale is the same as that of the greatest Arabic scholar of Christendom, whose remarks upon it I here translate.

"The history of the loves of Ḳamar-ez-Zemán, prince of the island of the children of Khálidán, an island which is situate at the distance of twenty days' sail from the coasts of Persia, in the Ocean, and of Budoor,[1] princess of China, is no more Indian or Persian than the others. The King, the father of Ḳamar-ez-Zemán, has Muslims for subjects; the mother of the young prince is named Fáṭimeh; and Ḳamar-ez-Zemán, in his prison, occupies himself in reading [or rather reciting] the Ḳur-án. The genii who interpose in these adventures are, again, of those who had concerns with Solomon. In fine, all that is said, in this tale, of the city of the Magians, as well as of the worshippers of fire, would suffice to shew that one should not expect to find in it anything but the production of a Muslim writer."[2]

Note 2. So in the edition of Breslau. In the Cairo edition, by a mistake of a copyist, "Shahramán."

---

1 In the French, "Badoure."—I write this and the other Arabic words in the above paragraph according to my usual system.

2 Mémoire sur l'origine du recueil de contes intitulé Les Mille et Une Nuits. (Mémoires d'Histoire et de Littérature Orientale, extraits des tomes ix. et x. des Mémoires de l'Institut, Académie des Inscriptions et Belles Lettres. Par M. le Baron De Sacy.—Paris, 1832.)—Page 237.

Note 3. This sentence is from the Breslau edition; but I have put "Islands" for "Island," to agree with the sequel.—It must be observed here, that the scenes of the events described in this tale are in the regions of fiction. I am at a loss to assign a position to the Islands of Khálidán, otherwise than in the vague manner in which they are mentioned in the old version, as being situate at the distance of about twenty days' sail from the coasts of Persia, in the Ocean; for Galland, in this case, appears to have followed his original. De Sacy, who seems from his own words to have founded his observations respecting the Thousand and One Nights chiefly upon an examination of Galland's original, mentions these Islands (calling them, as in Galland's version, the Islands of the children of Khálidán,) in the same manner, as already shewn in the first note of the present series. "Khálidán" may be a corruption of "El-Khálidát" or "El-Khálidetán," which names are given by the Arabs to the Fortunate Islands, or Canaries. Our author might have heard of these Islands, and, ignorant of their situation, supposed them to be in the sea which washes the coasts of Persia and India; of which sea, as well as of the sea of China, he evidently entertained most erroneous ideas. It should also be here observed, that the Arabic word ("jezeereh") which generally signifies "an island" is often applied to a peninsula, and may frequently, with propriety, be translated "country;" Arabia, Persia, India, &c., being, by many Arab writers, termed Islands. It is implied in the tale under consideration, that there was a route by land from the "Islands of Khálidán" to the "Ebony Islands" and the "Interior Islands of the region of China." The inhabitants of all these "Islands" are described as Muslims; and in manners, dress, &c., as Arabs. But this, in a tale of fiction, will not surprise those who are acquainted with the works of Arab geographers, and their accounts of places visited by their own countrymen. Ibn-El-Wardee, in describing "the Sea of Eẓ-Ẓulmeh, which is the western [portion of the] Circumambient Ocean" (that is, the Atlantic), says, "Among its islands are the Khálidetán [above mentioned]. These are two islands whereon are two images [or idols] constructed of hard stone: each of them is a hundred cubits high, and upon the top of each is a figure of copper, pointing with its hand backwards, as though it would say, 'Return; for there is nothing behind me.' Zu-l-Menár the Ḥemyeree, one of the Tubbas [or ancient Kings of the Yemen], constructed them. He was [the son of] Zu-l-Ḳarneyn; but not of the one mentioned in the Ḳur-án."[3]—But the Canary Islands were only known to *Europeans*, at the time when Ibn-El-Wardee wrote, from the accounts of the *Ancients*. They were rediscovered by some Genoese and Spanish seamen in 1345, three or four years before the death of that geographer.

Note 4. In the original, "el-'Ajam;" the sense of which appears to be here restricted to signify the Persians. Otherwise the text would mean, that the Islands of Khálidán were at the limits of the extra-Arabian world. It would be quite consistent with Arabian notions to speak thus of the Fortunate Islands, El-Khálidetán; but the former sense of the passage is more agreeable with the whole character of the tale.

Note 5. It is a common custom of the Arabs in the present day to perform the prayers of two rek'ahs[4] with the view of obtaining offspring; and more especially on the occasion of a man's first visit to his bride, as mentioned in the last paragraph of Note 39 to Chapter iv.

Note 6. This sentence, again, is from the Breslau edition. It describes a custom which, like that mentioned in the note immediately preceding, is often observed by Arabs in the present day to propitiate Providence, and obtain offspring. For the same purpose, alms are frequently given to the poor, to obtain their prayers; and visits are performed to the tombs of saints to request their intercession.

Note 7. "Ḳamar-ez-Zemán" signifies "the Moon of the Age."

---

[3] Khareedet el-'Ajáïb (MS. in my possession).

[4] See Note 1 to the Introduction.

NOTE 8.—*On the manner in which the Arab Ladies dress their Hair.* Two of the customs here mentioned, the dyeing of the fingers with ḥennà, and the blackening of the edges of the eyelids with koḥl, have been noticed before.[5] The manner in which the Arab ladies usually dress their hair may now be described.

They are extremely fond of full and long hair; and, however amply endowed with this natural ornament, to add to its effect they have recourse to art. But the Prophet, abhorring all false attractions that might at first deceive a husband and then disappoint him, "cursed the woman who joined her own hair to that of another, or other hair to her own without her husband's permission: if she do it, therefore, with his permission, it is not prohibited, unless she so make use of human hair; for this is absolutely forbidden."[6] Hence the Arab women prefer strings of silk to add to their hair.—Over the forehead, the hair is cut rather short; but two full locks hang down on each side of the face: these are often curled in ringlets, and sometimes plaited. The rest of the hair is arranged in plaits or braids, which hang down the back. They are generally from eleven to twenty-five in number; but always of an uneven number: eleven is considered a scanty number: thirteen and fifteen are more common. Three times the number of black silk strings (three to each plait of hair, and each three united at the top), from sixteen to eighteen inches in length, are braided with the hair for about a quarter of their length; or they are attached to a lace or band of black silk which is bound round the head, and in this case hang entirely separate from the plaits of hair. These strings, together with certain ornaments of gold, &c., compose what is termed the "ṣafà." Along each string, except from the upper extremity to about a quarter or (at most) a third of its length, are generally attached nine or more little flat ornaments of gold, which are usually all of the same form. The most common form is oblong, round at the lower extremity and pointed at the upper, or the reverse. They are affixed (each by a little ring at its upper extremity) about an inch, or a little more, apart; but those of each string are purposely placed so as not exactly to correspond with those of the others. At the end of each string is a small gold tube, or a small polygonal gold bead, beneath which is most commonly suspended (by a little ring) a gold coin, a little more than half an inch in diameter. Such is the most general kind of ṣafà; but some ladies substitute, for the gold coin, a fanciful ornament of the same metal, either simple, or with a pearl in the centre; or they suspend, in the place of this, a little tassel of pearls; or attach alternately pearls and emeralds to the bottom of the triple strings, and a pearl with each of the little ornaments of gold first mentioned. Coral beads are also sometimes attached in the same manner as these pearls.—The ṣafà I think the prettiest, as well as the most singular, of all the ornaments worn by the Arab ladies. The glittering of the little ornaments of gold, and their chinking together as the wearer walks, have a peculiarly lively effect.[7]

The ornamented strings, though not alluded to in the verses to which this note immediately refers, are afterwards mentioned in the tale. The passages relating to them, with many others in the present collection of stories, shew that the costumes described in this work were nearly the same as those which still prevail in Arabian countries.

NOTE 9. Here follows, in the old version, a discussion on the subject of marriage, between Ḳamar-ez-Zemán and his mother Fáṭimeh, who had been desired by Sháh-Zemán to try if her powers of persuasion would induce him to comply with the King's request. But not a word of all this occurs in the edition of Cairo or in that of Breslau. I do not, however, ascribe it to Galland's invention; for De Sacy, who examined the original, mentions it, and partly founds an argument upon it, as I have already shewn.

---

[5] The former, in Note 36 to Chapter iv.: the latter, in Note 34 to Chapter ii.

[6] Kitáb el-'Onwán fee Mekáïd en-Niswán.

[7] This description of the ṣafà is abridged from my work on the Modern Egyptians, Appendix A.

NOTE 10. In illustration of this expression, see Note 14 to Chapter iii.

NOTE 11. "Eṭ-Ṭághoot" is a name given to the Devil, or any seducer, and to any idol. It is therefore to be understood here in the first of these senses.

NOTE 12. His eye-lashes are said to have scorned the sharp sword, because they were themselves more piercing.

NOTE 13. This is said to shew his excessive submission. In the usual posture of a subject before his prince, or a servant before his master, a posture maintained also in some other cases, especially by the son or daughter before the parent, the hands are placed together, the left within the right, before the girdle.

NOTE 14. Perhaps it is needless to comment upon this reply of Ḳamar-ez-Zemán, and to remind the reader of the extreme respect which is generally shewn by the Arab son to his father. But though no reader will regard it as a light offence, some might not imagine the degree of indignation which such expressions would excite in the mind of an Eastern parent.

NOTE 15. These words, addressed by a King to his son, gross as they are, and reflecting upon the honour of the former and his wife, convey a correct idea of the extravagancies into which an Arab, however high his rank, is sometimes betrayed by anger.

NOTE 16. The farrásh is a servant who spreads the carpets, mattresses, &c., takes care of these and other articles of the furniture of the house, and, on a journey, pitches the tents.

NOTE 17. By Muslims of education, the Ḳur-án is usually recited by heart, and to do so is, with many, a daily exercise: with others, it is also very common.—The same Arabic word is employed to signify both reading a book and reciting by heart.

NOTE 18. The chapter of "The Cow" is the second; "The Family of 'Emrán," the third; "Yá-Seen," the thirty-sixth; "The Compassionate," the fifty-fifth; "Blessed be He in whose hand is the Kingdom," the sixty-seventh; and the "Two Preventives" are the last two. These two are so named[8] because they serve as preventives of, or antidotes against, the effects of the evil eye, or enchantment. They are said to have been revealed to the Prophet in order that he might liberate himself from an enchantment by repeating them; and they are often employed as preservative charms.—Ḳamar-ez-Zemán's recitation of these chapters of the Ḳur-án is to be understood as supererogatory; but it is often that a Muslim, in solitude, terminates his prayers in this manner. By his "supplication," is meant a short petition in words of his own choice. In repeating this, the worshipper looks at the palms of his two hands, which he holds like an open book before him; and when he has finished, he draws them over his face, from the forehead downwards. By the "seeking refuge with God," is meant repeating the words, "I seek refuge with God from Satan the accursed."—See Note 44 below.

NOTE 19. "Maạdinee" signifies "mineral" and "metallic," and may perhaps here denote the *colour* of the satin; but it may, more probably, signify "of the fabric of a place called Maạdin;" for silks, &c., are often called after the names of the places where they are made. I cannot offer any other conjecture as to its meaning in this case; and as my sheykh has not explained it, I infer that he, also, was in doubt respecting it; which is not to be wondered at, as many similar terms are no longer understood. In the Breslau edition it is not mentioned. A large and populous town called Maạdin en-Naḳrah, or ——en-Naḳireh, is mentioned by Arab geographers as situate at the point where the pilgrim-routes from El-Baṣrah and El-Koofeh unite.

[8] In Arabic, "el-mo'owwidhetán," vulg., "el-mo'owwizeteyn."

NOTE 20. The word which I render "kerchief" (namely "miḳna'") is a kind of veil, similar to the ḳináạ,[9] but narrower, and seldom worn but by women. It is probably meant, that Ḳamar-ez-Zemán used it to keep off mosquitoes.

NOTE 21. I have substituted "tower" for "saloon;" the sequel requiring this alteration.

NOTE 22. In the original, "Roománee." This term, and the collective "Roomán," are used in modern Arabic to signify, respectively, "Roman" and "Romans." The terms "Roomán" and "Roománeeyoon" (plural of "Roománee") are applied to the inhabitants of Italy, and the Greeks of late ages ("el-Arwám"), and other people, who became subject to the Roman Empire.[10] Hence my interpretation of "Roomán" in Note 13 to Chapter ii. But "Room" is the more proper appellation of the subjects of the Eastern Roman, or later Greek, Empire, and of the modern Greeks.

NOTE 23. "Meymooneh" (feminine of "Meymoon") signifies "Fortunate."

NOTE 24. "Jánn" is here synonymous with "Jinn."—See Note 21 to the Introduction.

NOTE 25. She ascended towards the confines of the lowest of the seven heavens to listen by stealth to the conversation of the Angels.—See the note just before referred to, and Note 36 in the present series.

NOTE 26. We may suppose that she entered the saloon either by a window or by passing through the solid wall.

NOTE 27.—*On Talismans.* "Talisman" is a corruption of the Arabic word "ṭalsam." I write this latter word in accordance with the manner in which it is generally pronounced by the Arabs, and the manner in which my sheykh has written it here and in other parts of the work: by some it is written "ṭilsem," and "ṭilism." It is a term applied to mystical characters; and also to seals, images, &c., upon which such characters are engraved or inscribed. These characters are astrological, or of some other magical kind. The purposes for which ṭalsams are contrived are various; one has the property of preserving from enchantment, or from a particular accident, or a variety of evils; another protects a treasure with which it is deposited; a third, by being rubbed, procures the presence and services of a Jinnee.

NOTE 28. The upper order of Jinn are those who inhabit the higher regions, and do good acts; the lower are those who inhabit low places, such as the *latrinæ*, and do evil acts; and the third class are those who dive in the seas.[11]

NOTE 29. My sheykh remarks that this name is commonly written "Shemhoorish;" but correctly, "Shemharoosh."

NOTE 30. I have already remarked that the scenes of the events related in this tale are in the regions of fiction. When China, and the Islands of its Sea, are mentioned in the present work, we must dismiss from our minds all correct notions of those parts and their inhabitants, who are generally here described as similar to the Arabs in religion, manners, dress, &c.

NOTE 31. "El-Ghayoor" signifies "the Jealous" (with respect to love or honour), or "the Zealous;" and in some cases, "the Changeable."

NOTE 32. The foregoing description is somewhat abridged. Its extravagance in the original may partly be attributed to the excitement of Dahnash.

---

[9] See Note 2 to Chapter iii.

[10] For instance, they are thus applied in a dictionary of the names of places, &c., prefixed by the sheykh Rifá'ah to his "Ḳaláïd el-Mefákhir," (printed at Booláḳ, the port of Cairo, in 1833,) an Arabic translation of Depping's "Aperçu Historique sur les Mœurs et Coutumes des Nations."

[11] From marginal notes by the sheykh Moḥammad 'Eiyád.

NOTE 33. The number of these palaces, and the costly materials of which they are said to have been constructed, are probably designed to convey a comparison to the seven heavens, or to the seven stages of paradise.—See Note 2 to the Introduction.

NOTE 34. "Budoor" is the plural of "bedr," and signifies "Full Moons." She was thus named to imply that, "by the excess of her beauty she was [to be compared to nothing less than] a number of full moons; not one only."[12] In the old version she is improperly called "Badoura."

NOTE 35. I give the Arabic appellation of "ḳahramáneh" for want of an English synonym. It sometimes signifies "a female confidant" (as I have before rendered it); in other cases, "an intriguing waiting-woman," "a duenna," and "a woman of gallantry." But it is generally applied, as in the present instance, to an experienced, confidential female slave, who is set over others, or intrusted with some office of importance. It is from the Persian "ḳahramán," signifying "a valiant warriour," the name of a celebrated fabulous hero of Persia.

NOTE 36. The reader may perhaps say, "How did Meymooneh become acquainted with the youth's history?"—Probably, before she met Dahnash, she had reached the confines of the lowest heaven, and there heard the Angels conversing upon the subject; such being the usual way by which the Jinn arrive at the knowledge of things which would otherwise remain hidden from them.

NOTE 37. The fire here mentioned is that of which the Jinn are created.—See Note 21 to the Introduction.

NOTE 38. The chinking of the ornaments of the head has been mentioned in the eighth note of the present series. The anklets, also, knocking together, produce a tinkling. The odour alluded to in the last of these characteristic verses is that arising from perspiration. A beautiful Arab damsel is often described as diffusing a natural perfume of this kind, like the blessed in Paradise, whose perspiration will be odoriferous as musk. Thus, in the Mo'allaḳah of Imra-el-Ḳeys, in allusion to two former objects of the poet's love, it is said,—

> "When they rise, the odour of musk is diffused from them, as the breathing of the zephyr bringing the fragrance of the clove."

Many similar examples might be added: but they are often misunderstood: one of them is quoted with the view of proving the fondness of the Oriental ladies for perfumes, while it only implies such fondness in the men. It is true, however, that both sexes take great delight in perfumes, and few of the women comply with the injunction in the latter part of the following saying of the Prophet; that, "the perfume for a man should have smell, but not colour; and the things which women rub on must have colour, but not smell."[13]—[The odour of the Prophet's perspiration may also be here cited, although hardly applicable to the particular instance in the text. The Muslim's praise of this quality appears, in general, not to have been suggested by this pretended characteristic of the Prophet.—ED.]

NOTE 39. My sheykh explains the word "ḳuṭrub" as signifying here, "an animal with long fore-legs; one of those which early in the morning puts itself in motion." In the Ḳámoos it is described as "a small beast that ceases not from moving about all the day;" and the same term (ḳuṭrub) is also there rendered, "a bald wolf," and "the male of the Ghool,"[14] &c.

---

[12] Marginal note by the sheykh Moḥammad 'Eiyád.

[13] Mishkát el-Maṣábeeḥ, vol. ii. p. 361.

[14] See Note 21 to the Introduction of the present work. [El-Maḳreezee relates, as a historical fact, that the great cemetery of Cairo (the Ḳaráfeh) was frequented by one of these fabulous animals, which he wrongly calls Ḳuṭrubeh and describes as a female; and that, in consequence of its violation of the tombs, the people abstained for a time from burying their dead in the tract.—ED.]

NOTE 40. So in the edition of Breslau. In the Cairo edition, "äwi-l-ḳubbeti-l-mebneeyeh," which may be rendered "or [like] the dome-crowned structure."

NOTE 41. See Note 15 to Chapter iii.

NOTE 42. The word here rendered "quinary," which is its literal sense, is generally used to signify "of five spans." We may perhaps here understand it as meaning "of five *feet*." The Arabs especially admire damsels who have not attained their full growth; and at witnessing a bridal procession, disapprobation is often expressed, or indicated by looks, if the bride is of the average stature of women.

NOTE 43. This is here interpreted by my sheykh as meaning "narrow."—The former part of Note 11 to Chapter iii. will explain this interpretation.

NOTE 44. When the Muslim has finished the prayers ordained by the Ḳur-án and the Sunneh, if he would acquit himself of supererogatory acts, he remains sitting (but may then sit more at his ease), and recites the "Throne-Verse," which is the 256th of the second chapter of the Ḳur-án (beginning with the words, "God! There is no deity but He;" and ending with, "He is the High, the Great"); and generally adds, "O High! O Great! Thy perfection [I extol]." He then repeats "The perfection of God!" (thirty-three times). "The perfection of God, the Great, with his praise for ever!" (once). "Praise be to God!" (thirty-three times). "Extolled be his dignity! There is no deity but He!" (once). "God is most great!" (thirty-three times). "God is most great in greatness, and praise be to God in abundance!" (once). He counts these repetitions with a string of beads, which are ninety-nine in number, and have a mark between each thirty-three: they are of aloes or other odoriferous or precious wood, or of coral, or of certain fruit-stones, or seeds, &c.

NOTE 45. This exclamation ("Allah preserve thy youth!"), being only used by women, is, as my sheykh remarks, improper from the mouth of the Wezeer.

NOTE 46. This, again, is an ejaculation of women.—See Note 65 to Chapter iv.

NOTE 47. The word here rendered "news" generally signifies "happy news." My sheykh observes that it is used to excite laughter.

NOTE 48. Of the various significations of "ḳubbeh," the most appropriate here seems to be either "a dome" or "a building or chamber &c. surmounted by a dome."

NOTE 49. These are the names of the twelve lunar months which compose the Mohammadan year. They are mentioned in the order of their succession; but Moḥarram is that with which the year commences.—The questions here put are those which are generally addressed by the Arabs to a person to try if he be sane.

NOTE 50. "Kisrà," or "Kesrà," from the Persian "Khusrow," which signifies "a great king," and which the Romans converted into "Cosroes" (a surname that they gave to almost every King of the Sásánian dynasty), is an appellation applied by the Arabs (like Cæsar among the Romans) to many ancient Kings of Persia. According to the Persian and Arab historians, the Kings of Persia prior to El-Islám composed four dynasties; namely, the Péshdádians, the chronology of which is unknown; the Kayánians, which ended in the year 331 B.C., when Persia was conquered by Alexander the Great; the Áshkánians, which terminated A.D. 202; and the Sásánians, the last of whom was overcome by the Arabs, A.D. 636.

NOTE 51. From the commencement of this sentence to the end of the paragraph is from the Breslau edition.

NOTE 52. In the Cairo edition, the lady Budoor is said to have killed the old woman; but in the edition of Breslau, and the old version, she is described as having only beaten her.

NOTE 53. Maniacs, in the madhouse in Cairo, are thus chained by the neck, each in a separate cell. They are treated there, I fear, with unnecessary rigour; but travellers are often deceived on this point; for it is a custom of visiters to take with them bread to distribute to the lunatics, many of whom consequently cry out for it, when any stranger enters the court, as if they were starving. Sometimes, when a lunatic has received his cake of bread, he throws it back in the face of the giver. [Since this note was written, the madhouse in Cairo has been removed from the old Máristán, founded by the Sulṭán, El-Melik el-Manṣoor Ḳaláoon, which is situate in the main street of the city, to the European district. It is now organized by French physicians, and the condition of the patients is considerably improved.—ED.]

NOTE 54. So in the edition of Breslau, and apparently in the MS. from which Galland translated, being written in his version "Torf." In the Cairo edition, "Eṭ-Ṭeyreb."

NOTE 55. These are female proper names, used as fictitious names. "Suleymà" is the diminutive of "Selmà;" and, like the latter, is often employed to designate a beautiful woman. "Er-Rabáb" signifies "the white cloud," and "the viol;"[15] and "Rabáb" is also applied to "a cloud which is now white, and presently black;" and hence it is a term applied to "a woman," denoting changeableness. "Ten'om" is the third person singular feminine of the aorist of a verb signifying "to be soft, gentle, &c."[16]

NOTE 56. "'Andam" is an Arabic name of "Brazil-wood" (also called "baḳḳam"), and of the resinous substance termed by us "dragon's blood."

NOTE 57. The meaning is, "My fingers are not dyed with ḥennà."—See Note 36 to Chapter iv.

NOTE 58. This and the next preceding verse, on the superior merit of the precedent, are often repeated by the learned.[17]

NOTE 59. She hath Luḳmán's[18] wisdom (which is proverbial among the Muslims), Joseph's beauty (which is alike celebrated), David's sweet voice (on the effects of which see Note 18 to Chapter i.), and the chastity of the Virgin Mary; while *I* have grief like that which Jacob felt (for the loss of Joseph), regret such as Jonas suffered (when swallowed by the fish), affliction like that endured by Job (when God tried him, on his marrying the wife of the man whom He sent, and not being content with the wives whom he had before),[19] and am in a state like that of Adam expelled from Paradise.

NOTE 60. This is equivalent to saying, she is in a state of affliction that cannot be described.

---

15 There are two kinds of viol called "rabáb," which I have described in my work on the Modern Egyptians, vol. ii. ch. v.

16 Chiefly from a marginal note by the sheykh Moḥammad 'Eiyád.

17 Marginal note by the same.

18 The country and age of this famous person are unknown. He is generally described as an ugly black slave, and said to have lived in the time of David; though some assert that he was son of a sister, or of a maternal aunt, of Job. Some suppose him to be Æsop.

19 So says my sheykh, from whom the above note is chiefly taken. Various reasons are given by Arab writers for God's empowering the Devil to afflict Job. One says, that a sick man came to him, and he looked at him with disgust, and sent him away from the court of his house: so God afflicted him with the like disease. Another, that a poor beggar stopped at his door, and he turned him away disappointed. A third, that a person who was oppressed implored his aid, and he did not assist him against his oppressor. A fourth, that there was in his time a tyrannical King who assigned him a portion of land whereon to pasture his horses, and the learned men went in to the King and reproved him for his tyranny, except Job, who did not forbid his tyranny, on account of the pasture of his beasts.—The Arab writers assert that Job was an inhabitant of Syria (possessing El-Bethneh and El-Jábiyeh and [other places in] the province of Dimashḳ, or Damascus); and almost all of them agree that he never quitted that country. It is also their general belief that he was the great-grandson of Esau, whom they call 'Eeṣoo.—Mir-át ez-Zemán.

NOTE 61. This, I suppose, is said from politeness; for, as my sheykh remarks, it is not consistent with the story; since Ḳamar-ez-Zemán acquainted his father and others with the adventure, and the lady Budoor did not acquaint *her* father.

NOTE 62. See the fiftieth note of the present series.

NOTE 63.—*On Geomancy.* On the science and practice of Geomancy, called "'Ilm er-Raml" and "Ḍarb er-Raml," there are several treatises by Eastern writers; but I have not met with any of these; nor have I seen a geomantic tablet; which, probably, I should be unable to describe satisfactorily if I had. Geomancy is a mode of divination from the combinations of certain marks or dots made, apparently at random, upon sand (whence its appellation) or on paper; but I have been informed that it is chiefly founded upon astrology; so I suppose the geomantic tablet to be an instrument engraved with astrological diagrams, &c. I have only seen the mode of performing geomantic experiments upon paper. The invention of the science is ascribed by some to Idrees, or Enoch; by some, to Daniel; by some, to Ham the son of Noah; and by others, to Hermes Trismegistus.

NOTE 64. Literally, "I write the book," or "—— the writ." This phrase is employed to signify writing, or, more commonly, merely repeating, a form of words constituting a contract of marriage. It is evident that this is its meaning here, and that it alludes to astrological calculations which are often made previously to marriage, and which I have described in Note 74 to Chapter v.—See that note, and Note 147 in the present series.

NOTE 65. See the fifty-sixth note of the present series.

NOTE 66. Amulets thus engraved with talismanic characters are worn by many Muslims in the present day; but a more common kind of amulet is a piece of paper partly inscribed with such characters and enclosed in a case of gold or silver or leather, &c.

NOTE 67. In the times of the early 'Abbásee Khaleefehs, in the eighth and ninth centuries of our era, popular European tales may have found their way among the Arabs, as well as Persian and Indian tales of the same nature; and the establishment of an Arab empire in Spain, the Crusades, and the extensive commerce of the Venetians with Egypt and Syria, doubtless occasioned the transmission of similar tales from the Arabs to Europe, and *vice versâ.* On the subject of such transmissions, and the resemblance of popular tales and fictions of different countries, much information and entertainment may be derived from a work by Mr. Keightley, from which I must here insert an extract.

"In that pleasing old French romance of Peter of Provence and the fair Maguelone, ... there is a circumstance so like one in the Arabian Nights, that it may have come from the East. I know not the age of the romance, but it is certainly posterior to the establishment of the Angevin dynasty at Naples. As it does not appear to have ever existed in verse, I would refer it to the fifteenth century.

"Peter, son to the Count of Provence, hearing of the beauty of Maguelone, daughter of the King of Naples, determined to go thither in person, and view the peerless maiden. He accordingly went in disguise to the Neapolitan court, and there, as an unknown knight, so distinguished himself in the tournaments, that he won the favour of the King, and the heart of the lovely Maguelone. After some time, being desirous to return to Provence, he persuaded the princess to fly with him. She yielded her assent, and they secretly left the palace and departed on horseback, taking a third horse laden with provisions. On the second day they came to a dense wood on a mountain near the sea, and being fatigued and overcome with the heat, they alighted from their horses to rest them; and the princess, laying her head on the lap of Peter, fell fast asleep and ——[20]

[20] "I translate," says Mr. Keightley, "from a Spanish translation of the romance in the King's Library, printed at Seville in 1519; possibly the very edition that Cervantes had read."

"'While Magalona, as has been said, was sleeping on the lap of her dear friend Peter, the said Peter delighted his whole heart by gazing on the sovereign beauty of his lady; and when he had to his pleasure contemplated her beautiful countenance, and had well admired and kissed that sweet and agreeable, small and beautiful mouth, he could not satiate himself with looking at it more and more: then he could not refrain from uncovering her a little, and gazing on her most beautiful and white bosom, that was whiter than the crystal; and he touched her sweet bosom, and when he did so he was so penetrated with love that it seemed to him that he was in paradise, and that nothing could ever cause him any affliction. But that pleasure did not last long; for he suffered the most inestimable pain and ill-fortune, as you shall hear, that man could ever think of. And the noble Magalona suffered not less, for she afterwards passed through many great afflictions.

"'For while Peter thus admired and touched the sweet Magalona, he found in her bosom a coloured piece of silk, which was folded up, and he had a very great desire to know what was in it. And he began to unfold it, and he found in it three of his mother's rings, which he had given to Magalona, and she had kept them out of good love. And when Peter had seen them, he folded them up again, and placed them near him on a stone; and he turned his eyes to the noble Magalona, and regarded her with good love, and he almost fainted away with love and with pleasure. But our Lord shewed that in this world there is not pleasure without pain, nor perfect happiness. For a bird of prey, thinking that that coloured silk was a piece of flesh, came flying, and took that silk, and went away with it, and flew to the mountain, and seated itself on a very lofty tree.

"'When Peter saw this he was greatly grieved, and he thought that Magalona would be grieved at it, whom he wished to please more than any person in the world. He put his cloak under the head of Magalona, and then got up very quietly, without her perceiving anything. And he began to follow that bird, and to pelt it with stones, to make it drop the silk it was carrying. And there was there a little rock near the land. Yet between the rock and the land there was a great quantity of water, and no one could pass to that rock without swimming. And this bird went flying from tree to tree to settle on that perilous rock, and Peter flung a stone at it, so that that bird went from thence, and let that silk fall into the sea; and the said Peter could not pass thither, because he knew not how to swim. Nevertheless, as the distance was not great, he began to search on one side and the other if he could find anything in which he could pass to the rock to go to look for it. Then said Peter, Would to God that I had not taken the rings or the silk from where I took them, and that I had not meddled with them, for they will cost me dear, and Magalona still more; for if I delay much longer Magalona will go look for me. And as Peter was thus searching along the shore of the sea, he found an old boat, which the fishers had abandoned because it was worth nothing; and Peter went into it, and was greatly joyed, but his joy lasted not long. And he took some sticks that he had picked up to row with, and went off for the rock. But God, who does all things at his pleasure, caused to rise a great wind, cold and strong, from the land side, which carried Peter and his bark, against his will, very far out to sea, and all his rowing availed him nought; for the sea was very high and very deep, and he could not get to land, and the wind carried him along in despite of himself.'

"I need not tell how Peter was taken up by a ship and brought to Egypt, where he became a great favourite with the Sultan, and how Maguelone went to Provence, and was made directress of an hospital, whither Peter was brought as a pauper, and how she recognised him, and made herself known to him, and how they were united, and passed their days in uninterrupted felicity."[21]

---

21 "Tales and Popular Fictions; their Resemblance, and Transmission from Country to Country," pp. 82—86.

Mr. Keightley proceeds to remark upon the similar incident in the tale of Ḳamar-ez-Zemán, "the main story of which (for the episodic ones certainly are not) is possibly," he says, "of Persian origin;" but, like De Sacy, as I have already said, I see no foundation for such an opinion; and there is certainly much that is utterly inconsistent with it. Mr. Keightley afterwards mentions another point of resemblance between the story of Ḳamar-ez-Zemán and that of Peter of Provence, which I shall notice in its proper place; and he adds, "It is therefore, I think, by no means unlikely that some part at least of the oriental tale travelled westwards." To me it seems more probable that the writers of these two stories were alike indebted to some tale much older than that of Ḳamar-ez-Zemán—to one which offered little that was worthy of imitation. The resemblances, being only in two points, I regard as tending to confirm my opinion, that the tales of the Thousand and One Nights, in general, differ extremely from any others upon which they may have been founded. For the incomparable superiority of the tale of Ḳamar-ez-Zemán over that of Peter of Provence renders it, I think, highly improbable that the latter could have been founded upon the former; or that the former could have been indebted, otherwise than in the points here noticed, to any tale of which the latter may be an imitation. The chief merit of the former tale I most confidently ascribe to an Arab writer.

Note 68. It is perhaps unnecessary to observe to the reader, that the danger which Ḳamar-ez-Zemán is said to have incurred in the city of the Magians is inconsistent with the idea that his story may be one borrowed from the "Hezár Afsáneh;" that is, of an ancient Persian origin. So, too, is the treatment experienced by El-As'ad, later in the tale.

Note 69. "El-Islám" is a term often used to signify "the Muslims."

Note 70. In a former tale, "the king of the further parts of India" is called "lord of the Ebony Island."—See vol. i. p. 143.

Note 71. The same principle which induced Moḥammad to forbid all games of chance was strictly regarded by him in his laws relating to commerce and industry, as in the cases of "musáḳáh" and "muzára'ah." "Musáḳáh signifies a man's giving over his trees in charge to another, to attend upon them and improve them, by watering them for a fixed proportion of their produce; such as half, a third, or a fourth. Muzára'ah is the giving of land in charge, to be cultivated on similar conditions."[22] It appears that Moḥammad forbade the latter practice, and consequently the former also, under certain circumstances. "My two uncles," says Ráfe' the son of Khadeej, "informed me, that the companions of the Prophet used to let land by this agreement, that the sower should sow his own seed, and that whatever grew upon the sides of small ponds should be for them; or they fixed on a part of the ground, and said, 'Whatever grows on this is for us, and the rest for you.' Then the Prophet forbade it, because peradventure nothing might grow on it:" that is, on one part of it. But it is also said, by one of the companions of Moḥammad, "Verily the Prophet of God has forbidden muzára'ah in this sense, by saying, 'Whatever may be produced in this part is for me, and in the other part for you;' and ordered fixed rent, and said, 'In this there is no fear.'" It is evident, therefore, that he prohibited certain modes of muzára'ah, which were unfair; but I think it is also clear that he did not forbid the practice in cases in which the proprietor of the land and the labourer incurred a similar risk. 'Omar, the second Khaleefeh, "settled with the people, that if he found the seed, he should have half its produce; and if the labourers brought the seed, then two-thirds [should be] for them, and the remainder for him." Moḥammad himself, also, "delivered over, to a Jew of Kheyber, the trees and grounds of Kheyber, by this stipulation, that he should work on them at his own expense, and give him half their produce."[23]—I

---

[22] Mishkát el-Maṣábeeḥ, vol. ii. p. 48, note.

[23] *Idem*, vol. ii. pp. 48—51.

should be extremely glad to see a similar plan adopted in Egypt: the revenue of the government would be greatly increased by it; and the chief evil of which the peasants complain, remedied.

In the tale which this note is designed to illustrate, Ḳamar-ez-Zemán was merely an assistant: therefore a fourth of the produce of the garden was a fair remuneration for him.

NOTE 72. See Note 25 to Chapter iv.

NOTE 73. See Note 32 to Chapter vi.

NOTE 74. "Ḥayát-en-Nufoos" signifies "the Life of Souls."

NOTE 75. This he did to obtain a blessing.[24]

NOTE 76. Thamood and 'Ád were two tribes of ancient Arabs, said to have been of enormous stature, who, with few exceptions, were destroyed for their obstinate idolatry. The tribe of 'Ád was the more ancient; but both lived before the time of Abraham.

NOTE 77. In the original, "amṭár," plural of "maṭr." The terms "maṭr" and "maṭrah" are applied to a large jar or bottle of wood or leather, used for water, &c.

NOTE 78. I do not know of any kind of olives called "'aṣáfeeree;" nor do I find this appellation in any dictionary.

NOTE 79. "Just so Peter of Provence, when leaving Egypt, put his valuables into barrels, which he filled with salt; and, having fallen asleep in the isle of Sagona, the ship sailed away, leaving him behind. On arriving at the place where Maguelone dwelt, the captain gave her the barrels of salt for the use of the hospital, and in them she found the treasure."[25]

NOTE 80. This is a common expression of humility. An Arab, writing to a superior, often terms himself the latter's slave.

NOTE 81. From this we must understand that the gardener had left no natural heir.

NOTE 82. Tamarind, in Arabian countries, is generally formed into round, flattish cakes, which have a hole in the middle. When dry, they are strung together.

NOTE 83. The Muslims are forbidden not only to swear frequently and vainly by God, but especially to swear by any created thing. There are few of them, however, who are not in the constant habit of acting contrary to both these prohibitions. Their most common forms of oath are "By God!" and "By the existence of the Prophet!" but they also often swear by the life of any respected person; and by the life, head, or beard, of a man whom they are addressing.

NOTE 84.—*On Polygamy, &c.* In a former Note[26] I have mentioned certain beneficial results of the law of the separation of the sexes; its promoting a more free and extensive intercourse among persons of the same sex and of different ranks, and its tendency, with Muslims, to increase what *they* consider domestic happiness. I must now remark upon some other effects of the same law.

First, the restriction of intercourse between the sexes before marriage renders indispensable, to some, the facility of divorce; for it would be unjust for a man who finds himself disappointed in his expectations of a wife whom he has never before seen, not to be enabled to put her away. Secondly, it sometimes renders indispensable the licence of polygamy; for a man who finds his first wife unsuited to him may not be

---

[24] Marginal note by the sheykh Moḥammad 'Eiyád.

[25] Keightley's Tales and Popular Fictions, p. 88.

[26] Note 4 to Chapter ix.

able to divorce her without reducing her to want; and the licence of polygamy becomes as necessary in this case as that of divorce in another. Thirdly, the liberty of polygamy renders the facility of divorce more desirable for the happiness of women; since, when a man has two or more wives, and one of them is dissatisfied with her situation, he is enabled to liberate her. Fourthly, the licence of divorce often acts as a check upon that of polygamy; for the fear of being obliged, by the influence of his first wife, or by that of her relations, to divorce her if he take a second, often prevents a man from doing this. Thus both these licences are required by the most important principle of the constitution of Muslim society, and each is productive of some moral benefit. In considering the question of their expediency, we should also remember, that barrenness is much more common in hot climates than in those which are temperate.

Christianity is plainly opposed to polygamy; but as to divorce, some have contended that it only forbids putting away a wife against her will, unless for one cause.[27] Christians are often most unjust in their condemnation of Muslim laws and tenets, and especially condemn those which agree with the Mosaic code and the practices of holy men; such as polygamy (which Moḥammad *limited*), divorce, war for the defence of religion, purifications, and even minor matters.[28] Moḥammad endeavoured to remove one of the chief causes of polygamy and divorce, by recommending that a man should see a woman whom he proposed to take as his wife.[29] We might imagine that he could have made these practices less common than they now are, and always have been, among his followers, had he given more licence, allowing the man to enjoy a limited intercourse with the object of his choice in the presence of her female or male relations (the former of whom might be veiled), without infringing further the general law of the separation of the sexes. But he saw that such liberty would very seldom, if ever, be allowed: scarcely any parents, among the Arabs, except those of the lower classes, permit the little licence which he recommended. Instead of condemning him for allowing a plurality of wives, I think we should be more reasonable if we commended him for diminishing and restricting the number. I think too, that, as Moses allowed his people, for the hardness of their hearts, to put away their wives, and God denounced not polygamy when the patriarchs practised it, we should be more consistent as believers in the Scriptures if we admitted the permission of these practices to be more conducive to morality than their prohibition, *among a people similar to the ancient Jews* to whom Moses allowed such liberty. As to the privilege which Moḥammad assumed to himself, of having a greater number of wives than he allowed to others, I have elsewhere remarked, that, in doing so, he may have been actuated by the want of male offspring rather than impelled by voluptuousness; he seems, however, to have been influenced by both these motives.

"On the subject of polygamy," says a recent writer who has deeply studied Muslim institutions and their effects, "a European has all the advantage in discussion with a Turkish woman, because her feelings are decidedly on the side of her antagonists; but then she has a tremendous power of reply, in the comparison of the practical effects of the two systems, and in the widely-spread rumours of the heartlessness and the profligacy of Europe.—All the convictions of our habits and laws stand in hostile array against the country where the principle of polygamy is admitted into the laws of the state; but yet, while we reproach Islamism with polygamy, Islamism may reproach us

---

27 "The Protestants of Hungary admit the plea of 'irrevocabile odium.'"—Urquhart's Spirit of the East, vol. ii. p. 416.

28 A religious lady once asked me if I so conformed with the manners of the Easterns as to eat in their "beastly manner." I replied, "Do not call it a 'beastly manner:' call it the manner of our Lord and his Apostles." But some excuse may be made in this case. I was determined, when I first went to the East, never to conform to the practice of eating with the fingers when I could avoid it; however, after I had first seen the manner of doing this, I immediately adopted the custom, and continued it.

29 See Mishkát el-Maṣábeeḥ, vol. ii. p. 81.

with practical polygamy, which, unsanctioned by law, and reproved by custom, adds degradation of the mind to dissoluteness of morals."[30]—It should further be remarked, that, by sanctioning polygamy, Moḥammad did not make the practice general: nay, he could not. It is a licence for the *hard-hearted*, which restrains them from worse conduct, and in some cases, as already shewn, a resource for the tender-hearted. "The permission," observes the author just cited, "does not alter the proportions of men and women. While, therefore, the law of nature renders this practice an impossibility as regards the community, it is here still further restrained among the few who have the means of indulging in it, both by the domestic unquiet that results from it, and by the public censure and reprobation of which it is the object."[31]—I have remarked in a former work, that polygamy "is more rare among the higher and middle classes [in Egypt, and I believe in other Arab countries,] than it is among the lower orders; and it is not very common among the latter. A poor man may indulge himself with two or more wives, each of whom may be able, by some art or occupation, nearly to provide her own subsistence; but most persons of the higher and middle orders are deterred from doing so by the consideration of the expense and discomfort which they would incur. A man having a wife who has the misfortune to be barren, and being too much attached to her to divorce her, is sometimes induced to take a second wife, merely in the hope of obtaining offspring; and from the same motive, he may take a third, and a fourth; but fickle passion is the most evident and common motive both to polygamy and to repeated divorces. They are comparatively few who gratify this passion by the former practice. I believe that not more than one husband among twenty has two wives."[32]

I hope I have shewn, that, though I consider polygamy as necessary in the constitution of Muslim society, to prevent a profligacy that would be worse than that which prevails to so great a degree in European countries, where parties are united in marriage after an intimate mutual acquaintance, I consider it as a necessary *evil*.—When two or more wives of the same man live together, or when they visit each other, feelings of jealousy are generally felt, and often manifested, and especially on the part of the wife or wives who cannot claim precedence by having been married before the other or others, or by reason of being more favoured by the husband.[33] The wife first married usually enjoys the highest rank: therefore parents often object to giving a daughter in marriage to a man who has already another wife; and it frequently happens that the female who is sought in marriage objects to such a union. The law provides in some measure against the discomforts arising from polygamy, by giving to each wife a claim to a distinct lodging, affording conveniences for sleeping, cooking, &c.; and further enjoins the husband to be strictly impartial to his wives in every respect. But fruitfulness and superior beauty are qualifications that often enable a second, third, or fourth wife to usurp the place of the first; though in many cases, as I have remarked in another note, the lasting favourite is not the most handsome.

There are, however, many instances of sincere affection existing in the hearts of fellow-wives. The following story of two wives of the father of El-Jabartee, the modern Egyptian historian, related by himself, and of undoubted truth, is a pleasing example.—Speaking of the first of these two wives, the historian says,—

"Among her acts of conjugal piety and submission was this, that she used to buy

---

[30] Urquhart's Spirit of the East, vol. ii. pp. 415 & 416. I may here recommend the perusal of its two chapters on "The Life of the Harem," and "State of Women," which I think its most valuable portion.

[31] *Idem.*

[32] Modern Egyptians, vol. i. ch. vi.

[33] A fellow-wife is called, in Arabic, "ḍarrah," a word derived from "ḍarar," which signifies "injury," because fellow-wives usually experience injurious treatment, one from another. The word "ḍarrah," in vulgar or colloquial Arabic (by substituting a soft for an emphatic d, and u for a), is pronounced "durrah," which properly signifies "a parrot." "The life of a fellow-wife is bitter" ("'eeshet ed-durrah murrah") is a common proverb.—From one of my sheykh's marginal notes to the story of Ḳamar-ez-Zemán.

for her husband beautiful concubine slaves, with her own wealth, and deck them with ornaments and apparel, and so present them to him, confidently looking to the reward and recompense which she should receive [in Paradise] for such conduct. He took, in addition to her, many other wives from among free women, and bought female slaves; but she did not in consequence conceive any of that jealousy which commonly affects women. Among other strange events which happened, was the following. When the subject of this memoir [the author's father] performed the pilgrimage, in the year 1156 (A.D. 1743-4), he became acquainted, at Mekkeh, with the sheykh 'Omar El-Ḥalabee, who commissioned him to purchase for him a white female slave, who should be a virgin, not arrived at womanhood, and having such and such other qualifications. So when he returned from the pilgrimage, he searched for female slaves among the slave-dealers, to choose from them such a one as was wanted, and ceased not until he found the object of his desire, and bought her. He brought her to his wife, above mentioned, to remain with her until he should send her with a person to whom he was commissioned to intrust her for the journey; and when the period at which she was to depart arrived, he informed his wife of it, that she might prepare the provisions for the way, and other necessaries. But she said to him, 'I have conceived a great love for this maid, and I cannot endure separation from her: I have no children, and I have taken her as a daughter.' The girl also wept, and said, 'I will not part from my mistress, nor ever leave her.' 'Then what is to be done?' he asked. She answered, 'I will pay her price from my own property, and do thou buy another.' He did so. She then emancipated the girl, gave her to him by a marriage-contract, prepared her paraphernalia, and furnished for her a separate apartment; and he took her as his wife in the year 65. The former wife could not bear to be separated from her even for an hour, although she had become her fellow-wife, and borne him children. In the year 82 before mentioned, the [emancipated] slave fell sick, and she [the first wife] fell sick on account of her [friend's] sickness. The illness increased upon both of them; and in the morning the slave arose, and looked at her mistress when she seemed about to die, and wept, and said, 'O my God and my Lord, if Thou hast decreed the death of my mistress, make my day to be before her day.' Then she lay down, and her disease increased, and she died the next night; and they wrapped her up by the side of her mistress. And her mistress awoke at the close of the night, and felt her with her hand, and began to say, 'Zeleekhà! Zeleekhà!'[34] They said to her, 'She is asleep.' But she replied, 'My heart telleth me that she is dead: and I saw in my sleep what indicated this event.' They then said to her, 'May thy life be prolonged!'[35] And when she had thus ascertained the event, she raised herself, and sat up, and said, 'No life remaineth to me after her.' And she wept and wailed until the day appeared, when they began to prepare for the speedy burial of the slave; and they washed the corpse before her, and carried it to the grave. Then she returned to her bed, and fell into the agonies of death, and died at the close of the day; and on the following day they carried her corpse to the grave in like manner.—This was one of the strangest of the things that I have witnessed and seen and remembered. My age at that time was fourteen years."[36]

NOTE 85. "El-Amjad" signifies "the More, or the Most, Glorious."

NOTE 86. "El-As'ad" signifies "the More, or the Most, Fortunate, Prosperous, or Happy."

NOTE 87. I here omit an explanation which is of a nature to disgust every person

---

[34] This was the slave's name.

[35] This is the usual way of informing a person that another is dead. Many say in the same case, Mayest thou live!" and then, being asked, "Who is dead?" mention the name.

[36] Modern Egyptian History (MS. in my possession), vol. i. obituary of the year of the Flight 1188.

of good taste. In this case, and in several others of a similar kind, the old version agrees with the original, being faithful to the latter when, to say the least, it is utterly unnecessary to be so, and unfaithful when fidelity is most desirable. He who is unacquainted with the original should be informed, that it contains many passages which seem as if they were introduced for the gratification of the lowest class of the auditors of a public reciter at a coffee-shop. These passages exhibit to us persons of high rank, both men and women, as characterized by a grossness which is certainly not uncommon among Arabs of the inferior orders; but this is all that I can venture to assert; for although there are numerous anecdotes which might be adduced with the view of justifying our original in the cases here alluded to, they are obviously of suspicious authority. It is highly probable that Hároon Er-Rasheed often exercised the wit of Aboo-Nuwás by relating to him exaggerated or even fictitious accounts of occurrences in his own ḥareem; and, still more so, that the latter person, in reciting his anecdotes to his friends, disregarded truth in a much greater degree.

Note 88. See Note 8 in the present series.—By sending, with the letter, the silk strings of her hair, we are to understand that the lady designed to testify the most abject submission. The same meaning is conveyed in a more forcible manner by sending the hair itself. Thus, when Cairo was besieged by the Franks in the year of the Flight 564 (A.D. 1168), El-'Áḍid, the last Khaleefeh of the house of Fáṭimeh, sent letters to Noor-ed-Deen Maḥmood, Sulṭán of Syria, imploring succour, and with them sent his women's hair,[37] to shew their subjection and his own.

Note 89. This is one of the passages alluded to at the close of Note 8 in the present series.

Note 90. By "drinking of the anguish of another" is meant "partaking of his anguish by witnessing it." The same and a similar expression occur shortly afterwards, where the meaning is more obvious.

Note 91. The person here designated the "Treasurer" ("Kházindár," as generally pronounced,) is called in the Breslau edition "the Emeer Jendár," and in the old version, "an emeer called Giondar." Dr. Scott has converted "Giondar" into "Jehaun-dar." But "Jendár" is not a proper name. This term, more properly written "Jándár," was a title common to a class of officers under the Sulṭáns of Egypt, whose duty was to guard the door of the Sulṭán, to convey or enforce his orders with respect to emeers, and to guard the prison called the Zardakhánáh, in which persons of rank were confined. The Emeer Jándár was the chief of these officers.

It is important to remark, that the present work exhibits but a very imperfect acquaintance with the offices held under the Sulṭáns whose dominion was subverted by the Turkish conqueror Seleem. Such we should expect to be the case in a work either composed or remodelled *after* the Turkish conquest of Syria and Egypt, A.D. 1517.

Note 92. This prayer is addressed to God.

Note 93. When God desireth anything, He saith unto it, "Be," and it is.[38]

Note 94. In the original, three pieces of poetry are here put into the mouth of El-As'ad. That which I have given is the second of them.

Note 95. The saráb (generally called by Europeans "mirage") is that remarkable vapour which is so often seen in the desert, tormenting the thirsty traveller by presenting the appearance of a lake. So complete is the illusion, that I have seen the

[37] Ibn-Esh-Sheḥneh. [So too El-Maḳreezee, with a slight variation. It was in this siege that the old town now called, erroneously, Miṣr (or Maṣr) El-'Aṭeeḳah was burnt by order of the Wezeer Sháwir; the conflagration lasting 54 days. —The Khiṭaṭ; account of the ruin of El-Fusṭáṭ; and reign of El-'Áḍid.—Ed.]

[38] Marginal note by my sheykh. The saying, somewhat varied, occurs in several places in the Ḳur-án.

images of objects situate within or beyond it distinctly reflected by its surface.—In the verse in which this vapour is mentioned, the word "kaḥal," which I have rendered "the black-edged eyelid," literally signifies "the natural blackness round the eye, resembling the artificial blackness which is produced by the powder called koḥl."

NOTE 96. This sentence I have inserted from the Breslau edition.

NOTE 97. A small oratory, with a niche indicating the direction of Mekkeh, is often seen in Muslim countries, by the side of a spring, a well, a reservoir, or a large water-jar which is daily replenished for the use of travellers. Sometimes it is designed also as a place of repose, being a small, roofed chamber, open towards the north.

NOTE 98. In the story of the Young King of the Black Islands, the Muslims, Christians, Jews, and Magians, who composed his subjects, are said to have been transformed, respectively, into white, blue, yellow, and red, fish; and here a Magian is described with a red turban. When the Christians and Jews were compelled to distinguish themselves by wearing, respectively, blue and yellow turbans (as mentioned in Note 55 to Chapter ii.), and the white turban was made peculiar to the Muslims, the Samaritans were also compelled to wear *red* turbans; and our author appears to have made red the distinguishing colour of the *Magians* from this circumstance; for an Arab writer quoted by El-Maḳreezee, in his account of the Samaritans,[39] says that the tenets of this latter people were a mixture of Judaism and *Magism*.—This explanation I think more probable than one which might be deduced from the Turkish term "Ḳizil-básh," or "Red-head," a nickname applied by the Turks to a Persian, and so applied by the Persians themselves. It is said to have been derived from a red cap first worn by the Persian soldiers under the Sháh Ismá'eel, about the commencement of the sixteenth century. I prefer the explanation first proposed because it would account for the distinctive colours of *all* the fish above mentioned.

NOTE 99. "Ghaḍbán" signifies "enraged," or "angry."

NOTE 100. The remainder of this paragraph is from the Breslau edition.—Here I may mention that, in the old version, the old man orders his "daughters, Bostama and Cavama," to undertake the office of torturing El-As'ad: in the Breslau edition, he is said to have so commissioned his "daughter Bustán and slave-girl Ḳäwám." This shews that he is the same person who is afterwards mentioned by the name of Bahrám; which, in the Cairo edition, is not so clearly shewn. Agreeably with this edition, I have not here mentioned Bahrám's daughter; as I think that an incident at the close of the story is rendered needlessly improbable by describing her as the torturer of El-As'ad.

NOTE 101.—*On the Magian Festivals of Fire.* As the present tale exhibits scarcely any acquaintance with the religion of the Magians, I consider it almost unnecessary to attempt any illustration of its allusions to the rites of that people. The "Blue Sea and the Mountain of Fire" I suppose to be purely imaginary. But the idea of the human sacrifice at a particular period of the year, on the occasion of "the Festival of the Fire" (as afterwards said), may have been derived from a vague notion of the rites of two Magian festivals. The first of these was celebrated in the month of Ádur, or Ázur, which (except in the middle ages of Persia, when the calendar was altered,) corresponded with November. The angel after whom this month was named "presided over fire; in consequence of which, on the ninth, his name-day, the country blazed all around with flaming piles; whilst the Magi, by the injunction of Zoroaster, visited, with great solemnity, all the temples of that element throughout the empire, which, upon this occasion, were adorned and illuminated in a splendid manner. On this day it was reckoned a point of religion to pare the nails and to shave the hair, under the idea that,

[39] In his "Khiṭaṭ."

with these excrescences, they threw away, at the same time, all their sins and defects."[40] —In the following month (Dei), "on the 11th, or the angel's day," the other "great festival of fire was celebrated all over the kingdom; for the origin of which solemnity, a variety of traditional reasons have been handed down; one of them is curious: Winter, they say, having once, on the anniversary of that day, taken a fancy to come from hell, which was, it seems, too hot for him, their ancestors had lighted up immediately those piles of fire, to convince him that he had got into a still more infernal place, and force him again from earth to the shades of darkness. In order to improve the general scene of nocturnal splendour, on this occasion, it was usual for the King and his courtiers to set fire to large bunches of dry herbs, fastened to wild beasts and birds, who being then let loose, the fields, mountains, and the air itself were immediately in one universal temporary blaze, heightened often by the accidental firing of the neighbouring woods, to which those terrified animals naturally fled for shelter. . . . A custom similar to this prevailed even in England within this century; it having been customary, on Twelfth-night, in Shropshire and other places, to kindle bonfires on the mountain-tops and other high grounds, as a farewell to winter, and a welcome to the spring. The 15th of this month was remarkable for another singular ceremony: they formed a number of images of paste or clay, representing those deceased personages whom they meant to honour, which they placed in the most public places, especially where many roads or streets met, and, after paying them great homage, burnt them with much formality."[41]—Might not this last practice have given rise to a vulgar belief among the Arabs, that the Magians offered human sacrifices?

Note 102.—*On the* Ṣoofees. On this characteristic passage, my sheykh remarks, in a marginal note, that it is usual with the Ṣoofees thus to beg for an increase of the afflictions that they suffer.—The Ṣoofees are so called either from the Arabic word "ṣoof," signifying "wool," on account of their wearing woollen garments, or from the Greek word *σοφὸς*, because of their philosophical tenets. There is an order of Muslim darweeshes called Ṣoofees, "who make profession of a more regular and more contemplative life than darweeshes in general; and many of this class have written books of spirituality, of devotion, and of contemplation, which mostly bear the title of 'Taṣowwuf,' that is, of spiritual life."[42] The first convent of this order in Egypt was founded by Ṣaláḥ-ed-Deen, who is commonly called by European writers Saladin. But the title of Ṣoofee is adopted by many who do not belong to this order of darweeshes; by those who lead a life of contemplation, and of philosophical religion; and of this class are many excellent men, who regard with especial veneration the moral and most other doctrines of the Gospel. Their grand principle seems to be love of God.—The Sunnee Ṣoofees are in a great degree mystical and latitudinarian; but not so much so as the Ṣoofees of the Persian sect.

Note 103. So in the Breslau edition and in the old version. In the Cairo edition, the distance by sea is said to be *six* months. The preferable reading is "four months," because this city is evidently the same as that in the neighbourhood of which Ḳamar-ez-Zemán resided with the gardener. The two princes are said to have performed in three months a journey which usually occupied a year; and we must therefore suppose that they did it in that comparatively short space of time by taking a route too arduous to be generally followed, and impracticable for caravans. This is implied by El-Amjad's remark on the first discovery of the city.

Note 104. The Muslims hold (and I believe adduce a saying of their Prophet in confirmation of their opinion) that it is improper to eat in a street or other place where

---

40 Richardson's Dictionary, Persian, Arabic, and English (Johnson's edition), *voce* "máh."

41 *Idem.*

42 D'Herbelot, Bibliothèque Orientale, art. "sofi."

many people are passing; because a person who does so cannot give to all who pass by and desire to partake; and when he has given all that he can spare, the remainder may be looked upon by an envious eye, which renders it injurious, or at least unprofitable.

NOTE 105. In the present day, in many parts of the East, the Frank Christian may dress as a Muslim: but formerly, Muslims were distinguished from all other persons, especially by the colour and form of the turban. The Eastern Christians and Jews, with few exceptions, are still distinguished by the turban, which is generally black or blue, or of a greyish, or light-brown, colour.—See Note 55 to Chapter ii., and Note 98 in the present series.

NOTE 106. The meaning of this is, "Thy beauty is continually increasing."[43]

NOTE 107. See Note 59 in the present series.

NOTE 108. By "the thorns of lances," it is perhaps needless to state, that piercing eyes or eyelashes are meant.

NOTE 109. This sentence commences the thirty-eighth verse of the fourth chapter of the Ḳur-án. By "He whose name be exalted" we are always to understand God. The Muslim never quotes the Ḳur-án but as the word of God, and generally in doing so says, "He whose name be exalted hath said, in the Excellent Book,"—never mentioning the Prophet in this case unless he use some such phrase as this, "God hath said by the tongue of his Prophet."

NOTE 110. The word which I render "flowers" (namely "ṣoḥbeh") also signifies "a branched candlestick, or candelabrum, with many candles." Either sense would be appropriate here; but in speaking of wine, it generally signifies "a bunch of flowers," which are often placed in a candlestick in the midst of the wine-service.[44]

NOTE 111. The wooden lock which is in general use in Arabian countries for the doors of houses and chambers is described and figured in the Introduction to my work on the Modern Egyptians.

NOTE 112. See Note 12 to Chapter iii.

NOTE 113. In a MS. Arabic dictionary of my own composition I see that the only meaning that I have given to "sidilleh" (a word that I do not find in any other dictionary) is that of "a long seat, or couch;" and accordingly, in a former instance (vol. i. p. 122), I have rendered the plural of this word, with that of "maṣṭabah" preceding it, by "benches of different kinds." In the present case, my sheykh has explained the plural of "sidilleh" by words signifying "places elevated a little, like the ṣuffeh;" which last term is applied to "a kind of shelf or sill of stone," and "a bench or sofa." The term "sidilleh" is applied in Cairo to a slightly-elevated recess, without a window; and to a platform of stone, for a deewán, generally about half a foot high.

NOTE 114. The clothes here mentioned are those which were usually worn at wine-parties.—See Note 22 to Chapter iii. (vol. i. p. 197).

NOTE 115. The most appropriate meaning of "sufreh" here appears to be "a round cloth." A stool with a round tray upon it are also called a sufreh; and this term is applied to a round piece of leather, which serves as a table for meals, and which is usually spread on the ground; chiefly used by travellers, whence its name.

NOTE 116. This word is Persian and Turkish, and signifies "courageous," "bold," "a hero." It is pronounced by the Arabs as I have written it; by the Persians, "Bahádar;" and by the Turks, "Behádir." Turkish and Persian names became

---

[43] Note by the sheykh Moḥammad 'Eiyád.

[44] See Note 22 to Chapter iii. (vol. i. p. 198).

familiar to the Arabs in the times of the 'Abbásee Khaleefehs, and were still more so in later times.

NOTE 117. This is said to shew more strongly the disturbed state of his mind; for it is usual to put the feet into the shoes or slippers on stepping off the carpeted portion of the floor.

NOTE 118. "Bahrám" is a common Persian name. It is also a name of the planet Mars; and signifies "a king," "a sword," &c.

NOTE 119. See Note 100 in the present series.

NOTE 120. "Marjáneh" (vulg., "murjáneh"), in modern Arabic, signifies "a piece of coral." It also signifies "a small pearl," and "a kind of spring pot-herb."

NOTE 121. This sentence I insert from the Breslau edition.

NOTE 122. Here, again, I insert a few words from the Breslau edition, ending with "El-Moaṭarr."

NOTE 123. "El-Moaṭarr" signifies "the Poor," "the Indigent," "He who dares not ask for what he needs." It is a name assumed as the opposite of "El-As'ad," or "the Most Fortunate." In the old version, it is written "Motar," and rendered "Devoted to be sacrificed."

NOTE 124. "These two verses are by one of the sect of the Murjiäh, or Murjis,[45] and one of the Sunnees (or orthodox Muslims) answered them, and said,—

'If God protect him, no moisture will touch him, and he need not care for being hand-bound and thrown;[46]

But if the Lord have decreed that he shall be drowned, he will be drowned though he be cast upon a desert.'"

Thus my sheykh comments upon the two verses to which this note relates. The tale itself also shews their fallacy, by a subsequent incident (of no very improbable nature) in the history of El-As'ad. In their place are inserted, in the Breslau edition, with some slight variations and errors, the verses of which a translation has been given in a former tale, in page 299 of the first volume of this work; and the same appears to be the case in the manuscript from which Galland translated.

NOTE 125. The drum and pipe are the instruments most commonly used in Arabian countries on occasions of festivity; as in the procession of a bride or bridegroom, that of a boy about to be circumcised, and that of a pilgrim approaching his home on his return from the holy places.

NOTE 126. The burial-grounds adjacent to Arab towns generally contain a number of dome-crowned structures erected over graves, which often afford shelter to benighted travellers.

NOTE 127. "Bustán" signifies "a garden."

NOTE 128. This is said in allusion to his name, which signifies "more, or most, fortunate."

NOTE 129. See Note 9 to Chapter vi.

---

[45] A sect of Muslims who seem to have been chiefly distinguished by the very small importance that they attached to works. This sect is divided into four classes; and the person here alluded to appears to have been of the Jeberee class, who deny free agency in man, ascribing his actions wholly to God. I believe that most of the Murjis were of this class.

[46] The meaning I suppose to be this, that, as a man can never foresee his fate, he should not neglect to make use of means which God may have decreed for his preservation. This, at least, is the orthodox doctrine.

NOTE 130. In the edition of Breslau, this story occupies a different place, commencing the seventh volume.

NOTE 131. "El-Koofeh" is the city commonly called by European writers "Kufah" and "Cufa," situate on the west bank of the Euphrates. It was founded in the reign of the Khaleefeh 'Omar, and was a famous seat of Arabian learning.—The inhabitants of El-Koofeh were a people difficult to please, always ready to revolt, and continually complaining of their Governors. A party of them one day urging a complaint, to the Khaleefeh El-Ma-moon, against one of his officers, one of them abused this person in such gross terms that the Khaleefeh took his officer's part, and highly praised him for the strict justice which he rendered to every one. Upon this, one of the complainants replied that all which the Khaleefeh said was very true, and that all the accusations which his townsmen had advanced against the officer were pure calumnies: yet, as it was necessary that justice should be rendered everywhere, it was not right that the people of El-Koofeh alone should enjoy the advantage of possessing such a man, while all the other provinces of the Empire were deprived of him. "Cause thy people, then, O our lord," he continued, "to praise and bless thee equally, by sending him elsewhere."[47]

NOTE 132. "Neạmet-Allah" signifies "the Boon of God."

NOTE 133. The meaning of "Towfeeḳ" is "a causing to be prosperous, or agreeable," &c.

NOTE 134. "Saạd" signifies "prosperity," "happiness," "good fortune."

NOTE 135. "Noạm" is synonymous with "Saạd." The name was changed that it might agree with that of Neạmet-Allah.

NOTE 136. In "Neạmet-Allah" and similar names, the latter word is often dropped. In this case, the final t in the former is changed into h.

NOTE 137. That is, each of them was in some respects more beautiful than the other.

NOTE 138. I here put "four" instead of "nine," as the sequel requires it.

NOTE 139. "Zeyd" and "'Amr" are here used as fictitious names, in the same manner as they are by the Arab grammarians.

NOTE 140.—*Of El-Ḥajjáj and his Character.* El-Ḥajjáj the son of Yoosuf Eth-Thaḳafee was Governor of the Ḥejáz and of the Arabian 'Eráḳ under 'Abd-El-Melik and his son El-Weleed, the fifth and sixth Khaleefehs of the house of Umeiyeh, for a space of about twenty years, until the period of his death, which happened in the year of the Flight 95 (A.D. 713-14). He was highly celebrated for his eloquence and courage, but execrated for his tyranny. His cruelty, however, has perhaps been exaggerated by the Shiya'ees, or Shee'ees, to whom he rendered himself especially odious; and I do not place entire reliance on the correctness of the following illustrations of his character, which I insert on account of their singular nature.

In his last illness, "he ventured to consult an astrologer whether the position of the stars, that year, prognosticated the demise of any person in power. To which the astrologer replied, that a prince would shortly die, who either bore or had borne the appellation of Kuleyb; and El-Ḥajjáj confessing that his mother had in his infancy been accustomed to address him by that name (puppy, perhaps[48]), the astrologer rashly

---

47 D'Herbelot, Bibliothéque Orientale, art. "Coufah."

48 "Kuleyb" signifies "a little dog." It was a common custom among the Arabs to give names of this kind, and among the Bedawees the custom still prevails, though it is not often followed by other Arabs. Speaking of the Bedawees, Burckhardt says, "A name is given to the infant immediately on his birth. The name is derived from some trifling accident, or from some object which

declared that the person whose death was indicated could be no other than himself. 'At least thou shalt precede me,' said El-Ḥajjáj, and the unfortunate wizard was ordered to be immediately despatched by the attendants.—This ferocious tyrant, whose memory has been indeed loaded with sufficient obloquy by the Shiya'ees, and whom he on his part never ceased to persecute with unsparing vengeance, expired, at the age of fifty-four, about the twenty-fifth day of the month of Ramaḍán, in the ninety-fifth year of the Hijrah. Some time previous to his death he complained that his bowels were lacerated by dogs; and a roll of flexible silk being passed down his throat, by the physicians who attended, it was drawn up, covered with vermin. And though it does not appear to have rendered his government at all more palatable, it is recorded, probably as a proof of his boundless prodigality in the public expenditure, that among the disciples of the Ḳur-án, he was the first who, on one occasion, displayed a thousand tables for the entertainment of the people; or in a single donation disbursed a million of dirhems.—Exclusive of those who perished in battle, the amount of whom could be estimated by Him alone who knows all things, there fell by the arbitrary mandates of El-Ḥajjáj, not less than one hundred and twenty thousand persons. Nevertheless, in a dream, in which he is said to have appeared to some one a short time after his death, he is made to declare, that, though for each of this numerous list of the victims of his fury, divine justice was satisfied with inflicting on him the punishment of a single death, yet that for the execution of Sa'eed[49] alone, he was condemned to suffer seventy times the agony of dissolution. There were, after all, found in the different prisons of his government, when Providence thought fit to relieve mankind from his oppressions, no less than thirty thousand men, and twenty thousand women; many of these confined in that species of prison invented by himself, without roof; in which, alternately exposed to the scorching rays of the sun, and the vicissitudes of cold, heat, and rain, the unhappy victims were left to suffer under every variety of pain and wretchedness."[50]

NOTE 141. See a note at the foot of page 59 in this volume.

NOTE 142. It is a custom of many Muslim devotees to hang to the neck, in several circumvolutions, a string of many hundreds of beads. The object is either to employ these beads in repeating certain ejaculations in praise of God, or to make others believe that the wearer is accustomed so to employ them.—See the forty-fourth note of the present series.—A string of a thousand beads, and the use to which it is applied, have been mentioned in Note 15 to Chapter iv.

The whole description of the costume, manners, and expressions, of the hypocritical old woman in this tale is admirably just. It is perfectly applicable to persons who may be seen occasionally in the streets of Cairo in the present day, though probably the character of many of these may be sincere. The female devotees who thus distinguish themselves are very few in comparison with the male.—I should also add that the conduct of Noạm towards the old woman described in this story is consistent with that of the generality of Arab women in similar cases. Indeed the story altogether is as true a picture of Arab manners as any of the present collection.

NOTE 143. In some Arab houses, in one or more of the apartments, a niche is formed or painted, in or upon one of the walls, indicating the direction of Mekkeh. But more commonly a prayer-carpet answers the same purpose, its pattern presenting

---

had struck the fancy of the mother, or any of the women present at the child's birth. Thus, if the dog happened to be near on this occasion, the infant is probably named 'Kiláb,' from 'Kelb' a dog," of which it is the plural. (Notes on the Bedouins and Wahábys, 8vo. ed. vol. i. p. 97.)

[49] See Note 30 to Chapter ii.

[50] Price's Retrospect of Mahommedan History, vol. i. pp. 479 *et seq.*—As justice should be rendered to every one, however bad, it may here be remarked, that many of these prisoners had probably been before accustomed to the vicissitudes here mentioned. [Another anecdote of El-Ḥajjáj occurs after the Notes to Chapter XIV.—ED.]

the form of a niche, the point of which is turned towards Mekkeh, so that a visiter need not ask of his host in what direction he is to turn his face in prayer.

NOTE 144. These words are the commencement of the seventieth verse of the twenty-fifth chapter of the Ḳur-án. They follow a denunciation against the wicked, and Noạm is supposed to know what precedes them, as well as the remainder of the verse, which is this:—"for unto them God will change their evil works into good; and God is ready to forgive, and merciful."

NOTE 145. By "the sheykhs" we are here to understand the saints, or persons who devote themselves to religious exercises. And "the holy places" mentioned in the same passage are those mosques and other buildings containing the tombs or cenotaphs of saints; such buildings being frequently visited by men and women, in the belief that the prayers there offered up are especially efficacious.—See Note 63 to Chapter iii.

NOTE 146. By this is meant, that she was a *descendant* of the Kings of El-Koofeh; but the author was probably ignorant that there were no such Kings. If by "Kings" are meant merely "Governors," he is still in error; for the Governors of El-Koofeh were, from its foundation, Muslims; and their daughters could not be sold as slaves.

NOTE 147.—*On Astrological Calculations.* My sheykh remarks, in a marginal note, that the calculation here spoken of is founded upon the numerical values of the letters composing the name. Thus, Noạm (in Arabic) consists of three letters, Noon, 'Eyn, and Meem: Noon is 50; 'Eyn, 70; and Meem, 40: the sum of the three is therefore 160: subtract from this 9 and 9, or 12 and 12, and so on until there remains either 12 or less than 12: the remainder is the number of the sign of the Zodiac that influences the person to whom the name belongs: 1, being Aries; 2, Taurus; 3, Gemini; and so on.

I have mentioned two other modes of making calculations of the same kind;[51] but from the above it appears, that I should have stated, in explaining the former of those two modes, that the calculation is sometimes (and perhaps generally) founded upon the numerical values of the letters composing only the name of the person whose sign is sought, and that then the number of the sign is obtained in the manner above described. The reader has seen that two different results may be obtained according to my sheykh's directions. He does not state whether it is the general practice to subtract 9 or 12 from the number of the name.

NOTE 148. "O brother of the Persians" (yá akhà-l-Furs) is synonymous with "O Persian." "O brother of the Arabs" is a common expression used in addressing an Arab.

NOTE 149. Arab shopkeepers very often make their calculations by writing on the palm of the hand.

NOTE 150. "Soạdà" and "Juml" are fictitious names of women. They are chosen for the sake of a play upon words, which I could not preserve in the translation.

NOTE 151.—*On the* Koofee *Character.* The Koofee character (generally called by European writers "Cufic") was so termed from the city of El-Koofeh, in which, without doubt, it originated, and which was founded in the seventeenth year of the Flight. Some papyri lately discovered in Egypt shew that the character employed by the Arabs of the Ḥejáz before this differed little from that which superseded the Koofee, and which has generally been employed by the Arabs to the present day.[52] But the character, as well as the language (called Ḥemyeree, or Himyaritic,) used in El-Yemen, and probably in several other parts of Arabia, before the time of the Prophet, is unknown. My learned friend M. Fulgence Fresnel has discovered a language still

[51] In Note 74 to Chapter v.

[52] See De Sacy's Grammaire Arabe, 2nd. ed. vol. i. p. 5.

spoken in some parts of El-Yemen, a dialect of the ancient Ḥemyeree; and it may be hoped that his discovery will be productive of important results, and be of value in biblical literature.

A flexuous Koofee character, an ornamental style, which came into use in the fourth century of the Flight, has been erroneously called, by many European writers, the Carmatic character, and supposed to have been invented by the nation or people called the Ḳarmaṭees.[53] This mistake seems to have originated in a misinterpretation of the word "ḳarmaṭah," which is defined in the Ḳámoos as signifying "a diminutive style of writing, and a close [or short] step [in walking]."[54]

Note 152. It is related in the Soorat Yoosuf (the twelfth chapter of the Ḳur-án), that Jacob's eyes became white with mourning for Joseph; but that the latter, when he had discovered himself to his brethren in Egypt, gave to them his inner garment, desiring them to throw it on his father's face; and when this was done, Jacob recovered his eyesight.—This garment, we are told in the Commentary of the Jeláleyn, "was the shirt of Ibráheem, which he wore when he was thrown into the fire.[55] It was on his [Yoosuf's] neck in the well; and it was from Paradise. Jibreel [or Gabriel] ordered him to send it, and said that in it was its odour, [i. e. the odour of Paradise,] and it should not be thrown on any one afflicted [with a disease] but he should be restored to health."

Note 153. For the insertion of the words enclosed between crotchets in this sentence, I have the authority of my sheykh.

Note 154. See Note 65 to Chapter viii.

Note 155. In my original it is here added, "and her name was Noạm," which would explain what the Khaleefeh's sister wished as yet to conceal.

Note 156. Marjáneh, we may suppose, came thither with him.

Note 157. The words "And God is all-knowing" are added by the narrator to imply that the story may perhaps be not entirely true!

[53] The Arabic words at the head of Chapter ix., commencing this volume, (signifying, "In the name of God, the Compassionate, the Merciful,") present an example of this style.

[54] This error was, I believe, first exposed and confuted by M. Fræhn, in the 5th No. of the Nouveau Journal Asiatique, May, 1828.

[55] This was done by order of Numrood (or Nimrod), and is mentioned in the twenty-first chapter of the Ḳur-án. The patriarch came forth from the fire unhurt.

CHAPTER XI.

COMMENCING WITH PART OF THE TWO HUNDRED AND FORTY-NINTH NIGHT, AND ENDING WITH PART OF THE TWO HUNDRED AND SIXTY-NINTH.

THE STORY OF 'ALÁ-ED-DEEN ABU-SH-SHÁMÁT.[1]

It hath been told me, O happy King, that there was, in ancient times, a merchant in Cairo,[2] named Shems-ed-Deen. He was one of the best and the most veracious in speech of all the merchants, and was possessor of servants and other dependants, and male black slaves, and female slaves, and memlooks, and of great wealth, and was Sháh-Bandar[3] of the merchants in Cairo. And there resided with him a wife whom he loved, and who loved him: but he had lived with her forty years, and had not been blessed with a daughter nor with a son by her. And he sat one day in his shop, and saw the other merchants, every one of them having a son, or two sons, and the greater number of these sons were sitting in shops like their fathers. That day was Friday: so this merchant entered the bath, and performed the ablution of Friday;[4] and when he came forth [from the inner apartment], he took the barber's looking-glass, and, looking at his face in it, said, I testify that there is no deity but God, and I testify that Moḥammad is God's Apostle![5] He then looked at his beard, and saw that the white eclipsed the black; and he reflected that hoariness was the monitor of death.

Now his wife knew the time of his coming, and she used to wash and prepare herself to receive him; and when he came home to her that day, she said to him, Good evening:—but he replied, I have seen no good. She had said to the slave-girl, Bring the supper-table. So she brought the repast; and the merchant's wife said to him, Sup, O my master.—I will not eat anything, he replied. And he turned away his face from the table. She therefore said to him, What is the reason of this, and what hath grieved thee? He answered her, Thou art the cause of my grief.—Wherefore? she asked. And he answered her, When I opened my shop this day, I saw that every one of the merchants had a son, or two sons, and most of the sons were sitting in the shops like their fathers; whereupon I said within myself, Verily he who took thy father will not leave thee.[6] And when I first visited thee (he continued), thou madest me swear that I would not take another wife in addition to thee, nor take an Abyssinian nor a Greek nor any other slave-girl as a concubine; and

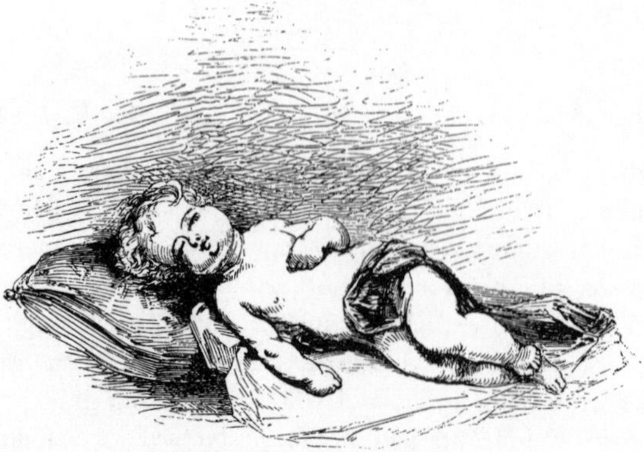

thou art barren.—But his wife reproved him in such a manner that he passed the night and arose in the morning repenting that he had reproached her, and she also repented that she had reproached him. And soon after this, his wife informed him that his wish was likely to be accomplished.

The son was born, and the midwife charmed him by repeating the names of Moḥammad and 'Alee,[7] and she pronounced in his ear the tekbeer and the adán,[8] and wrapped him up and gave him to his mother, who nursed him, and he took his nourishment until he was satiated, and slept. The midwife remained with them three days, until they had made the sweetmeat to distribute on the seventh day; and then they sprinkled the salt for the infant.[9] And the merchant went in and congratulated his wife on her safety, and said to her, Where is God's deposite?[10] Whereupon she presented to him an infant of surprising loveliness, the work of the Ever-present Governor. He was an infant of seven days; but he who beheld him would say that he was a child a year old; and the merchant looked in his face, and saw that it was like a shining full moon, with moles upon the cheeks. He said to his wife, What hast thou named him? And she answered, Were it a girl, I had named her; but this is a boy; so no one shall name him but thyself.[11] The people of that age used to name their children from an omen; and while they were consulting upon the name of the merchant's son, lo, one said to his companion, O my master 'Alá-ed-Deen. So the merchant said to his wife, We will name him 'Alá-ed-Deen Abu-sh-Shámát.[12] He commissioned the nurses to rear him, and the child drank the milk for two years; after which they weaned him, and he grew up, and walked upon the floor. And when he had attained the age of seven years, they put him in a chamber beneath a trap-door,[13] fearing the influence of the eye upon him, and his father said, This boy shall not come forth from beneath the trap-door until his beard groweth.[14] The merchant appointed a slave-girl and a male black slave to attend upon him: the slave-girl prepared the table for him, and the black slave carried it to him. Then his father circumcised him, and made for him a magnificent banquet; and after this, he brought to him a professor of religion and law to teach him; and the professor taught him writing and the Ḳur-án and science until he became skilful and learned.

But it happened that the black slave took to him the table one day, and inadvertently left the trap-door open; whereupon 'Alá-ed-Deen came forth from it, and went in to his mother. There was with

her a party of women of rank, and while they were conversing with her, lo, he came in to them, resembling an intoxicated memlook, in the excess of his beauty. So when the women saw him, they covered their faces, and said to his mother, Allah requite thee, O such-a-one! How dost thou cause this strange memlook to come in to us? Dost thou not know that modesty is one of the points of the faith?—But she said to them, Pronounce the name of Allah![15] Verily this is my son, and the darling of my heart, the son of the Sháh-Bandar of the merchants, and the child of the nurse and the necklace and the crust and the crumb![16]—They replied, In our lives we never saw a son of thine. So she said, Verily his father feared for him from the influence of the eye, and therefore made as his nursery a subterranean chamber under a trap-door; and probably the eunuch hath inadvertently left the trap-door open, and he hath in consequence come up from it; but it was not our desire that he should come out from it until his beard should grow. The women therefore congratulated her upon this. And the youth went forth from them into the court of the house, and then ascended into the maḳ'ad,[17] and there seated himself; and while he was sitting there, the slaves entered the house with the mule of his father; whereupon 'Alá-ed-Deen said to them, Where hath this mule been? They answered him, We have conducted thy father to the shop, mounted upon her, and brought her back. And he asked them, What is the trade of my father?—Thy father, they answered him, is Sháh-Bandar of the merchants in the land of Egypt, and he is Sulṭán of the Sons of the Arabs.[18]

And upon this, 'Alá-ed-Deen went in to his mother, and said to her, O my mother, what is the trade of my father? She answered him, O my son, thy father is a merchant, and he is Sháh-Bandar of the merchants in the land of Egypt, and Sulṭán of the Sons of the Arabs. His slaves consult him not respecting the sale of anything except that of which the smallest price is a thousand pieces of gold. As to the sale of a thing for nine hundred pieces of gold or less, they consult him not respecting it, but sell it of their own free will. And there cometh not merchandise from other parts, little or much, but it is submitted to him, and he disposeth of it as he willeth; and no merchandise is packed up and goeth to other parts, but it is under the disposal of thy father. God (whose name be exalted!) hath given to thy father, O my son, great wealth, that cannot be calculated. —So he said to her, O my mother, praise be to God that I am the son of the Sulṭán of the Sons of the Arabs, and that my father is Sháh-Bandar of the merchants! But for what reason, O my mother, do ye put me in a chamber beneath a trap-door, and leave me there imprisoned?—She answered him, O my son, we put thee not in the chamber beneath the trap-door but in our fear for thee from the influence of the eyes of men; for the influence of the eye is true,[19] and most of the inhabitants of the graves are victims of the eye. But he said to her, O my mother, and where is a place of refuge from destiny? Caution preventeth not fate, and from that which is written there is no escape. Verily he who took my grandfather will not leave my father: so if he is alive to-day, he will not be alive to-morrow; and when my father dieth, and I go forth and say, I am 'Alá-ed-Deen the son of the merchant Shems-ed-Deen,—not one of the people will believe me, and the aged will say, In our lives we never saw a son nor a daughter of Shems-ed-Deen:—then the officers of the government-treasury will come down and take my father's wealth. Allah have mercy upon him who said, The liberal-minded man dieth, and his wealth departeth, and the meanest of men taketh his women. Do thou, then, O my mother, speak to my father, that he may take me with him to the market-street and open for me a shop, and I will sit in it with merchandise, and he shall teach me the art of selling and buying, and taking and giving.—She replied, O my son, when thy father cometh I will acquaint him with thy wish.

And when the merchant returned to his house, he found his son 'Alá-ed-Deen Abu-sh-Shámát sitting with his mother: so he said to her, Wherefore hast thou taken him forth from beneath the trap-door?—O son of my uncle, she answered, I did not take him forth; but the servants inadvertently left the trap-door open, and while I was sitting with a party of women of rank, lo, he came in to us. And she acquainted him with that which his son had said; whereupon the merchant said to him, O my son, to-morrow, if it be the will of God (whose name be exalted!), I will take thee with me to the market-street; but, O my son, sitting in the market-streets and shops requireth polite and accomplished manners under every circumstance.

So 'Alá-ed-Deen passed the next night full of joy at the words of his father; and when the morning came, his father took him into the bath, and clad him in a suit worth a large sum of money. And after they had breakfasted, and drunk the sherbet, the merchant mounted his mule, and put his son upon another mule, and, taking him behind him, repaired with him to the market-street; and the people of the market-street saw the Sháh-Bandar of the merchants approaching, followed by a youth whose face was like the moon in its fourteenth night. It was customary, when the Sháh-Bandar came from his house in the morning and sat in his shop, for the Naḳeeb[20] of the market to approach the merchants and recite the Fáteḥah to them, whereupon they arose and came with him to the Sháh-Bandar of the merchants and recited the Fáteḥah to him,[21] and wished him good morning: then each of them departed to his shop. But when the Sháh-Bandar of the merchants seated himself in his shop on that day according to his custom, the merchants came not to him as they were wont to do. So he called the Naḳeeb (who was named the sheykh Moḥammad Simsim,[22] and who was a poor man), and said to him, Wherefore have not the merchants come together according to their custom? The Naḳeeb answered him, that they were disputing on the subject of the youth who was with him, wondering who he could be, and he said, Is he thy memlook, or is he related to thy wife?—

He is my son, said the Sháh-Bandar. The Naḳeeb replied, In our lives we have never seen a son of thine. The Sháh-Bandar therefore said, In my fear for him from the influence of the eye, I reared him in a subterranean chamber beneath a trap-door, and it was my desire that he should not come up from it until he could hold his beard with his hand; but his mother would not consent; and he requested me to open a shop, and to give him merchandise, and teach him the art of selling and buying. So the Naḳeeb went to the merchants, and acquainted them with the true state of the case; upon which all of them arose and went with him to the Sháh-Bandar, and, standing before him, recited the Fáteḥah, and congratulated him on his having this youth for a son, and said to him, May our Lord preserve the root and the branch! But (they added) the poor among us, when a son or a daughter is born to him, is required to make for his brothers a saucepan of 'aṣeedeh,[23] and to invite his acquaintances and relations, and yet thou hast not done this.—So he said to them, I will give you the entertainment, and our meeting shall be in the garden.

Accordingly, when the next morning came, he sent the farrásh[24] to the saloon and the pavilion[25] which were in the garden, and desired him to spread the furniture in them. He sent also the necessaries for cooking, as lambs and clarified butter, and such other things as the case required, and prepared two tables, one in the pavilion and one in the saloon. The merchant Shems-ed-Deen girded himself, and so did his son 'Alá-ed-Deen, and the former said to the latter, O my son, when the hoary man cometh in, I will meet him, and seat him at the table which is in the pavilion; and thou, O my son, when the beardless youth cometh in, shalt take him and conduct him into the saloon, and seat him at the table there. His son said to him, Wherefore, O my father? What is the reason of thy preparing two tables, one for the men and one for the youths?—O my son, answered the merchant, the beardless youth is ashamed to eat in the presence of men.[26] So his son approved of this. And when the merchants came, Shems-ed-Deen met the men, and seated them in the pavilion; and his son 'Alá-ed-Deen met the youths, and seated them in the saloon. Then the servants placed the food, and the party ate and drank, and enjoyed themselves and were delighted, and they drank the sherbet, and the servants gave vent to the smoke of the perfume; after which, the aged men sat conversing upon science and tradition.[27]

Meanwhile, the youths had seated 'Alá-ed-Deen among them at the upper end of the chamber, and one of them said to his companion, O my master Ḥasan, acquaint me respecting the capital in thy possession, by means of which thou sellest and buyest, how it came to thee. He replied, When I grew up, and attained to manhood, I said to my father, O my father, give me some merchandise:—but he replied, O my son, I have none; go, however, and procure money from some merchant, and traffic with it, and learn the art of selling and buying, and taking and giving. So I repaired to one of the merchants, and borrowed of him a thousand pieces of gold, and, having bought some stuffs with it, I journeyed with them to Syria, where I obtained double the cost-price. Then I took merchandise from Syria, and journeyed with it to Baghdád, where I sold it, and again obtained double the cost-price; and I ceased not to traffic until my capital became about ten thousand pieces of gold.—And each of the youths said to his companion the like of this until the turn to speak came round to 'Alá-ed-Deen Abu-sh-Shámát; when they said to him, And thou, O our master 'Alá-ed-Deen. So he replied, I was reared in a subterranean chamber beneath a trap-door, and came forth from it this week, and I go to the shop and return from it to the house. And upon this they said to him, Thou art accustomed to remain in the house, and knowest not the delight of travel, and travel is for none but men. He replied, I have no need to travel; and ease is invaluable. And one of them said to his companion, This is like the fish: when he quitteth the water he dieth. They then said to him, O 'Alá-ed-Deen, the glory of the sons of the merchants consisteth in nothing but travel for the sake of gain.

At these words, 'Alá-ed-Deen became enraged, and he went forth from among the youths, with weeping eye and sorrowful heart, and, having mounted his mule, repaired to the house. And his mother saw him in a state of excessive rage, and weeping: so she said to him, What maketh thee weep, O my son? He therefore answered her, All the sons of the merchants have reproached me, and said to me, The glory of the sons of the merchants consisteth in nothing but travel for the sake of gaining pieces of silver and gold. His mother said to him, O my son, dost thou desire to travel? He answered, Yes. And she asked him, To what country wouldst thou travel?—To the city of Baghdád, he answered; for there a man gaineth double the cost-price of his merchandise. His mother then said to him, O my son, thy father hath great wealth; but if he prepare not merchandise for thee with his wealth, I will prepare for thee some with mine. And he replied, The best of favours is that which is promptly bestowed; and if there be kindness to be shewn, this is the time for it. She therefore summoned the slaves, and sent them to the persons who packed up stuffs, and, having opened a magazine, took from it some stuffs for him, and they packed up for him ten loads.

His father, in the mean time, looked around, and found not his son 'Alá-ed-Deen in the garden. So he inquired respecting him, and they told him that he had mounted his mule and gone to the house; whereupon he mounted and went after him; and when he entered his abode, seeing the loads packed up, he asked concerning them. His wife therefore informed him of the manner in which the sons of the merchants had acted towards his son 'Alá-ed-Deen. And upon this he said to him, O my son, malediction be upon foreign travel! for the Apostle of God (may God bless and save him!) hath said, It is of a man's good fortune that he be sustained in his own country;—and the ancients have said, Abstain from travel, though it be but a mile's journey.—Then he said to his son, Hast thou determined to travel, and wilt thou not relinquish thy purpose? His son answered him, I must travel to Baghdád with merchandise, or I will pull off my clothes, and put on the habit of the darweeshes, and go forth a wanderer through the countries. So his father said to him, I am not in need, nor destitute: but, on the contrary, I have great wealth. And he shewed him all the wealth and merchandise and stuffs that he possessed, and said to him, I have stuffs and other merchandise suitable for every country. And he shewed him, of such goods, forty loads packed up, upon each of which was written its price, a thousand pieces of gold. He then said to him, O my son, take the forty loads, and the ten loads which are given thee by thy mother, and journey under the protection of God, whose name be exalted! But, O my son, I fear for thee on account of a forest in thy way, called the Forest of the Lion, and a valley there called the Valley of the Dogs; for lives are sacrificed in those two places without pity.—How so, O my father? said his son. The merchant answered, By a Bedawee, an intercepter of the way, who is named 'Ejlán. But his son replied, The means of preservation are from God, and if I have any share in them left, no harm will happen to me.

Then he mounted with his father, and went to the market of the beasts of burden; and lo, an 'Akkám[28] dismounted from his mule, and, kissing the hand of the Sháh-Bandar of the merchants, said to him, By Allah, for a long time, O my master, thou hast not employed us in the transaction of mercantile business. The Sháh-Bandar replied, Every time hath its fortune and its men.[29] O Muḳaddam,[30] it is none but this my son who desireth to travel.—And the 'Akkám said, God preserve him to thee! The Sháh-Bandar then made a covenant between his son and the 'Akkám, that the former should be as a son of the latter, and gave the 'Akkám a charge respecting 'Alá-ed-Deen, and said to him, Take these hundred pieces of gold for thy young men. After which he bought sixty mules, and a covering for Seyyidee 'Abd-El-Ḳádir El-Geelánee,[31] and said to his son, O my son, while I am absent, this 'Akkám shall be thy father in my stead, and with whatever he saith to thee do thou comply. Then he returned, with the mules and the young men, and the next night they caused a recitation of the whole of the Ḳur-án to be performed, and celebrated a festival in honour of the sheykh 'Abd-El-Ḳádir El-Geelánee.[32] And when the following morning came, the Sháh-Bandar of the merchants gave to his son ten thousand pieces of gold, saying to him, When thou enterest Baghdád, if thou find the stuffs of easy sale, sell them; but if thou find them not in request, expend of these pieces of gold.

They then loaded the mules, and bade one another farewell, and the party went forth from the city. They continued their way over the deserts and wastes until they came in sight of Damascus, and from Damascus they proceeded until they entered Aleppo, and thence they continued their route until there remained between them and Baghdád one day's journey. Still they advanced till they descended into a valley, and 'Alá-ed-Deen desired that they should halt there; but the 'Akkám said, Halt ye not here: continue on your way and hasten in your pace: perhaps we may reach Baghdád before its gates be closed; for the people open them not nor close them but when the sun is up, in their fear lest the Ráfiḍees[33] should take the city and throw the books of science into the Tigris. 'Alá-ed-Deen, however, replied, O my father, I came not with this merchandise unto this town for the sake of traffic, but for the sake of amusing myself by the sight of foreign countries.—O my son, rejoined the 'Akkám, we fear for thee and for thy property on account of the Arabs. But 'Alá-ed-Deen said, O man, art thou a servant or a person served? I will not enter Baghdád but in the morning, that the sons of Baghdád may see my merchandise, and may know me.—So the 'Akkám replied, Do what thou wilt; for I have advised thee, and thou canst judge for thyself. And 'Alá-ed-Deen ordered them to take down the burdens from the backs of the mules; and they did so, and pitched the pavilion, and remained until midnight.

'Alá-ed-Deen then went forth from the pavilion, and saw something glittering in the distance. So he said to the 'Akkám, O Muḳaddam, what is this thing that is glittering? And the 'Akkám, looking attentively and with a scrutinizing eye, saw that what glittered was the points of spears and the iron of Bedawee weapons and swords. And lo, they were Arabs, whose chief was named the Sheykh of the Arabs 'Ejlán Aboo-Náïb; and when these Arabs drew near them and saw their packages, they said, one to another, O night of spoil! As soon as the travellers heard them say this, the Muḳaddam Kemál-ed-Deen, the 'Akkám, exclaimed, Avaunt, O least of Arabs! But Aboo-Náïb smote him with his spear upon his breast, and it protruded glittering from his back; whereupon he fell at the door of the tent, slain. Then the Saḳḳà[34] exclaimed, Avaunt, O basest of Arabs! And one of them struck him upon his shoulder with a sword, and it passed forth glittering from his vitals, and he, also, fell down slain.

All this took place while 'Alá-ed-Deen stood looking on. The Arabs surrounded and fiercely assaulted the caravan, and killed the attendants of 'Alá-ed-Deen, not sparing one of them; after which, they placed the loads upon the backs of the mules, and retired. 'Alá-ed-Deen then said to himself, Nothing will occasion thy slaughter but thy mule and this thy dress. So he arose, and pulled off the dress, and threw it upon the back of his mule, remaining in the shirt and drawers alone; and, looking before him, towards the door of the tent, he found a pool of blood, flowing from the slain; and he rolled himself in it with the shirt and the drawers, so that he appeared like one slain, drowned in his blood.

Meanwhile, the Sheykh of the Arabs, 'Ejlán, said to his troops, O Arabs, was this caravan entering from Egypt, or going forth from Baghdád? They answered him, Coming from Egypt into Baghdád. And he said to them, Return to the slain; for I imagine that the proprietor of this caravan hath not died. So the Arabs returned to the slain, and proceeded to pierce and strike them again until they came to 'Alá-ed-Deen. He had thrown himself among the slain;

and when they came to him they said, Thou hast feigned thyself to be dead; so we will complete thy slaughter. And a Bedawee took his spear, and was about to thrust it into the breast of 'Alá-ed-Deen; whereupon 'Alá-ed-Deen said, O thy blessing,[35] O my lord 'Abd-El-Ḳádir, O Geelánee! And he saw a hand turn away the spear from his breast to the breast of the Muḳaddam Kemál-ed-Deen, the 'Akkám; so that the Bedawee pierced the latter with it, and left 'Alá-ed-Deen; after which, the Arabs replaced the burdens on the backs of the mules, and departed with them.

'Alá-ed-Deen then looked, and, seeing that the birds had flown with their spoils, rose and ran away. But, lo, the Bedawee Aboo-Náïb said to his companions, I saw a faint appearance of an object in the distance, O Arabs. One of them, therefore, came forth, and beheld 'Alá-ed-Deen running; upon which he said to him, Flight will not profit thee while we are behind thee. And he struck his mare with his fist, and she hastened after him. Now 'Alá-ed-Deen had seen before him a tank containing water, and by the side of it was a cistern: so he ascended to a window of the cistern, and there stretching himself along, feigned himself asleep, and said, O kind Protector, cover me with the veil of thy protection that cannot be removed![36] And behold, the Bedawee stopped beneath the cistern, and stretched forth his hand to seize 'Alá-ed-Deen; whereupon the latter said, O thy blessing, O my lady Nefeeseh! This is thy time![37]—And lo, a scorpion stung the Bedawee in the palm of his hand; and he cried out and said, O Arabs, come to me, for I am stung! And he alighted from the back of his mare, and his companions, coming to him, mounted him again, and said to him, What hath befallen thee? He answered them, A scorpion hath stung me. And they then took the property of the caravan, and departed.

'Alá-ed-Deen remained a while sleeping in the window of the cistern. Then arising, he proceeded, and entered Baghdád. The dogs barked behind him as he passed through the streets, and in the evening, while he was walking on in the dark, he saw the door of a mosque, and entering its vestibule, he concealed himself in it. And lo, a light approached him, and as he looked attentively at it, he perceived two lanterns in the hands of two black slaves, who were walking before two merchants. One of these was an old man of comely countenance, and the other was a young man; and he heard the latter say to the former, By Allah, O my uncle, I conjure thee to restore to me my cousin, thy daughter. To which the old man replied, Did I

not forbid thee many times, when thou wast making divorce thy muṣ-ḥaf?[38] Then the old man looked to the right, and saw 'Alá-ed-Deen, appearing like a piece of the moon; and he said to him, Peace be on thee! 'Alá-ed-Deen, therefore, returned his salutation, and the old man said to him, O youth, who art thou? He answered him, I am 'Alá-ed-Deen, the son of Shems-ed-Deen the Sháh-Bandar of the merchants in Cairo. I requested my father to give me merchandise, and he prepared for me fifty loads of goods, and gave me ten thousand pieces of gold; and I journeyed until I arrived at the Forest of the Lion, when the Arabs came upon me and took my wealth and my packages; and I entered this city, not knowing where to pass the night: so, seeing this place, I concealed myself in it.—The old man then said to him, O my son, what sayest thou of my giving thee a thousand pieces of gold, and a suit of clothing of the price of a thousand pieces of gold?—For what purpose, said 'Alá-ed-Deen, wilt thou give me these things, O my uncle? He answered him, This young man who is with me is the son of my brother, and his father hath no son but him; and I have a daughter, and have none but her, who is named Zubeydeh El-'Oodeeyeh.[39] She is endowed with beauty and loveliness, and I married her to him, and he loveth her; but she hateth him; and he swore an oath of triple divorcement, and scarcely had his wife heard it when she separated herself from him. And he employed all the people of his acquaintance to intercede with me, that I should restore her to him: so I said to him, This will not be right unless by means of a mustaḥall:[40]—and I agreed with him that we should employ some foreigner as a mustaḥall, in order that no one might reproach him on account of this affair. Since, then, thou art a foreigner, come with us, that we may write thy contract of marriage to her, and to-morrow thou shalt divorce her, and we will give thee what I have mentioned.—So 'Alá-ed-Deen said within himself, To do what he proposeth will be better than passing the nights in the by-streets and vestibules.

Accordingly he went with the two men to the Ḳáḍee. And when the Ḳáḍee saw him, his heart was moved with affection for him, and he said to the father of the damsel, What is your desire? The old man answered, It is our desire to employ this person as a mustaḥall for our daughter; but we will write a bond against him, stating that the portion of the dowry to be paid in advance is ten thousand pieces of gold; and if he divorce her to-morrow-morning, we will give him a dress of the price of a thousand pieces of gold, and a mule of the same price, and a thousand pieces of gold besides; but if he divorce her not, he will pay ten thousand pieces of gold.[41] So they settled the contract on this condition, and the father of the damsel received a bond to this effect. He then took 'Alá-ed-Deen with him, clad him with the suit, and proceeded with him until they came to the house of his daughter, when he stationed him at the door of the house, and, going in to his daughter, said to her, Receive the bond of thy dowry; for I have written thy contract of marriage to a comely young man, named 'Alá-ed-Deen Abu-sh-Shámát: so consider thyself under a most strict charge respecting him. And he gave her the bond, and repaired to his house.

Now the damsel's cousin (her former husband) had a ḳahramáneh who frequently visited Zubeydeh El-'Oodeeyeh, and he used to treat her with beneficence; and he said to her, O my mother, if Zubeydeh, the daughter of my uncle, see this comely young man, she will not accept me after; so I desire of thee that thou contrive a stratagem to restrain the damsel from him.—By thy youth, she replied, I will not suffer him to go near her. She then went to 'Alá-ed-Deen, and said to him, O my son, I give thee good advice for the sake of God (whose name be exalted!); therefore do thou accept my advice, and approach not that damsel, but let her remain alone, and neither touch her nor draw near to her.—Wherefore? said he. And she answered him, Verily her whole skin is affected with elephantiasis, and I fear for thee lest she communicate the disease to thy comely, youthful person.[42] So he replied, I have no need of her. Then she went to the damsel, and said to her as she had said to 'Alá-ed-Deen; and the damsel replied, I have no need of him: on the contrary, I will leave him to remain alone, and in the morning he shall go his way. And she called a slave-girl, and said to her, Take the table with the food, and give it to him that he may sup. The slave-girl, therefore, carried to him the table with the food, and placed it before him, and he ate until he was satisfied, and then sat reciting the chapter of Yá-Seen,[43] with a charming voice; and the damsel, listening to him, found that his voice was like the sounds of the Psalms sung by the family of Dáood.[44] So she said within herself, Allah send trouble upon this old woman who told me that he was afflicted with elephantiasis! for he who is in such a state hath not a voice of this kind. Surely this assertion is a lie against him.—Then taking in her hands a lute of Indian manufacture, she tuned its chords, and sang to it, with a voice that would stay the birds in the midst of the sky, these two verses:—

I am enamoured of a fawn with languishing black eyes: the willow-branches envy him when he walketh.
He rejecteth *me*, and another enjoyeth his society, which is a boon that God will grant to whom He pleaseth.

And when he heard her words, after he had finished his recitation of the Chapter he sang this verse in reply:—

My salutation to the form concealed within the garments, and to the roses in the gardens of the cheeks.

And upon this, the damsel's love for him increased, and she lifted up the curtain; and when 'Alá-ed-Deen beheld her, he recited these two verses:—

She appeared as a moon, and inclined as a willow-branch; diffused an odour like ambergris, and looked with eyes like a gazelle's.
It seemed as though grief were enamoured of my heart, and when she should depart, would obtain possession of it.

She then advanced with a graceful gait; but as she approached him he said to her, Retire from me, lest thou communicate thy disease to me. So she uncovered her wrist, which was bipartite,[45] and its whiteness was like that of silver; after which she said to him, Retire from me; for thou art afflicted with elephantiasis, and perhaps thou wilt communicate the disease to me. He therefore asked her, Who informed thee that I was afflicted with elephantiasis? She answered him, The old woman acquainted me with it. And he replied, The old woman also informed me that thou wast afflicted with leprosy. Then he uncovered to her his arms, and she found that his skin was like pure silver. So she accepted him as her husband.

And on the following morning he said to her, Alas for joy that is not complete! The raven hath taken it and flown away![46]—She therefore said, What is the meaning of these words? And he answered her, O my mistress, I have only this hour to remain with thee.—Who saith so? she asked.—Thy father, he answered her, wrote a bond against me, obliging me to pay ten thousand pieces of gold towards thy dowry; and if I produce it not this day, they imprison me for it in the house of the Ḳáḍee; and now my hand is unable to advance a single half-dirhem[47] of the sum of ten thousand pieces of gold. But she said to him, O my master, is the matrimonial tie in thy hand, or in their hands? He answered her, The tie is in my hand; but I have nothing in my possession.—The affair, she rejoined, is easy; and fear nothing; but take these hundred pieces of gold. Had I more, I would give thee what thou desirest. This, however, I cannot do; for my father, from the affection that he beareth for the son of his brother, hath transferred all his property from my hands to his house: even all my ornaments he took. But when they send to thee a sergeant from the court of justice, this morning, and the Ḳáḍee and my father say to thee, Divorce,—do thou say to them, By what code is it ordained as proper that I should marry at nightfall and divorce in the morning? Then thou shalt kiss the hand of the Ḳáḍee, and give him a present; and in like manner thou shalt kiss the hand of each Sháhid,[48] and give him ten pieces of gold. And all of them will speak with thee: and if they say to thee, Wherefore wilt thou not divorce, and receive a thousand pieces of gold, and the mule and the dress, according to the condition which we imposed upon thee?—do thou answer them, Every hair of her head is in my estimation worth a thousand pieces of gold, and I will never divorce her, nor will I receive a dress or anything else. If the Ḳáḍee then say to thee, Pay the dowry,—reply, I am at present unable to pay. And thereupon the Ḳáḍee and the Sháhids will treat thee with benevolence, and will grant thee a delay.

Now while they were thus conversing, the sergeant of the Ḳáḍee knocked at the door. So he went forth to him, and the sergeant said to him, Answer the summons of the Efendee;[49] for thy father-in-law citeth thee. And 'Alá-ed-Deen gave to him five pieces of gold, saying, O sergeant, by what code am I required to marry at nightfall and to divorce in the morning? He answered him, To do so is not held proper by us in any case; and if thou be ignorant of the law, I will act as thy deputy. And they proceeded to the court of justice, and the Ḳáḍee said to 'Alá-ed-Deen, Wherefore dost thou not divorce the woman, and receive what the contract hath prescribed for thee? And upon this he advanced to the Ḳáḍee, and, kissing his hand, put into it fifty pieces of gold, and said to him, O our lord the Ḳáḍee, by what code is it allowable that I should marry at nightfall and divorce in the morning by compulsion? The Ḳáḍee therefore answered, Divorce by compulsion is not allowable by any of the codes of the Muslims. Then the father of the damsel said, If thou divorce not, pay me the dowry, ten thousand pieces of gold. 'Alá-ed-Deen replied, Give me three days' delay. But the Ḳáḍee said, Three days will not be a sufficient period of delay: he shall grant thee ten days. And to this they agreed, binding him, after the ten days, either to pay the dowry or to divorce.

On this condition, therefore, he went forth from them, and, having procured the meat and rice and clarified butter and other eatables that the case required, returned to the house and went in to the damsel and related to her all that had happened to him. She replied, Between night and day, wonders take place; and divinely gifted was he who said,—

Be mild when thou art troubled by rage, and be patient when calamity befalleth thee;
For the nights are pregnant with events, and give birth to every kind of wonder.

She then arose, prepared the food, and brought the table, and they ate and drank, and enjoyed themselves, and were moved with merriment; and he requested her to perform a piece of music. So she took the lute, and performed a piece in such a manner that a rock would have danced at it as if with joy, the sounds of the chords vying with the voice of Dáood;[50] and she began the more rapid part of the performance.[51]

But while they were full of delight and jesting, and mirth and gladness, the door was knocked. She therefore said to him, Arise, and see who is at the door. Accordingly, he went down, and, opening the door, found four darweeshes standing there, and he said to them, What do ye desire?—O my master, answered one of them, we are foreign darweeshes: the food of our souls consisteth in music and in the delicacies of poetry, and we desire to recreate ourselves with thee this night, until the morning, when we will go our way; and thou wilt receive thy recompense from God (whose name be exalted!); for we are passionately fond of music, and there is not one among us who doth not retain in his memory odes and other pieces of poetry and lyric songs.[52] 'Alá-ed-Deen replied, I must consult. And he went up, and informed the damsel; and she said to him, Open the door to them. So he opened to them the door, and, having conducted them up, seated them and welcomed them, and brought them food. But they declined eating, and one of them said to him, O my master, verily our victuals are the commemoration of God with our hearts, and the hearing of songs with our ears; and divinely was he gifted who said,—

> Our desire is for nought but the enjoyment of society; and eating is nought but a characteristic of the brutes.

We just now heard some pleasant music in thine abode; but when we came up, it ceased; and we would that we knew whether she who was performing is a white or a black slave-girl, or a lady.—'Alá-ed-Deen replied, She is my wife. And he related to them all that had happened to him, and said to them, My father-in-law hath bound me to pay ten thousand pieces of gold as her dowry, and they have given me ten days' delay. Upon this, one of the darweeshes said to him, Grieve not, nor anticipate anything but good fortune; for I am the Sheykh of the Convent, having under me forty darweeshes over whom I exercise authority, and I will collect for thee the ten thousand pieces of gold from them, and thou shalt discharge the dowry that thou owest to thy father-in-law. But desire her (he added) to perform a piece of music for us, that we may be rejoiced and enlivened; for music is to some people like food; and to some, like a remedy; and to some, like a fan.—Now these four darweeshes were the Khaleefeh Hároon Er-Rasheed, and the Wezeer Jaạfar El-Barmekee, and Aboo-Nuwás El-Ḥasan the son of Hánee,[53] and Mesroor the Executioner. And the reason of their passing by this house was that the bosom of the Khaleefeh was contracted; so he said to the Wezeer, O Wezeer, it is our desire to descend and to go about through the city; for I experience a contraction of the bosom. They therefore clad themselves in the apparel of darweeshes, and went down into the city, and, passing by this house, they heard the music, and desired to ascertain the cause. They passed the night there in happiness and good order, and in relating stories one after another, until the morning came, when the Khaleefeh put a hundred pieces of gold beneath the prayer-carpet, and he and his companions took leave of 'Alá-ed-Deen, and went their way.

When the damsel, therefore, lifted up the prayer-carpet, she saw the hundred pieces of gold beneath it. And she said to her husband, Take these hundred pieces of gold that I have found under the prayer-carpet; for the darweeshes put them before they went, without our knowledge. So 'Alá-ed-Deen took them, and, repairing to the market, bought the meat and the rice and the clarified butter, and all that he required. And on the following night he lighted the candles, and said to his wife, The darweeshes have not brought the ten thousand pieces of gold which they promised me; but they are poor men. While they were talking, however, the darweeshes knocked at the door; and she said to him, Go down, and open to them. He therefore did so, and they came up, and he said to them, Have ye brought the ten thousand pieces of gold that ye promised me? They answered him, Nothing of the sum hath been provided; but fear no evil: if it be the will of God (whose name be exalted!), to-morrow we will perform an alchymical process for thee; and now do thou desire thy wife to gratify our ears by an excellent performance of music, that our

hearts may be enlivened by it; for we love music. So she performed a piece for them upon the lute, such as would make a rock to dance. And they passed the night in enjoyment and happiness, and conversation and cheerfulness, until the morning came and diffused its light; whereupon the Khaleefeh again put a hundred pieces of gold beneath the prayer-carpet, and he and his companions took leave of 'Alá-ed-Deen, and departed from him and went their way.

Thus they continued to do for a period of nine nights; the Khaleefeh every night putting beneath the prayer-carpet a hundred pieces of gold, until the tenth night, when they came not; and the cause of their ceasing their visits was this. The Khaleefeh sent to a great merchant, saying to him, Make ready for me fifty loads of stuffs, such as come from Cairo, each load of the price of a thousand pieces of gold, and write upon each the amount of its price; and provide for me a male Abyssinian slave. So the merchant made ready for him all that he ordered him to provide, after which the Khaleefeh committed to the slave a basin and ewer of gold, and another present, and the fifty loads, and wrote a letter as from Shems-ed-Deen the Sháh-Bandar of the merchants in Cairo, the father of 'Alá-ed-Deen, and said to the slave, Take these loads and the things that are with them, and repair with them to such a quarter, in which is the house of the Sháh-Bandar of the merchants, and say, Where is my master 'Alá-ed-Deen Abu-sh-Shámát? Then the people will direct thee to the quarter and to the house.—The slave therefore took the loads and what was with them, and went as the Khaleefeh commanded him.

In the mean time, the damsel's cousin repaired to her father, and said to him, Come, let us go to 'Alá-ed-Deen, that we may effect the divorce of my cousin. So the father descended and went with him to 'Alá-ed-Deen; but when they arrived at the house, they found fifty mules, upon which were fifty loads of stuffs, attended by a black slave upon a mule; and they said to him, To whom belong these loads? He answered, To my master 'Alá-ed-Deen Abu-sh-Shámát; for his father prepared for him merchandise, and despatched him on a journey to the city of Baghdád, and the Arabs came upon him, and took his wealth and his loads; and the news reached his father; wherefore he sent me to him with loads in their stead. He sent with me also a mule laden with fifty thousand pieces of gold, and a wrapper of clothes worth a large sum of money, and a furred robe of sable, and a basin and ewer of gold.—Upon this, the father of the damsel said, This person is my son-in-law, and I will shew thee the way to the house.

And while 'Alá-ed-Deen was sitting in the house in a state of violent grief, the door was knocked; and he said, O Zubeydeh, God is all-knowing; but it seemeth that thy father hath sent to me a sergeant from the Ḳáḍee or from the Wálee. She replied, Go down and see what is the case. So he went down and opened the door, and beheld his father-in-law, who was the Sháh-Bandar of the merchants, the father of Zubeydeh; and he found there an Abyssinian slave of dark complexion and of pleasant countenance, mounted upon a mule. And the slave, having descended from the mule, kissed his hands; and he said to him, What dost thou desire? He answered, I am the slave of my master 'Alá-ed-Deen Abu-sh-Shámát, the son of Shems-ed-Deen the Sháh-Bandar of the merchants in the land of Egypt; and his father hath sent me to him with this deposite. He then gave him the letter; and 'Alá-ed-Deen took it and opened it and read it, and found written in it these words:—

After perfect salutations, and compliments and respectful greetings, from Shems-ed-Deen to his son 'Alá-ed-Deen Abu-sh-Shámát.—Know, O my son, that the news of the slaughter of thy men, and of the plunder of thy wealth and thy loads, hath reached me; and I have therefore sent to thee, in their stead, these fifty loads of Egyptian stuffs, and the suit of dress, and the furred robe of sable, and the basin and ewer of gold. And fear no evil; for the wealth is thy ransom, O my son; and may grief never affect thee. Thy mother and the people of the house are well, in prosperity and health; and they greet thee with abundant salutations. Moreover, O my son, news hath reached me that they have employed thee as a mustaḥall for the damsel Zubeydeh El-'Oodeeyeh, and have imposed upon thee the payment of ten thousand[54] pieces of gold as her dowry. Therefore fifty thousand pieces of gold will be brought to thee with the loads, attended by thy slave Seleem.[55]

As soon as 'Alá-ed-Deen had finished reading the letter, he took possession of the loads, and, looking towards his father-in-law, said to him, O my father-in-law, receive the ten thousand pieces of gold, the amount of the dowry of thy daughter Zubeydeh: receive also the loads, and dispose of them, and the profit shall be thine; only do thou restore to me the cost-price. But he replied, Nay, by Allah, I will take nothing; and as to the dowry of thy wife, do thou make an agreement with her respecting it. So 'Alá-ed-Deen arose, together with his father-in-law, and they went into the house, after the loads had been brought in. And Zubeydeh said to her father, O my father, to whom belong these loads? He answered her, These loads belong to 'Alá-ed-Deen, thy husband. His father hath sent them to him in the place of those which the Arabs took from him; and he hath sent to him fifty thousand pieces of gold, and a wrapper of clothes, and a furred robe of sable, and a mule, and a basin and ewer of gold: and as to thy dowry, it is for thee to decide respecting it. Then 'Alá-ed-Deen arose, and, having opened the chest, gave her her dowry. The damsel's cousin said, O my uncle, let 'Alá-ed-Deen divorce my wife for me. But the father of the damsel replied, This is a thing that now can by no means be, as the matrimonial tie is in his hand. And upon this the young man went away, grieved and afflicted, and laid himself down sick in his house, and there he died.

As to 'Alá-ed-Deen, he went forth to the market, after he had received the loads, and, having procured what he desired of food and drink and clarified butter, made the same regular preparations as on each preceding night, and said to Zubeydeh, See, these lying darweeshes gave us a promise and broke it. She replied, Thou art the son of a Sháh-Bandar of the merchants, and yet thy hand was unable to produce a half-dirhem. What then is the case of the poor darweeshes?—God (whose name be exalted!), he rejoined, hath rendered us independent of them, and I will not again open the door to them if they come to us. But she said to him, Wherefore, seeing that good fortune happened not unto us but in consequence of their coming; for every night they put for us beneath the prayer-carpet a hundred pieces of gold? It is absolutely necessary, then, that thou open the door to them if they come.—And when the day departed with its brightness, and the night came, they lighted the candles, and 'Alá-ed-Deen said to his wife, O Zubeydeh, arise, and perform a piece of music for us. And immediately the door was knocked: so she said to him, Arise, and see who is there. He descended, therefore, and opened the door, and seeing the darweeshes, he said, Oh! Welcome to the liars! Come up.—Accordingly they went up with him, and he seated them, and brought the table of food to them; and they ate and drank, and enjoyed themselves and were merry. They then said to him, O our master, verily our hearts have been troubled respecting thee. What hath happened to thee with thy father-in-law?—God, he answered them, hath granted us a recompense above our desires. And they said to him, By Allah, we were in fear for thee, and nothing prevented our coming to thee again but the inadequacy of our means to procure the money. He replied,

Speedy relief hath come to me from my Lord, and my father hath sent to me fifty thousand pieces of gold, and fifty loads of stuffs, each load of the price of a thousand pieces of gold, and a suit of dress, and a furred robe of sable, and a mule and a slave, and a basin and ewer of gold: a reconciliation hath taken place between me and my father-in-law, and my wife hath become lawful to me;[56] and praise be to God for this!

The Khaleefeh then arose and withdrew; and the Wezeer Jaạfar, inclining towards 'Alá-ed-Deen, said to him, Impose upon thyself the obligation of good manners; for thou art in the company of the Prince of the Faithful.—What have I done, asked 'Alá-ed-Deen, inconsistently with good manners in the company of the Prince of the Faithful, and which of you is the Prince of the Faithful? The Wezeer answered him, He who was speaking to you, and who hath just now retired, is the Prince of the Faithful, Hároon Er-Rasheed, and I am the Wezeer Jaạfar, and this is Mesroor, the Khaleefeh's executioner, and this is Aboo-Nuwás El-Ḥásan the son of Hánee. Reflect then with thy reason, O 'Alá-ed-Deen, and consider how many days are required for the journey from Cairo to Baghdád.—He replied, Five and forty days. Then said Jaạfar, Thy loads were carried off only ten days ago; and how could the news reach thy father, and how could he pack up the other loads for thee, and these loads traverse a space of five and forty days' journey in ten days?—O my master, said 'Alá-ed-Deen, and whence came they unto me? The Wezeer answered him, From the Khaleefeh, the Prince of the Faithful, on account of his excessive affection for thee.—And while they were thus conversing, lo, the Khaleefeh approached. So 'Alá-ed-Deen arose, and kissed the ground before him, and said to him, God preserve thee, O Prince of the Faithful, and prolong thy life, and may mankind never be deprived of thy bounty and beneficence! And the Khaleefeh said, O 'Alá-ed-Deen, let Zubeydeh perform for us a piece of music, as a gratuity for thy safety.[57] She therefore performed a piece on the lute, of the most admirable kind, such as would make a rock to shake as with joy, and the sounds of the lute vied with the voice of Dáood.[58] They passed the night in the happiest manner until the morning, when the Khaleefeh said to 'Alá-ed-Deen, To-morrow come up to the court. And 'Alá-ed-Deen replied, I hear and obey, O Prince of the Faithful, if it be the will of God (whose name be exalted!), and mayest thou continue in prosperity.

Then 'Alá-ed-Deen took ten trays, and put on them a costly present; and on the following day he went up with them to the court. And while the Khaleefeh was sitting upon the throne in the council-chamber, lo, 'Alá-ed-Deen advanced from the door, reciting these two verses:—

May prosperity and glory attend thee each morning, and the nose of thine envier be rubbed in the dust;
And may the days never cease to be white unto thee, and the days of him who is thine enemy be black!

The Khaleefeh replied, Welcome, O 'Alá-ed-Deen. And 'Alá-ed-Deen said, O Prince of the Faithful, verily the Prophet (God bless and save him!) accepted a present; and these ten trays with what is upon them are a present from me unto thee. And the Prince of the Faithful accepted them from him. He gave orders also to invest him with a robe of honour, appointed him Sháh-Bandar of the merchants, and seated him in the council-chamber. And while 'Alá-ed-Deen was sitting there, lo, his father-in-law, the father of Zubeydeh, approached, and, finding him sitting in his place, and wearing the robe of honour, said to the Prince of the Faithful, O King of the age, wherefore is this person sitting in my place, and wearing this robe of honour? The Khaleefeh answered him, I have appointed him Sháh-Bandar of the merchants; and offices are conferred by investiture, not granted for perpetuity; and thou art displaced. And he replied, He is of our family and our connexions, and excellent is that which thou hast done, O Prince of the Faithful. May God always make the best of us to preside over our affairs! And how many a small person hath become great!—The Khaleefeh then wrote a diploma for 'Alá-ed-Deen, and gave it to the Wálee, and the Wálee gave it to the executioner, and he proclaimed in the court, None is Sháh-Bandar of the merchants but 'Alá-ed-Deen Abu-sh-Shámát; and his word is to be heard, and respect is to be paid to him: he is entitled to honour and reverence and exaltation!—And when the court was dissolved, the Wálee descended with the crier before 'Alá-ed-Deen, and the crier proclaimed, None is Sháh-Bandar of the merchants but my master 'Alá-ed-Deen Abu-sh-Shámát! And they went about with him through the great thoroughfare-streets of Baghdád, the crier repeating the same proclamation.

On the following morning, therefore, 'Alá-ed-Deen opened a shop for the slave, and seated him in it to sell and buy, while he rode, and took his place in the court of the Khaleefeh. And it happened that he was sitting in his place one day according to his custom, and as he sat, lo, a person said to the Khaleefeh, O Prince of the Faithful, may thy head long survive such-a-one, the boon-companion;[59] for he hath been admitted to the mercy of God (whose name be exalted!), and may thy life be prolonged! And the Khaleefeh said, Where is 'Alá-ed-Deen Abu-sh-Shámát? So he presented himself before the Khaleefeh, who, when he saw him, bestowed upon him a magnificent robe of honour, appointed him his boon-companion, and assigned him a monthly salary of a thousand pieces of gold; and 'Alá-ed-Deen continued with him as his boon-companion. And it happened again that he was sitting one day in his place according to his custom, in the service of the Khaleefeh, when an Emeer came up into the court with a sword and shield, and said, O Prince of the Faithful, may thy head long survive the Raees es-Sitteen;[60] for he hath died this day. And the Khaleefeh gave orders to bring a robe of honour for 'Alá-ed-Deen Abu-sh-Shámát, and appointed him Raees es-Sitteen in the place of the deceased. The latter had no son nor daughter nor wife: so 'Alá-ed-Deen went down and put his hand upon his wealth; and the Khaleefeh said to him, Inter him, and take all that he hath left of wealth and male slaves and female slaves and eunuchs. Then the Khaleefeh shook the handkerchief,[61] and the court dispersed; and 'Alá-ed-Deen departed, with the Muḳaddam Aḥmad Ed-Denef, the Muḳaddam of the right division of the Khaleefeh's guard, attended by his forty followers, by his stirrup, on the right; and on his left, the Muḳaddam Ḥasan Shoomán, the Muḳaddam of the left division of the Khaleefeh's guard, together with his forty followers. And 'Alá-ed-Deen looked towards the Muḳaddam Ḥasan Shoomán and his followers, and said to them, Be ye intercessors with the Muḳaddam Aḥmad Ed-Denef, that he may accept me as his son by a covenant before God. And he accepted him, and said to him, I and my forty followers will walk before thee to the court every day.

After this, 'Alá-ed-Deen continued in the service of the Khaleefeh for many days. And it happened that he descended from the court one day, and went to his house, and, having dismissed Aḥmad Ed-Denef and his attendants, seated himself with his wife Zubeydeh El-'Oodeeyeh, who, after she had lighted the candles, went into an adjoining chamber; and while he was sitting in his place, he heard a great cry. He therefore arose quickly to see who it was that cried, and beheld, in the person from whom the sound proceeded, the form of his wife Zubeydeh El-'Oodeeyeh, lying extended upon the floor; and he put his hand upon the bosom of the prostrate damsel, and found her dead. Her father's house was opposite to that of 'Alá-ed-Deen, and he (the father) also heard her cry: so he came, and said to her husband, What is the matter, O my master 'Alá-ed-Deen? The latter replied, May thy head, O my father, long survive thy daughter Zubeydeh El-'Oodeeyeh: but now, O my father, we must pay respect to the dead by its burial. And when the following morning came, they interred the damsel's body; and 'Alá-ed-Deen and the father of Zubeydeh consoled each other. 'Alá-ed-Deen put on the apparel of mourning, separated himself from the court, and continued with weeping eye and mourning heart.

So the Khaleefeh said to Jaạfar, O Wezeer, what is the reason of 'Alá-ed-Deen's absenting himself from the court? The Wezeer answered him, O Prince of the Faithful, he is mourning for his wife Zubeydeh, and engaged in receiving the visits of consolation for her loss. Upon this the Khaleefeh said, It is incumbent on us to console him. And the Wezeer replied, I hear and obey. The Khaleefeh therefore descended with Jaạfar and some of the household attendants, and they mounted, and repaired to the house of 'Alá-ed-Deen. And as he was sitting, lo, the Khaleefeh and the Wezeer and their attendants approached him; whereupon he rose to meet them, and kissed the ground before the Khaleefeh, who said to him, May God compensate thee happily! 'Alá-ed-Deen replied, May God prolong thy life to us, O Prince of the Faithful! And the Khaleefeh said, O 'Alá-ed-Deen, what is the reason of thy separating thyself from the court? He answered, My mourning for my wife Zubeydeh, O Prince of the Faithful. The Khaleefeh replied, Dispel anxiety from thy mind; for she hath departed to receive the mercy of God (whose name be exalted!), and mourning will never avail thee aught. But 'Alá-ed-Deen said, I will not cease to mourn for her until I die and they bury me by her. The Khaleefeh rejoined, Verily with God is a compensation for every loss, and neither stratagem nor wealth will save one from death. Divinely gifted was he who said,—

Every son of woman, though he be long preserved, must one day be carried upon the curving bier.[62]
How then shall he on whose cheeks the dust is to be placed find diversion or delight in life?

—And when he had made an end of consoling him, he charged him that he should not separate himself from the court, and returned.

'Alá-ed-Deen then passed the night, and when the morning came, he mounted, and repaired to the court, and, going in to the Khaleefeh, kissed the ground before him. And the Khaleefeh raised himself to him slightly from the throne,[63] welcoming him and saluting him; and after he had desired him to take the place belonging to him, he said to him, O 'Alá-ed-Deen, thou art my guest this night. Then the Khaleefeh took him into his palace, and called a slave-girl named Ḳoot-el-Ḳuloob,[64] and said to her, 'Alá-ed-Deen had a wife whose name was Zubeydeh El-'Oodeeyeh, and she used to divert him from anxiety and grief; but she hath departed to receive the mercy of God (whose name be exalted!), and I desire that thou gratify his ears by a performance on the lute, of the most admirable kind, in order that he may be diverted from anxiety and sorrows. So the damsel performed an admirable piece of music; and the Khaleefeh said, What sayest thou, O 'Alá-ed-Deen, of the voice of this slave-girl?—Verily, he answered, Zubeydeh had a better voice than hers; but she is eminently skilled in playing on the lute; for she would make a rock to dance. And the Khaleefeh said to him, Hath she pleased thee? He answered him, She hath pleased me, O Prince of the Faithful. Then said the Khaleefeh, By my head, and by the tombs of my ancestors, verily she is a present from me unto thee, with her female slaves also. And 'Alá-ed-Deen imagined that the Khaleefeh was jesting with him. But when the Khaleefeh arose in the morning, he went to his slave-girl Ḳoot-el-Ḳuloob, and said to her, I have made thee a present to 'Alá-ed-Deen. And she rejoiced at this; for she had seen him and loved him. He then went from the pavilion of the palace to the council-chamber, and, having summoned the porters, said to them, Remove the goods of Ḳoot-el-Ḳuloob, and put her in the litter,[65] and convey her together with her female slaves to the house of 'Alá-ed-Deen. So they conveyed her with her female slaves and her goods to the house, and conducted her into the pavilion. And the Khaleefeh remained sitting in the hall of judgment until the close of the day, when the court broke up, and he retired to his pavilion.

Now as to Ḳoot-el-Ḳuloob, when she had entered the pavilion of 'Alá-ed-Deen, with her female slaves, who were forty in number, and the eunuchs also, she said to two of the eunuchs, One of you two shall sit on a chair on the right of the door, and the other shall sit on a chair on the left of it; and when 'Alá-ed-Deen cometh, kiss his hands, and say to him, Our mistress Ḳoot-el-Ḳuloob requesteth thy presence in the pavilion; for the Khaleefeh hath given her to thee, together with her female slaves. And they replied, We hear and obey. They then did as she commanded them. So when 'Alá-ed-Deen arrived, he found the two eunuchs of the Khaleefeh sitting at the door, and he wondered at the event, saying within himself, Perhaps this is not my house; or if it be, what hath occurred? And when the eunuchs saw him, they rose to him, and kissed his hands, and said, We are of the dependants of the Khaleefeh, and the slaves of Ḳoot-el-Ḳuloob, and she saluteth thee, and saith to thee, that the Khaleefeh hath given her to thee, together with her female slaves, and she requesteth thy company. 'Alá-ed-Deen, however, replied, Say to her, Thou art welcome; but as long as thou art in his abode, he will not enter the pavilion in which thou residest; for it is not fit that what hath belonged to the master should become the property of the servant:—and say to her, What was the amount of thy daily expenditure with the Khaleefeh? They therefore went up to her, and said to her as he desired them; and she replied, A hundred pieces of gold each day. So he said to himself, I have no need of the Khaleefeh's giving to me Ḳoot-el-Ḳuloob, that I should expend in this manner upon her; but I have no means of avoiding this.

She then remained in his abode many days, he assigning to her daily a hundred pieces of gold, until he absented himself one day from the court; whereupon the Khaleefeh said, O Wezeer Jaạfar, I gave not Ḳoot-el-Ḳuloob to 'Alá-ed-Deen but that she might divert him from mourning for his wife; and what is the cause of his absenting himself from us? The Wezeer answered, O Prince of the Faithful, he hath spoken truth who hath said, Whoso findeth his friends, forgetteth his mere acquaintances. The Khaleefeh, however, replied, Probably nothing hath caused him to absent himself from us save some event that rendereth him excusable; but we will visit him.—Now, some days before this, 'Alá-ed-Deen had said to the Wezeer, I complained to the Khaleefeh of the grief that I suffered for the loss of my wife Zubeydeh El-'Oodeeyeh, and he gave to me Ḳoot-el-Ḳuloob. And the Wezeer said, If he did not love thee, he had not given her to thee. And hast thou visited her, O 'Alá-ed-Deen?—He answered, No, by Allah; nor do I know the difference between her height and breadth.[66]—And why so? said the Wezeer. 'Alá-ed-Deen answered, O Wezeer, what is suited to the master is not suited to the servant. —Then the Khaleefeh and Jaạfar disguised themselves, and went to visit 'Alá-ed-Deen; and they proceeded without stopping until they went in to him; whereupon he recognised them, and arose, and kissed the Khaleefeh's hands. And when the Khaleefeh saw him, he found the impress of mourning upon his countenance: so he said to him, O 'Alá-ed-Deen, what is the cause of this mourning which thou sufferest? Hast thou not visited Ḳoot-el-Ḳuloob?—O Prince of the Faithful, he answered, what is suited to the master is not suited to the servant; and verily to the present time I have not visited her, nor do I know the difference between her height and her breadth: therefore quit me of her. The Khaleefeh said, I desire an interview with her, that I may ask her respecting her state. And 'Alá-ed-Deen replied, I hear and obey, O Prince of the Faithful. The Khaleefeh therefore went in to her; and when she beheld him, she arose, and kissed the ground before him; and he said to her, Hath 'Alá-ed-Deen visited thee? She answered, No, O Prince of the Faithful: I sent to invite him; but he would not. And the Khaleefeh gave orders for her return to the palace, and said to 'Alá-ed-Deen, Absent not thyself from us. And he then went back to his palace.

So 'Alá-ed-Deen passed that night, and in the morning mounted and repaired to the court, and seated himself in the place of the Raees es-Sitteen. And the Khaleefeh ordered the Treasurer to give to the Wezeer Jaạfar ten thousand pieces of gold. He therefore gave him that sum; and the Khaleefeh said to the Wezeer, I require of thee that thou go down to the market of the female slaves, and that thou purchase a slave-girl for 'Alá-ed-Deen with the ten thousand pieces of gold. And the Wezeer obeyed the command of the Khaleefeh. He went down, taking with him 'Alá-ed-Deen, and proceeded with him to the market of the female slaves.

Now it happened this day, that the Wálee of Baghdád, who held his office by the appointment of the Khaleefeh, and whose name was the Emeer Khálid, went down to the market for the purpose of buying a slave-girl for his son; and the cause was this. He had a wife named Khátoon,[67] and he had, by her, a son of foul aspect, named Ḥabaẓlam Baẓáẓah,[68] who had attained to the age of twenty years and knew not how to ride on horseback. But his father was bold, valiant, stout in defence, one who was practised in horsemanship, and who waded through the seas of night.[69] And his mother said to his father, I desire that we marry him; for he is now of a fit age. The Emeer, however, replied, He is of foul aspect, of disgusting odour, filthy, hideous: no woman will accept him. So she said, We will buy for him a slave-girl.—And it happened, in order to the accomplishment of an event which God (whose name be exalted!) had decreed, that on the same day on which the Wezeer and 'Alá-ed-Deen went down to the market, the Emeer Khálid, the Wálee, went thither also, with his son Ḥabaẓlam Baẓáẓah. And while they were in the market, lo, there was a slave-girl endowed with beauty and loveliness, and justness of stature, in the charge of a broker; and the Wezeer said, Consult, O broker, respecting a thousand pieces of gold for her. But the broker passed with her by the Wálee, and Ḥabaẓlam Baẓáẓah beholding her, the sight drew from him a thousand sighs, and he was enamoured of her, and love of her took entire possession of him: so he said, O my father, buy for me this slave-girl. The Wálee therefore called the broker, and asked the slave-girl her name. She answered him, My name is Yásemeen.[70] And the Wálee said to his son, O my son, if she please thee, bid higher for her. Accordingly he said, O broker, what price hath been offered thee? The broker answered, A thousand pieces of gold. And Ḥabaẓlam Baẓáẓah said, Let her be mine for a thousand and one pieces of gold. So the broker went to 'Alá-ed-Deen, and he bid for her two thousand; and every time that the son of the Wálee bid one piece of gold more, 'Alá-ed-Deen bid a thousand. And the son of the Wálee was enraged at this, and said, O broker, who outbiddeth me in the price of the slave-girl? The broker answered him, The Wezeer Jaafar desireth to buy her for 'Alá-ed-Deen Abu-sh-Shámát. And at last 'Alá-ed-Deen bid for her ten thousand pieces of gold; whereupon her master gave him his assent, and received her price; and 'Alá-ed-Deen took her, and said to her, I emancipate thee for the sake of God, whose name be exalted! He then wrote his contract of marriage to her, and repaired with her to the house.

The broker returned with his brokerage; and the son of the Wálee called him, and said to him, Where is the slave-girl? He answered him, 'Alá-ed-Deen hath purchased her for ten thousand pieces of gold, and hath emancipated her, and written his contract of marriage to her. And upon this, the young man was incensed; his sighs were many, and he returned to the house in a state of infirmity in consequence of his love for the damsel, and threw himself upon the bed. He abstained from food, and his love and desire were excessive. So when his mother saw him in this state of debility, she said to him, Allah preserve thee, O my son! What is the cause of thine infirmity? —He answered, Buy me Yásemeen, O my mother. And his mother said, When the seller of sweet-scented flowers passeth by, I will buy for thee a pannier full of jasmine.[71] He replied, What I mean is not the jasmine that people smell; but a slave-girl whose name is Yásemeen, whom my father would not buy for me. So she said to her husband, Why didst thou not buy for him this slave-girl? He answered her, What is suited to the master is not suited to the servant; and I have no power to take her; for none purchased her but 'Alá-ed-Deen, the Raees es-Sitteen.

In consequence of this, the illness of the young man so increased that he abandoned sleep and food; and his mother bound her head with the kerchiefs of mourning. And while she was sitting in her house, mourning for her son, lo, an old woman came in to her. She was the mother of Aḥmad Ḳamáḳim the arch thief; and this arch thief used to break through a middle-wall, and to scale an upper one, and steal the koḥl from the eye.[72] He was distinguished by these abominable practices in the beginning of his career. Then they made him chief of the watch, and he stole a sum of money, and was discovered in consequence: the Wálee came upon him suddenly, and took him and led him before the Khaleefeh, who gave orders to slay him in the place of blood.[73] But he implored the protection of the Wezeer, whose intercession the Khaleefeh never rejected; and he interceded for him. The Khaleefeh said to him, How is it that thou intercedest for a viper, noxious to mankind? But he replied, O Prince of the Faithful, imprison him; for he who built the first prison was a wise man, since the prison is the sepulchre of the living, and a cause of the exultation of the enemies over those who are confined in it. And upon this the Khaleefeh gave orders to put him in chains, and engraved upon his chains, Appointed to remain until death: they shall not be loosed but on the bench of the washer of the dead. And they put him chained in the prison.

Now his mother used to frequent the house of the Emeer Khálid, the Wálee, and to go in to her son in the prison, and say to him, Did I not say to thee, Repent of unlawful deeds? And he used to reply, God decreed this to befall me: but, O my mother, when thou goest in to the wife of the Wálee, induce her to intercede for me with him.

And when the old woman went in to the Wálee's wife, and found her with her head bound with the kerchiefs of mourning, she said to her, Wherefore art thou mourning? She answered, For the loss of my son Ḥabaẓlam Baẓáẓah. And the old woman said, Allah preserve thy son! What hath befallen him?—The wife of the Wálee, therefore, related to her the story. And upon this the old woman said, What sayest thou of him who will achieve an extraordinary feat by which thy son shall be preserved?—And what wouldst thou do? said the Wálee's wife. The old woman answered, I have a son named Aḥmad Ḳamáḳim the arch thief, and he is chained in the prison, and on his chains are engraved the words, Appointed to remain until death. Do thou, therefore, attire thyself in the most magnificent apparel that thou hast, and adorn thyself in the best manner: then present thyself before thy husband with a cheerful and smiling countenance, and say to him, When a man requireth aught of his wife, he importuneth her until he obtaineth it from her; but if the wife require aught of her husband, he will not perform it for her. And he will say to thee, What is it that thou wantest? And do thou answer, When thou hast sworn, I will tell thee. But if he swear to thee by his head, or by Allah, say to him, Swear by thy divorce from me.[74] And when he hath sworn to thee by divorce, do thou say to him, Thou hast, in the prison, a Muḳaddam named Aḥmad Ḳamáḳim, and he hath a poor mother, who hath had recourse to me, and urged me to conciliate thee, saying to me, Induce him to intercede for my son with the Khaleefeh, that my son may repent, and thy husband will be recompensed.—And the Wálee's wife replied, I hear and obey.

Accordingly, when the Wálee came to his wife, she addressed him with the words which the old woman had dictated; and he swore to her by the oath of divorce. And on the following morning he performed the morning-prayers, and, going to the prison, said, O Aḥmad Ḳamáḳim, O arch thief, wilt thou repent of thy conduct? He answered, Verily I do turn unto God with repentance, and forsake my sins, and say from my heart and with my tongue, I beg forgiveness of God.—So the Wálee released him from the prison, and took him with him to the court, still in his chains. Then advancing towards the Khaleefeh, he kissed the ground before him; whereupon the Khaleefeh said to him, O Emeer Khálid, what dost thou desire? And he led forward Aḥmad Ḳamáḳim, swinging his arms in the chains as he advanced, before the Khaleefeh, who, on seeing him, said, O Ḳamáḳim, art thou still alive?—O Prince of the Faithful, he answered, verily the life of the wretch is protracted. And the Khaleefeh said, O Emeer Khálid, for what purpose hast thou brought him hither? The Wálee answered him, Verily he hath a poor, desolate mother, who hath no son but him, and she hath had recourse to thy slave, that he should intercede with thee, O Prince of the Faithful, and beg thee to release him from the chains, and he will repent of his former conduct; and do thou appoint him Muḳaddam of the watch, as he was at first. Upon this the Khaleefeh said to Aḥmad Ḳamáḳim, Dost thou repent of thy former conduct? And he answered him, I do turn unto God with repentance, O Prince of the Faithful. And the Khaleefeh gave orders to bring the blacksmith, and he unfastened his chains upon the bench of the washer of the dead.[75] The Khaleefeh then appointed him again Muḳaddam of the watch, and charged him to conduct himself well and uprightly. So he kissed the hands of the Khaleefeh, and descended with the robe of his investiture as Muḳaddam of the watch, and they proclaimed his appointment.

After this, when he had remained some time in his office, his mother went in to the wife of the Wálee, and the latter said to her, Praise be to God who hath released thy son from the prison, and that he is at present in health and safety! But now, she added, why dost thou not tell him to contrive some means of bringing the damsel Yásemeen to my son Ḥabaẓlam Baẓáẓah?—The old woman answered, I will tell him. So she departed from her, and went in to her son, whom she found intoxicated; and she said to him, O my son, no one was the cause of thy release from the prison but the wife of the Wálee, and she desireth of thee that thou contrive some means of killing 'Alá-ed-Deen Abu-sh-Shámát, and that thou bring the damsel Yásemeen to her son Ḥabaẓlam Baẓáẓah. He replied, This will be the easiest of things. I must contrive some means this night.—Now that night was the first of the new month, and it was the custom of the Prince of the Faithful to pass it with the lady Zubeydeh, for the purpose of emancipating a female slave or a memlook, or with some similar intention. And it was his habit to take off the royal apparel, and to leave the rosary and the dagger and the royal signet, putting them all upon the chair in the sitting-room. The Khaleefeh had also a lamp of gold, to which were attached three jewels disposed upon a gold wire; and that lamp was dear in his estimation. He charged the eunuchs with the care of the suit of apparel, and the lamp and the rest of the things, and entered the private apartment of the lady Zubeydeh. Then Aḥmad Ḳamáḳim waited until the night was half spent, and Canopus shone, and mankind slept, and the Creator covered them with the curtain of darkness; when he drew his sword and took it in his right hand, and took his grappling-instrument in his left, and, approaching the Khaleefeh's sitting-room, fixed his scaling-ladder. He threw his grappling-instrument upon the sitting-room, and it caught hold upon it, and he mounted the ladder, ascended to the roof, lifted up the trap-door of the saloon, and descended into it, and found the eunuchs sleeping; and he administered some benj[76] to them, took the Khaleefeh's suit of apparel, with the rosary and the dagger, and the handkerchief and the signet, and the lamp that was adorned with jewels, and descended by the same way by which he had made his ascent. He then repaired to the house of 'Alá-ed-Deen Abu-sh-Shámát, who was this night occupied with the damsel's wedding-festivities, and who had retired to her. And Aḥmad Ḳamáḳim the arch thief descended into 'Alá-ed-Deen's saloon, pulled up a slab of marble in its durḳá'ah,[77] and, having dug a hole beneath it, deposited there some of the things that he had stolen, retaining the rest in his possession. After this, he cemented the marble slab with gypsum as it was before, and de-

scended by the way he had ascended, and said within himself, I will sit and get drunk, and put the lamp before me, and drink the cup by its light. He then returned to his house.

Now when the morning came, the Khaleefeh went into the saloon (his sitting-room), and found the eunuchs stupified with benj. So he awoke them, and, putting his hand upon the chair, he found not the suit of apparel nor the signet, nor the rosary nor the dagger, nor the handkerchief nor the lamp; whereupon he was violently enraged, and put on the apparel of anger, which was a suit of red,[78] and seated himself in the council-chamber. And the Wezeer advanced, and, having kissed the ground before him, said, May God avert evil from the Prince of the Faithful!—O Wezeer, replied the Khaleefeh, the evil is enormous. And the Wezeer said to him, What hath occurred? The

Khaleefeh therefore related to him all that had happened. And lo, the Wálee came up, with Aḥmad Ḳamáḳim the arch thief by his stirrup, and found the Khaleefeh in an excessive rage. And when the Khaleefeh saw the Wálee he said to him, O Emeer Khálid, what is the state of Baghdád? He answered, Safe and secure. The Khaleefeh replied, Thou liest.—How so, O Prince of the Faithful? said the Wálee. And the Khaleefeh explained to him the affair, and said to him, I require thee to bring to me all those things. The Wálee replied, O Prince of the Faithful, the worms of the vinegar are of it and in it; and a stranger can never obtain access to this place. But the Khaleefeh said, If thou bring me not these things I will put thee to death. So the Wálee replied, Before thou slay me, slay Aḥmad Ḳamáḳim the arch thief; for none knoweth the robber and the traitor but the Muḳaddam of the watch. And upon this, Aḥmad Ḳamáḳim said to the Khaleefeh, Accept my intercession for the Wálee, and I will be responsible to thee for the thief, and I will trace him until I discover him: but give me two persons on the part of the Ḳáḍee, and two on the part of the Wálee; for he who did this deed feareth not thee, nor doth he fear the Wálee nor anyone else. And the Khaleefeh replied, Thou shalt have what thou hast desired; but the search shall be first made in my palace, and then in the palace of the Wezeer, and in that of the Raees es-Sitteen.—Thou hast spoken rightly, O Prince of the Faithful, said Aḥmad Ḳamáḳim: probably he who did this deed is one who hath been brought up in the palace of the Prince of the Faithful, or in the palace of one of his chief officers. And the Khaleefeh said, By my head, whosoever shall appear to have done this deed shall surely be slain, though he be my son!

Then Aḥmad Ḳamáḳim took what he desired, and received a written order authorizing him to force his entrance into the houses, and to search them. Accordingly he went down, having in his hand a rod, one third of which was of bronze, and one third of copper, and one third of iron;[79] and he searched the palace of the Khaleefeh, and that of the Wezeer Jaạfar, and went about to the houses of the chamberlains and lieutenants, until he passed by the house of 'Alá-ed-Deen Abu-sh-Shámát. And when 'Alá-ed-Deen heard the clamour before his house, he arose from the presence of Yásemeen his wife, and, descending, opened the door; whereupon he found the Wálee in the midst of a tumult. So he said to him, What is the matter, O Emeer Khálid? The Wálee therefore related to him the whole affair; and

'Alá-ed-Deen said, Enter my house and search it. The Wálee replied, Pardon, O my master: thou art surnamed[80] Faithful; and God forbid that the Faithful should become treacherous. But 'Alá-ed-Deen said, My house must be searched. The Wálee therefore entered, and the Ḳáḍees and the witnesses; and Aḥmad Ḳamáḳim, advancing to the durḳá'ah of the saloon, came to the slab of marble beneath which he had buried the stolen things; when he let fall the rod upon the slab with violence, and the marble broke, and lo, something shone beneath it; whereupon the Muḳaddam exclaimed, In the name of Allah! Wonderful is Allah's will![81] Through the blessing attendant upon our coming, a treasure hath opened unto us! Let me descend into this hoarding-place, and see what is in it.—And the Ḳáḍee and witnesses looked into this place, and found the stolen things. So they wrote a paper stating that they had found the things in the house of 'Alá-ed-Deen, and, after they had put their seals upon the paper, commanded to seize 'Alá-ed-Deen; and they took his turban from his head, and registered all his wealth and property.

Aḥmad Ḳamáḳim the arch thief then seized the damsel Yásemeen, and gave her to his mother, saying to her, Deliver her to Khátoon, the wife of the Wálee. The old woman therefore took Yásemeen, and went in with her to the Wálee's wife; and when Ḥabaẓlam Baẓáẓah saw her, vigour returned to him, and he arose instantly, rejoicing excessively, and approached her. But she drew a dagger from her girdle, and said to him, Retire from me, or I will kill thee and kill myself! His mother Khátoon exclaimed, O impudent wench, suffer my son to take thee as his wife!—O brutish woman, said Yásemeen, by what code is it allowed a woman to marry two husbands; and what shall admit the dogs to the abode of the lions?—So the young man's desire increased, passion and distraction enfeebled him, and he again relinquished food, and took to the pillow. The wife of the Wálee said to Yásemeen, O impudent wench, how is it that thou causeth me to sorrow for my son? Thou shalt surely be punished, and as to 'Alá-ed-Deen, he will inevitably be hanged.—But Yásemeen replied, I will die in my love for him. And upon this, the wife of the Wálee arose, and pulled off from her the ornaments and silken apparel that were upon her, and, having clad her in drawers of canvass and a shirt of hair-cloth, sent her down into the kitchen, and made her one of the menial slave-girls, and said to her, Thy recompense shall be that thou break up the wood and peel the onions and put the fire under the cooking-pots. Yásemeen replied, I will consent to every kind of torment, but I will not consent to see thy son. God, however, moved the hearts of the female slaves with sympathy for her, and they worked in her stead in the kitchen.—Such was the case of Yásemeen.

As to 'Alá-ed-Deen, they took him, together with the articles belonging to the Khaleefeh, and proceeded with him until they arrived at the council-chamber; and while the Khaleefeh was sitting upon the throne, lo, they came up with 'Alá-ed-Deen and the stolen things, and the Khaleefeh said, Where did ye find them? They answered him, In the midst of the house of 'Alá-ed-Deen Abu-sh-Shámát. And upon this the Khaleefeh was enraged, and he took the things, but found not among them the lamp: so he said, O 'Alá-ed-Deen, where is the lamp? He answered, I have not stolen nor known nor seen, nor have I any information. But the Khaleefeh said to him, O traitor, how is it that I draw thee near unto me and thou rejectest me, and that I confide in thee and thou actest towards me with treachery? And he gave orders to hang him. The Wálee therefore descended with him, and the crier proclaimed before him, This is the recompense, and the smallest recompense, of him who acteth treacherously towards the orthodox Khaleefehs! And the populace collected at the gallows.

Meanwhile, Aḥmad Ed-Denef, the chief of 'Alá-ed-Deen, was sitting with his followers in a garden. And as they were seated there in joy and happiness, lo, a water-carrier, one of those belonging to the court, came in to them, and, kissing the hand of Aḥmad Ed-Denef, said, O Muḳaddam Aḥmad, O Denef, thou art sitting in enjoyment, with the water running beneath thy feet, and hast thou no knowledge of that which hath happened? So Aḥmad Ed-Denef said to him, What is the news? The water-carrier answered, Verily thy son by a covenant before God, 'Alá-ed-Deen, they have taken down to the gallows. Upon this, Aḥmad Ed-Denef said, What stratagem hast thou to propose, O Ḥasan, O Shoomán? He answered, Verily, 'Alá-ed-Deen is innocent, and this is a plot that hath been practised against him by some enemy.—And what is thy advice? said Aḥmad Ed-Denef.—His deliverance, he answered, shall be accomplished by us, if the Lord will. Then Ḥasan Shoomán repaired to the prison, and said to the jailer, Give us some one who is deserving of being put to death. And he gave him one who was the nearest of men in resemblance to 'Alá-ed-Deen Abu-sh-Shámát. And he covered his head, and Aḥmad Ed-Denef took him, between him and 'Alee Ez-Zeebaḳ[82] of Cairo. They had then brought forward 'Alá-ed-Deen to hang him; and Aḥmad Ed-Denef advanced, and put his foot upon the foot of the executioner. The latter therefore said to him, Give me room, that I may perform my office. And Aḥmad Ed-Denef replied, O accursed, take this man, and hang him in the place of 'Alá-ed-Deen Abu-sh-Shámát; for he is unjustly accused, and we will ransom Ismá'eel with the ram.[83] So the executioner took that man, and hanged him instead of 'Alá-ed-Deen.

Then Aḥmad Ed-Denef, and 'Alee Ez-Zeebaḳ of Cairo, took 'Alá-ed-Deen and repaired with him to the saloon of Aḥmad Ed-Denef, and 'Alá-ed-Deen said to Aḥmad, May God recompense thee well, O my chief. But Aḥmad Ed-Denef said, O 'Alá-ed-Deen, what is this deed that thou hast committed? God have mercy upon him who hath said, Whoso confideth in thee, act not treacherously towards him, though thou be a traitor. The Khaleefeh established thee in his court, and surnamed thee the Trusty and the Faithful. How then couldst thou act towards him in this manner, and take his goods?—'Alá-ed-Deen replied, By the Most Great Name, O my chief, it was not my deed: I am not guilty of it; nor do I know who did it. So Aḥmad Ed-Denef said, Verily none committed this deed except a manifest enemy, and he who committeth a deed will be requited for it: but, O 'Alá-ed-Deen, thou canst no longer reside in Baghdád; for Kings do not relinquish one object for another, and great is the fatigue of him of whom they are in quest!—Whither shall I go, O my chief? said 'Alá-ed-Deen.—I will conduct thee, answered Aḥmad Ed-Denef, to Alexandria; for it is a blessed place, and its threshold is green,[84] and life there is agreeable. To this, 'Alá-ed-Deen replied, I hear and obey, O my chief. And Aḥmad Ed-Denef said to Ḥasan Shoomán, Be mindful, and if the Khaleefeh inquire respecting me, answer, He is gone to make a circuit through the provinces.

He then took 'Alá-ed-Deen, and went forth from Baghdád, and they proceeded without stopping until they arrived at the vineyards and gardens, where they found two Jews, of the Khaleefeh's collectors of the revenue, mounted on two mules; and Aḥmad Ed-Denef said to them, Give me the fee for watching.—On what account, said they, shall we give thee the fee for watching? He answered them, I am the watchman of this valley. And upon this, each of them gave him a hundred pieces of gold. After which, Aḥmad Ed-Denef slew them,[85] and, having taken the two mules, he mounted one of them, and 'Alá-ed-Deen mounted the other, and they proceeded to the city of Ayás.[86]

There they put the mules in a Khán, and passed the night in it; and when the morning came, 'Alá-ed-Deen sold his mule, and charged the door-keeper with the care of the mule of Aḥmad Ed-Denef. Then embarking in a ship in the harbour of Ayás, they proceeded to Alexandria. And Aḥmad Ed-Denef landed with 'Alá-ed-Deen, and they walked to the market; and lo, a broker was crying for sale a shop, within which was a suite of rooms, announcing the sum bidden to be nine hundred and fifty;[87] whereupon 'Alá-ed-Deen said, Let them be mine for a thousand. And the seller assented to his offer for the property, which belonged to the government-treasury; and 'Alá-ed-Deen received the keys, and, opening the shop and the suite of rooms, found the latter spread with carpets, &c., and furnished with cushions. He saw there also a magazine containing sails and masts and ropes and chests, and leathern bags full of beads and shells, and stirrups and battle-axes and maces and knives and scissors, and other things; for its owner was a dealer in second-hand goods.[88] So 'Alá-ed-Deen seated himself in the shop, and Aḥmad Ed-Denef said to him, O my son, the shop and the suite of rooms and what they contain have become thy property: sit therefore in the shop, and sell and buy; and be not displeased; for God (whose name be exalted!) hath blessed commerce. And he remained with him three days, and on the fourth day he took leave of him, saying to him, Continue in this place until I shall have gone and returned to thee with news of thy safety from the Khaleefeh, and seen who hath practised this plot against thee. He then set forth on his voyage, and proceeded until he arrived at Ayás, when he took the mule from the Khán, and went on to Baghdád, and, meeting with Hasan Shoomán and his followers, he said to

him, O Ḥasan, hath the Khaleefeh inquired respecting me?—No, answered Ḥasan; nor hast thou occurred to his mind.

After this, Aḥmad Ed-Denef continued in the service of the Khaleefeh, and endeavoured to learn news [respecting the case of 'Alá-ed-Deen]. And he saw the Khaleefeh look towards the Wezeer Jaạfar one day, saying to him, See, O Wezeer, how 'Alá-ed-Deen hath acted towards me. The Wezeer replied, O Prince of the Faithful, thou hast recompensed him with hanging, and hath not his recompense been accomplished upon him?—O Wezeer, rejoined the Khaleefeh, I desire to go down and see him hanging.[89] And the Wezeer said, Do as thou wilt, O Prince of the Faithful. So the Khaleefeh went down, accompanied by the Wezeer Jaạfar, and proceeded to the gallows, and, raising his eyes, he saw that the body which was hanging there was not that of 'Alá-ed-Deen, the Trusty and the Faithful. He said therefore, O Wezeer, this is not 'Alá-ed-Deen.—How knowest thou, said the Wezeer, that it is not he? The Khaleefeh answered, 'Alá-ed-Deen was short, and this is tall. The Wezeer replied, A person when hanged becomes lengthened. The Khaleefeh then said, 'Alá-ed-Deen was fair, and the face of this person is black. But the Wezeer replied, Knowest thou not, O Prince of the Faithful, that death is followed by blackness? And the Khaleefeh gave orders to take down the body from the gallows; and when they had done so, he found written upon the heels of the corpse the names of the two Sheykhs;[90] whereupon he said, O Wezeer, 'Alá-ed-Deen was a Sunnee, and this was a Ráfiḍee. So the Wezeer replied, Extolled be the perfection of God, who is omniscient with respect to the things that are hidden from the senses! We know not whether this be 'Alá-ed-Deen or some other person.—The Khaleefeh then gave orders to bury the body, and they buried it; and 'Alá-ed-Deen became utterly forgotten.

Now as to Ḥabaẓlam Baẓáẓah, the son of the Wálee, his passion and desire were protracted until he died; and they interred him. And as to the damsel Yásemeen, when she had accomplished her time of nine months after her marriage to 'Alá-ed-Deen, she gave birth to a male child, like the moon. The female slaves said to her, What wilt thou name him? And she answered, Were his father living, he had named him, but I will name him Aṣlán.[91] She nursed him two successive years, and weaned him; and he crawled and walked. And it happened that his mother was occupied with the service of the kitchen one day, and the boy walked forth, and, seeing the stairs of the maḳ'ad, he went up them. The Emeer Khálid, the Wálee, was sitting

there; and he took him and seated him in his lap, extolling the perfection of his Lord in respect of that which He had created and formed; and he looked at his face, and saw that he was the nearest of beings in resemblance to 'Alá-ed-Deen Abu-sh-Shámát. Then his mother Yásemeen searched for him, but found him not: so she went up into the maḳ'ad, and beheld the Emeer Khálid sitting, with the child playing in his lap; God having instilled an affection for the boy into the heart of the Emeer. And the child looked aside, and, seeing his mother, would have thrown himself upon her; but the Emeer Khálid held him tightly in his lap, and said to his mother, Come hither, O slave-girl. And when she had come, he said to her, Whose son is this child? She answered him, This is my son, and the darling of my heart.—And who, said he, is his father? She answered, His father was 'Alá-ed-Deen Abu-sh-Shámát; but now he hath become thy son. The Emeer replied, 'Alá-ed-Deen was a traitor. But she said, Allah preserve him from the imputation of treachery! Allah forbid it should ever be said that the Faithful was a traitor!—And he said to her, When this boy groweth up, and saith to thee, Who is my father?—do thou answer him, Thou art the son of the Emeer Khálid, the Wálee, the Chief of the Police. So she replied, I hear and obey.

—Then the Emeer Khálid circumcised the boy, and educated him carefully, and brought him a professor of religion and law, skilled in caligraphy, who taught him the arts of writing and reading; and he read the Ḳur-án the first and second times, and recited the whole of it; and as he grew up he used to say to the Emeer Khálid, O my father. The Wálee also used to exercise his followers in the horse-course, collect the horsemen, and descend and teach the youth the different modes of battle, and thrusting and striking, until he became accomplished in horsemanship, acquired courage, attained the age of fourteen years, and gained the rank of an Emeer.

After this it happened that Aṣlán met one day with Aḥmad Ḳamáḳim the arch thief, and they became companions. And Aṣlán followed him to the vintner's; and lo, Aḥmad Ḳamáḳim took forth the lamp ornamented with jewels, which he had taken from the things belonging to the Khaleefeh, and, placing it before him, drank the cup by its light, and intoxicated himself; and Aṣlán said to him, O Muḳaddam, give me this lamp. He replied, I cannot give it thee.—Why so? said Aṣlán. He answered, Because lives have been lost on account of it. Aṣlán therefore said, What life hath been lost on account of it? And Aḥmad Ḳamáḳim answered him, There was a person who came to us here and was made Raees es-Sitteen, named 'Alá-ed-Deen Abu-sh-Shámát, and he died on account of this lamp.—And what is his story? said Aṣlán, and what was the cause of his death?—Thou hadst a brother, answered Aḥmad Ḳamáḳim, named Ḥabaẓlam Baẓáẓah, and when he attained a fit age for marriage, his father desired to purchase for him a slave-girl.—Then Aḥmad Ḳamáḳim proceeded, and acquainted him with the story from beginning to end, informing him of the illness of Ḥabaẓlam Baẓáẓah, and of the unmerited fate of 'Alá-ed-Deen. So Aṣlán said within himself, Probably that damsel is Yásemeen, my mother, and none was my father but 'Alá-ed-Deen Abu-sh-Shámát. And the youth Aṣlán went forth from him sorrowful, and he met the Muḳaddam Aḥmad Ed-Denef, who, when he saw him, exclaimed, Extolled be the perfection of Him unto whom none is like! Upon this, Ḥasan Shoomán (being with him) said to him, O my chief, at what dost thou wonder? He answered, At the form of this youth Aṣlán; for he is the nearest of mankind in resemblance to 'Alá-ed-Deen Abu-sh-Shámát. And he called him, saying, O Aṣlán! And Aṣlán having answered him, he said, What is the name of thy mother? He answered, She is named the slave-girl Yásemeen. So Aḥmad Ed-Denef said to him, O Aṣlán, be of good heart and cheerful eye; for none was thy father but 'Alá-ed-Deen Abu-sh-Shámát: but, O my son, go in to thy mother and ask her respecting thy father. And he replied, I hear and obey. Accordingly he went in to his mother and asked her, and she answered him, Thy father is the Emeer Khálid. But he replied, None was my father but 'Alá-ed-Deen Abu-sh-Shámát. And his mother wept, and said to him, Who acquainted thee with this, O my son? He answered, The Mukaddam Aḥmad Ed-Denef. She therefore related to him all that had happened, and said to him, O my son, the truth hath appeared, and falsity is withdrawn; and know that thy father was 'Alá-ed-Deen Abu-sh-Shámát. None, however, reared thee but the Emeer Khálid, and he adopted thee. And now, O my son, when thou meetest with the Mukaddam Aḥmad Ed-Denef, say to him, O my chief, I conjure thee by Allah that thou take my revenge for me upon him who killed my father 'Alá-ed-Deen Abu-sh-Shámát.

So he went forth from her to the Mukaddam Aḥmad Ed-Denef, and kissed his hand; and Aḥmad Ed-Denef said, What dost thou want, O Aṣlán? He answered, I have known of a certainty that my father was 'Alá-ed-Deen Abu-sh-Shámát, and I request of thee that thou take my revenge for me upon him who killed him. Aḥmad Ed-Denef said, Who killed thy father? And Aṣlán answered him, Aḥmad Ḳamáḳim the arch thief.—And who, said Aḥmad Ed-Denef, acquainted thee with this? The youth answered, I saw in his possession the lamp ornamented with jewels that was lost with the other things belonging to the Khaleefeh, and I said to him, Give me this lamp:—but he would not; and he replied, Lives have been lost on account of this. He told me also that he was the person who descended into the chamber of the Khaleefeh and stole the things, and that he deposited them in the house of my father.—Upon this, Aḥmad Ed-Denef said to him, When thou seest the Emeer Khálid attiring himself in the apparel of war, say to him, Clothe me like thyself. And when thou goest up with him, and performest some feat of valour before the Prince of the Faithful, the Khaleefeh will say to thee, Request of me what thou desirest, O Aṣlán. Thou shalt then reply, I request of thee that thou avenge my father for me upon him who killed him. The Khaleefeh thereupon will say to thee, Thy father is living, and he is the Emeer Khálid, the Wálee. And thou shalt reply, Verily my father was 'Alá-ed-Deen Abu-sh-Shámát; and Khálid, the Wálee, hath a claim upon me only for his having reared me. Acquaint him also with all that hath happened between thee and Aḥmad

Ḳamáḳim the arch thief; and say to him, O Prince of the Faithful, give orders to search him, and I will produce the lamp from his pocket.—So Aṣlán replied, I hear and obey.

He then went forth, and found the Emeer Khálid preparing himself to go up to the court of the Khaleefeh, and he said to him, I would that thou clothe me with the apparel of war like thyself, and take me with thee to the Khaleefeh's court. And he clad him, and took him to the court. The Khaleefeh then went down with the troops, without the city, and they pitched the pavilions and tents, and the ranks were formed, and they proceeded to play with the ball and the goff-stick, one of the horsemen striking the ball with the goff-stick, and another striking it back to him. Now there was among the troops a spy, who had been incited to kill the Khaleefeh; and he took the ball and struck it with the goff-stick, aiming it at the face of the Khaleefeh. But, lo, Aṣlán warded it off from the Khaleefeh, and smote with it him who had impelled it, and it struck him between the shoulders, whereupon he fell on the ground; and the Khaleefeh exclaimed, God bless thee, O Aṣlán! They then alighted from the backs of their horses, and seated themselves upon the chairs, and the

Khaleefeh gave orders to bring the man who had struck the ball at him. And when he was brought before him, he said to him, Who incited thee to do this deed; and art thou an enemy or a friend? He answered, I am an enemy, and I was purposing to kill thee.—For what reason? said the Khaleefeh. Art thou not a Muslim?—No, he answered; but I am a Ráfiḍee.[92] So the Khaleefeh gave the order to put him to death.

And he said to Aṣlán, Request of me what thou desirest. He therefore replied, I request of thee that thou avenge my father for me upon him who killed him. The Khaleefeh said to him, Thy father is living, and he is standing upon his feet.—Who is my father? said Aṣlán. The Khaleefeh answered him, The Emeer Khálid, the Wálee. —O Prince of the Faithful, replied Aṣlán, he is not my father save in having reared me; and none was my father but 'Alá-ed-Deen Abu-sh-Shámát. The Khaleefeh said, Thy father was a traitor. But Aṣlán replied, O Prince of the Faithful, God forbid it should be said that the Faithful was a traitor! And in what, said he, did he act treacherously towards thee? The Khaleefeh answered, He stole my suit of apparel, and the things that were with it.—O Prince of the Faithful, replied Aṣlán, God forbid it should be said that my father was a traitor! But, O my lord, he added, when thy suit of apparel was lost and returned to thee, didst thou see the lamp brought back to thee also? The Khaleefeh answered, We found it not. Then said Aṣlán, I saw it in the possession of Aḥmad Ḳamáḳim, and begged it of him; but he would not give it me; and he said, Lives have been lost on account of this. And he told me of the illness of Ḥabaẓlam Baẓáẓah, the son of the Emeer Khálid, and his passion for the damsel Yásemeen, and his own release from the chains, and informed me that he was the person who stole the suit of apparel, and the lamp. Do thou, therefore, O Prince of the Faithful, avenge my father for me upon him who killed him.—So the Khaleefeh said, Seize Aḥmad Ḳamáḳim. And they did so. And he said, Where is the Muḳaddam Aḥmad Ed-Denef? He therefore came before him; and the Khaleefeh said to him, Search Ḳamáḳim. And he put his hands into his pocket, and took forth from it the lamp ornamented with jewels: whereupon the Khaleefeh said, Come hither, O traitor. Whence came to thee this lamp?—He answered, I bought it, O Prince of the Faithful. But the Khaleefeh said to him, Whence didst thou buy it; and who could possess himself of such a thing, that he should sell it to thee? They then beat him; and he confessed that he was the person who stole the suit of apparel, and the lamp. And the Khaleefeh said to him, Wherefore didst thou these deeds, to destroy 'Alá-ed-Deen Abu-sh-Shámát, who was the Trusty and Faithful? And he commanded to seize him, and the Wálee also. But the Wálee said, O Prince of the Faithful, I am injured. Thou gavest me the order to hang him, and I had no knowledge of this plot; for the thing was contrived by the old woman and Aḥmad Ḳamáḳim and my wife, and I had no information of it. I implore thy protection, O Aṣlán!—So Aṣlán interceded for him with the Khaleefeh. The Prince of the Faithful then said, What hath God done with the mother of this youth? The Wálee answered, She is in my house. And the Khaleefeh said, I command that thou order thy wife to attire her in her apparel and ornaments, and to restore her to her rank of a lady, and that thou take off the seals that are upon the house of 'Alá-ed-Deen, and give to his son his possessions and wealth. The Wálee replied, I hear and obey. And he descended, and gave the orders to his wife, who attired Yásemeen in her apparel; and he took off the seals from the house of 'Alá-ed-Deen, and gave Aṣlán the keys.

The Khaleefeh then said, Request of me what thou desirest, O Aṣlán. Aṣlán replied, I request that thou unite me with my father. And the Khaleefeh wept, and said, It is most probable that thy father was the person who was hanged, and died; but, by my ancestors, whosoever bringeth me the good news of his being alive, I will give him all that he shall require. So upon this, Aḥmad Ed-Denef advanced, and, having kissed the ground before him, said to him, Grant me indemnity, O Prince of the Faithful. The Khaleefeh replied, Thou hast indemnity. And Aḥmad Ed-Denef said, I give thee the good news that 'Alá-ed-Deen Abu-sh-Shámát, the Trusty and Faithful, is well, and still living. The Khaleefeh said to him, What is it thou assertest? He answered, By thy head, my words are true; for I ransomed him by substituting another, from among such as deserved to be put to death, and conducted him to Alexandria, where I opened for him a shop of a dealer in second-hand goods. So the Khaleefeh said, I require thee to bring him. He replied, I hear and obey. And the Khaleefeh commanded to give him ten thousand pieces of gold, and he departed on his way to Alexandria.

But as to 'Alá-ed-Deen Abu-sh-Shámát, he sold all that he had in the shop, except a few articles, and a leathern bag. And he shook this bag, and there dropped from it a bead, large enough to fill the hand, attached to a chain of gold, and having five faces, whereon were names and talismans like the tracks made by the creeping of ants. And he rubbed the five faces; but no one answered him.[93] So he said within himself, Probably it is a bead of onyx.[94] He then hung it up in the shop. And lo, a Consul[95] passed along the street, and, raising his eyes, saw the bead hung up; whereupon he seated himself at 'Alá-ed-Deen's shop, and said to him, O my master, is this bead for sale? 'Alá-ed-Deen answered him, All that I have is for sale. And the Consul said to him, Wilt thou sell it to me for eighty thousand pieces of gold? 'Alá-ed-Deen answered, May God open a better way to dispose of it.[96] The Consul then said, Wilt thou sell it for a hundred thousand pieces of gold? And he answered, I sell it thee for a hundred thousand pieces of gold: so pay me the coin. But the Consul replied, I cannot carry the sum; and in Alexandria are robbers and sharpers: do thou therefore come with me to my ship, and I will give thee the price, together with a bale of Angora wool, and a bale of satin, and a bale of velvet, and a bale of broad-cloth. So 'Alá-ed-Deen arose, and closed the shop, after he had delivered to him the bead; and he gave the keys to his neighbour,[97] saying to him, Keep these keys in thy charge while I go to the ship with this Consul and bring the price of my bead: but if I remain long away from thee, and the Muḳaddam Aḥmad Ed-Denef who established me in this place come to thee, give him the keys, and acquaint him with this circumstance.

He then repaired with the Consul to the ship; and when he went on board with him, the Consul put him a chair, and seated him upon it, and said, Bring the money. And having paid him the price, and given him the four bales which he had promised him, he said to him, O my master, I desire that thou refresh my heart by taking a mouthful of food, or a draught of water. 'Alá-ed-Deen replied, If thou have water, give me to drink. And the Consul gave orders to bring sherbet; and there was benj in it. So when he had drunk, he fell down on his back. And they took away the chairs, and put by the poles,[98] and loosed the sails, and the wind favoured them until they advanced into the midst of the sea. The Captain then gave orders to bring up 'Alá-ed-Deen from the cabin; and they brought him up, and made him smell the antidote of benj: so he opened his eyes, and said, Where am I? The Captain answered, Thou art here with me, bound and in custody; and hadst thou said again, May God open a better way to dispose of it,—I had increased my offer to thee.—And what, said 'Alá-ed-Deen, is thy occupation? He answered, I am a Captain, and I desire to take thee to the beloved of my heart.

Now while they were talking, there appeared a ship, on board of which were forty Muslim merchants; and the Captain attacked them, fixed the grappling-irons in their ship, and, boarding her with his men, they plundered her and took her, and proceeded with her to the city of Genoa. The Captain with whom 'Alá-ed-Deen was a prisoner then went to a door of a palace, opening upon the sea;[99] and lo, a damsel came down, drawing a lithám before her face, and said to him, Hast thou brought the bead and its owner? He answered her, I have brought both. And she said to him, Give me the bead. So he gave it to her. And after this, he returned to the port, and fired the guns[100] to announce his safe return; and the King of the city, becoming acquainted with his arrival, came forth to welcome him, and said to him, How hath been thy voyage? He answered, It hath been very prosperous, and I have captured, in the course of it, a ship containing forty-one Muslim merchants. The King then said to him, Bring them forth into the port. And he brought them forth in irons, with 'Alá-ed-Deen among them; and the King and the Captain mounted and made the prisoners walk before them until they arrived

at the council-chamber, when they seated themselves, and caused the first of the prisoners to be led forward; and the King said to him, Whence art thou, O Muslim? He answered, From Alexandria. And the King said, O executioner, slay him. The executioner therefore struck him with the sword, and severed his head from his body. Thus was done to the second also, and the third, and to their companions successively, until forty had been put to death. 'Alá-ed-Deen remained to the last: so he drank their sighs, and he said to himself, The mercy of God be on thee, O 'Alá-ed-Deen! Thy life hath expired!—Then the King said, And from what country art thou? He answered, From Alexandria. And the King said, O executioner, strike off his head!

The executioner accordingly raised his hand with the sword, and was about to strike off the head of 'Alá-ed-Deen; but, lo, an old woman, of venerable appearance, advanced before the King; whereupon he rose to her, to shew her honour; and she said, O King, did I not say to thee, When the Captain cometh with the captives remember to supply the convent with a captive or two to serve in the church?—O my mother, he answered, would that thou hadst come a little earlier: but take this captive that remaineth. And the old woman, looking towards 'Alá-ed-Deen, said to him, Wilt thou serve in the church, or shall I suffer the King to slay thee? He answered her, I will serve in the church. So she took him, and, going forth with him from the council-chamber, repaired to the church; and 'Alá-ed-Deen said to her, What service am I to perform? She answered, Thou shalt arise early in the morning, and take five mules and repair with them to the forest, cut dry firewood, and break it up, and bring it to the kitchen of the convent. After that, thou shalt take up the carpets, and sweep and wipe the stone and marble pavements, and spread the carpets again as they were. And thou shalt take half an ardebb [101] of wheat, and sift it, and grind it, and knead it, and make it into mineenehs [102] for the convent; and thou shalt take a weybeh [103] of lentils, and grind them with the hand-mill, and cook them. Then thou shalt fill the tanks of the four fountains with water, and convey it in barrels, and fill three hundred and sixty-six wooden bowls, and crumble the mineenehs into them, and pour into them some of the lentil-porridge, and take in to each monk or patriarch his bowl.—To this, 'Alá-ed-Deen replied, Return me to the King and let him slay me; for death will be easier to me than this work. She said to him, If thou work, and perform the service that is required of thee, thou wilt escape slaughter; and if thou perform it not, I will cause the King to put thee to death. So 'Alá-ed-Deen sat, full of trouble. And there were in the church ten blind and impotent men, who employed him in the most degraded of services. Then the old woman came, and said to him, Wherefore hast thou not done the work in the church?—How many hands have I, said he, that I should be able to accomplish this work?—Thou fool, she replied, I brought thee not but to work. She then said, Take, O my son, this rod (and it was of brass, with a cross at the top), and go forth into the great thoroughfare-street; and when the Wálee of the town approaches thee, say to him, I summon thee to the service of the church. And he will not disobey thee. So make him take the wheat, and sift it and grind it, and pass it through the second sieve, and knead it and bake mineenehs of it; and whoever shall disobey thee, beat him, and fear not anyone.—So he replied, I hear and obey. He did as she had told him, and ceased not to compel great and small to work, gratuitously, for the space of seventeen years.

After this, as he was sitting in the church, lo, the old woman came in to him, and said to him, Go without the convent.—Whither shall I go? said he. She answered him, Pass this night in a tavern, or in the house of one of thy companions. He said, Wherefore dost thou send me away from the church? And she answered, Ḥosn-Maryam,[104] the daughter of the King Yooḥannà,[105] the King of this city, desireth to pay a visit to the church, and it is not proper that anyone should be in her way. So he professed his assent to her order, and rose, pretending to her that he was going out from the church; but he said within himself, I wonder whether the daughter of the King is like our women, or more beautiful than they. I will not go, therefore, until I have gratified myself by the sight of her.—Accordingly he concealed himself in a closet which had a window looking into the church. And while he was looking thence into the church, lo, the daughter of the King approached, and he directed at her a glance which occasioned him a thousand sighs; for he found her to be like the full moon when it appeareth from behind the clouds; and with her was a damsel, to whom she was saying, Thou hast cheered me by thy society, O Zubeydeh. And 'Alá-ed-Deen, looking intently at that damsel, saw that she was his wife Zubeydeh El-'Oodeeyeh, who (as he supposed) had died. The King's daughter then said to Zubeydeh, Perform for us now a piece of music on the lute. But Zubeydeh replied, I will not perform it for thee until thou accomplish for me my desire, and fulfil thy promise to me.—What have I promised thee? said the daughter of the King. Zubeydeh answered her, Thou promisedst me to reunite me with my husband 'Alá-ed-Deen Abu-sh-Shámát, the Trusty and the Faithful. And the King's daughter said to her, O Zubeydeh, be of good heart and cheerful eye, and perform for us a piece of music as a gratuity for our union with thy husband 'Alá-ed-Deen. So Zubeydeh said, And where is he?—Verily, answered the King's daughter, he is in this closet, hearing our words. And upon this, Zubeydeh performed a piece of music upon the lute, such as would make a rock to dance; and when 'Alá-ed-Deen heard it, longing desires were excited in his heart, and he went forth from the closet, and, rushing upon them, took his wife Zubeydeh El-'Oodeeyeh in his bosom, and she recognised him.

They embraced each other, and fell down upon the floor senseless; and the Princess Ḥosn-Maryam came, and sprinkled some rose-water upon them, and recovered them, and said, God hath united you! 'Alá-ed-Deen replied, Through thy kindness, O my mistress. Then looking towards his wife, he said to her, Thou wast dead, O Zubeydeh, and we buried thee in the grave. How then didst thou return to life, and come unto this palace?—O my master, she answered, I died not; but one of the 'Óns[106] of the Jánn carried me off, and flew with me to this place; and as to her whom ye buried, she was a Jinneeyeh, who assumed my form and feigned herself dead, and after ye had buried her she clove open the grave and came forth from it, and betook herself to the service of her mistress Ḥosn-Maryam, the daughter of the King. But as to myself, I was possessed,[107] and, opening my eyes, I saw that I was with Ḥosn-Maryam, the King's daughter, who is this lady; and I said to her, Wherefore hast thou brought me hither? She answered me, I am predestined to marry thy husband 'Alá-ed-Deen Abu-sh-Shámát. And she said, Wilt thou accept me, O Zubeydeh, as thy fellow-wife? I answered her, I hear and obey, O my mistress: but where, said I, is my husband? And she said, Upon his forehead is written what God hath decreed to happen unto him,[108] and when he hath experienced the accomplishment of events that are written upon his forehead, he cannot fail to come unto this place; but thou shalt console thyself for his separation by melodious sounds, and playing upon musical instruments, until God unite us with him. So I remained with her during this period, till God united me with thee in this church.[109]

Then Ḥosn-Maryam looked towards him and said to him, O my

master 'Alá-ed-Deen, wilt thou accept me as a wife, and be to me a husband?—O my mistress, said he, I am a Muslim, and thou art a Christian: how then should I marry thee?[110] But she replied, God forbid that I should be an infidel! Nay, I am a Muslimeh, and for eighteen years I have held fast the religion of El-Islám, and I am guiltless of following any religion that is at variance with that of El-Islám.—He then said to her, O my mistress, I desire to return to my country. And she replied, Know that I have seen written upon thy forehead events of which thou must experience the accomplishment, and thou shalt attain thy wish. Be rejoiced also, O 'Alá-ed-Deen, by the information that a son of thine hath made his appearance, whose name is Aṣlán, and he is now sitting in thy place in the court of the Khaleefeh, and hath attained the age of eighteen years. Know, too, that the truth hath appeared, and falsity is withdrawn, and our Lord hath removed the veil of his protection from him who stole the goods of the Khaleefeh: he is Aḥmad Ḳamáḳim the arch thief and traitor; and he is now in prison, confined and chained. Know, moreover, that I am the person that sent to thee the bead, and caused it to be put for thee in the leathern bag in the shop; and I am the person who sent to thee the Captain who brought thee and the bead. And know that this Captain is enamoured of me, and desireth to possess me; but I would not yield to him, and I said to him, I will not grant thy request unless thou bring to me the bead and its owner. And I gave him a hundred purses,[111] and sent him in the garb of a merchant, though he was a Captain. Then, when they had brought thee forward to slay thee, after the slaughter of the forty captives with whom thou wast, I sent unto thee the old woman.—So 'Alá-ed-Deen said to her, May God recompense thee for me with every blessing!—Then Ḥosn-Maryam renewed to him her profession of conversion to El-Islám; and when he was convinced of the truth of her avowal, he said to her, Acquaint me with the virtue of this bead, and tell me whence it came.

She replied, This bead is from a charmed treasure, and possesseth five virtues, which will profit us in the time when we need them. My grandmother, the mother of my father, was an enchantress, who solved mysteries, and carried off treasures, and from a treasure this bead came into her possession. And when I had grown up, and attained the age of fourteen years, I read the Gospels and other books, and saw the name of Moḥammad (God bless and save him!) in the four books, the Pentateuch and the Gospels and the Psalms and the Furḳán:[112] so I believed in Moḥammad, and became a Muslimeh, and was convinced in my mind that none is to be worshipped in truth but God (whose name be exalted!), and that the Lord of mankind approveth of no faith but that of El-Islám. My grandmother, when she fell sick, made me a present of this bead, and acquainted me with the five virtues that it possesseth. And before my grandmother died, my father said to her, Perform for me an operation of geomancy, and see the end of my history, and what will happen to me. And she said to him, Verily the remote[113] will die slain by a captive who will come from Alexandria. So my father swore that he would put to death every captive that should come from that city, and acquainted the Captain with his vow, and said to him, Thou must attack the vessels of the Muslims, and whomsoever thou seest from Alexandria, thou must kill him, or bring him unto me. The Captain therefore complied with his command until he had slain a number as many as the hairs of his head. Then my grandmother perished; and I performed an operation of geomancy, considering in my mind and saying, I would know who will marry me. And it was revealed to me that none would marry me but one named 'Alá-ed-Deen Abu-sh-Shámát, the Trusty and Faithful; whereat I wondered; and I waited until the time came, and I met with thee.

'Alá-ed-Deen then married her,[114] and said to her, I desire to return to my country. She replied, If the case is so, come with me. And she took him and concealed him in a closet in her palace, and went in to her father, who said to her, O my daughter, I am to-day suffering from excessive oppression of spirits: sit therefore that I may intoxicate myself with thee. So she sat; and he called for the wine-table; and she proceeded to fill and to hand to him until he became insensible, when she put some benj into his cup, and he drank the cup, and fell down upon his back. She then came to 'Alá-ed-Deen, and, taking him forth from the closet, said to him, Thine adversary is laid prostrate upon his back; so do with him what thou wilt; for I have intoxicated him, and stupified him with benj. 'Alá-ed-Deen therefore went in, and beheld him stupified with benj; and he bound his hands tightly behind him, and chained him; after which he gave him the antidote of benj, and he recovered his senses, and found 'Alá-ed-Deen and his daughter sitting on his bosom. So he said, O my daughter, dost thou act thus towards me? She replied, If I am thy daughter, embrace El-Islám; for I have done so. The truth hath become manifest to me, and I have followed it, and falsity I have abandoned; and I have humbled my face unto God, the Lord of all creatures, and am guiltless of following any religion that is at variance with the religion of El-Islám in this world and in that which is to come. If then thou become a Muslim, we will treat thee with affection and honour; but if not, thy slaughter will be better than thy life.—Then 'Alá-ed-Deen also admonished him. But he refused and was obstinate: so 'Alá-ed-Deen drew forth a dagger, and cut his throat from one jugular vein to the other, and, having written a paper stating what had happened, put it upon his forehead.

After this, they took what was light to carry and great in value, and went forth from the palace, and repaired to the church. She then brought out the bead, and, putting her hand upon one of the faces of it, whereon was engraved a couch, she rubbed it; and lo, a couch was placed before her. And she mounted with 'Alá-ed-Deen and his wife

Zubeydeh El-'Oodeeyeh upon this couch, and said, By virtue of the names and talismans and scientific characters that are inscribed upon this bead, rise with us, O couch! And the couch rose with them, and conveyed them to a valley wherein was no vegetation.[115] Then she turned up the other four faces of the bead towards the sky, turning downwards the face whereon the couch was figured, and it descended with them to the earth. And she turned round a face upon which was figured the form of a pavilion, and rubbed it, saying, Let a pavilion be set up in this valley. Whereupon the pavilion was set up, and they seated themselves in it. Now that valley was a waste, destitute alike of vegetation and water: so she turned four faces of the bead towards the sky, and said, By virtue of the names of God, let trees spring up here, with a large river by their side! And the trees sprang up immediately, and by them ran a large murmuring river, agitated with waves; and they performed the ablution with its water, and prayed and drank. The King's daughter then turned round the three faces yet undescribed, until she came to a face upon which was represented a table of viands, and said, By virtue of the names of God, let the table be spread! And lo, a table was spread, whereon were all kinds of rich viands; and they ate and drank, and were full of joy and merriment.

Meanwhile, the King's son went in to wake his father, and found him slain; and he found also the paper which 'Alá-ed-Deen had written: so he read it, and became acquainted with its contents. He then searched for his sister, and, not finding her, he repaired to the old woman in the church, and inquired of her respecting her; and she answered, Since yesterday I have not seen her. He therefore returned and betook himself to the troops, and said to them, To horse, O riders! And he acquainted them with that which had happened: whereupon they mounted their horses, and proceeded until they drew near to the pavilion, when Ḥosn-Maryam turned her eyes, and saw that the dust had obstructed the view of the adjacent tracts; and after it had risen high and spread, it dispersed, and there appeared beneath it her brother and the troops, who were calling out, Whither will ye go when we are behind you? So the damsel said to 'Alá-ed-Deen, How is thy stability in war and combat? And he answered her, As that of the stake in bran; for I am not acquainted with war and battle, nor with swords and spears. She therefore took forth the bead, and rubbed a face upon which were figured a horse and rider; and lo, a horseman appeared from the desert, and ceased not to smite with the sword among them until he had routed and repelled them.

The King's daughter then said to 'Alá-ed-Deen, Wilt thou journey to Cairo or to Alexandria? He answered, To Alexandria. So they mounted the couch, and after she had pronounced a spell upon it, it conveyed them to Alexandria in the twinkling of an eye; and 'Alá-ed-Deen, having taken them into a cavern, went to the city, and brought them thence apparel, with which he clad them. He then conducted them to the shop and the suite of rooms, and went forth to procure dinner for them; and, lo, the Muḳaddam Aḥmad Ed-Denef approached, arriving from Baghdád. 'Alá-ed-Deen saw him in the street, and he met him with open arms, saluting him and welcoming him; and Aḥmad Ed-Denef gave him good news of his son Aṣlán, telling him that he had attained the age of twenty years; after which, 'Alá-ed-Deen related to the Muḳaddam all that had happened to him from first to last, and took him to the shop and the suite of rooms; and Aḥmad Ed-Denef wondered extremely at his story. They passed the next night, and when they arose in the morning, 'Alá-ed-Deen sold the shop, and put its price with the rest of his money. Then Aḥmad Ed-Denef informed him that the Khaleefeh desired his presence. But 'Alá-ed-Deen replied, I am going to Cairo, to salute my father and mother and the other members of my family. So they mounted the couch, all together, and repaired to the fortunate city of Cairo, and alighted in the Darb el-Aṣfar;[116] for the house of 'Alá-ed-Deen's family was in that quarter; and he knocked at the door; whereupon his mother said, Who is at the door after the loss of the beloved? He answered her, I am 'Alá-ed-Deen. And on hearing this, the family came down and embraced him. He then sent his two wives, and the property that he had brought with him, into the house, and entered himself, accompanied by Aḥmad Ed-Denef, and they rested three days; after which, he desired to depart to Baghdád. His father said to him, O my son, remain with me. But he replied, I cannot endure the separation from my son Aṣlán. And he took his father and his mother with him, and they journeyed to Baghdád.

Then Aḥmad Ed-Denef went in to the Khaleefeh, and imparted to him the happy news of the arrival of 'Alá-ed-Deen; on hearing which, the Khaleefeh went forth to meet him, taking with him his son Aṣlán, and they met and embraced him. And the Khaleefeh gave orders to bring Aḥmad Ḳamáḳim, the arch thief, and, when he came before him, said, O 'Alá-ed-Deen, avenge thyself upon thine adversary.

So 'Alá-ed-Deen drew his sword, and, smiting Aḥmad Ḳamáḳim, severed his head. The Khaleefeh then made a magnificent entertainment for 'Alá-ed-Deen, after he had summoned the Ḳáḍees and witnesses, and written 'Alá-ed-Deen's contract of marriage to Ḥosn-Maryam. He also appointed his son Aṣlán to the office of Raees es-Sitteen, and bestowed upon both of them sumptuous robes of honour; and they passed a most comfortable and agreeable life, until they were visited by the terminator of delights, and the separator of companions.[117]

NOTES TO CHAPTER ELEVENTH.

Note 1. This story is in the edition of Breslau, as well as in that of Cairo, from which I translate it. In the former, it occupies the next place to the story of Neạmeh and Noạm. It appears to be comprised also in the MS. of Von Hammer; but with a title not exactly the same; for in a list of the contents of his MS., prefixed to Trébutien's "Contes Inédits des Mille et une Nuits," I find, in the place corresponding with that in which the story of 'Alá-ed-Deen Abu-sh-Shámát occurs in the Cairo edition, a tale entitled "Aladdin le père des Envieux," with the words "Traduit par Caussin" added. Caussin's translation of this story, I believe, forms part of an edition, of which I have in vain endeavoured to procure a copy, published in Paris, by Lenormant, in 1806.

In presenting the story of 'Alá-ed-Deen Abu-sh-Shámát to the English reader, I may give my opinion that it is a purely Arab tale, of Egyptian character, either wholly composed, or in some parts altered, since the conquest of Egypt by the Turkish Sulṭán Seleem; faithfully describing Arab manners and customs, as existing during the last three or four centuries.

Note 2. That Cairo is here meant, as usual, by "Miṣr" (vulg. "Maṣr"), is proved afterwards, towards the close of the story, by the mention of a street.

Note 3. "Sháh-Bandar" is a title given to the chief, or general syndic, of the merchants of Cairo; but in some parts of the East it is applied to the receiver-general of duties or tribute.

Note 4. It is a duty of the Muslim to perform a lustration of the whole person before the congregational prayers of Friday.

Note 5. To utter an ejaculation of this kind on looking at his face in a glass is a usual custom of a Muslim; but I believe it is more common to say in this case, "O God, bless our lord Moḥammad!"—a person being often fearful even of the influence of his own admiring glance; for these words are generally used to counteract the influence of the evil eye, which is always dreaded when a look of admiration is cast.—When a person is about to leave the bath, the barber's glass is presented to him, and upon it he places the money that he has to pay.

Note 6. The allusion here is to Death, or the Angel of Death.

Note 7. This custom prevails in the present day among the women. They say to the infant, "In the name of the Prophet and of his cousin (the son of his paternal uncle) 'Alee!"[1] The object is, to preserve the child from the influence of the Jinn.

Note 8. This, also, is done with the view of preventing any mischief from the Jinn.—The "tekbeer" is the exclamation of "God is most great!" and the "adán," or "adhán," the call to prayer. See Note 24 to Chapter iv.

Note 9.—*On the Customs observed on the Seventh Day after the Birth of a Child.* The messes which are distributed after the birth of a child I have described in my work on the Modern Egyptians, vol. ii. ch. xiv. They are generally prepared on the fourth or fifth day after the birth. In the work above mentioned, in the same chapter, I have described the customs observed on the seventh day, and I must here repeat, nearly in the same words, what I have there said on this subject.—In the families of the higher classes, professional female singers are hired to entertain a party of ladies, friends of the infant's mother, who visit her on this occasion, in the ḥareem; or a concert of instrumental music, or a recitation of the whole of the Ḳur-án, is performed below by men. The mother, attended by the midwife, being seated on a chair[2] which is the property of the latter, the child is brought, wrapped in a handsome shawl, or something costly; and, to accustom it to noise, that it may not be frightened afterwards by the music, and other sounds of mirth, one of the women takes a brass mortar, and strikes it repeatedly with the pestle, as if pounding. After this, the child is put into a sieve, and shaken; it being supposed that this operation is beneficial to its stomach. Next, it is carried through all the apartments of the ḥareem, accompanied by several women or girls; each of whom bears a number of wax candles, sometimes of various colours, cut in two, lighted, and stuck into small lumps of paste of ḥennà, upon a small round tray. At the same time, the midwife, or another female, sprinkles, upon the floor of each room, a mixture of salt with seed of the fennel-flower, or salt alone, which has been placed during the preceding night at the infant's head; saying, as she does this, "The salt be in the eye of the person who doth not bless the Prophet!" or "The foul salt be in the eye of the envier!" This ceremony of the sprinkling of salt is considered a preservative, for the child and mother, from the evil eye; and each person present should say, "O God, bless our lord Moḥammad!"[3] The child, wrapped up, and placed on a fine mattress, which is sometimes laid on a silver tray, is shewn to each of the women present, who looks at its face, says, "O God, bless our lord Moḥammad! God give thee long life!" &c., and usually puts an embroidered handkerchief, with a gold coin (if pretty or old the more esteemed) tied up in one of the corners, on the child's head, or by its side. This giving of handkerchiefs and gold is considered as imposing a debt, to be repaid by the mother, if the donor should give her the same occasion; or as the discharge of a debt for a similar offering. The coins are generally used, for some years, to decorate the head-dress of the child. After these presents for the child, others are given for the midwife. During the night before the seventh-day's festivity, a water-bottle full of water (a dóraḳ in the case of a boy, and a ḳulleh in that of a girl[4]), with an embroidered handkerchief tied round the neck, is placed at the child's head while it sleeps. This, with the water it contains, the midwife takes, and puts upon a tray, and presents it to each of the women, who put presents of money for her into the tray.—In the evening, the husband generally entertains a party of his friends.

---

[1] Marginal note by my sheykh.

[2] This is used for the purpose mentioned in Exodus i. 16.

[3] See above, Note 5 in the present series.

[4] The dóraḳ has a long, narrow neck: the ḳulleh, a short, wide one. The tail-piece to the Notes to Chapter vi. of this work shews the most common forms of the latter.

Note 10. That is, Where is the new-born child, which is God's deposite? For he belongeth to God, who hath intrusted him to us; and when He desireth to take him, He taketh him by death. The poet saith,—

> Wealth and families are nought but deposites, and a day must come when deposites shall be restored.[5]

Note 11. The daughter is named by her mother; and the son, by his father.[6]

Note 12. "'Alá-ed-Deen" signifies "the Nobility of the Religion;" and "Abu-sh-Shámát," "Having Moles" (literally, "Father of the Moles"). The former is changed by the vulgar into "'Aláy-ed-Deen," and is generally written by us "Aladdin."—The custom of deriving a name from an omen is still general among the Bedawees.

Note 13. Many a house in Cairo has a trap-door in some apartment (often in a cupboard), opening into a secret chamber, or into a passage by which the tenant may make his escape in any case of danger.

Note 14. When a youth has attained to years of discretion, and begun to say his prayers and to acquit himself of other religious duties, he is believed to be less obnoxious to the influence of the eye: still more so, when his beard is grown; for then he is less likely to be admired, or envied, or coveted. Many Arabs preserve their children from the public gaze with a care almost as ridiculous as that of which 'Alá-ed-Deen Abu-sh-Shámát is said to have been the object. On this subject I have made some remarks in Note 24 to Chapter iv.

Note 15. When a person admires a child or any other object, he should say, "In the name of Allah!" or utter some similar words, as "Má sháa-lláh" (explained in Note 81 in this series). Such expressions are believed to prevent and to counteract the influence of the eye.

Note 16. These are metaphorical expressions, alluding to the careful manner in which the boy had been reared, and to his gentility.[7]

Note 17. See Note 20 to Chapter viii.

Note 18. Since Egypt has been under the dominion of foreign princes, the great officers of the state have generally been, almost exclusively, foreigners. On this account, the Sháh-Bandar of the merchants is here called "Sulṭán of the Sons of the Arabs," being the chief man of substance among them. The term "'Arab" is now given only to the Bedawees, or Arabs of the desert: the townspeople and villagers call themselves "Owlád el-'Arab," or "Sons of the Arabs."

Note 19. This is a saying of the Prophet.

Note 20. The "Naḳeeb" of a sooḳ, or market, is an officer under its Sheykh, or syndic. The Sháh-Bandar, being chief of all the merchants, was of course chief of the market in which he had his shop.

Note 21. It is customary to recite the Fáteḥah (or opening chapter of the Ḳur-án) on making for the first time, and on renewing, a profession of submission to the authority of another, as well as in concluding a bargain, and on various other occasions.

Note 22. "Simsim," here used as a surname, is the name of the grain which we call sesame.

Note 23. "'Aṣeedeh" is a kind of custard, made with boiling water, flour, clarified butter, and honey.

---

[5] Marginal note by my sheykh. [6] *Idem.* [7] *Idem.*

NOTE 24. See Note 16 to Chapter x.

NOTE 25. The word which I render "pavilion" is "ḳaṣr." This word is used to signify a palace; a mansion; and a pavilion (or a piece of building, or set of apartments, isolated, or only connected with another piece of building on one side; or an upper room, generally isolated, or nearly so): the same as the Turkish "kyúshk," generally called by us "kiosk" and "kiosque." The term "pavilion," when used in this work, except when it evidently signifies "a large tent," may be understood in either of the senses in which it is explained above.

NOTE 26. Among the Arabs, it is very seldom that a beardless youth, in genteel society, can be persuaded to eat with men, unless with those who are much inferior to him in rank. That this is a result of an education which inculcates an *affectionate* respect for elders, and superiors in station, is evident to every person familiar with Muslim society; for he will often hear a servant address his master by the appellation of father. In the tale upon which I am commenting, a servant of 'Alá-ed-Deen becomes his adopted father. 'Alá-ed-Deen disobeys him on one occasion; but his doing so is an exception to a general rule. The kind of respect shewn by Muslims to parents and other elders, and to masters, excited my high admiration during my residence among the Arabs. This respect of servants for masters is attributable in a great measure to the occasional presents which the former receive from the latter. Mr Urquhart has well observed, "The habit of irregular remuneration, in lieu of fixed, invariable, and *actionable* wages, produces a difference of mental habits, as regards servants and masters, that I am sure is not to be understood through description; and yet every day you see Europeans, those men who affect such comprehensive views and such powers of logic, reviling the habit of giving presents, not perceiving that this practice leads to the preservation of those interesting domestic relations which I conceive to be the greatest lesson, political and moral, that is presented to us by the Eastern world."[8] The Muslim servant generally *feels* far greater respect for his master, though he often *shews* less, than the European.

NOTE 27. Here, in the original, is introduced a character of a disgusting description, and unnecessary to the carrying on of the story.

NOTE 28. The appellation of "'Akkám" is here applied to a person who ties and loads camels and other beasts of burden. It is also often applied to one who has the charge of the tents and baggage.

NOTE 29. The meaning is, This is not my time; for I am grown old.[9]

NOTE 30. "Muḳaddam" signifies "one placed before, or over, others; a superior, chief, or overseer."

NOTE 31. The kind of "covering" here mentioned is placed over the oblong monument that is erected over the grave of a saint; and is like the covering of the Kaạbeh, at Mekkeh.[10] 'Abd-El-Ḳádir El-Geelánee was a very famous saint, and founder of a celebrated order of Darweeshes called the Ḳádireeyeh, who died at Baghdád, in the year of the Flight 561 (A.D. 1165-6). The Sháh-Bandar is said to have bought a covering for him because his son was going to Baghdád, where this saint is buried; and by carrying with him this offering, he might hope to obtain the saint's favour and intercession.—A new covering for the Kaạbeh is sent from Cairo every year with the great caravan of pilgrims: it is carried in procession through that city, and is believed to be one of the chief means of procuring safety to the attendants during their arduous and dangerous journey.[11]—The reader needs not to be informed

---

[8] Spirit of the East, vol. ii. p. 402.

[9] Marginal note by my sheykh.

[10] It is generally ornamented with one or more inscriptions from the Ḳur-án.

[11] For an account of the covering of the Kaạbeh, and of the departure and return of the pilgrim-caravan, at Cairo, see the Modern Egyptians, vol. ii. chaps. xi. and xii.—ED.

that camels are the beasts generally employed in Arabian countries to carry the baggage on long journeys: but mules are preferred by the rich, when camels are not necessary.

Note 32. The festival here alluded to is similar to those periodical festivals which I have described in Note 63 to Chapter iii., and further illustrated by Note 37 to Chapter viii.

Note 33. The "Ráfiḍees" are the Mohammadan sect of the Shiya'ees, or Shee'ees; the followers of 'Alee; who are regarded by the Sunnees as heretics. The principal point wherein they differ from the Sunnees is their denying the right of the first three Khaleefehs, Aboo-Bekr, 'Omar, and 'Othmán; asserting the only legitimate successors of the Prophet to be 'Alee and his descendants, called by them their Imáms; the twelfth and last of whom (El-Mahdee) they believe to be still living, though invisible. The Shiya'ee faith became the national religion of Persia about the commencement of the sixteenth century of our era, under the Sháh Ismá'eel, the founder of the Ṣafee Dynasty; and since that period (a period with which the character of the story of 'Alá-ed-Deen Abu-sh-Shámát appears best to agree), the adjacent territories of Sunnee princes and governors have always been coveted, and often invaded, by the Ráfiḍees. The first war between the 'Osmánlee Sunnees under the Sulṭán Seleem, and the Persian Shiya'ees under the Sháh above mentioned, occasioned the conquest of Syria and Egypt by the former monarch; for though the inhabitants of these countries were Sunnees, they were in alliance with the Sháh Ismá'eel.

Note 34. A Saḳḳà is a water-carrier, or a person who has the charge of supplying water.

Note 35. "O thy blessing!" is an invocation for supernatural aid, which is generally signified by the word "blessing" when it is employed with reference to a saint. The hand afterwards mentioned is to be understood as that of Seyyidee 'Abd-El-Ḳádir, or as the result of a miracle performed by him.

Note 36. This prayer is addressed not to Seyyidee 'Abd-El-Ḳádir, but to God.

Note 37. The Seyyideh Nefeeseh, who was the great-granddaughter of the Imám El-Ḥasan, was a very celebrated saint, and many miracles are related to have been performed by her. Her tomb, which is greatly venerated, is in a mosque in a southern suburb of Cairo. [She died in the year of the Flight 208.—Ed.]

Note 38. The meaning is, Thou wast always swearing by divorce, as though it were thy muṣ-ḥaf (or copy of the Ḳur-án) in which thou wast constantly reading.[12]

Note 39. "El-'Oodeeyeh" is derived from "'ood," which signifies "wood," and particularly "aloes-wood," and also "a lute," &c. As Zubeydeh was very skilful in playing on the lute, I think that "El-'Oodeeyeh" here signifies "the Lute-player." My sheykh has remarked, in a marginal note, "Probably she was so called because her odour was sweet, like that of aloes-wood;" but I find the term "'oodeeyeh" used to signify "a female lute-player" in the Breslau edition of the Thousand and One Nights (for instance, in vol. vii. p. 205,) instead of the more proper term "'Owwádeh."

Note 40. I have before mentioned that when a Muslim has divorced his wife three times, or by a triple divorce expressed in one sentence, he cannot take her again, unless by her own consent and by a new contract, and after another man has consummated a marriage with her and divorced her. When a man is employed to do this, he is called a "mustaḥall" or "mustaḥill," or a "moḥallil:" but such a proceeding is regarded by all respectable persons as disgraceful, and is clearly contrary

[12] Marginal note by my sheykh.

to the spirit of the law, which has ordained this consequence of a third or triple divorce as a check upon the husband, and as an indulgence to the wife. As I am not desirous of expatiating here on this subject, if any reader require further information respecting it, I beg to refer him to my work on the Modern Egyptians, vol. i. ch. vi. I have there mentioned a plan which is sometimes pursued to defeat the mustaḥall if he refuses to divorce. The wife also may withhold her consent to a reunion with her former husband, unless she is not of age, which we must understand to have been Zubeydeh's case. A girl who is not of age may be married by her father or other lawful guardian to whom he pleases.

NOTE 41. This impudent avowal of the design is contrary to the law; but there are doubtless Ḳáḍees who would listen to such a proposition. The ten thousand pieces of gold which 'Alá-ed-Deen was required to pay in case of his not divorcing, we are to understand as constituting that portion of the dowry which is usually paid before concluding the marriage-contract; for the remainder is not paid but on the occasion of a divorce, or from the property which the husband leaves at his death. But if 'Alá-ed-Deen divorced his wife at the time promised, no dowry was to be required of him.

NOTE 42. The Prophet denied the communication of diseases from one person to another; but said, "Run from the person afflicted with *elephantiasis* as you would from a tiger:" yet he himself took hold of the hand of a person who had that disease, and put it into a dish out of which he was eating, and said, "I depend upon God." [13]—On this subject, see Note 5 to Chapter i.

NOTE 43. This is the thirty-sixth Chapter of the Ḳur-án. It is one which is very frequently recited.

NOTE 44. By "the family of Dáood" is meant Dáood (or David) himself, agreeably with a common form of speech.[14] On David's recitation of the Psalms, see Note 18 to Chapter i.

NOTE 45. This expression, according to my sheykh, alludes to the appearance of the *veins* in the midst of the wrist, dividing it as the spine does the back.

NOTE 46. The raven is regarded as an omen of separation.

NOTE 47. In the original, "nuṣf faḍḍah." The same coin is also called simply "nuṣf," and vulgarly "nuṣṣ." See Note 17 to Chapter iii.

NOTE 48. The "Sháhids" of a Ḳáḍee's court are officers whose business is to hear and write the statements of the cases to be submitted for judgment. The same term is also applied to witnesses.

NOTE 49. "Efendee" is a Turkish title, given to judges, ministers of religion, learned men, writers, and others. It is here improperly applied to the Ḳáḍee of an Arabian city at a period when that city had not become subject to Turkish dominion.

NOTE 50. In the original, the chords are said to have called out, O Dáood!—See above, Note 44.

NOTE 51. It is a common custom of Arab musicians to commence a piece slowly, and afterwards, as if becoming excited, to perform with a rapid measure. The word which I have rendered "the more rapid part" (agreeably with an explanation given by my sheykh) also signifies "trilling" or "quavering."

NOTE 52. By the term "lyric songs" I render the Arabic word "muweshshaḥát," plural of "muweshshaḥ." This word is used, it appears, by the Persians, to signify an acrostic; but I have heard, and possess copies of, many Arabic poems so entitled, none

---

13 Mishkát el-Maṣábeeḥ, vol. ii. pp. 381 *et seq.*

14 Marginal note by my sheykh.

of which is of this character: they are poems in stanzas; all the stanzas of the same muweshshaḥ agreeing in the last rhyme, or the last two or more rhymes. In many instances, all the stanzas of the same poem end with two pairs of hemistichs rhyming alternately; the preceding hemistichs of each stanza also rhyming alternately, but the rhymes of these being different in different stanzas. This kind of poem is generally sung.

Note 53. Aboo-Nuwás was a celebrated poet and wit, who stood high in the favour of Hároon Er-Rasheed. He was surnamed "Aboo-Nuwás" from his having two long locks of hair which hung down upon his shoulders. He died (according to Abu-l-Fidà) in the year of the Flight 195, aged fifty-nine years.

Note 54. So in the Breslau edition, both here and where the dowry is next mentioned. In the Cairo edition, in both cases, fifty thousand.

Note 55. "Seleem" (generally written by European authors "Selim") signifies "sound," "safe," "entire," &c.—The inappropriate style of this letter seems to be intentional.

Note 56. Until he had paid that portion of the dowry which he had agreed to give in case of his refusing to divorce, his marriage was not lawful.

Note 57. It often happens in Cairo (as my sheykh mentions in a marginal note), that when a person arrives from a journey, his friends say to him, "Make an entertainment for us as a gratuity for thy safety" (ḥaláwet es-selámeh): so also when a person recovers from a sickness, and on other occasions. I was often required there to comply with this custom.

Note 58. What I have said in the fiftieth note of the present series applies also to this passage.

Note 59. "May thy head long survive (or, literally, May thy head [long] live with respect to, or in comparison of,) such-a-one!" is a common form of speech used in announcing a person's death; for, in communicating any bad news, it is a general custom among the Arabs to greet the individual addressed with some kind of salutation.[15] It is meant that the person here mentioned was one of the Khaleefeh's appointed boon-companions. I use the term "boon-companion" for the Arabic "nedeem," which properly signifies "a cup-companion," but is employed in a more extended sense, applied to one who is a regular associate on occasions of conviviality or diversion; generally a poet, wit, musician, or any other who is an amusing companion, or a favourite.

Note 60. "Raees es-Sitteen" signifies "Chief of the Sixty;" and I believe it is improperly used here as the title of some great officer of the state. In the Breslau edition we find, in its place, a title which appears to me still more improper, namely, "Básh es-Sitteen Sulṭán," or "Chief of the Sixty Sulṭáns;" and the palaces of the Sixty Sulṭáns are afterwards mentioned. "Raees es-Sitteen" seems to be of similar import to "Emeer 'Asharah," "Emeer Miäh," &c., which we meet with in the histories of the Memlook Sulṭáns, signifying "Emeer of Ten Memlooks," "—— of a Hundred Memlooks," &c.; the chief of hired soldiers being commonly called "Muḳaddam."[16]

Note 61. Shaking the handkerchief is a common signal for the dispersion of an assembly.

Note 62. The poet calls the bier "curving" (literally "humpbacked") "in allusion

---

[15] See, on this subject, a note at the foot of page 213 in this volume.

[16] See Quatremère, Histoire des Sultans Mamlouks, vol. i. p. 173.

to the bier of the Arabs [i. e. of the Bedawees]; for they used to carry the dead upon cords interwoven between two poles, so that the corpse lay depressed within them."[17]

NOTE 63. The Khaleefeh's making this motion to welcome 'Alá-ed-Deen was a proof of most extraordinary condescension.

NOTE 64. See Note 21 to Chapter vii.

NOTE 65. The kind of litter here mentioned is the takht-rawán, described in Note 8 to Chapter viii.

NOTE 66. From this we must infer, that when 'Alá-ed-Deen heard Ḳoot-el-Ḳuloob perform on the lute in the Khaleefeh's palace, she was concealed from him by a curtain, or a screen of lattice-work, in accordance with usual custom.

NOTE 67. "Khátoon," here used as a proper name, is a Persian and Turkish word, signifying "a lady" and "a matron."

NOTE 68. "Ḥabaẓlam" and "Baẓáẓah" are, I believe, words of no meaning; but chosen for the uncouthness of their sound, as composing a suitable name for an uncouth person.

NOTE 69. This is a metaphorical expression, signifying the rushing headlong into peril.[18]

NOTE 70. "Yásemeen," or "yásimeen," signifies "jasmine."

NOTE 71. This is explained by the note immediately preceding.

NOTE 72. "He would steal the koḥl from the eye" is a phrase often used to denote wonderful expertness in thieving.—See Note 34 to Chapter ii.

NOTE 73. See Note 39 to Chapter vi.

NOTE 74. On the oath of divorce, see Note 48 to Chapter viii., Note 40 in the present series, and Note 39 to Chapter iv.

NOTE 75. This was done in order to fulfil the Khaleefeh's oath. Arabs often have recourse to shifts of this kind in similar cases.

NOTE 76. Respecting benj, see Note 46 to Chapter ii.—The following remarks by the celebrated Von Hammer, who regards the benj as hyoscyamus (or henbane), should have been there added. "'Bendj,' the plural of which in Coptic is 'nibendj,' is without doubt the same plant as the 'nepenthe,' which has hitherto so much perplexed the commentators of Homer. Helen evidently brought the nepenthe from Egypt, and bendj is there still reputed to possess all the wonderful qualities which Homer attributes to it."[19]

NOTE 77. The "durḳá'ah" is the depressed portion of the paved floor. See Note 12 to Chapter iii.

NOTE 78. I do not remember to have found this custom mentioned in any other Arabic work; but Mr. Salamé, whom I have consulted on the subject, has informed me of a similar custom among the Turks. The billets of the tribute exacted from unbelievers have occasionally been of red paper, and the issuing of these has spread consternation among the tributaries; red being the colour significant of anger, as white and black (or blue) are, respectively, the colours appropriated to joy and mourning. But red, among the *Arabs*, was certainly not always indicative of anger;

---

17 Marginal note by my sheykh.

18 *Idem.*

19 Trébutien, Contes Inédits des Mille et une Nuits, vol. i. p. 12, note.

for Arabs at *carousals* used to wear dresses of this colour, and of yellow, and green;[20] and red dresses are very commonly worn by them. Their princes, however, may have been accustomed to exhibit the striking and dramatic spectacle described by our author; which, I conceive, may have been more effective than any words could be.

NOTE 79. In the description of this rod or staff in the Cairo edition, there is an error: I therefore follow the edition of Breslau. I suppose this kind of rod to have been employed for the purpose of inducing a belief that it possessed some magical property.

NOTE 80. I have inserted the word "surnamed," as the Khaleefeh is afterwards said to have surnamed 'Alá-ed-Deen "the Trusty and Faithful."

NOTE 81. The words which I render "Wonderful is Allah's will!" (Má sháa-lláh!) are sometimes used to signify literally "What God hath willed:" in other cases, as in the present instance, "What hath God willed!" i. e. "How wonderful is the event that God hath brought to pass!"

NOTE 82. "Ez-Zeebaḳ" is a surname, or nickname, signifying "quicksilver." Many traditional stories of extraordinary feats said to have been performed by 'Alee Ez-Zeebaḳ are related in Cairo. I believe that there really was a famous thief so named in that city; but have met with no authentic record of him stating the age in which he lived.

NOTE 83. "It is the most received opinion among the Mohammadans that the son whom Abraham offered was Ismael, and not Isaac; Ismael being his only son at that time: for the promise of Isaac's birth is mentioned lower [in the Ḳur-án], as subsequent in time to this transaction. They also allege the testimony of their prophet, who is reported to have said, 'I am the son of the two who were offered in sacrifice;' meaning his great ancestor, Ismael, and his own father, 'Abd-Allah: for 'Abd-El-Muṭṭalib[21] had made a vow, that if God would permit him to find out and open the well Zemzem, and should give him ten sons, he would sacrifice one of them; accordingly, when he had obtained his desire in both respects, he cast lots on his sons, and the lot falling on 'Abd-Allah, he redeemed him by offering an hundred camels, which was therefore ordered to be the price of a man's blood in the Sunneh."[22]

NOTE 84. This expression is to be understood as metaphorical; for there is no city to which, in the literal sense, it is more inapplicable than Alexandria, which is encompassed by sea and desert.

NOTE 85. It is here proper to mention that Aḥmad Ed-Denef, in other stories of the Thousand and One Nights, is said to have been an iniquitous character; and so is Ḥasan Shoomán.

NOTE 86. A small village, I believe, now occupies the site of the city of Ayás (supposed to be that of the ancient Ægæ), on the shore of the Gulf of Iskenderoon.

NOTE 87. The coin is not specified here, and I cannot attempt to supply the omission, the property being so vaguely described.

NOTE 88. The Arabic term "suḳaṭee" I render "a dealer in second-hand goods." My sheykh remarks, in a marginal note, that this term is here improperly applied; and that it denotes one who sells the pluck and the feet &c. of animals. So it generally does; but it has another application in Egypt; and it is singular that I should be

---

[20] See Note 22 to Chapter iii.

[21] By Sale, and most others of our Orientalists, this name is erroneously written "Abd'almotalleb." The chief emphasis in "Muṭṭalib" is on the second syllable, though its vowel is short; and hence may have arisen the mistake.

[22] Sale's note on verse 101 of the 37th chapter of the Ḳur-án.

acquainted with a sense in which it is there employed, and that a learned native of that country should not. In inquiring for a sprinkling-bottle and perfuming-vessel of brass or bronze and of old workmanship, I was told that I should apply for them to a sukaṭee; and being directed to a person so called, I found that he dealt in a variety of old and damaged articles, chiefly of metal, and mostly purchased at sales of old furniture, &c. Professor Habicht, in the seventh volume of the Breslau edition of the Thousand and One Nights, page 5 of the Glossary, explains this term in a similar manner.

NOTE 89. That a corpse should remain hanging during the period required to go from Baghdád to Alexandria and to return, is too improbable. The remains of a person who has been executed are generally left exposed for three days, and then interred.

NOTE 90. By "the two sheykhs" are meant Aboo-Bekr and 'Omar, the first two Khaleefehs. Many of the Ráfiḍees, or Shiya'ees, it is said, write the names of the first two Khaleefehs, or only the name of 'Omar, whom they especially hate, upon the upper surface of the soles of their shoes, and upon their heels, to be habitually trodden upon, by way of shewing contempt. See above, Note 33.

NOTE 91. "Aṣlán" is a Turkish word, signifying "a lion."

NOTE 92. This might convey, to some readers, a wrong notion; for the Ráfiḍees do call themselves Muslims, though the Sunnees often deny them to be so. The passage reminds me of an anecdote related by Burckhardt. A Bedawee one day presented himself before Moḥammad 'Alee, during his war with the Wahhábees, "kissed his beard, and exclaimed, 'I have abandoned the religion of the Muslims' (or 'True Believers,' as the Wahhábees style themselves); 'I have adopted the religion of the heretics' (so the Wahhábees entitle all those Mohammadans who are not of their own creed); 'I have adopted the religion of Moḥammad 'Alee.' This unintended blunder caused a general laugh; and the Páshá answered through his interpreter (for he but imperfectly understood Arabic), 'I hope you will always be a stanch heretic.'"[23]

NOTE 93. He rubbed the bead to try if it were a talisman, and if this process would procure the presence of some obedient Jinnee; for in this manner the virtues of a talisman are generally proved.

NOTE 94. That is, Probably it is a stone naturally variegated or marked.

NOTE 95. "Consul" (pronounced by the Arabs "Ḳunṣul") is a title often given in Egypt, not merely to those to whom it justly belongs, but also to any wealthy Frank.

NOTE 96. The Arabic phrase thus rendered literally signifies "May God open," or "—— assist." It is commonly used by Arab shopkeepers in the present day.

NOTE 97. This incident deserves especial remark. What 'Alá-ed-Deen is here described to have done is an act very common with Arab shopkeepers, and is a proof of their general good faith. When an Arab quits his shop intending to return to it the same day, he usually hangs a net before the front. [Frequently, also, he leaves his goods in the charge of a casual visiter to his shop. I have often been thus left sitting among valuable property, while its owner has gone, perhaps, to the congregational Friday-prayers, or on some business occupying a considerable time. Once a money-changer thus intrusted me with the care of his money, which, probably uncounted, was

---

[23] "Notes on the Bedouins and Wahábys," 8vo. ed. vol. ii. pp. 284-5.

deposited in the open drawers of a small chest within the reach of my arm. I was not aware of having ever seen him before: certainly I had never sat in his shop.—Ed.]

Note 98. The poles here mentioned are those which are used in shoving off a small vessel from the shore, or from a bank on which it has run, in propelling it in a calm in shallow water, and also in sounding.

Note 99. The Arabic words "báb ḳeyṭoon," which I render "a door opening upon the sea," my sheykh explains as applied to a door which opens upon a river, as the doors opening upon the canal in Cairo.

Note 100. Cannons are mentioned in several places in the Thousand and One Nights; but perhaps by copyists.

Note 101. See Note 10 to Chapter v.

Note 102. The "mineeneh" is a kind of small biscuit or cracknel made of fine wheat-flour with a little clarified butter.[24]

Note 103. The "weybeh" is the sixth part of the ardebb; consequently nearly equivalent to six English gallons and two-thirds.

Note 104. "Ḥosn-Maryam" (literally "the Beauty of Maryam") is here used to signify "Beautiful as Maryam," i. e. "——as the Virgin Mary."

Note 105. "Yooḥannà" is the Arabic *Christian* name corresponding to "John:" the corresponding *Muslim* name is "Yaḥyà."

Note 106. "'Ón" is used as synonymous with "Márid,"[25] an appellation already explained as applied to an evil Jinnee of the most powerful class.

Note 107. In the original, "ṣureaṭu," which literally signifies "I was prostrated," particularly "by an epileptic fit." My sheykh explains it by the words "iltebestu bi-l-jinneeyi," or "I was possessed by the Jinnee;" the belief that epilepsy is thus occasioned generally prevailing among the Arabs. A person under the influence of this malady they term "melboos," or "possessed."

Note 108. See the last paragraph of Note 5 to Chapter i.

Note 109. I have remarked before, that we must suppose Zubeydeh to have been under age when 'Alá-ed-Deen married her; consequently, at the time of her reunion with him, we need not infer that her age was much more than thirty years: for some Arab girls are married at the age of ten years; and we may imagine Zubeydeh to have been eleven or twelve years old at the time of her second marriage; yet in person, notwithstanding, nearly a woman.

Note 110. The marriage of a Muslim with a Christian woman is not absolutely forbidden; but it is generally disapproved.

Note 111. The sum called "a purse" in Egypt is five hundred Egyptian piasters, now nearly equivalent to five pounds sterling.

Note 112. "The Furḳán" is an appellation of the Ḳur-án, and sometimes applied to "other books of scripture," "from the verb 'faraḳa,' 'to divide' or 'distinguish;' not, as the Mohammadan doctors say, because those books are divided into chapters or sections, or to distinguish between good and evil; but in the same notion that the Jews use the word 'Perek,' or 'Pirka,' from the same root, to denote a section or

---

[24] Marginal note by my sheykh. [25] *Idem.* See also Note 21 to the Introduction.

portion of scripture."[26]—The Muslims believe that the copies of the Pentateuch, Psalms, and Gospels, now existing, have been corrupted, and that the passages in them wherein Moḥammad is foretold have been altered or expunged: yet they pretend to trace a prophecy of him in the modern copies of the Gospel of St. John, reading, instead of "Paraclete," "Periclyte," which is similar in signification to "Moḥammad" and "Aḥmad," both of which are names of the Arabian Prophet; the former of these two names signifying "greatly praised;" the latter, "more or most laudable."—Here it is worthy of remark, that the name of Moḥammad, pronounced as Europeans generally write it, with an "e" instead of an "a" in the last syllable, might be understood by an Arab in an active instead of a passive sense, as meaning "greatly praising."

NOTE 113. Shahrazád, in relating this story, says, "the *remote* will die," instead of "*thou* wilt die," as the latter expression might seem to be intended as a prophecy of the death of the King Shahriyár, whom she is addressing. See note 8 to Chapter ii.

NOTE 114. A marriage without witnesses in this case was perfectly lawful.

NOTE 115. Thrones, carpets, &c., of this kind are mentioned in several Eastern tales,[27] the authors of which may have all taken the idea from the tradition of Solomon's mode of travelling through the air. It is said "that he had a carpet of green silk, on which his throne was placed, being of a prodigious length and breadth, and sufficient for all his forces to stand on, the men placing themselves on his right hand, and the spirits [or Jinn] on his left; and that when all were in order, the wind, at his command, took up the carpet, and transported it, with all that were upon it, wherever he pleased; the army of birds at the same time flying over their heads, and forming a kind of canopy, to shade them from the sun."[28]

NOTE 116. The "Darb el-Aṣfar" is a street in the Jemáleeyeh, in the northern part of Cairo.

NOTE 117. Here it becomes necessary to mention, that many anecdotes are inserted among the longer stories of the Thousand and One Nights. They are chiefly, I believe, extracted from other works, and many are historical; but most of them are very inferior in interest to the longer stories; and, from a hasty perusal of them, I found that it would be advisable to omit, in my translation, the greater number; introducing the rest in their proper places, but appending them to my notes.[29]

Almost the whole of that portion of the Thousand and One Nights which is wanting in Galland's version was translated into French by the late Baron Von Hammer Purgstall; and from his manuscript French version, a German translation was made by Professor Zinserling; but the latter alone was published; the former being afterwards most unfortunately lost by a person to whose care it was intrusted to bring it to England for the purpose of publication. Again, from the German version, a French translation was made, by M. Trébutien, and published in Paris in 1828; and likewise an English translation of most of the longer stories, and four anecdotes, by the Rev. George Lamb, published in London in 1829. I regret extremely that I am unable to read the German version; for it is natural to infer that the merits of the version of Von Hammer are more imperfectly reflected in the second, than in the first, of two succes-

---

26 Sale's Preliminary Discourse, Sect. iii.

27 So also (as I learn from Mr. Keightley) "in a poem of the old poet Occleve, in Browne's Shepherd's Pipe."

28 Sale's note to verse 20 of the 27th chapter of the Ḳur-án.

29 A few of these anecdotes have been already given from other sources; for at the time of my inserting them, I had not received from Cairo the whole of the copy from which my translation is made, and had no means of knowing that it contained those anecdotes. Their places in the original will be mentioned as they occur in order. As they rest on better authority than that of the Thousand and One Nights, and illustrate the notes in which they are inserted, it has been thought best to retain them in their present form in this edition.

sive translations of which one has been made from the other. With respect to Von Hammer's version, the only remarks that I can venture to make are these; 1st, that he appears to have considerably abridged the stories; 2ndly, that he has omitted very few of them altogether but such as had been previously translated, and not all of these; and, 3rdly, that he has generally preserved the best of the verses with which they are interspersed. Thus, in two respects, his plan differs from that which is pursued by me; for I scarcely ever abridge in the smallest degree, except in the omission of many of the pieces of poetry; but reject entirely those stories which I think the English reader would find tedious, or otherwise displeasing. And here I must remark, that some pieces of appropriate poetry occur in the versions above mentioned in places where none, or some slightly different, are found in mine, because the pieces in my original do not always admit of being rendered as they are in the former versions. Of this, the reader may judge by comparing my translation of the first poetical quotation in the third of the following anecdotes with the corresponding couplet in M. Trébutien's version (vol. iii. pp. 280-1), which runs thus:—

> "Le ciel a récompensé ceux qui honorèrent Joseph lorsqu'il était encore dans sa prison; ainsi le ciel me mettra peut-être un jour en état de reconnaître vos bienfaits envers moi."

In my original, as follows:—

> "Wa-'asa-lledhee ahdà li-yoosufa ahlahu: wa-a'azzahu fi-s-sejni wa-hwa aseeru:
> An yestejeeba lanà wa-yejma'a shemlanà: wa-lláhu rabbu-l-'álameena ḳadeeru."

The same remark applies also in many cases to the prose. M. Trébutien's version I consider superior to that of Mr. Lamb; but I regret his having endeavoured to imitate the style of Galland.—I have deemed it necessary to make the above observations in justice to Von Hammer and his translators, and to myself; as my reader has now arrived at the point where he is first enabled to compare the versions above mentioned with my own.

The following anecdotes are selected from a series of nine, commencing with part of the two hundred and sixty-ninth Night, and ending with part of the two hundred and eighty-fifth.

Liberality of Ḥátim Eṭ-Ṭáee *after his Death.*

It is related of Ḥátim Eṭ-Ṭáee,[30] that, when he died, he was buried on the summit of a mountain,[31] and they made over his grave two troughs of stone, and stone images of damsels with dishevelled hair. Beneath that mountain ran a river; and when travellers arriving there alighted at that place, they heard a loud crying during the whole night, from nightfall until morn; but when they arose in the morning, they found no one save only the damsels carved of stone. And when Zu-l-Keláạ,[32] the King

[30] Ḥátim Eṭ-Ṭáee (i. e. Ḥátim of the tribe of Ṭeiyi) was most highly celebrated for his generosity. He lived in "the Time of Ignorance;" but his son 'Adee became a Muslim, and is numbered among the Companions of the Prophet. Ḥátim's most famous act of liberality was that which he shewed to an ambassador of the Greek Emperor, sent to demand of him, as a present for his master, a horse of very great price. The generous Arab, before he knew the object of this person's mission, slaughtered his horse to regale him, having nothing at the time in his house to serve in its stead.—It is also said that he often caused as many as forty camels to be slaughtered for the entertainment of his neighbours and the poor Arabs of the desert. (D'Herbelot.)

[31] Called 'Owáriḍ, in the district of Ṭeiyi. (Ḳámoos.)

[32] So in the edition of Breslau: in the Cairo edition, Zu-l-Kuráạ. Two Kings of El-Yemen named Zu-l-Keláạ are mentioned in the Ḳámoos, surnamed the Greater and the Less.—My sheykh remarks that this anecdote is related at length in the "Aghánee;" but that the person who demanded Ḥátim's hospitality was a man named Abu-l-Kheyberee. Zu-l-Keláạ, he adds, lived a long time before Ḥátim.

of Ḥemyer, alighted in that valley, going forth from his tribe, he passed a night there, and, approaching the place, he heard the crying: so he said, What is this lamentation that is on the summit of this mountain? They answered him, Here is the sepulchre of Ḥátim Eṭ-Ṭáee, over which are two troughs of stone, with stone images of damsels with dishevelled hair, and every night, persons who alight in this place hear this lamentation and crying. Upon this, Zu-l-Keláạ said, in mockery of Ḥátim Eṭ-Ṭáee, O Ḥátim, we are this night thy guests, and lank with hunger. And after sleep had overcome him, he awoke in alarm, exclaiming, O Arabs, come hither to me and to my beast! And when they came, they found the she-camel convulsed: so they slaughtered her, and roasted her flesh, and ate. They then asked him the cause of this; and he answered, I was sleeping, and saw in a dream Ḥátim Eṭ-Ṭáee, who came to me with a sword, and said, Thou hast visited us when we have nothing in our possession. And he wounded my she-camel with the sword. Had ye not slaughtered her, she had died.

And when the next morning came, Zu-l-Keláạ mounted the beast of one of his companions, taking the man up behind him; and at mid-day they saw a man riding a beast and leading another beast by his hand; and they said to him, Who art thou? He answered, I am 'Adee the son of Ḥátim Eṭ-Ṭáee. And where, he added, is Zu-l-Keláạ, the Prince of Ḥemyer? So they answered him, This is he. And he said to Zu-l-Keláạ, Mount this she-camel, instead of thine own; for thy she-camel, my father hath slaughtered for thee.—And who, said Zu-l-Keláạ, informed thee? 'Adee answered, My father came to me in sleep this last night, and said to me, O 'Adee, Zu-l-Keláạ, the King of Ḥemyer hath demanded my hospitality, and I have slaughtered for him his she-camel: so repair thou to him with a she-camel for him to ride; for I have nothing in my possession.—Zu-l-Keláạ therefore took her, and wondered at the generosity displayed by Ḥátim while living and when dead.

Anecdote of Maạn *the Son of* Záïdeh.

As Maạn the son of Záïdeh[33] was hunting, one day, he thirsted, and found not any water with his young men. But while he was in this state, lo, three damsels approached him, carrying three skins of water. He therefore requested drink of them, and they gave it him; and he demanded something of his young men, to give it to the damsels; but found that they had no money. So he presented to each of the damsels ten arrows from his quiver, the heads of which were of gold. Whereupon one of them said to her companions, This generous conduct cannot proceed from any but Maạn the son of Záïdeh: do ye each, then, recite some poetry in his praise. Accordingly, the first said,—

---

[33] Maạn the son of Záïdeh was compared, for his liberality, to Ḥátim Eṭ-Ṭáee. He was one of the chief captains of Marwán, the last of the Umawee Khaleefehs, and was eventually received into the favour of the 'Abbásee Khaleefeh El-Manṣoor. (See D'Herbelot, *art.* "Mán ou Mâan, fils de Zaïdeh," where another and more interesting anecdote of him is given.)

He headeth his arrows with points of gold, and in smiting his enemies dispenseth his munificence,
Affording the wounded a means of cure, and grave-clothes for him whose abode is the tomb.

And the second said,—

A warriour of such excessive liberality, that his benefits are bestowed both on friends and foes.
The heads of his arrows are made of gold, that war may not hinder him from acts of munificence.

Then the third recited a couplet, in substance the same as that of the first.

Adventures of Ibráheem *the Son of* El-Mahdee.[34]

Ibráheem the son of El-Mahdee,[35] and brother of Hároon Er-Rasheed, when the office of Khaleefeh devolved to El-Ma-moon the son of his brother Er-Rasheed, refused to vow allegiance to him, and repaired to Er-Rei,[36] where he assumed to himself the title of Khaleefeh, and thus he continued to do for the space of one year and eleven months and twelve days. His brother's son, El-Ma-moon, remained expecting his return to obedience, and his ranging himself among the number of his followers, until at length, despairing of his doing so, he mounted and set forth with his horsemen and foot-soldiers to Er-Rei. And when the news of his approach was brought to Ibráheem, he found no resource but that of going to Baghdád, where he hid himself, fearing for

---

34 This anecdote is related, nearly word for word as in the Cairo edition, by El-Is-ḥáḳee, from the "Kowkab el-Wahháj" of Ibráheem El-Andalusee, afterwards Ed-Dimashḳee.

35 This celebrated personage was a very skilful musician, an admirable singer, remarkably polite and liberal and eloquent. His complexion was very dark; his mother being a black slave, named Shekleh, or Shikleh, whom El-Mahdee had married; and he was so corpulent, that he received the nickname of Et-Teen, or The Fig. (D'Herbelot, *art.* "Ibrahim Abou Ishák Ben Mahadi;"—and Ibn Khallikán.)

36 A city in the north of the Persian 'Eráḳ.

his life; and El-Ma-moon offered to any one who would point out his place of concealment a hundred thousand pieces of gold.

Now when I heard of this reward that was offered, says Ibráheem, I feared for myself, and was perplexed at my case. So I went forth from my house at the hour of mid-day, not knowing whither to repair, and I entered a great street that was not a thoroughfare, and, seeing at the upper end of it a barber[37] standing at the door of his house, I advanced towards him, and said to him, Hast thou any place in which I may conceal myself for a while? He answered, Yes:—and opened the door, and I entered a clean house. Then, after he had brought me in, he closed the door upon me, and went away. I suspected, therefore, that he had heard of the reward that was offered, and said within myself, He hath gone forth to betray me. So I remained in a state of agitation like the pot upon the fire, reflecting upon my case; but while I was in this state, lo, he came, attended by a porter with all that he required; and, looking towards me, he said to me, May I be thy ransom!—I was in want of food, and prepared for myself a saucepan-full, the like of which I do not remember ever to have eaten before; and when I had satisfied myself with it, he said, O my master, it is not consistent with

---

[37] In the Breslau edition, and in Trébutien's version, and also in El-Is-ḥáḳee, the barber is described as a negro; but in an account of the occurrence resting on good authority (in D'Herbelot, *ubi suprà*), he is said to have been a person of very dark complexion, much resembling, in this respect, Ibráheem himself.

my station to converse with thee; but if thou desire to honour thy slave, thine own surpassing judgment will determine. I therefore said to him, not imagining that he knew me, And whence hast thou learned that I excel in conversation? Whereupon he exclaimed, Extolled be the perfection of Allah! Our lord is too celebrated for me to be ignorant of that. Thou art my master Ibráheem the son of El-Mahdee, respecting whom El-Ma-moon hath announced that he will give to him who discovereth thee a hundred thousand pieces of gold.—And when he said this, he became exalted in my eye, and his generosity was established in my opinion: so I complied with his desire, and, the remembrance of my children and my family occurring to my mind, I said,—

> Perhaps He who restored to Yoosuf his family, and aggrandized him in the prison when he was a captive,
> May answer our prayer, and reunite us; for God, the Lord of all creatures, is able.

And when he heard these words from me, he said, O my master, wilt thou permit me to repeat what hath suggested itself to my mind? I answered, Do so. And he recited two pieces of poetry; on hearing which, I was filled with the utmost wonder at him, and moved with extreme delight. I then took a purse that I had with me, containing a number of pieces of gold, and threw it towards him, saying to him, I commend thee to the care of God; for I am about to depart from thee; I beg thee to employ the contents of this purse in the purchase of some of the things that thou requirest, and thou wilt receive from me an abundant recompense when I am secure from that which I fear. But he gave me back the purse, and said, O my master, paupers like myself are of no estimation with you; yet, consistently with my feelings of generosity, how can I accept payment for the boon which fortune had granted me in causing thee to shew me such favour and to visit my abode? By Allah, if thou repeat those words, and throw the purse to me a second time, I will kill myself. So I took the purse, putting it into my sleeve,[38] and the weight of it incommoded me; and I turned to leave him; but when I came to the door of his house, he said, O my master, this place is more suited for thy concealment than another, and the supplying thee with provisions is no burden to me; therefore remain with me until God dispel thy trouble. So I replied, On the condition that thou expend from this purse. And he deceived me by professing his assent to this condition. Accordingly, I remained with him some days; but he expended nothing from the purse.

I then attired myself in women's apparel, with the khuff[39] and the veil, and went forth from his house. But when I was in the street, excessive fear overcame me; and as I was about to pass over the bridge, I found myself in a place sprinkled with water,[40] and a trooper, one of those who had been in my service, saw me and recognised me; whereupon he called out and said, This is the person of whom El-Ma-moon is in quest! And he laid hold upon me. I however pushed him and his horse, and threw both down in that slippery place, so that the rider became an example to him who would be admonished, and the people hastened towards him.

I therefore hurried on until I had passed the bridge, when I entered a great street, and, seeing the door of a house, and a woman standing in the passage, I said, O my mistress, save my life; for I am a man in fear. She replied, No harm shall befall thee. And she took me up into a supping-room, where she spread furniture for me, and brought to me some food, saying to me, Let thy terror subside. And while she was thus comforting me, the door was knocked with violence. So she went forth and

---

[38] An Arab often carries things in his long and ample sleeve, gathering up the greater part of its edge in his hand.

[39] A kind of socks, or short boots, of yellow morocco, still worn by Arab and some other Eastern ladies, within the slipper, when walking abroad, or riding.

[40] The ground is generally sprinkled in the streets &c. of Arab cities, during the summer, to cool the air as well as to lay the dust; but a narrow space is usually left dry, in the middle; this being especially necessary for the camels.

opened it; and, lo, my acquaintance whom I had pushed upon the bridge came forward, with his head bound, and his blood running down upon his clothes, and his horse was not with him. She said to him, What is this? What calamity hath befallen thee?—He answered, I caught the man, and he made his escape from me. And he related to her the whole affair. And she took forth a piece of rag, with which she bound his head; after which, she spread a bed for him, and he lay sick. Then coming up to me, she said to me, I imagine that thou art the person in question. I replied, Yes. And she said, No harm shall befall thee. She then renewed her generous conduct to me, and I remained with her three days; at the expiration of which, she said to me, I am in fear for thee from this man, lest he come up to thee, and thou fall into the misfortune that thou dreadest: therefore save thyself by flight. But I requested her to delay my departure until the night; and she said, There will be no harm in that.

So when the night came, I put on the women's apparel, and, going forth from her, repaired to the house of an emancipated female slave who had belonged to us; and when she saw me, she wept, and appeared grieved, and praised God (whose name be exalted!) for my safety, and went forth as though she would go to the market to procure what was requisite for my entertainment. But suddenly I beheld Ibráheem El-Mósilee,[41] approaching in the midst of his young men and troopers, with a woman before them; and, looking narrowly at her, I found that she was the emancipated slave, the owner of the house where I was. She walked on before them until she delivered me into their hands, and I was carried, in the women's attire, to El-Ma-moon.

He held a general council, and caused me to be brought in before him; and when I entered, I saluted him as Khaleefeh;[42] but he replied, May God not preserve thee nor bless thee! So I said to him, Act according to thy good pleasure, O Prince of the Faithful: thou hast the command; therefore decide upon punishment or pardon; but pardon is the more agreeable with piety. God hath made thy pardon to excel that of every other person, as He hath made my offence to exceed every other offence, O Prince of the Faithful; and if thou take vengeance it will be in thy justice, and if thou pardon it will be in thy generosity. Then I recited these verses:—

My offence against thee is great; but thou art greater than it:
So exact thy due, or else, in thy clemency remit it.
If *I* have not been of the generous in conduct, do *thou* be so.

El-Ma-moon then raised his head, and I quickly recited these other verses:—

---

[41] See Note 22 to Chap. iii.

[42] Saying, "Peace be on thee, O Prince of the Faithful!"

I have committed an enormous offence; but thou art disposed to pardon.
If thou pardon, thou wilt be gracious; and if thou punish, thou wilt be just.

And El-Ma-moon hung down his head, and repeated this couplet:—

When a friend desireth to enrage me, and causeth me to be choked in my anger,
I forgive his offences, and pardon him, fearing lest I should live friendless.

So when I heard these words from him, I perceived from them the odour of mercy. He then addressed the son of his uncle, and his brother Is-ḥáḳ, and all his chief officers who were present, and said to them, What course do ye see to be suitable to his case? Whereupon every one of them advised him to slay me; but they differed as to the mode of slaughter. El-Ma-moon, however, said to Aḥmad the son of Khálid, What sayest thou, O Aḥmad?—O Prince of the Faithful, he answered, if thou slay him, we find an instance of such a person as thyself who hath slain such as he is; and if thou pardon him, we find not an instance of any like thee who hath pardoned one like him. And when El-Ma-moon heard the words of Aḥmad the son of Khálid, he hung down his head, and repeated the saying of the poet:—

My family have slain Umeym, my brother: so if I shoot at them, my arrow will revert to me.
If I pardon, I shall grant an egregious pardon; and if I assault, I shall weaken my own bones.[43]

And he recited also these words of the poet:—

Forgive thy brother when he mingleth what is right with what is wrong;
And continue thy kindness to him, whether he be thankful or ungrateful;
And abstain thou from reproaching him, whether he err or act justly.
Dost thou not see that what thou lovest and what thou hatest are conjoined?
And that the delight of long life is disturbed by the mixture of grey hairs?
And that the thorns[44] appear upon the branches together with the fruit that is gathered?
Who is he that hath never done evil? And who hath done good alone?
If thou triedst the sons of this age, thou wouldst find that most of them had erred.

On hearing these verses from him, I removed the veil from my head, loudly exclaiming, God is most great![45]—and said, May God pardon *thee*, O Prince of the Faithful! He replied, No harm shall befall thee, O uncle.—O Prince of the Faithful, I rejoined, my offence is too great for me to utter any thing in excuse of it, and thy pardon is too great for me to express my thanks. Then, with mirth-exciting modulations, I sang these verses:—

Verily the Author of all virtues collected them in the loins of Adam for the Seventh Imám.[46]
Thou hast filled men's hearts with reverence for thee, and with an humble heart thou guardest them all.
I rebelled not against thee, overwhelmed by delusion, from any motive but that of covetousness;[47]
And thou hast pardoned one whose like never was pardoned before, though none interceded with thee,
And hast pitied little-ones like those of the ḳaṭà,[48] and the yearning of a mother with impatient heart.

To this, El-Ma-moon replied, I say, in imitation of the example of our lord Yoosuf (upon our Prophet and upon him be blessing and peace!), There shall be no reproach cast on you this day: God forgive you; for He is the most merciful of those who shew mercy.[49]

---

[43] This latter verse is omitted in my original, but supplied by my sheykh in the margin.

[44] In the original, "And that the *rose* appeareth." The requisite correction is made, as usual, by my sheykh.

[45] This is the usual Muslim cry of victory.

[46] By "the Seventh Imám" is meant El-Ma-moon, the seventh of the 'Abbásee Khaleefehs

[47] Or, as explained by my sheykh, "coveting thy pardon."

[48] The ḳaṭà is a kind of grouse, that deposits its eggs in the desert, at a great distance from any water. The comparison in the verse is therefore apt and strong.—See De Sacy, Chrestomathie Arabe, 2nd. ed., vol. ii. p. 370. See also Note 30 to the Introduction of the present work.

[49] These words, beginning, "There shall be no reproach," are from the Ḳur-án, ch. xii. v. 92.

And I restore to thee thy wealth and thy lands, O uncle, and no harm shall befall thee. —So I devoutly supplicated blessings upon him, and recited these verses:—

Thou hast restored my wealth, and not been avaricious of it; and before thou didst this, thou sparedst my life.
I would give my blood to obtain thine approval, and my wealth till I drew off the shoe from my foot.
Were I ungrateful for the favours thou hast granted me, I should be more base than thou art generous.

El-Ma-moon then treated me with honour and beneficence, and said to me, O uncle, verily Aboo-Is-ḥáḳ and El-'Abbás advised me to slay thee. I replied, Verily Aboo-Is-ḥáḳ and El-'Abbás advised thee faithfully, O Prince of the Faithful; but thou hast acted as became thyself, and averted that which thou fearedst by doing what thou desiredst. And he said, I have extinguished my rancour by sparing thy life, and I have pardoned thee without burdening thee by obligations to intercessors. Then he prostrated himself in adoration for a long time; after which he raised his head, and said, O uncle, knowest thou wherefore I prostrated myself? I answered, Perhaps thou didst so to thank God for his having made thee master of thine enemy. He replied, I desired not that; but to thank God that He had inspired me to pardon thee.—I then explained to him my case, and told him what had happened to me with the cupper [or barber], and with the trooper and his wife, and the emancipated female slave who betrayed me: whereupon El-Ma-moon gave orders to bring that emancipated female slave. She was in her house, expecting the reward to be sent to her; and when she came before El-Ma-moon, he said to her, What induced thee to act as thou didst to thy master? She answered, Desire for the money. And he said, Hast thou a child or a husband? She answered, No. And upon this he gave orders to inflict upon her a hundred lashes, and commanded that she should be imprisoned for life. He then caused the trooper and his wife and the cupper to be brought; and when they had all come, he asked the trooper the cause of his having acted as he had done. He answered, Desire for the money. And El-Ma-moon replied, Thou must be a cupper. And accordingly he commissioned a person to place him in the shop of a cupper that he might teach him his art. But the trooper's wife he treated with honour, and he took her into the palace, and said, This is a sensible woman, fit to be employed in affairs of importance. Then he said to the cupper, There hath been such evidence of thy generosity as requireth that extraordinary honour should be paid to thee. And he commanded that the house of the trooper should be given up to him, and bestowed upon him, in addition to that, fifteen thousand pieces of gold.

The Discovery and History of Irem Zát el-'Emád, *the Terrestrial Paradise of* Sheddád *the Son of* 'Ád.[50]

It is related that 'Abd-Allah the son of Aboo-Ḳilábeh went forth to seek a camel that had run away, and while he was proceeding over the deserts of El-Yemen and the district of Sebà, he chanced to arrive at a vast city encompassed by enormous fortifications, around the circuit of which were pavilions rising high into the sky. So when he approached it, he imagined that there must be inhabitants within it, of whom he might inquire for his camel; and accordingly he advanced to it; but on coming to it, he found that it was desolate, without any one to cheer its solitude.

I alighted, says he, from my she-camel, and tied up her foot; and then, composing my mind, entered the city. On approaching the fortifications, I found that they had two enormous gates, the like of which, for size and height, have never been seen elsewhere in the world, set with a variety of jewels and jacinths, white and red and yellow

---

50 The Breslau edition merely gives a brief account of the *construction* of Irem Zát el-'Emád, and mentions, at its close, that 'Abd-Allah the son of Aboo-Ḳilábeh discovered it.—On the stature of the 'Ádites, see Note 37 to Chapter ii.

and green; and when I beheld this, I was struck with the utmost wonder at it, and the sight astonished me. I entered the fortifications in a state of terror, and with a wandering mind, and saw them to be of the same large extent as the city, and to comprise elevated pavilions, every one of these containing lofty chambers, and all of them constructed of gold and silver, and adorned with rubies and chrysolites and pearls and various-coloured jewels. The folding-doors of these pavilions were like those of the fortifications in beauty, and their floors were overlaid with large pearls and with balls like hazel-nuts composed of musk and ambergris and saffron. And when I came into the midst of the city, I saw not in it a created being of the sons of Adam; and I almost died of terror. I then looked down from the summits of the lofty chambers and pavilions, and saw rivers running beneath them; and in the great thoroughfare-streets of the city were fruit-bearing trees, and tall palm-trees; and the construction of the city was of alternate bricks of gold and silver: so I said within myself, No doubt this is the Paradise promised in the world to come.

I carried away, of the jewels which were as its gravel, and the musk that was as its dust, as much as I could bear, and returned to my district, where I acquainted the people with the occurrence. And the news reached Mo'áwiyeh the son of Aboo-Sufyán (who was then Khaleefeh) in the Ḥejáz: so he wrote to his lieutenant in Ṣan'à of El-Yemen, saying, Summon that man, and inquire of him the truth of the matter. His lieutenant therefore caused me to be brought, and demanded of me an account of my adventure, and of what had befallen me; and I informed him of what I had seen. He then sent me to Mo'áwiyeh, and I acquainted him also with that which I had seen; but he disbelieved it: so I produced to him some of those pearls and the little balls of ambergris and musk and saffron. The latter retained somewhat of their sweet scent; but the pearls had become yellow and discoloured.

At the sight of these, Mo'áwiyeh wondered, and he sent and caused Kaạb-el-Aḥbár[51] to be brought before him, and said to him, O Kaạb-el-Aḥbár, I have called thee on account of a matter of which I desire to know the truth, and I hope that thou mayest be able to certify me of it.—And what is it, O Prince of the Faithful? asked Kaạb-el-Aḥbár. Mo'áwiyeh said, Hast thou any knowledge of the existence of a city constructed of gold and silver, the pillars whereof are of chrysolite and ruby, and the gravel of which is of pearls, and of balls like hazel-nuts, composed of musk and ambergris and saffron? He answered, Yes, O Prince of the Faithful. It is Irem Zát el-'Emád,[52] the like of which hath never been constructed in the regions of the earth; and Sheddád the son of 'Ád the Greater built it.—Relate to us, said Mo'áwiyeh, somewhat of its history. And Kaạb-el-Aḥbár replied thus:—

'Ád the Greater had two sons, Shedeed and Sheddád; and when their father perished, they reigned conjointly over the countries after him, and there was no one of the Kings of the earth who was not subject to them. And Shedeed the son of 'Ád died: so his brother Sheddád ruled alone over the earth after him. He was fond of reading the ancient books; and when he met with the description of the world to come, and of Paradise with its pavilions and lofty chambers and its trees and fruits, and of the other things in Paradise, his heart enticed him to construct its like on the earth, after this manner which hath been above mentioned. He had under his authority a hundred thousand Kings, under each of whom were a hundred thousand valiant chieftains, and under each of these were a hundred thousand soldiers. And he summoned them all before him, and said to them, I find in the ancient books and histories the description of the Paradise that is in the other world, and I desire to make its like upon the earth. Depart ye therefore to the most pleasant and most spacious vacant tract in the earth, and build for me in it a city of gold and silver, and spread, as its gravel, chrysolites and rubies and pearls, and as the supports of the vaulted roofs of that city make columns of chrysolite, and fill it with pavilions, and over the pavilions construct lofty chambers, and beneath them plant, in the by-streets and great thoroughfare-streets, varieties of trees bearing different kinds of ripe fruits, and make rivers to run beneath them in channels of gold and silver.—To this they all replied, How can we accomplish that which thou hast described to us, and how can we procure the chrysolites and rubies and pearls that thou hast mentioned? But he said, Know ye not that the Kings of the world are obedient to me, and under my authority, and that no one who is in it disobeyeth my command? They answered, Yes, we know that.—Depart then, said he, to the mines of chrysolite and ruby, and to the places where pearls are found, and gold and silver; and take forth and collect their contents from the earth, and spare no exertions. Take also for me from the hands of men such of those things as ye find, and spare none, nor let any escape you; and beware of disobedience.

---

51 A famous traditionist, of the tribe of Ḥemyer, who embraced El-Islám in the reign of 'Omar, and died in the year of the Flight 32, during the reign of 'Othmán. (Miskát el-Maṣábeeḥ, vol. i. p. 161.) The anecdote therefore presents an anachronism.

52 "Irem Zát el-'Emád" is generally understood to signify "Irem with the Lofty Buildings:" but Von Hammer has remarked (see Trébutien's translation, vol. iii. p. 286), that the story of this city, though related as true by Arab historians and others, is pronounced by Ibn-Khaldoon to be an invention of the commentators of the Ḳur-án; this judicious critic asserting, that "Irem" is the name of an ancient tribe, and that "'emád" is to be understood in this case as meaning "a tent-pole;" so that "Irem Zát el-'Emád" signifies "Irem with the [numerous] tent-poles, or tents." In like manner, the expression "ahlu-l-'emád" is used to signify "people dwelling in tents."

He then wrote a letter to each of the Kings in the regions of the earth, commanding them to collect all the articles of the kinds above-mentioned that their subjects possessed, and to repair to the mines in which these things were found, and extract the precious stones that they contained, even from the beds of the seas. And they collected the things that he required in the space of twenty years;[53] after which, he sent forth the geometricians [54] and sages, and labourers and artificers, from all the countries and regions, and they dispersed themselves through the deserts and wastes, and tracts and districts, until they came to a desert wherein was a vast open plain, clear from hills and mountains, and in it were springs gushing forth, and rivers running. So they said, This is the kind of place which the King commanded us to seek, and called us to find. They then busied themselves in building the city according to the direction of the King Sheddád, King of the whole earth, in its length and breadth; and they made through it the channels for the rivers, and laid the foundations conformably with the prescribed extent. The Kings of the various districts of the earth sent thither the jewels and stones, and large and small pearls, and carnelion and pure gold, upon camels over the deserts and wastes, and sent great ships with them over the seas; and a quantity of those things, such as cannot be described nor calculated nor defined, was brought to the workmen, who laboured in the construction of this city three hundred years. And when they had finished it, they came to the King and acquainted him with the completion; and he said to them, Depart, and make around it impregnable fortifications, of great height, and construct around the circuit of the fortifications a thousand pavilions, each with a thousand pillars[55] beneath it, in order that there may be in each pavilion a Wezeer. So they went immediately, and did this in twenty years; after which they presented themselves before Sheddád, and informed him of the accomplishment of his desire.

He therefore ordered his wezeers, who were a thousand in number, and his chief officers, and such of his troops and others as he confided in, to make themselves ready for departure, and to prepare themselves for removal to Irem Zát el-'Emád, in attendance upon the King of the world, Sheddád the son of 'Ád. He ordered also such as he chose of his women and his ḥareem, as his female slaves and his eunuchs, to fit themselves out. And they passed twenty years in equipping themselves. Then Sheddád proceeded with his troops, rejoiced at the accomplishment of his desire, until there remained between him and Irem Zát el-'Emád one day's journey; when God sent down upon him and upon the obstinate infidels who accompanied him a loud cry from the heaven of his power, and it destroyed them all by the vehemence of its sound.[56] Neither Sheddád nor any of those who were with him arrived at the city or came in sight of it, and God obliterated the traces of the road that led to it; but the city remaineth as it was in its place until the hour of the judgment.

At this narrative related by Kaạb-el-Aḥbár, Mo'áwiyeh wondered, and he said to him, Can any one of mankind arrive at that city?—Yes, answered Kaạb-el-Aḥbár: a man of the companions of Moḥammad (upon whom be blessing and peace!), in appearance like this man who is sitting here, without any doubt.—Esh-Shaạbee[57] also saith, It is related on the authority of the learned men of Ḥemyer, in El-Yemen, that when Sheddád and those who were with him were destroyed by the loud cry, his son

---

[53] Here it is added, "and the number of the Kings ruling in the earth was three hundred and sixty Kings:" but this does not agree with what has been said before.

[54] In the original, "muhendiseen," a term often applied to architects, and engineers.

[55] Instead of "'alam" (standard or banner, &c.,) in the Cairo edition, I read "'amood" (pillars), agreeably with the description in the edition of Breslau.

[56] This was not the final catastrophe of the tribe of 'Ád. The whole of this tribe, except a few persons, rejecting the admonitions of the prophet Hood, were destroyed by a hot and suffocating wind.

[57] There was a traditionist surnamed Esh-Shaạbee, another surnamed Esh-Shoạbee, and a third surnamed Esh-Sheạbee; and which of them is here meant I know not, the short vowel-signs not being written.

Sheddád the Less reigned after him; for his father Sheddád the Greater had left him as successor to his kingdom, in the land of Ḥaḍramót and Sebà, on his departure with the troops who accompanied him to Irem Zát el-'Emád. And as soon as the news reached him of the death of his father on the way before his arrival at the city of Irem, he gave orders to carry his father's body from those desert tracts to Ḥaḍramót, and to excavate a sepulchre for him in a cavern. And when they had done this, he placed his body in it, upon a couch of gold, and covered the corpse with seventy robes interwoven with gold and adorned with precious jewels; and he placed at his head a tablet of gold, whereon were inscribed these verses:—

Be admonished, O thou who art deceived by a prolonged life!
I am Sheddád the son of 'Ád, the lord of the strong fortress;
The lord of power and might and of excessive valour.
The inhabitants of the earth obeyed me, fearing my severity and threats;
And I held the east and west under a strong dominion.
And a preacher[58] of the true religion invited us to the right way;
But we opposed him, and said, Is there no refuge from it?
And a loud cry assaulted us from a tract of the distant horizon;
Whereupon we fell down like corn in the midst of a plain at harvest;
And now, beneath the earth, we await the threatened day.

—Eth-Tha'álibee also saith, It happened that two men entered this cavern, and found at its upper end some steps; and having descended these, they found an excavation, the length whereof was a hundred cubits, and its breadth forty cubits, and its height a hundred cubits. And in the midst of this excavation was a couch of gold, upon which was a man of enormous bulk, occupying its whole length and breadth, covered

58 The Prophet Hood, vulgarly believed to be Heber.

with ornaments and with robes interwoven with gold and silver; and at his head was a tablet of gold, whereon was an inscription. And they took that tablet, and carried away from the place as much as they could of bars of gold and silver, and other things.

Anecdote of Is-ḥáḳ El-Móṣilee *and* Khadeejeh *and* El-Ma-moon.

I went forth one night, says Is-ḥáḳ El-Móṣilee,[59] from the presence of El-Ma-moon, and, turning into a by-street, I saw something hanging from one of the houses there. So I felt it, to discover what it was, and found that it was a large basket,[60] with four handles, and covered with brocade; whereupon I said within myself, There must be some cause for this. And I was perplexed at my case.

Intoxication induced me to seat myself in the basket; and when I had done so, lo, the people of the house drew it up with me in it, thinking that I was the person whom they were expecting. And when they had raised it to the top of the wall, behold, four damsels were there, and they said to me, Descend, and may ample enjoyment attend thee. Then a damsel walked before me with a candle until I descended into a mansion in which were sitting-rooms spread [with carpets and other furniture], the like of which I had never seen except in the palace of the Khaleefeh. And after I had sat a while, suddenly some curtains were raised on one side of the apartment, and, lo, maids walked in with candles in their hands, and with perfuming-vessels containing aloes-wood; and among them was a damsel like the rising full moon. So I rose; and she said, Thou art a welcome visiter. Then having desired me to be seated, she inquired of me my story. I therefore answered her, I came forth from certain of my brethren, and, turning into this street, found a basket let down; whereupon the wine induced me to seat myself in it, and it was drawn up, with me in it, to this house. This, said I, is my case.—And she said, No harm shall befall thee, and I hope thou wilt approve of the result of thine adventure. And what, she added, is thine occupation? I answered, That of a merchant in the market of Baghdád. And she said, Canst thou repeat any verses?—Some trifling pieces, I answered.—Then mention them to us, said she, and recite to us somewhat of them. But I replied, The visiter is bashful: do thou begin.—Thou hast spoken truly, she said. And she recited some elegant verses, of the poetry of ancient and of recent composers, some of their most admirable effusions; and I listened, and knew not whether to wonder most at her beauty and loveliness, or at the charming style of her rehearsal. After this she said, Hath thy bashfulness passed away?—Yea, by Allah, I answered. And she said, If thou wilt, recite to us somewhat of that which thou art able to rehearse. So I recited to her an abundance of pieces by a number of old writers; and she approved them, and said, By Allah, I did not imagine that there existed among the sons of the common people such a person as this.

---

59 A very famous musician, and the favourite boon-companion of El-Ma-moon. He was the son of Ibráheem El-Móṣilee. See Note 22 to Chapter iii.

60 This kind of basket, called "zembeel" or "zimbeel," is formed of palm-leaves.

She then gave orders to bring the food; and it was brought, and she began to take and to put before me; and varieties of sweet-smelling flowers were there, with rare fruits, such as are usually found nowhere but in the abodes of Kings. Afterwards she called for the wine, and she drank a cup, and handed one to me, saying, This is the time for conversation and relating stories. I therefore began to converse with her, and to say, I have been told that such and such things happened, and there was a man who said so and so,—until I had related to her a number of agreeable stories; with which she was delighted; and she said, I wonder how it is that one of the merchants is able to repeat stories like these; for they are such as are proper for Kings. So I said, I had a neighbour who used to converse with the Kings, and serve as their boon-companion; and when he was unoccupied, I used to visit his house, and sometimes he would relate what thou hast heard. And she replied, By my life, thou hast retained them well. We continued our conversation, whenever I was silent she beginning, until we had passed the greater part of the night, the fumes of the aloes-wood imparting a constant odour to the air; and I was in such a state that if El-Ma-moon could have imagined it, he would have flown with desire to enjoy it. She then said, Verily thou art one of the most pleasant and polished of men; for thou art a person of surpassing good breeding; and there is but one thing wanting.—And what, said I, is that? She answered, Couldst thou sing verses to the sounds of the lute? So I replied, I used to devote myself to this art of old; but not being endowed with a talent for it, I relinquished it; and my heart is inflamed on that account. I should be glad to sing something well on the present occasion, that my night's enjoyment might be complete.

On hearing this, she said, It seemeth thou hast proposed that the lute should be brought. I replied, It is thine to decide: thou art the conferrer of favours, and art entitled to thanks for thy kindness. And she gave orders to bring a lute; and when it was brought, she sang with a voice which I had never heard equalled in sweetness, with a charming manner, and admirable skill in striking the chords, and altogether with consummate excellence; after which she said, Knowest thou by whom this air was composed, and whose are the verses? I answered, No. And she said, The verses are by such-a-one, and the air is Is-ḥáḳ's. I said, And is Is-ḥáḳ (may I be thy ransom!) endowed with such talent?—Wonderful! wonderful! she exclaimed: Is-ḥáḳ surpasseth all in this art. And I said, Extolled be the perfection of Allah, who hath given to this man what He hath not given to any beside him!—And how then wouldst thou be charmed, she added, if thou heardest this air sung by him!—Thus we continued to pass the time until daybreak, when an old woman, who seemed to be her nurse, addressed her and said, The time hath arrived. So she arose at her words, and said, Keep thou our conduct secret; for social meetings are confidential.—May I be thy ransom! I replied: I required no charge on that subject. I then bade her farewell, and she sent a damsel to walk before me to the door of the house, and she opened to me, and I went forth to my own abode.

Having arrived there, I performed the morning-prayers, and slept; and the messenger of El-Ma-moon came to me; so I repaired to him, and remained with him that day. And when the hour of nightfall came, I reflected upon the pleasure that I had enjoyed during the preceding night, and it was such as none but the fool could be withheld from. I therefore went forth, and, coming to the basket, seated myself in it, and was drawn up to the place in which I was the night before. The damsel said to me, Thou hast been assiduous. But I replied, I do not think myself to have been otherwise than neglectful. We then chatted together, as in the preceding night, each of us supplying subjects of conversation, and reciting poetry, and relating strange tales, until dawn; when I departed to my abode, and performed the morning-prayers, and slept.

The messenger of El-Ma-moon then came to me, and I repaired to him; and after I had passed the day with him, and the hour of nightfall arrived, the Prince of the

Faithful said to me, I conjure thee to sit here until I have gone and accomplished an object that I have in view and come back. But when the Khaleefeh had gone away from me, disquieting thoughts arose in my mind, and, reflecting upon my late enjoyment, what I might experience from the Prince of the Faithful seemed of little moment to me. So I sprang up and retired, and went forth running until I came to the basket; whereupon I seated myself in it, and it was drawn up with me to the place of my former visits; and the damsel said, Probably thou art our friend?—Yea, by Allah, I answered.—And she said, Hast thou made our house thine abode? I answered, May I be thy ransom! The right of a stranger to hospitality is for three days; and if I return after that period, ye shall be free to shed my blood.—We then sat amusing ourselves as on the former occasions; and when the time of departure drew near, knowing that El-Ma-moon would certainly question me, and would not be content with any thing but an explanation of the affair, I said to her, I see thee to be one of those who take pleasure in singing, and I have a cousin who is more comely than myself in countenance, and of higher rank, and more accomplished manners, and he is most nearly acquainted of all the creatures of God (whose name be exalted!) with Is-ḥáḳ. Upon this she said, Art thou a spunger and dost thou urge an impertinent request? I answered her, Thou art the arbitress of the matter. And she replied, If thy cousin be as thou hast described him, we shall have no dislike to be acquainted with him.—Then the time came, and I arose and went homewards.

But before I arrived at my house, the messengers of El-Ma-moon rushed upon me, and violently bore me away to him. I found him sitting upon a throne, and incensed against me; and he said, O Is-ḥáḳ, hast thou swerved from allegiance? I answered, No, by Allah, O Prince of the Faithful.—What then is thy story? said he: relate the affair to me with truth. So I replied, Well; but in privacy. He therefore made a sign to those who were before him; whereupon they retired; and I told him the story, and said to him, I promised her that thou wouldst pay her a visit. And he said, Thou hast done well. We then occupied ourselves with our usual pleasures that day; but the heart of El-Ma-moon was intent upon the damsel; and scarcely had the appointed time arrived when we departed. I charged him, saying, Refrain from calling me by my name before her; and be as though thou wert my attendant [61] in her presence. And we agreed on this subject.

We proceeded until we came to the place where the basket had been hung, and we found two baskets: so we seated ourselves in them, and they were drawn up with us to the same place. The damsel then advanced and saluted us; and when El-Ma-moon beheld her, he was astonished at her beauty and loveliness. She began to relate stories to him, and to recite verses, and afterwards caused the wine to be brought, and we drank; she making him the object of her particular favour, and rejoicing in his society, and he shewing the same favour to her, and alike delighted with her. And she took the lute, and sang these verses:—[62]

> The beloved visited me towards the close of night. I stood, to shew him honour, until he sat down.
> I said, O my intimate, and all my desire, hast thou come this night and not feared the watch?
> He answered, The love-smitten feared; but his desire had forcibly deprived him of his reason.

---

[61] So in the Calcutta edition of the first two hundred Nights: in the Cairo edition, "but I will be thy attendant."

[62] From the Calcutta edition of the first two hundred Nights, vol. i. p. 425. [These verses, slightly varied, form the conclusion of one of the muweshshaḥs, or religious love-odes, usually sung at zikrs in Egypt, and cited in the Modern Egyptians. As specimens of the religious poetry of the Muslims, these odes deserve attention from their striking similarity to the Song of Solomon; and, as Mr. Lane remarks, decide the question of the object of the latter. They are confessedly addressed to the Prophet, in a spiritual sense, and so understood by the persons who sing them, although the vulgar apply them to human love. See the Modern Egyptians, vol. ii. ch. xi.—Ed.]

She then said to me, And is thy cousin of the merchants? And she pointed towards El-Ma-moon. I answered, Yes. And she said, Verily ye nearly resemble each other. I replied, Yes.

And when El-Ma-moon had drunk three pints,[63] being moved with joy and merriment, he called out and said, O Is-ḥáḳ! I replied, At thy service, O Prince of the Faithful.—Sing, said he, this air. And when the damsel discovered that he was the Khaleefeh, she retired into another apartment. So after I had finished my song, El-Ma-moon said to me, See who is the master of this house. Whereupon an old woman quickly answered and said, It belongeth to El-Ḥasan the son of Sahl. And he said, Bring him hither unto me. The old woman, therefore, was absent for a short time, and, lo, El-Ḥasan came in. El-Ma-moon said to him, Hast thou a daughter? He answered, Yes: her name is Khadeejeh.[64]—Is she married? said the Khaleefeh. El-Ḥasan answered, No, by Allah. Then, said El-Ma-moon, I demand her of thee as my wife. El-Ḥasan replied, She is thy handmaiden, and at thy disposal, O Prince of the Faithful. And the Khaleefeh said, I marry her on the condition of paying in ready money, as her dowry, thirty thousand pieces of gold, which shall be brought to thee this next morning: so, after thou shalt have received the money, do thou convey her to us in the following night. He replied, I hear and obey. We then went forth; and he said, O Is-ḥáḳ, tell not this story to any one. I therefore kept it a secret until El-Ma-moon died.

Never have such pleasures altogether fallen to the lot of any one, as those which I enjoyed during these four days, keeping company with El-Ma-moon by day, and with Khadeejeh by night. By Allah, I have seen no one among men like El-Ma-moon, and I have not beheld among women the like of Khadeejeh, nor any who approached her in intelligence and sense and elocution.—And God is all-knowing.

[Some Arab authors have, not without reason, pronounced this anecdote an invention of Is-ḥáḳ. It is well known that El-Ma-moon married the daughter of his Wezeer El-Ḥasan the son of Sahl; but that he became acquainted with her in the manner above described is highly improbable. The marriage took place at Fem eṣ-Ṣilḥ, on the bank of the Tigris, near Wásiṭ, and was celebrated with a magnificence scarcely credible. El-Ḥasan, the father of the bride, scattered, among the officers and other chief persons who were present, balls of musk of the size of hazel-nuts, containing papers inscribed with the names of lands and of female slaves, and the descriptions of beasts &c., and into whose hand soever a ball fell, the property of which the name or description was written upon the enclosed paper was delivered to him, whether it were a piece of land, or other possession, or a horse, or a female slave, or a memlook. After that, he scattered, among the rest of the people, pieces of gold and silver, and bags of musk, and balls[65] of ambergris. He expended upon the entertainment of El-Ma-moon and his companions, and all his troops and other attendants, the number of whom was incalculable, even the camel-drivers, and the hired conductors of beasts, and the boatmen, so that none had occasion to purchase any thing for himself or for his beast. It is said that El-Ma-moon remained with El-Ḥasan nineteen days, the latter providing the Khaleefeh and all who were with him, each day, with every thing that they required; and that the sum which he expended upon them was fifty millions of pieces of silver.[66] El-Ma-moon, on his departure, gave orders to present him with ten millions of pieces of silver, and allotted him Eṣ-Ṣilḥ as a possession; whereupon El-Ḥasan sat, and distributed the money among his grandees and companions and retinue. El-Ma-moon likewise gave up to him the revenue of Fáris and of the cities of El-Ahwáz for the period of a year. It is related also, that when El-Ma-moon first

---

63 See vol. i. p. 197.

64 Her true name, or that by which she was generally known, was Boorán.

65 Literally, "eggs."

66 Equivalent to about a million and a quarter of pounds sterling.

entered the apartment of the bride, and seated himself with her, her grandmother scattered over them both a thousand large pearls from a tray of gold; and that a candle of ambergris,[67] weighing forty menns,[68] in a lantern[69] of gold, was lighted that night; but that El-Ma-moon disapproved of it, and pronounced it an act of prodigality.[70]]

---

[67] Probably of wax, with an admixture of ambergris.

[68] The "menn" is generally said to be two pounds.

[69] In the text from which I translate, "toor" or "towr;" but this I suppose to be an error of the press, and the right reading to be "tennoor."

[70] Ibn-Khallikán, De Slane's edition, vol. i. pp. 136-8.

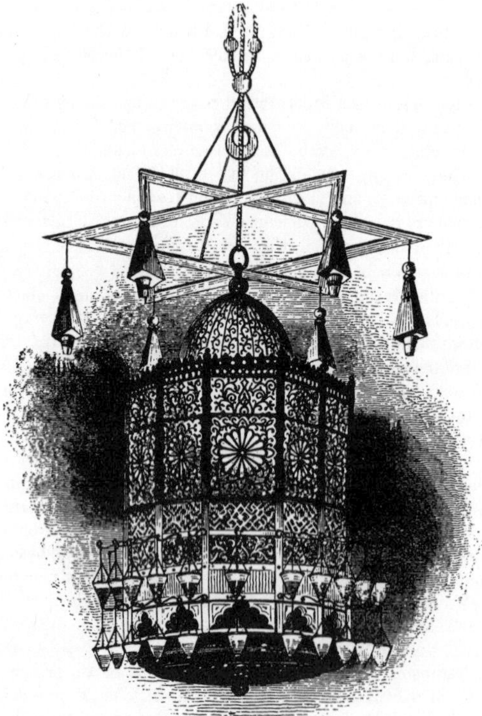

CHAPTER XII.

CHIEFLY FROM THE EDITION OF BRESLAU, COMMENCING WITH PART OF THE TWO HUNDRED AND SEVENTY-FIRST NIGHT, AND ENDING WITH THE TWO HUNDRED AND NINETIETH.

THE STORY OF ABU-L-ḤASAN THE WAG, OR THE SLEEPER AWAKENED.[1]

There was a merchant in Baghdád, in the reign of the Khaleefeh Hároon Er-Rasheed, and he had a son named Abu-l-Ḥasan the Wag.[2] And this merchant died, leaving to his son vast wealth: whereupon Abu-l-Ḥasan divided his property into two equal portions, one of which he laid aside, and of the other he expended. He took as his familiar friends a number of the sons of the merchants, and others, and gave himself up to the delights of good drinking and good eating, until all the wealth that he had appropriated to this purpose was consumed. And upon this he repaired to his associates and relations and boon-companions, and exposed to them his case, shewing them how little property remained in his possession; but none of them paid any regard to him, or uttered a word in reply. So he returned to his mother, with a broken heart, and told her of the treatment that he had experienced from his associates, that they would neither do him justice nor even reply to him. But she said, O Abu-l-Ḥasan, thus are the sons of this age: as long as thou hast any thing, they draw thee near to them; and when thou hast nothing, they cast thee off. She was grieved for him, and he sighed and wept.

He then sprang up, and went to the place in which was deposited the other half of his wealth, and upon this he lived agreeably. He took an oath that he would not thenceforth associate with any one of those whom he knew, but only with the stranger, and that he would not associate with any person but for one night, and on the following morning would not recognise him. Accordingly, every night, he went forth and seated himself on the bridge, and when a stranger passed by him, he invited him to an entertainment, and took him to his house, where he caroused with him that night, until the morning: he then dismissed him; and after that, he would not salute him if he saw him.

Thus he continued to do for a whole year; after which, as he was sitting one day upon the bridge as usual, to see who might come towards him, Er-Rasheed and certain of his domestics passed by in disguise; for the Khaleefeh had experienced a contraction of the bosom, and come forth to amuse himself among the people. So Abu-l-Ḥasan laid hold upon him, and said to him, O my master, hast thou any desire for a repast and beverage? And Er-Rasheed complied with his request, saying to him, Conduct us. And Abu-l-Ḥasan knew not who was his guest. The Khaleefeh proceeded with him until they arrived at Abu-l-Ḥasan's house: and when Er-Rasheed entered, he found in it a saloon, such that if thou beheldest it, and lookedst towards its walls, thou wouldst behold wonders; and if thou observedst its conduits of water, thou wouldst see a fountain encased with gold. And after he had seated himself there, Abu-l-Ḥasan called for a slave-girl, like a twig of the Oriental willow, who took a lute, and extemporized and sang these verses:—

O thou who ever dwellest in my heart, while thy person is distant from my sight!
Thou art my soul; though I see it not, it is nearer to me than any thing beside.

And when Er-Rasheed heard these verses, he said to her, Thou hast performed well. God bless thee!—Her eloquence pleased him, and he wondered at Abu-l-Ḥasan and his entertainment.

He then said to Abu-l-Ḥasan, O young man, who art thou? Acquaint me with thy history, that I may requite thee for thy kindness.—But Abu-l-Ḥasan smiled, and replied, O my master, far be it from me that what hath happened should recur, and that I should be in thy company again after this time!—And why so? said the Khaleefeh, and why wilt thou not acquaint me with thy case?—So Abu-l-Ḥasan told him his story, and when the Khaleefeh heard it, he laughed violently, and said, By Allah, O my brother, thou art excusable in this matter. Then a dish of roast goose was placed before him, and a cake of fine bread;[3] and Abu-l-Ḥasan sat, and cut off the meat, and put morsels into the mouth of the Khaleefeh, and they continued eating until they were satisfied; when the basin and ewer were brought, with the potash;[4] and they washed their hands. After this, Abu-l-Ḥasan lighted for his guest three candles and three lamps, spread the wine-cloth, and brought clear, strained, old, perfumed wine, the odour of which was like fragrant musk, and, having filled the first cup, said, O my boon-companion, bashfulness is dismissed from us, with thy permission. Thy slave is by thee, may I never be afflicted by the loss of thee!—And he drank the cup, and filled the second, which he handed to the Khaleefeh, waiting upon him as a servant. And the Khaleefeh was pleased with his actions, and the politeness of his words, and said within himself, By Allah, I will certainly requite him for this! Abu-l-Ḥasan then, after he had kissed the cup, handed it to the Khaleefeh, who accepted it from his hand, kissed it and drank it, and handed it back to him. Abu-l-Ḥasan still continued serving him. He filled and drank, and filled again and handed the cup to the Khaleefeh, after he had kissed it three times, reciting these verses:—

Thy presence with us is an honour, and we confess it to be so;
And if thou absent thyself from us, we have none to fill thy place.

Drink, he added, and may it be attended with health and vigour.—And they drank and caroused until midnight.[5]

After this, the Khaleefeh said to his host, O Abu-l-Ḥasan, is there any service that thou wouldst have performed, or any desire that thou wouldst have accomplished? And Abu-l-Ḥasan answered, In our neighbourhood is a mosque, to which belong an Imám and four sheykhs, and whenever they hear music or any sport, they incite the Wálee against me, and impose fines upon me, and trouble my life, so that I suffer torment from them. If I had them in my power, therefore, I would give each of them a thousand lashes, that I might be relieved from their excessive annoyance.

Er-Rasheed replied, May Allah grant thee the accomplishment of thy wish! And without his being aware of it, he put into a cup a lozenge of benj, and handed it to him; and as soon as it had settled in his stomach, he fell asleep immediately. Er-Rasheed then arose and went to the door, where he found his young men waiting for him, and he ordered them to convey Abu-l-Ḥasan upon a mule, and returned to the palace; Abu-l-Ḥasan being intoxicated and insensible. And when the Khaleefeh had rested himself in the palace, he called for his Wezeer Jaạfar, and 'Abd-Allah the son of Ṭáhir, the Wálee of Baghdád, and certain of his chief attendants, and said to them all, In the morning, when ye see this young man (pointing to Abu-l-Ḥasan) seated on the royal couch, pay obedience to him, and salute him as Khaleefeh, and whatsoever he commandeth you, do it. Then going in to his female slaves, he directed them to wait upon Abu-l-Ḥasan, and to address him as Prince of the Faithful; after which he entered a private closet, and, having let down a curtain over the entrance, slept.

So when Abu-l-Ḥasan awoke, he found himself upon the royal couch, with the attendants standing around, and kissing the ground before him; and a maid said to him, O our lord, it is the time for morning-prayer:—upon which he laughed, and, looking round about him, he beheld a pavilion whose walls were adorned with gold and ultramarine, and the roof bespotted with red gold, surrounded by chambers with curtains of embroidered silk hanging before their doors; and he saw vessels of gold and China-ware and crystal, and furniture and carpets spread, and lighted lamps, and female slaves, and eunuchs and other attendants; whereat he was perplexed in his mind, and said, By Allah, either I am dreaming, or this is Paradise, and the Abode of Peace. And he closed his eyes. So a eunuch said to him, O my lord, this is not thy usual custom, O Prince of the Faithful. And he was perplexed at his case, and put his head into his bosom, and then began to open his eyes by little and little, laughing, and saying, What is this state in which I find

myself? And he bit his finger; and when he found that the bite pained him, he cried, Ah!—and was angry. Then raising his head, he called one of the female slaves, who answered him, At thy service, O Prince of the Faithful! And he said to her, What is thy name? She answered, Shejeret-ed-Durr.[6] And he said, Knowest thou in what place I am, and who I am?—Thou art the Prince of the Faithful, she answered, sitting in thy palace, upon the royal couch. He replied, I am perplexed at my case, my reason hath departed, and it seemeth that I am asleep; but what shall I say of my yesterday's guest? I imagine nothing but that he is a devil or an enchanter, who hath sported with my reason.

All this time, the Khaleefeh was observing him, from a place where Abu-l-Ḥasan

could not see him.—And Abu-l-Ḥasan looked towards the chief eunuch, and called to him. So he came, and kissed the ground before him, saying to him, Yes, O Prince of the Faithful. And Abu-l-Ḥasan said to him, Who is the Prince of the Faithful?—Thou, he answered. Abu-l-Ḥasan replied, Thou liest. And addressing another eunuch, he said to him, O my chief, as thou hopest for Allah's protection, tell me, am I the Prince of the Faithful?—Yea, by Allah, answered the eunuch: thou art at this present time the Prince of the Faithful, and the Khaleefeh of the Lord of all creatures. And Abu-l-Ḥasan, perplexed at all that he beheld, said, In one night do I become Prince of the Faithful? Was I not yesterday Abu-l-Ḥasan; and today am I Prince of the Faithful?—He remained perplexed and confounded until the morning, when a eunuch advanced to him and said to him, May Allah grant a happy morning to the Prince of the Faithful! And he handed to him a pair of shoes of gold stuff, reticulated with precious stones and rubies; and Abu-l-Ḥasan took them, and, after examining them a long time, put them into his sleeve. So the eunuch said to him, These are shoes, to walk in. And Abu-l-Ḥasan replied, Thou hast spoken truth. I put them not into my sleeve but in my fear lest they should be soiled.—He therefore took them forth, and put them on his feet. And shortly after, the female slaves brought him a basin of gold and a ewer of silver, and poured the water upon his hands; and when he had performed the ablution, they spread for him a prayer-carpet; and he prayed; but knew not how to do so. He continued his inclinations and prostrations until he had performed twenty rek'ahs;[7] meditating, and saying within himself, By Allah, I am none other than the Prince of the Faithful, in truth; or else this is a dream, and all these things occur not in a dream. He therefore convinced himself, and determined in his mind, that he was the Prince of the Faithful; and he pronounced the salutations,[8] and finished his prayers. They then brought him a magnificent dress; and, looking at himself, as he sat upon the couch, he retracted, and said, All this is an illusion, and a machination of the Jánn.

And while he was in this state, lo, one of the memlooks came in, and said to him, O Prince of the Faithful, the chamberlain is at the door, requesting permission to enter.—Let him enter, replied Abu-l-Ḥasan. So he came in, and, having kissed the ground before him, said, Peace be on thee, O Prince of the Faithful! And Abu-l-Ḥasan rose, and descended from the couch to the floor; whereupon the chamberlain exclaimed, Allah! Al-

lah! O Prince of the Faithful! Knowest thou not that all men are thy servants, and under thy authority, and that it is not proper for the Prince of the Faithful to rise to any one?—Abu-l-Ḥasan was then told that Jaạfar El-Barmekee, and 'Abd-Allah the son of Ṭáhir, and the chiefs of the memlooks, begged permission to enter. And he gave them permission. So they entered, and kissed the ground before him, each of them addressing him as Prince of the Faithful. And he was delighted at this, and returned their salutation; after which, he called the Wálee, who approached him, and said, At thy service, O Prince of the Faithful! And Abu-l-Ḥasan said to him, Repair immediately to such a street, and give a hundred pieces of gold to the mother of Abu-l-Ḥasan the Wag, with my salutation: then take the Imám of the mosque, and the four sheykhs, and inflict upon each of them a thousand lashes;[9] and when thou hast done that, write a bond against them, confirmed by oath, that they shall not reside in the street, after thou shalt have paraded them through the city, mounted on beasts, with their faces to the tails, and hast proclaimed before them, This is the recompense of those who annoy their neighbours!—And beware of neglecting that which I have commanded thee to do.—So the Wálee did as he was ordered. And when Abu-l-Ḥasan had exercised his authority until the close of the day, he looked towards the chamberlain and the rest of the attendants, and said to them, Depart.

He then called for a eunuch who was near at hand, and said to him, I am hungry, and desire something to eat. And he replied, I hear and obey:—and led him by the hand into the eating-chamber, where the attendants placed before him a table of rich viands; and

ten slave-girls, high-bosomed virgins, stood behind his head. Abu-l-Ḥasan, looking at one of these, said to her, What is thy name? She answered, Ḳaḍeeb-el-Bán.[10] And he said to her, O Ḳaḍeeb-el-Bán, who am I?—Thou art the Prince of the Faithful, she answered. But he replied, Thou liest, by Allah, thou slut! Ye girls are laughing at me.—So she said, Fear Allah, O Prince of the Faithful: this is thy palace, and the female slaves are thine. And upon this he said within himself, It is no great matter to be effected by God, to whom be ascribed might and glory! Then the slave-girls led him by the hand to the drinking-chamber, where he saw what astonished the mind; and he continued to say within himself, No doubt these are of the Jánn, and this person who was my guest is one of the Kings of the Jánn, who saw no way of requiting and compensating me for my kindness to him but by ordering his

'Ons to address me as Prince of the Faithful. All these are of the Jánn. May Allah then deliver me from them happily!—And while he was thus talking to himself, lo, one of the slave-girls filled for him a cup of wine; and he took it from her hand and drank it; after which, the slave-girls plied him with wine in abundance; and one of them threw into his cup a lozenge of benj; and when it had settled in his stomach, he fell down senseless.

Er-Rasheed then gave orders to convey him to his house; and the servants did so, and laid him on his bed, still in a state of insensibility. So when he recovered from his intoxication, in the latter part of the night, he found himself in the dark; and he called out, Ḳaḍeeb-el-Bán! Shejeret-ed-Durr!—But no one answered him. His mother, however, heard him shouting these names, and arose and came, and said to him, What hath happened to thee, O my son, and what hath befallen thee? Art thou mad?—And when he heard the words of his mother, he said to her, Who art thou, O ill-omened old woman, that thou addressest the Prince of the Faithful with these expressions? She answered, I am thy mother, O my son. But he replied, Thou liest: I am the Prince of the Faithful, the lord of the countries and the people.—Be silent, she said, or else thy life will be lost. And she began to pronounce spells and to recite charms over him, and said to him, It seemeth, O my son, that thou hast seen this in a dream, and all this is one of the ideas suggested by the Devil. She then said to him, I give thee good news, at which thou wilt be rejoiced.—And what is it? said he. She answered, The Khaleefeh gave orders yesterday to beat the Imám and the four sheykhs, and caused a bond to be written against them, confirmed by oath, that they shall not transgress henceforth against any one by their impertinent meddling; and he sent me a hundred pieces of gold,

with his salutation. And when Abu-l-Ḥasan heard these words from his mother, he uttered a loud cry, with which his soul almost quitted the world; and he exclaimed, I am he who gave orders to beat the sheykhs, and who sent thee the hundred pieces of gold, with my salutation, and I am the Prince of the Faithful.

Having said this, he rose up against his mother, and beat her with an almond-stick, until she cried out, O Muslims![11] And he beat her with increased violence, until the neighbours heard her cries, and came to her relief. He was still beating her, and saying to her, O ill-omened old woman, am I not the Prince of the Faithful? Thou hast enchanted me!—And when the people heard his words, they said, This man hath become mad. And not doubting his insanity, they came in and laid hold upon him, bound his hands behind him, and conveyed him to the madhouse.[12] There every day they punished him, dosing him with abominable medicines, and flogging him with whips, making him a madman in spite of himself. Thus he continued, stripped of his clothing, and chained by the neck to a high window, for the space of ten days; after which, his mother came to salute him. And he complained to her of his case. So she said to him, O my son, fear God in thy conduct: if thou wert Prince of the Faithful, thou wouldst not be in this predicament. And when he heard what his mother said, he replied, By Allah, thou hast spoken truth. It seemeth that I was only asleep, and dreamt that they made me Khaleefeh, and assigned me servants and female slaves.—So his mother said to him, O my son, verily Satan doeth more than this. And he replied, Thou hast spoken truth, and I beg forgiveness of God for the actions committed by me.

They therefore took him forth from the madhouse, and conducted him into the bath; and when he recovered his health, he prepared food and drink, and began to eat. But eating by himself was not pleasant to him; and he said to his mother, O my mother, neither life nor eating, by myself, is pleasant to me. She replied, If thou desire to do according to thy will, thy return to the madhouse is most probable. Paying no attention, however, to her advice, he walked to the bridge, to see for himself a cup-companion. And while he was sitting there, lo, Er-Rasheed came to him, in the garb of a merchant; for, from the time of his parting with him, he came every day to the bridge, but found him not till now. As soon as Abu-l-Ḥasan saw him, he said to him, A friendly welcome to thee, O King of the Jánn! So Er-Rasheed said, What have I done to thee?—What more couldst thou do, said Abu-l-Ḥasan, than thou hast done unto me, O filthiest of the Jánn? I have suffered beating, and entered the madhouse, and they pronounced me a madman. All this was occasioned by thee. I brought thee to my abode, and fed thee with the best of my food; and after that, thou gavest thy Devils and thy 'Óns entire power over me, to make sport with my reason from morning to evening. Depart from me, therefore, and go thy way.

The Khaleefeh smiled at this, and, seating himself by his side, addressed him in courteous language, and said to him, O my brother, when I went forth from thee, I inadvertently left the door open, and probably the Devil went in to thee.[13] Abu-l-Ḥasan replied, Inquire not respecting that which happened to me. And what possessed thee, he added, that thou leftest the door open, so that the Devil came in to me, and that such and such things befell me?—And he related to the Khaleefeh all that had happened to him from first to last, while Er-Rasheed laughed, but concealed his laughter: after which, the Khaleefeh said to him, Praise be to God that He hath dispelled from thee that which thou hatest, and that I have seen thee again in prosperity! But Abu-l-Ḥasan replied, I will not again take thee as my boon-companion, nor as an associate to sit with me; for the proverb saith, He who stumbleth against a stone and returneth to it is to be blamed and reproached:—and with thee, O my brother, I will not carouse, nor will I keep company with thee; since I have not found thy visit to be followed by good fortune to me.[14]—The Khaleefeh, however, said, I have been the means of the accomplishment of thy desire with regard to the Imám and the sheykhs.—Yes, replied Abu-l-Ḥasan. And Er-Rasheed added, Perhaps something will happen to thee that will rejoice thy heart more than that.—Then what dost thou desire of me? said Abu-l-Ḥasan.—My desire, answered Er-Rasheed, is to be thy guest this night. And at length Abu-l-Ḥasan said, On the condition that thou swear to me by the inscription on the seal of Suleymán the son of Dáood (on both of whom be peace!) that thou wilt not suffer thy 'Efreets to make sport with me. And Er-Rasheed replied, I hear and obey.

So Abu-l-Ḥasan took him to his abode, and put the food before him and his attendants, and they ate as much as satisfied them; and when they had finished eating, the servants placed before them the wine and exhilarating beverages, and they continued drinking and carousing until the wine rose into their heads. Abu-l-Ḥasan then said to the Khaleefeh, O my boon-companion, in truth I am perplexed respecting my case. It seemeth that I was Prince of the Faithful, and that I exercised authority and gave and bestowed: and truly, O my brother, it was not a vision of sleep.—But the Khaleefeh replied, This was a result of confused dreams. And having said this, he put a piece of benj into the cup, and said, By my life, drink this cup.—Verily I will drink it from thy hand, replied Abu-l-Ḥasan. So he took the cup, and when he had drunk it, his head fell before his feet. The Khaleefeh then arose immediately, and ordered his young men to convey Abu-l-Ḥasan to the palace, and to lay him upon his couch, and commanded the female slaves to stand around him; after which he concealed himself in a place where Abu-l-Ḥasan could not see him, and ordered a slave-girl to take her lute and strike its chords over Abu-l-Ḥasan's head, and desired the other slave-girls to play upon their instruments.

It was then the close of the night, and Abu-l-Ḥasan, awaking, and hearing the sounds of the lutes and tambourines and flutes, and the singing of the slave-girls, cried out, O my mother! Whereupon the slave-girls answered, At thy service, O Prince of the Faithful! And when he heard this, he exclaimed, There is no strength nor power but in God, the High, the Great! Come to my help this night; for this night is more unlucky than the former!—He reflected upon all that had happened to him with his mother, and how he had beaten

her, and how he had been taken into the madhouse, and he saw the marks of the beating that he had suffered there. Then looking at the scene that surrounded him, he said, These are all of them of the Jánn, in the shapes of human beings! I commit my affair unto Allah!—And looking towards a memlook by his side, he said to him, Bite my ear, that I may know if I be asleep or awake. The memlook said, How shall I bite thine ear, when thou art the Prince of the Faithful? But Abu-l-Ḥasan answered, Do as I have commanded thee, or I will strike off thy head. So he bit it until his teeth met together, and Abu-l-Ḥasan uttered a loud shriek.—Er-Rasheed (who was behind a curtain in a closet), and all who were present, fell down with laughter, and they said to the memlook, Art thou mad, that thou bitest the ear of the Khaleefeh? And Abu-l-Ḥasan said to them, Is it not enough that hath befallen me, O ye wretches of Jinn? But ye are not in fault: the fault is your chief's, who transformed you from the shapes of Jinn into the shapes of human beings. I implore help against you this night by the Verse of the Throne, and the Chapter of Sincerity, and the Two Preventives![15]—Upon this Er-Rasheed exclaimed from behind the curtain, Thou hast killed us, O Abu-l-Ḥasan! And Abu-l-Ḥasan recognised him, and kissed the ground before him, greeting him with a prayer for the increase of his glory, and the prolongation of his life. Er-Rasheed then clad him in a rich dress, gave him a thousand pieces of gold, and made him one of his chief boon-companions.

Abu-l-Ḥasan, after this, became a greater favourite with the Khaleefeh than all the other boon-companions, so that he sat with the Khaleefeh and his wife the lady Zubeydeh, the daughter of El-Ḳásim, and he married her female Treasurer, whose name was Nuzhet-el-Fuád.[16] With this wife he resided, eating and drinking, and enjoying a delightful life, until all the money that they possessed had gone; whereupon he said to her, O Nuzhet-el-Fuád! And she answered, At thy service. —I desire, said he, to practise a trick upon the Khaleefeh, and thou shalt practise a trick upon the lady Zubeydeh, and we will obtain from them immediately two hundred pieces of gold, and two pieces of silk.—Do what thou desirest, replied she: and what, she asked, is it? He answered, We will feign ourselves dead. I will die before thee, and lay myself out: then do thou spread over me a napkin of silk, and unfold my turban over me, and tie my toes, and put upon my stomach a knife and a little salt:[17] after which, dishevel thy hair, and go to thy lady Zubeydeh, and tear thy vest and slap thy face, and shriek. So she will say to thee, What is the matter with thee? And do thou answer her, May thy head long survive Abu-l-Ḥasan the Wag; for he is dead! Whereupon she will mourn for me, and weep, and will order her female Treasurer[18] to give thee a hundred pieces of gold, and a piece of silk,[19] and will say to thee, Go, prepare his corpse for burial, and convey it forth to the grave. So thou shalt receive from her the hundred pieces of gold, and the piece of silk, and come hither. And when thou comest to me, I will rise, and thou shalt lay thyself down in my place, and I will go to the Khaleefeh, and say to him, May thy head long survive Nuzhet-el-Fuád! And I will tear my vest, and pluck my beard; upon which he will mourn for thee, and will say to his Treasurer, Give to Abu-l-Ḥasan a hundred pieces of gold, and a piece of silk:—and he will say to me, Go, prepare her corpse for burial, and convey it forth to the grave. So I will come to thee.—And Nuzhet-el-Fuád was delighted with this, and replied, Truly this is an excellent stratagem!

She forthwith closed his eyes, and tied his feet, covered him with the napkin, and did all that her master told her; after which, she tore her vest, uncovered her head, and dishevelled her hair, and went in to the lady Zubeydeh, shrieking and weeping. When the lady Zubeydeh, therefore, beheld her in this condition, she said to her, What is this state in which I see thee, and what hath happened unto thee, and what hath caused thee to weep? And Nuzhet-el-Fuád wept and shrieked, and said, O my mistress, may thy head long survive Abu-l-Ḥasan the Wag; for he is dead! And the lady Zubeydeh mourned for him, and said, Poor Abu-l-Ḥasan the Wag! Then, after weeping for him a while, she ordered the female Treasurer to give to Nuzhet-el-Fuád a hundred pieces of gold, and a piece of silk, and said, O Nuzhet-el-Fuád, go, prepare his body for burial, and convey it forth. So she took the hundred pieces of gold, and the piece of silk, and, returning to her abode, full of joy, went in to Abu-l-Ḥasan, and acquainted him with what had happened to her; upon which he arose and rejoiced, and girded his waist and danced, and took the hundred pieces of gold, with the piece of silk, and laid them up.

He then extended Nuzhet-el-Fuád, and did with her as she had done with him; after which, he tore his vest and plucked his beard and disordered his turban, and ran without stopping until he went in to the Khaleefeh, who was in his hall of judgment; and in the condition above described, he beat his bosom. So the Khaleefeh said to him, What hath befallen thee, O Abu-l-Ḥasan? And he wept, and said, Would that thy boon-companion had never been, nor his hour come to pass![20] The Khaleefeh therefore said to him, Tell me. He replied, May thy head long survive, O my lord, Nuzhet-el-Fuád! And the Khaleefeh exclaimed, There is no deity but God!—and struck his hands together. He then consoled Abu-l-Ḥasan, and said to him, Mourn not: I will give thee a concubine in her stead. And he ordered his Treasurer to give him a hundred pieces of gold, and a piece of silk. The Treasurer therefore did as he was commanded, and the Khaleefeh said to Abu-l-Ḥasan, Go, prepare her corpse for burial, and convey it forth, and make a handsome funeral for her. And he took what the Khaleefeh gave him, and went to his abode joyful, and, going in to Nuzhet-el-Fuád, said to her, Arise; for our desire is accomplished. She therefore arose, and he put before her the hundred pieces of gold, and the piece of silk. So she rejoiced; and they put these pieces of gold on the other pieces, and the piece of silk on the former one, and sat conversing, and laughing at each other.

But as to the Khaleefeh, when Abu-l-Ḥasan departed from him, and went with the pretence of preparing the corpse of Nuzhet-el-Fuád for burial, he mourned for her, and, having dismissed the council, arose and went in, leaning upon Mesroor his executioner, to console the lady Zubeydeh for the loss of her slave-girl. He found her, however, sitting weeping, and waiting for his arrival, that she might console him for the loss of Abu-l-Ḥasan the Wag. The Khaleefeh said, May thy head long survive thy slave-girl Nuzhet-el-Fuád! But she replied, O my lord, Allah preserve my slave-girl! Mayest thou long survive thy boon-companion Abu-l-Ḥasan the Wag; for he is dead!—And the Khaleefeh smiled, and said to his eunuch, O Mesroor, verily women are of little sense. By Allah, was not Abu-l-Ḥasan just now with me?—Upon this, the lady Zubeydeh said, after uttering a laugh from an angry bosom, Wilt thou not give over thy jesting? Is not the death of Abu-l-Ḥasan enough, but thou must make my slave-girl to be dead, as though we had lost them both, and thou must pronounce me of little sense?—The Khaleefeh replied, Verily Nuzhet-el-Fuád is the person who is dead. And the lady Zubeydeh rejoined, In truth he was not with thee, nor didst thou see him; and none was with me just now but Nuzhet-el-Fuád, who was mourning and weeping, with her clothes rent in pieces; and I exhorted her to have patience, and gave her a hundred pieces of gold, and a piece of silk; and I was waiting for thee, that I might console thee for the loss of thy boon-companion, Abu-l-Ḥasan the Wag; and I was going to send for thee. On hearing this, the Khaleefeh laughed, and said, None is dead but Nuzhet-el-Fuád. And the lady Zubeydeh said, No, no, O my lord: none is dead but Abu-l-Ḥasan. But the Khaleefeh now became enraged; the vein between his eyes, which was remarkable in members of the family of Háshim,[21] throbbed, and he called out to Mesroor the Executioner, saying to him, Go forth and repair to the house of Abu-l-Ḥasan the Wag, and see which of the two is dead.

Mesroor, therefore, went forth running. And the Khaleefeh said to the lady Zubeydeh, Wilt thou lay me a wager? She answered, Yes, I will, and I say that Abu-l-Ḥasan is dead.—And I, replied the Khaleefeh, lay a wager, and say that none is dead but Nuzhet-el-Fuád; and our wager shall be, that I stake the Garden of Delight against thy pavilion, the Pavilion of the Pictures.[22] And they sat waiting for Mesroor to return with the information.—Now as to Mesroor, he ran without ceasing until he entered the by-street in which was the house of Abu-l-Ḥasan the Wag. Abu-l-Ḥasan was sitting reclining against the window, and, turning his eyes, he saw Mesroor running along the street. So he said to Nuzhet-el-Fuád, It seemeth that the Khaleefeh, after I went forth from him, dismissed the court, and hath gone in to the lady Zubeydeh to console her, and that she, on his arrival, hath arisen and consoled him, and said to him, May God largely compensate thee for the loss of Abu-l-Ḥasan the Wag!—whereupon the Khaleefeh hath said to her, None is dead but Nuzhet-el-Fuád. May thy head long survive her!—And she hath replied, None is dead but Abu-l-Ḥasan the Wag, thy boon-companion. And he hath said again to her, None is dead but Nuzhet-el-Fuád. So they have become obstinate, and the Khaleefeh hath been enraged, and they have laid a wager, in consequence of which, Mesroor the Executioner hath been sent to see who is dead. It is therefore the more proper that *thou* lay thyself down, that he may see thee, and go and inform the Khaleefeh, who will thereupon believe my assertion.

Accordingly, Nuzhet-el-Fuád extended herself, and Abu-l-Ḥasan covered her with her izár, and seated himself at her head, weeping. And, lo, Mesroor the eunuch came up into the house of Abu-l-Ḥasan, and saluted him, and saw Nuzhet-el-Fuád stretched out; upon which he uncovered her face, and exclaimed, There is no deity but God! Our sister Nuzhet-el-Fuád is dead! How speedy was the stroke of fate! May Allah have mercy upon her, and acquit thee of responsibility!—He then returned, and related what had happened before the Khaleefeh and the lady Zubeydeh, laughing as he spoke. So the Khaleefeh said to him, O thou accursed, this is not a time for laughing. Tell us which of them is dead.—He therefore replied, By Allah, O my lord, verily Abu-l-Ḥasan is well, and none is dead but Nuzhet-el-Fuád. And upon this the Khaleefeh said to Zubeydeh, Thou hast lost thy pavilion in thy play. And he laughed at her, and said, O Mesroor, relate to her what thou sawest. So Mesroor said to her, In truth, O my mistress, I ran incessantly until I went in to Abu-l-Ḥasan in his house; whereupon I found Nuzhet-el-Fuád lying dead, and Abu-l-Ḥasan sitting at her head, weeping; and I saluted him and consoled him, and seated myself by his side; and, uncovering the face of Nuzhet-el-Fuád, I beheld her dead, with her face swollen. I therefore said to him, Convey her forth presently to the grave, that we may pray over her. And he replied, Yes. And I came, leaving him to prepare her corpse for burial, in order to inform you.—Upon this, the Khaleefeh laughed, and said, Tell it again and again to thy mistress, the person of little sense. But when the lady Zubeydeh heard the words of Mesroor, she was enraged, and said, None is deficient in sense but he who believeth a slave. And she abused Mesroor, while the Khaleefeh continued laughing; and Mesroor was displeased, and said to the Khaleefeh, He spoke truth who said, that women are deficient in sense and religion.[23]

The lady Zubeydeh then said, O Prince of the Faithful, thou sportest and jestest with me, and this slave deceiveth me for the purpose of pleasing thee; but I will send, and see which of them is dead. The Khaleefeh replied, Do so. And she called to an old woman, a ḳahramáneh, and said to her, Repair quickly to the house of Nuzhet-el-Fuád, and see who is dead, and delay not thy return. And she threw money to her. So the old woman went forth running; the Khaleefeh and Mesroor laughing. The old woman ran without ceasing until she entered the street, when Abu-l-Ḥasan saw her and knew her; and he said to his wife, O Nuzhet-el-Fuád, it seemeth that the lady Zubeydeh hath sent to us to see who is dead, and hath not believed what Mesroor hath said respecting thy death: wherefore she hath sent the old woman, the ḳahramáneh, to ascertain the truth of the matter. It is therefore more proper now for *me* to be dead, that the lady Zubeydeh may believe thee.

Then Abu-l-Ḥasan laid himself along, and Nuzhet-el-Fuád covered him, and bound his eyes and his feet, and seated herself at his head, weeping. And the old woman came in to Nuzhet-el-Fuád, and saw her sitting at the head of Abu-l-Ḥasan, weeping, and enumerating his merits; and when Nuzhet-el-Fuád saw the old woman, she shrieked, and said to her, See what hath befallen me! Abu-l-Ḥasan hath died, and left me single and solitary!—Then she shrieked again, and tore her clothes in pieces, and said to the old woman, O my mother, how good he was! The old woman replied, Truly thou art excusable; for thou hadst become habituated to him, and he had become habituated to thee.—And knowing how Mesroor had acted to the Khaleefeh and the lady Zubeydeh, she said to Nuzhet-el-Fuád, Mesroor is about to cause a quarrel between the Khaleefeh and the lady Zubeydeh.—And what is this cause of quarrel, O my mother? said Nuzhet-el-Fuád. The old woman answered, O my daughter, Mesroor hath come to them and told them that thou wast dead, and that Abu-l-Ḥasan was well.—O my aunt, replied Nuzhet-el-Fuád, I was just now with my lady, and she gave me a hundred pieces of gold, and a piece of silk: and see thou my condition, and what hath befallen me. I am perplexed; and what shall I do, single and solitary? Would that I had died, and that he had lived!—Then she wept, and the old woman wept with her, and, advancing, and uncovering the face of Abu-l-Ḥasan, saw his eyes bound, and swollen from the bandage. And she covered him, and said, Truly, O Nuzhet-el-Fuád, thou hast been afflicted for Abu-l-Ḥasan. And she consoled her, and went forth from her running until she went in to the lady Zubeydeh, when she related to her the story; on hearing which, the lady Zubeydeh laughed, and said, Tell it to the Khaleefeh, who hath pronounced me of little sense, and caused this ill-omened, lying slave to behave arrogantly towards me. But Mesroor said, Verily this old woman lieth; for I saw Abu-l-Ḥasan in good health, and it was Nuzhet-el-Fuád who was lying dead. The old woman replied, It is thou who liest, and thou desirest to excite a quarrel between the Khaleefeh and the lady Zubeydeh. Mesroor rejoined, None lieth but thou, O ill-omened old woman, and thy lady believeth thee, for she is disordered in mind. And upon this, the lady Zubeydeh cried out at him, enraged at him and at his words; and she wept.

At length the Khaleefeh said to her, I lie, and my eunuch lieth, and thou liest, and thy female slave lieth. The right course, in my opinion, is this, that we four go together to see who among us speaketh truth. So Mesroor said, Arise with us, that I may bring misfortunes upon this ill-omened old woman, and bastinade her for her lying.—O thou imbecile in mind! exclaimed the old woman: is thy sense like mine? Nay, thy sense is like that of the hen.—And Mesroor was enraged at her words, and would have laid violent hands upon her; but the lady Zubeydeh, having pushed him away from her, said to him, Immediately will her veracity be distinguished from thine, and her lying from thine. They all four arose, laying wagers one with another, and went forth and walked from the gate of the palace until they entered the gate of the street in which dwelt Abu-l-Ḥasan the Wag; when Abu-l-Ḥasan saw them, and said to his wife Nuzhet-el-Fuád, In truth, every thing that is slippery is not a pancake, and not every time that the jar is struck doth it escape unbroken.[24] It seemeth that the old woman hath gone and related the story to her lady, and acquainted her with our case, and that she hath contended with Mesroor the eunuch, and they have laid wagers respecting our death: so the Khaleefeh and the eunuch and the lady Zubeydeh and the old woman have all four come to us.—And upon this, Nuzhet-el-Fuád rose from her extended position, and said, What is to be done? Abu-l-Ḥasan answered her, We will both feign ourselves dead, and lay ourselves out, and hold in our breath. And she assented to his proposal.

They both stretched themselves along, bound their feet, closed their eyes, and held in their breath, lying with their heads in the direction of the Ḳibleh,[25] and covered themselves with the izár. Then the Khaleefeh and Zubeydeh and Mesroor and the old woman entered the house of Abu-l-Ḥasan the Wag, and found him and his wife extended as if they were dead. And when the lady Zubeydeh saw them, she wept, and said, They continued to assert the death of my female slave[26] until she actually died; but I imagine that the death of Abu-l-Ḥasan so grieved her that she died after him in consequence of it. The Khaleefeh, however, said, Do not prevent me with thy talk and assertions; for she died before Abu-l-Ḥasan, because Abu-l-Ḥasan came to me with his clothes torn in pieces, and with his beard plucked, and striking his bosom with two clods;[27] and I gave him a hundred pieces of gold, with a piece of silk, and said to him, Go, prepare her body for burial, and I will give thee a concubine better than she, and she shall serve in her stead:—and it appears that her loss was insupportable to him; so he died after her. I have therefore overcome thee, and gained thy stake. — But the lady Zubeydeh replied in many words, and a long dispute ensued between them.

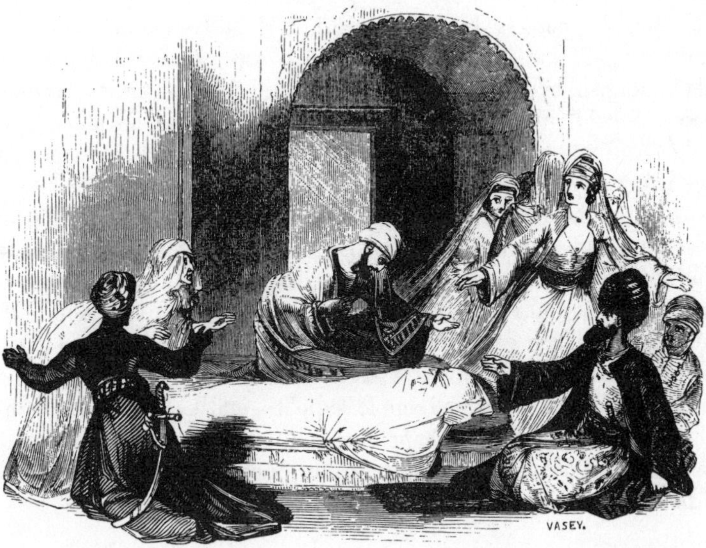

The Khaleefeh then seated himself at the heads of the two pretended corpses, and said, By the tomb of the Apostle of Allah (God bless and save him!), and by the tombs of my ancestors, if any one would tell me which of them died before the other, I would give him a thousand pieces of gold. And when Abu-l-Ḥasan heard these words of the Khaleefeh, he quickly rose and sprang up, and said, It was I who died first, O Prince of the Faithful. Give me the thousand pieces of gold, and so acquit thyself of the oath that thou hast sworn.—Then Nuzhet-el-Fuád rose and sat up before the Khaleefeh and the lady Zubeydeh, who rejoiced at their safety. But Zubeydeh chid her female slave. The Khaleefeh and the lady Zubeydeh congratulated them both on their safety, and knew that this pretended death was a stratagem for the purpose of obtaining the gold: so the lady Zubeydeh said to Nuzhet-el-Fuád, Thou shouldst have asked of me what thou desiredst without this proceeding, and not have tortured my heart on thine account.—I was ashamed, O my mistress, replied Nuzhet-el-Fuád.—But as to the Khaleefeh, he was almost senseless from laughing, and said, O Abu-l-Ḥasan, thou hast not ceased to be a wag, and to do wonders and strange acts. Abu-l-Ḥasan replied, O Prince of the Faithful, this stratagem I practised in consequence of the dissipation of the wealth that I received from thy hand; for I was ashamed to ask of thee a second time. When I was alone, I was not tenacious of wealth; but since thou hast married me to this female slave who is with me, if I possessed all thy wealth I should make an end of it. And when all that was in my possession was exhausted, I practised this stratagem, by means of which I obtained from thee these hundred pieces of gold, and the piece of silk, all of which are an alms of our lord. And now make haste in giving me the thousand pieces of gold, and acquit thyself of thine oath.

At this, the Khaleefeh and the lady Zubeydeh both laughed; and after they had returned to the palace, the Khaleefeh gave to Abu-l-Ḥasan the thousand pieces of gold, saying to him, Receive them as a gratuity on account of thy safety from death. In like manner also the lady Zubeydeh gave to Nuzhet-el-Fuád a thousand pieces of gold, saying to her the same words. Then the Khaleefeh allotted to Abu-l-Ḥasan an ample salary and ample supplies, and he ceased not to live with his wife in joy and happiness, until they were visited by the terminator of delights, and the separator of companions, the devastator of palaces and houses, and the replenisher of the graves.

NOTES TO CHAPTER TWELFTH.

NOTE 1. This story is not in the edition of Cairo, nor in the MS. of the Thousand and One Nights from which Galland translated,[1] though he has introduced it in his version; and I am not aware of its being found in any copy of that work, except the one from which the Breslau edition is printed. From these circumstances, and from my having discovered that its chief and best portion is a historical anecdote, related as a fact, I am inclined to think that it is not a genuine tale of the Thousand and One Nights, and that it has been inserted in some copies of that work (perhaps only in one) to supply a deficiency. But as it exists in one copy, and is one of the best tales in Galland's version, I have gladly given it a place in the present collection. The place which it occupies in the order of the Nights, in the edition of Breslau, I have mentioned at the head of this chapter; but in the order of the *Tales* in that edition, it follows the story of Es-Sindibád of the Sea and Es-Sindibád of the Land.

The author by whom I have found the chief portion of this tale related as a historical anecdote is El-Is-ḥáḳee, who finished his history shortly before the close of the reign of the 'Osmánlee Sulṭán Muṣṭafà, apparently in the year of the Flight 1032 (A.D. 1623). He does not mention his authority; and whether it is related by an older *historian*, I do not know; but perhaps it is founded upon fact.

The story is narrated in El-Is-ḥáḳee's work in a simple and agreeable manner: in the Breslau Thousand and One Nights it is given more fully, but in language of a vulgar style, and abounding with errors, of which a few will be found particularized in the following notes. I have, therefore, here availed myself of both these works, each of which, in this case, possesses merits that the other does not. To the former, as far as it has enabled me to do so, I have adhered more closely; but the additions I have made, of the best parts of the narrative in the latter work, constitute the main portion of my translation of the tale. Abu-l-Ḥasan's marriage, and the subsequent events, are not related by El-Is-ḥáḳee.

Galland has evidently added to this story considerable embellishments of his own invention, and made it in many parts inconsistent with Arab manners and customs.

---

[1] See Von Hammer's "Notice sur les douze Manuscrits connus des Mille et Une Nuits, qui existent en Europe," in Trébutien.

But his version of it appears to have been mainly derived from an Arabic original more full than the corresponding text in the Breslau edition; for I distinguish in it several poetical and other passages which are not in the tale as given in that edition, and which are certainly not invented by him. For instance, near the commencement of the story, I observe a loose translation of four verses occurring in the Cairo edition in an earlier tale: see page 305, in vol. i. of the present work.

NOTE 2. The word "khaleeạ," which I render "wag" (though this is not its primary meaning, nor do I find it so explained in any Dictionary, except one in MS. of my own composition), is generally used in the present day to signify "waggish," "frolicksome," or "witty," and has been so used by many good writers. That it is to be thus understood here, and not in the sense of an "abandoned person," or a "reprobate," is evident from the manner in which it is employed at the close of the tale. In like manner, "khalá'ah" signifies "waggishness," &c.

NOTE 3. In the original, "kumájeh." This word appears to be from the Persian "kumáj" or "kumásh" ("unleavened bread," or "bread baked in the ashes"); but it is commonly used to signify "fine flour," and I have not found it used in any other sense.

NOTE 4. Potash is used for washing the hands after eating; but the most common substitute for soap I have observed to be "duḳáḳ," which is the meal of the lupin, called in Arabic "turmus," vulgarly "tirmis."

NOTE 5. In illustration of this part of the story, as it respects the character of Hároon Er-Rasheed, see Note 22 to Chapter iii. (vol. i. p. 194).

NOTE 6. See Note 18 to Chapter vii.

NOTE 7. The morning-prayers consist of only four rek'ahs; namely, two sunneh (or ordained by the Prophet), and two farḍ (*i. e.* of divine appointment). Respecting the "rek'ah," see Note 1 to the Introduction.

NOTE 8. After the sunneh prayers, and after the farḍ, the worshipper, looking upon his right shoulder, says, "Peace be on you, and the mercy of God!" then, looking upon the left shoulder, he repeats the same words. These salutations are considered by some as addressed only to the guardian angels who watch over the believer and note all his actions; but others say that they are addressed both to angels and men (*i. e.* believers only), who may be present: no person, however, returns them. Some hold that every believer is attended by two angels; others say, five; others, sixty, or a hundred and sixty.

NOTE 9. In the Breslau edition, four hundred lashes.

NOTE 10. "Ḳaḍeeb-el-Bán" signifies "the Twig of the Oriental willow."

NOTE 11. See Note 78 to Chapter v.

NOTE 12. Or hospital. The same building, in an Arabian city, generally serves both as a hospital for the sick and an asylum for the mad.

NOTE 13. "Shut your doors at night," said the Prophet; "and at the time of doing it, remember [or rather repeat] God's name; because the Devil cannot open the door which has been shut in the name of God."[2]—As I have remarked in my work on the Modern Egyptians,[3] it is a common custom of many learned and devout persons, and some others, to say, "In the name of God, the Compassionate, the Merciful," on locking a door, covering bread, laying down their clothes at night, and on other occasions, to protect their property (as well as themselves) from evil genii, or devils.

---

[2] Mishkát el-Maṣábeeḥ, vol. ii. p. 341.

[3] Vol. i. ch. x.

NOTE 14. Literally, "I have not seen thee to have a heel prosperous to me."

NOTE 15. See Notes 44 and 18 to Chapter x. "The Chapter of Sincerity" is the 112th (or last but two) of the Ḳur-án.

NOTE 16. "Nuzhet-el-Fuád" signifies "the Delight of the Heart."

NOTE 17. Two of the customs here mentioned, namely, tying the toes of the corpse, and placing a knife, or rather, a sword, upon the body, are still common in some Muslim countries; but I did not hear of their being observed in Egypt, nor of the custom of putting the salt with the knife or sword. Iron and salt are both believed to repel genii, and to prevent their approach (see vol. i. pp. 30 and 32), and hence, perhaps, are thus used.

NOTE 18. Nuzhet-el-Fuád must have resigned her office of Treasurer on marrying Abu-l-Ḥasan.

NOTE 19. Abu-l-Ḥasan expected the present of the money for the purpose of defraying the expenses of the funeral, and the piece of silk for grave-clothing. See Note 11 to Chapter vi.

NOTE 20. This is a common kind of ejaculation. By the "hour," in this instance, we may understand either the hour of Abu-l-Ḥasan's birth, or that in which he was appointed the Khaleefeh's boon-companion.

NOTE 21. Literally, "the Háshimee vein." "The vein of anger between the eyes" appears to have been especially remarkable in descendants of Háshim. Whether it was so in Háshim himself, I do not find; but it is mentioned among the characteristics of his great-grandson, the Prophet.

NOTE 22. The word rendered "pictures" generally signifies "carved images," "effigies," or "models." I suppose pictures to be here meant because carved images are generally representations of living creatures, which representations are forbidden by the Muslim law. [The "Garden of Delight" has been mentioned in the story of Noor-ed-Deen and Enees-el-Jelees.—ED.]

NOTE 23. This is a saying of the Prophet, and is often quoted by a Muslim to silence his wife.

NOTE 24. The text here is faulty; but Dr. Habicht has pointed out the corrections, and I only differ from him in adding the article (in the Arabic) to the last word of the latter of the two proverbs.

NOTE 25. Here, also, the text appears to be faulty. I read "ḳibleh" for "ḳeeleh" or "ḳeyleh."—Some Muslims turn the *head* of the corpse in the direction of the Ḳibleh, or Mekkeh: others, the *right side*, inclining the *face* in that direction. In the latter position the corpse is placed in the tomb.

NOTE 26. In this passage, again, I am obliged to have recourse to a conjectural emendation.

NOTE 27. The word here rendered "two clods" also signifies "two lumps of stone," or "two bricks." Beating the bosom with two clods of hard, dry earth, in a case of extreme distress, is not an uncommon action with the Arabs of the lower orders.

CHAPTER XIII.

COMMENCING WITH PART OF THE TWO HUNDRED AND EIGHTY-FIFTH NIGHT, AND ENDING WITH PART OF THE TWO HUNDRED AND NINETY-FOURTH.

THE STORY OF MOḤAMMAD 'ALEE THE JEWELLER, OR THE FALSE KHALEEFEH.[1]

It is related that the Khaleefeh Hároon Er-Rasheed was troubled one night with an exceeding restlessness, in consequence of which he summoned his Wezeer Jaạfar El-Barmekee, and said to him, My bosom is contracted, and I desire this night to amuse myself in the streets of Baghdád, and to observe the employments of the people; but on the condition that we disguise ourselves in the garb of merchants, so that no one may know us. And the Wezeer replied, I hear and obey. They arose immediately, and, having pulled off the magnificent apparel with which they were then clad, put on the attire of merchants. And they were three; the Khaleefeh, and Jaạfar, and Mesroor the Executioner.

They walked from place to place until they arrived at the Tigris, when they saw an old man sitting in a boat; and approaching him, they saluted him, and said to him, O sheykh, we desire of thy favour and kindness that thou wouldst amuse us in this thy boat, and take this piece of gold as thy hire. But the sheykh said, Who is he that can amuse himself here? For the Khaleefeh Hároon Er-Rasheed embarketh every night on the river Tigris on board a small vessel, attended by a crier who proclaimeth and saith, O all ye companies of men, great and small, noble and plebeian, young men and youths, whosoever embarketh in a vessel and traverseth the Tigris, I will strike off his head, or hang him upon the mast of his vessel!—Ye have now almost encountered him; for his bark is approaching.—So the Khaleefeh and Jaạfar said, O sheykh, take these two pieces of gold, and convey us into one of those arches, that we may remain there until the bark of the Khaleefeh hath passed. And the sheykh replied, Give me the gold, and our reliance be upon God, whose name be exalted! He took the gold, set his boat afloat with them, and proceeded a little way; and, lo, the bark approached from the bosom of the Tigris, and in it were lighted candles and cressets.[2] The sheykh therefore said to them, Did I not tell you that the Khaleefeh passed along the river every night? Then he began to say, O excellent Protector, remove not the veils of thy protection! He conveyed them into an arch, and spread a black meezer[3] over them; and they gratified their curiosity by gazing at the spectacle from beneath the meezer. They beheld at the head of the bark a man having in his hand a cresset of red gold, in which he was burning aloes-wood: he wore a vest of red satin; upon one of his shoulders was a piece of yellow embroidered stuff;[4] upon his head, a muslin turban; and upon his other shoulder, a bag of green silk full of aloes-wood, from which he supplied the cresset with fuel instead of using common firewood. They saw likewise another man, at the stern of the bark, clad as the former one, and having in his hand a similar cresset. And there were also in the bark two hundred memlooks, standing on the right and left; and in it was placed a throne of red gold, upon which was sitting a handsome young man, like the moon, clad in a dress of black,[5] with embroidery of yellow gold. Before him was a man resembling the Wezeer Jaạfar, and at his head stood a eunuch like Mesroor, with a drawn sword in his hand. And they saw moreover twenty boon-companions.

Now when the Khaleefeh beheld this, he said, O Jaạfar. The

Wezeer replied, At thy service, O Prince of the Faithful. And the Khaleefeh said, Probably this is one of my sons; either El-Ma-moon, or El-Emeen. Then gazing at the young man as he sat on the throne, he beheld him to be of consummate beauty and loveliness, and justness of stature; and after attentively observing him, he looked towards the Wezeer, and said, O Wezeer.—At thy service, replied Jaạfar. And the Khaleefeh said, By Allah, this person sitting on the throne hath not omitted any thing appertaining to the distinctions of the Khaleefeh; and he who is before him is as though he were thyself, O Jaạfar; and the eunuch who is standing at his head, as though he were Mesroor; and these boon-companions are as though they were my boon-companions. My reason is confounded at this affair! By Allah, I am full of wonder at this event, O Jaạfar!—And I also, by Allah, O Prince of the Faithful! replied the Wezeer.—The bark then passed on until it disappeared from before their eyes; whereupon the sheykh put forth with his boat, and said, Praise be to God for our safety, and that no one hath fallen in with us! And the Khaleefeh said, O sheykh, doth the Khaleefeh every night embark on the Tigris? The sheykh answered, Yes, O my master; and for a whole year he hath continued to do so. And the Khaleefeh said, O sheykh, we desire of thy favour that thou wouldst wait for us here next night, and we will give thee five pieces of gold; for we are strangers, and wish to amuse ourselves, and we are lodging in [the quarter of] El-Khandaḳ. The sheykh replied, I am entirely at your service.

Then the Khaleefeh and Jaạfar and Mesroor departed from the sheykh and returned to the palace, and having taken off their merchants' attire, and put on the apparel of state, each seated himself in his place. The emeers and wezeers came in, and the chamberlains and lieutenants, and the council was fully attended. And when the day closed, and all ranks of the people had dispersed, each having gone his way, the Khaleefeh Hároon Er-Rasheed said, O Jaạfar, arise with us that we may amuse ourselves with the sight of the other Khaleefeh. Whereupon Jaạfar and Mesroor laughed.

They clad themselves again in the attire of merchants, and went forth and pursued their way through the city, in a state of the utmost hilarity. They went out from a private door; and when they arrived at the Tigris, they found the sheykh, the owner of the boat, sitting waiting for them. So they embarked with him in the boat; and they had not long sat with him when the bark of the False Khaleefeh[6] approached them; and looking attentively at it, they saw in it two hundred memlooks, different from those of the preceding night, and the bearers of the cressets proclaiming as usual. And the Khaleefeh said, O Wezeer, this is such a thing that if I heard of it I could not believe it; but I have beheld it with my eyes. He then said to the owner of the boat in which they were sitting, Take, O sheykh, these ten pieces of gold, and convey us towards them; for they are in the light, and we are in the dark; so we shall see them, and amuse ourselves by observing them, and they will not see us. The sheykh therefore took the ten pieces of gold, and, steering his boat towards them, proceeded in the gloom that surrounded the bark of the False Khaleefeh, until they arrived at the gardens, where they beheld a walled enclosure. At this enclosure the bark of the False Khaleefeh anchored; and, lo, young men were standing there, with a mule saddled and bridled; and the False Khaleefeh, having landed, mounted the mule, and proceeded in the midst of the boon-companions; the cresset-bearers vociferating, and the household-attendants busying themselves in performing their several services for the False Khaleefeh.

Hároon Er-Rasheed then landed, together with Jaạfar and Mesroor, and they made their way through the midst of the memlooks, and walked on before them. But the cresset-bearers, looking towards them, and beholding three persons whose dress was that of the merchants, and who appeared to be strangers, were displeased with them, and they made a sign, and caused them to be brought before the False Khaleefeh, who, when he saw them, said to them, How came ye to this place, and what brought you at this time? So they answered, O our lord, we are a party of foreign merchants: we arrived this day, and came forth to-night to walk, and, lo, ye approached, and these persons came and laid hold upon us, and placed us before thee. This is our story.—And the False Khaleefeh replied, No harm shall befall you, as ye are strangers; but had ye been of Baghdád, I had struck off your heads. Then looking towards his Wezeer, he said to him, Take these persons with thee; for they are our guests this night. And the Wezeer replied, I hear and obey, O our lord. After this, the False Khaleefeh proceeded, and they with him, until they arrived at a lofty and grand palace, strongly constructed, such as no Sulṭán hath possessed, rising from the dust, and reaching to the skirts of the clouds. Its door was of sáj,[7] adorned with brilliant gold; and through this door one passed into a

saloon with a fountain and a slightly-elevated platform,[8] and carpets, and cushions covered with brocade, and small pillows, and long mattresses;[9] in it a curtain was hung; and there was furniture that astonished the minds of the spectators, and that one would fail to describe; and upon the door were inscribed these two verses:—

This palace—on which be blessing and peace!—fortune hath invested with its loveliness:
In it are varieties of wonders and rarities, so that the penmen are perplexed in describing it.

The False Khaleefeh, having entered, together with the company, proceeded and seated himself upon a throne of jewelled gold, upon which was a prayer-carpet of yellow silk; and when the boon-companions had taken their seats, and the executioner had stationed himself before his master, the servants spread the table, and the party ate. The dishes were then removed, and the hands were washed, and the attendants brought the wine-service. The bottles and the cups were arranged, and the wine circulated until it came to the Khaleefeh Hároon Er-Rasheed; but he refused to drink; whereupon the False Khaleefeh said to Jaạfar, Wherefore doth not thy companion drink?—O my lord, answered the Wezeer, for a long time he hath not drunk of this beverage. The False Khaleefeh therefore said, I have another beverage, suitable to thy companion, and it is a kind of cider. And he gave orders to bring it. So they brought it immediately; and the False Khaleefeh, advancing towards Hároon Er-Rasheed, and standing before him, said to him, Whenever the turn cometh round to thee, drink of this beverage. They then continued merrily taking the cups of wine, until it rose into their heads and overpowered their reason; when the Khaleefeh Hároon Er-Rasheed said to his Wezeer, O Jaạfar, by Allah, we have not vessels like these. Would, then, that I knew the history of this young man!—But while they were talking together privately, the young man cast a glance towards them, and found the Wezeer whispering to the Khaleefeh: so he said, Whispering is an act of rudeness. The Wezeer therefore replied, No rudeness is committed here: but this my companion saith, Verily I have travelled into most countries, and caroused with the greatest of Kings, and associated with the warriours, yet I have not witnessed an entertainment better conducted than this, nor experienced a more joyous night than the present; save that the people of Baghdád say, Drink without music sometimes occasioneth the headache.

And when the False Khaleefeh heard these words, he smiled, and became cheerful. He had in his hand a rod, and he struck a round cushion[10] with it; whereupon a door opened, and there came forth from it a eunuch bearing a throne of ivory inlaid with brilliant gold, and followed by a damsel of surpassing beauty and loveliness and elegance and consummate grace. The eunuch placed the throne, and the damsel seated herself upon it, resembling the sun shining forth in the clear sky. In her hand was a lute of Indian manufacture, and she placed it in her lap, and, leaning over it as the mother leaneth over her child, sang to it. But first, with emotion, she played over four and twenty airs, so that she astonished the minds of her hearers. Then returning to her first air, with exhilarating modulations she sang these verses:—

The tongue of love in my heart addresseth thee, informing thee that I am enamoured of thee;
And I have evidence in the burning of a tortured heart, and a wounded eye, and incessant tears.
I knew not love until I loved thee; but God's decree overtaketh his creatures.

And when the False Khaleefeh heard these verses sung by the damsel, he uttered a great cry, and rent the dress that was upon him to the skirt; whereupon a curtain was let down over him, and the attendants brought him another dress, more handsome than the former one, and he put it on.

He then sat as before; and when the cup came to him, he again struck the rod upon the round cushion; and, lo, a door opened, and there came forth from it a eunuch bearing a throne of gold, and behind him was a damsel more beautiful than the first damsel. And she seated herself upon the throne, having in her hand a lute that would sadden the heart of the envious; and she sang to it these two verses:—

How can I be patient, with the fire of love in my heart, and the tears ever pouring in a flood from my eye?
By Allah, life hath no sweetness to rejoice me. And how can a heart filled with grief be happy?

And the young man, on hearing these verses, again uttered a great cry, and tore the clothes that were upon him to the skirt; and the curtain was let down over him, and they brought him another suit, which he put on.

Then composing himself upon his seat, he resumed his former state, entering cheerfully into conversation; and when the cup came to him, he struck the round cushion, and there came forth a eunuch followed by a damsel handsomer than the one who had just preceded her. The eunuch had with him a throne, and the damsel seated herself upon it, with a lute in her hand, and sang to it these verses:—

Cease from your abandonment, and abate your cruelty; for my heart, by your existence, hath not relinquished you!
Have mercy on a disordered, sad, mourning, lover, full of desire, and enslaved by his passion for you!
Sickness hath wasted him, through the excess of his ecstasy, and he hath supplicated the Deity for thine approval.
O full moon,[11] whose place is in my heart! how can I prefer any mortal to you?

And again, when the young man heard these verses, he uttered a great cry, rending the clothes that were upon him, and they let down the curtain over him, and brought him other clothes.

After this, he resumed his former state with his boon-companions, and the cups circulated; and when the cup came to him, he struck the round cushion as before; whereupon the door opened, and a page came forth from it with a throne, and behind him was a damsel. He set the throne for her, and she seated herself upon it, and, taking the lute, tuned it, and thus sang to it:—

When will disjunction and hatred cease, and the pleasures that have passed return unto me?
Yesterday we were united in the same abode, in happy converse, and saw the enviers heedless;
But fortune hath betrayed us and disunited us, having left our residence like the desert.
Wouldst thou have me relinquish the beloved, O my censurer? I find my heart will not comply with the censurer's wish.
Cease then to blame me, and leave me in my passion; for my mind hath not been void of cheering thoughts of the beloved.
O my lord,[12] who hast been faithless and changing, think not that my heart on account of thine estrangement hath relinquished thee.

And the False Khaleefeh, when he had heard the damsel's song, again uttered a great cry, tore the clothes that were upon him, and fell down in a fit; upon which the attendants would have let fall the curtain over him as usual; but its cords were immoveable; and Hároon Er-Rasheed, looking towards the young man, beheld upon his body the marks of beating with miḳra'ahs. So after he had looked, and certified himself of the fact, he said to his Wezeer, O Jaạfar, by Allah, he is a comely young man, but an abominable thief.—How, said Jaạfar, hast thou discovered that, O Prince of the Faithful? The Khaleefeh rejoined, Didst thou not see upon his sides the scars occasioned by whips?

Then the attendants let down the curtain over their master, and brought him another suit of clothing; and after he had put it on, he composed himself on his seat as at first, with his boon-companions; but looking towards the Khaleefeh and Jaạfar, he saw them conversing together privately; whereupon he said to them, What is the news, O ye two young men? So Jaạfar answered, O our lord, good news;[13] save that it is a fact not concealed from thee that this my companion is of the merchants, and he hath journeyed to all the great cities and the regions of the earth, and hath associated with the Kings and with the best of men, and he saith to me, Verily that which hath been done by our lord the Khaleefeh this night is excessive extravagance, and I have not seen any one do as he hath done in all the countries of the earth; for he hath rent such and such suits of apparel; each suit, of the value of a thousand pieces of gold; and this is exceeding extravagance.—But the False Khaleefeh replied, What is this! Verily the wealth is mine, and the stuff is mine; and this is one of the means of bestowing presents upon the servants and other attendants: for every suit of apparel that I have rent is for one of the boon-companions who are present, and I have assigned to them, with each suit of apparel, five hundred pieces of gold. The Wezeer therefore said, Excellently hast thou done, O our lord. And he recited these two verses:—

The virtues have built a mansion in the midst of thy hand, and thou hast made thy wealth common to all men.
If the virtues should ever close their doors, thy hands would be a key that would open their lock.

And when the young man heard these verses from the mouth of the Wezeer Jaạfar, he gave orders to present him with a thousand pieces of gold, and a suit of apparel.

The cups then circulated among them again, and the wine was pleasant to them, and Er-Rasheed, addressing his Wezeer, said, O Jaạfar, inquire of him respecting the marks of the beating upon his sides, that we may see what he will say in his answer. Jaạfar replied, Hasten not, O our lord, but sooth thy mind; for patience is more becoming. The Khaleefeh, however, said, By my head, and by the tomb of El-'Abbás,[14] if thou ask him not, I will assuredly stop thy breath. And upon this, the young man looked towards the Wezeer, and said, What is the matter with thee and thy companion, that ye are whispering together? Acquaint me with the subject of your conversation.—Jaạfar answered, It is good. But the young man replied, I conjure thee by Allah that thou tell me your story, and conceal from me nothing of your affair. So the Wezeer said, O my lord, he saw upon thy sides the marks occasioned by whips and miḳra'ahs, and he wondered thereat extremely, and said, How can the Khaleefeh be beaten?—and he desireth to know the cause.—And when the young man heard this, he smiled, and said, Know that my story is extraordinary, and my case is wonderful: if it were engraven upon the understanding, it would be a lesson to him who would be admonished. Then he groaned, and recited these verses:—

My story is wonderful, surpassing all wonders. I swear by love that my ways have become strait to me.
If then ye desire to hear me, listen; and let every one in this assembly be silent.
Attend to my words; for they are significant, and my speech is true: it is not false.

I am a victim of desire, and of ardent passion, and my murderess surpasseth all the high-bosomed damsels.
She hath a deep black eye, like an Indian sword, and she shooteth arrows from the bows of her eyebrows.
Now my heart feeleth that among you is our Imám, the Khaleefeh of this age, and of excellent descent;
And that the second of you is he who is called Jaafar, his Wezeer, a Ṣáḥeb[15] and the son of a Ṣáḥeb;
And that the third of you is Mesroor, his Executioner: then if this my assertion be not false,
I have attained the whole of what I wish by this occurrence; and in every respect my heart is rejoiced.

But when they heard these words from his mouth, Jaafar swore to him, making use of an ambiguous oath, that they were not the persons whom he had mentioned. And upon this, the young man laughed, and said,—

Know, O my lords, that I am not the Prince of the Faithful, but that I have only called myself by this title to obtain what I desire from the sons of the city. In truth, my name is Moḥammad 'Alee the son of 'Alee the Jeweller. My father was of the higher order of society, and he died, and left to me great wealth, in gold and silver, and pearls and coral, and rubies and chrysolites and other jewels, as well as landed property, baths and fields and gardens, and shops and ovens, and male black slaves and female slaves, and pages. And it happened one day, that I was sitting in my shop, with my servants

and dependants around me, and, lo, a damsel approached, mounted upon a mule, and attended by three other damsels, like moons; and when she came up to me, she alighted at my shop, and, seating herself with me, said to me, Art thou Moḥammad the Jeweller? I answered her, Yes, I am he, thy memlook and thy slave. And she said, Hast thou a necklace of jewels suitable to me?—O my mistress, I answered, what I have I will exhibit to thee and place before thee; and if any of them please thee, it will be of the good fortune of the memlook; and if none of them please thee, of his ill luck. I had a hundred necklaces of jewels, and I exhibited to her all of them; but none of those pleased her, and she said, I desire better than I have seen. Now I had a small necklace which my father had bought for a hundred thousand pieces of gold, and the like of it existed not in the possession of any one among the great Sulṭáns: so I said to her, I have yet a necklace of fine stones and jewels, the like of which no one of the great or of the small possesseth. And she replied, Shew it to me. And when she saw it, she said, This is the thing that I desire, and it is what I have wished for all my life. Then she said to me, What is its price? I answered her, Its price to my father was a hundred thousand pieces of gold. And she replied, And thou shalt have five thousand pieces of gold as profit. I said, O my mistress, the necklace and its owner are at thy service, and there is no opposition on my part. But she replied, Thou must receive a profit, and thou wilt still be entitled to abundant thanks. She then immediately arose, quickly mounted the mule, and said to me, O my master, in the name of Allah, do me the favour to accompany us, that thou mayest receive the price; for this thy day is to us like milk.[16]

I therefore arose, and, having closed the shop, proceeded with her in security until we arrived at the house; and I found it to be a mansion displaying evident signs of prosperity: its door was adorned with gold and silver and ultramarine, and upon it were inscribed these two verses:—

O mansion, may mourning never enter thee, nor fortune act treacherously to thine owner!
An excellent mansion to every guest art thou when other places are strait unto him.

The damsel alighted, and entered the house, ordering me to seat myself upon the maṣṭabah of the door until the money-changer should come.[17] So I sat a while at the door; and, lo, a damsel came forth to me and said to me, O my master, enter the vestibule; for thy sitting at the door is dishonourable. I rose, therefore, and entered the vestibule, where I seated myself upon the wooden sofa;[18] and while I was sitting there, a damsel came forth and said to me, O my master, my mistress saith to thee, Enter, and seat thyself at the door of the saloon, to receive thy money. Accordingly I rose, and entered the house, and when I had sat a moment, I beheld a throne of gold, with a silken curtain over it, and the curtain was raised, and there appeared beneath it the damsel who had purchased of me the necklace. She had displayed a face like the disk of the moon, and the necklace was upon her neck. My reason was disturbed, and my mind was confounded at the sight of that damsel, by reason of her excessive beauty and loveliness. And when she beheld me, she rose from the throne, and came towards me, saying to me, O light of my eye, is every one who is comely like thee, without sympathy for his beloved?—O my mistress, I replied, all beauty is centred in thee, and is one of thy charms. And she said, O Jeweller, know that I love thee, and I did not believe that I could bring thee into my abode. Then she bent over me, and I kissed her, and she kissed me; after which she said to me, I am a virgin whom no man hath approached, and I am not unknown in the city. Knowest thou who I am?—I answered, No, by Allah, O my mistress. And she rejoined, I am the lady Dunyà, the daughter of Yaḥyà the son of Khálid El-Barmekee, and my brother is Jaạfar, the Wezeer of the Khaleefeh. So when I heard these her words, I drew back from her, saying to her, O my mistress, I am not in fault in making advances towards thee. Thou excitedst my love.—But she replied, No harm shall befall thee; and thou must attain thy wish by the means that God approveth; for the disposal of myself is in my own power, and the Ḳáḍee shall officiate for me in performing the ceremony of my contract. I desire to be to thee a wife, and that thou be to me a husband.

She then summoned the Ḳáḍee and the witnesses, and busily occupied herself in preparing; and when they came, she said to them, Moḥammad 'Alee the son of 'Alee the Jeweller hath demanded me in marriage, and given me this necklace as my dowry; and I have accepted his proposal, and consented. So they performed the contract of my marriage to her, and I took her as my wife. And after this, she caused the wine-vessels to be brought, and the cups circulated in the most agreeable and perfect order; and when the wine penetrated into our heads, she ordered a damsel, a lute-player, to sing. She therefore did so, and others sang after her, one after another, until ten damsels had sung. Then the lady Dunyà took the lute, and, with delightful modulations, sang these verses:—

> I swear by the pliancy of thy gracefully-moving figure, that I am suffering the torture of thine estrangement.
> Pity then a heart that is burning with thy love, O bright as the full moon in the darkness of night!

And when she had finished, I took the lute from her, and, playing in an extraordinary manner, sang thus:—

> Extolled be the perfection of my Lord who hath given thee all beauty, so that I have become thy captive!
> O thou who hast an eye by which thou captivatest mankind, pray that I may be safe from the arrows that thou shootest!

And on hearing my song, she rejoiced exceedingly.

I resided with her a whole month, abandoning my shop and family and home; and she said to me one day, O light of the eye, O my master Moḥammad, I have determined to-day to visit the bath, and do thou remain upon this couch, and not move from thy place until I return to thee. She conjured me to do so, and I replied, I hear and obey. Then she made me swear that I would not move from my place, and, taking her female slaves with her, went to the bath. And by Allah, O my brothers, she had not arrived at the end of the street when the door was opened and there came in through it an old woman, who said, O my master Moḥammad, the lady Zubeydeh summoneth thee; for she hath heard of thy polite accomplishments, and elegance, and of the excellence of thy singing. I replied, By Allah, I will not rise from my place until the lady Dunyà cometh. But the old woman rejoined, O my master, cause not the lady Zubeydeh to be incensed against thee, and to become thine enemy. Arise then, and answer her summons, and return to thy place. So I arose immediately and repaired to her, the old woman preceding me, until she conducted me to the lady Zubeydeh; and when I came to her, she said to me, O light of the eye, art thou the beloved of the lady Dunyà? I answered, I am thy memlook and thy slave. And she said, He hath spoken truth who hath described thee as distinguished by beauty and loveliness and good breeding and every charming quality; for thou surpassest the description: but sing to me, that I may hear thee. So I replied, I hear and obey. And she gave me the lute, and I sang to it these verses:—

The heart of the lover is wearied in his suit, and his body becometh the spoil of diseases.
Among the riders of these haltered camels is none other than a lover whose beloved is among the caravan.
I commit to God's care a moonlike beauty in your tents, whom my heart loveth, but who is veiled from my eye;
Now consenting, now angry: how sweet is her feigned coyness! for every thing that the loved-one doth is loved.

And when I had finished the song, she said to me, Allah give health to thy body, and sweetness to thy voice! for thou art perfect in comeliness and polite accomplishments and in singing. And now arise and repair to thy place before the lady Dunyà cometh; lest she find thee not, and be incensed against thee.

So I kissed the ground before her, and went forth, and proceeded with the old woman before me until I arrived at the door from which I had come out. But when I entered, and came to the couch, I found that the lady Dunyà had returned from the bath, and she was sleeping upon the couch. I therefore seated myself at her feet, and pressed them with my hands;[19] whereupon she opened her eyes, and, seeing me, drew up her feet, and kicked me down from the couch, and said, O traitor, thou hast violated thine oath, and perjured thyself. Thou gavest me a promise that thou wouldst not move from thy place, and thou hast broken thy promise, and gone to the lady Zubeydeh. By Allah, were it not for my fear of disgracing myself, I would demolish her palace over her head!—She then said to her black slave, O Ṣawáb, arise, and strike off the head of this lying traitor; for we have no further need of him. So the slave advanced, and, having torn a strip from his skirt, bound my eyes with it, and was about to strike off my head. But the female slaves, great and small, came to her and said, O our mistress, this is not the first who hath been guilty of a fault, and he knoweth not thy temper, nor hath he committed an offence that requireth his slaughter. And upon this she said, By Allah, I must cause him to bear some mark of my resentment. Accordingly she gave orders to beat me, whereupon they beat me on my sides, and these scars which ye have beheld are the result. After that, she commanded that I should be turned out; and they took me forth to a distance from the mansion, and threw me down.

I raised myself, and walked on by a few steps at a time until I arrived at my abode, when I caused a surgeon to be brought, and shewed him the wounds occasioned by the beating; and he treated me with kindness, and applied himself to my cure. And when I recovered, and had entered the bath, and my pains and disorders had ceased, I went to the shop, and, taking all the goods that it contained, sold them, and with their united price I bought for myself four hundred memlooks, such as no King ever collected; and every day two hundred of them rode forth with me. I also made this bark, for the construction of which I expended five thousand pieces of gold; and I called myself the Khaleefeh, appointing each of my servants to the office of some one of the dependants of the Khaleefeh, and equipping him in his costume, and proclaimed, Whosoever amuseth himself upon the Tigris, I will strike off his head without delay. Thus I have continued to do for a whole year; but I have heard no tidings of the damsel, nor seen any trace of her.

Then the young man lamented, and poured forth tears, and recited these verses:—

By Allah, I shall never forget her, nor draw near to any but such as may draw her to me.
She is like the full moon in her aspect. Extolled be the perfection of her Maker! Extolled be her Creator!
She hath made me full of mourning, sleepless, love-sick; and my mind is confounded by her charms.

—And when Hároon Er-Rasheed heard his words, and knew his transport and ardour and desire, his mind was disturbed with sorrow for him, he was lost in wonder, and he said, Extolled be the perfection of God, who appointeth for every thing a cause!—Then they begged leave of the young man to depart; and he gave them permission; Er-Rasheed determining to do him justice, and to treat him with the utmost munificence.

They departed from him, proceeding to the palace; and when they had remained sitting there a while, and changed their clothes, and put on the robes of state, Mesroor the Executioner stood before the Khaleefeh and Jaạfar, and the Khaleefeh said to Jaạfar, O Wezeer, bring hither to me the young man with whom we were last night. The Wezeer replied, I hear and obey. And he repaired to him, and saluted him, and said to him, Answer the summons of the Prince of the Faithful, the Khaleefeh Hároon Er-Rasheed. So the young man went with him to the palace, with a heart contracted in consequence of the summons; and when he went in to the Khaleefeh, he kissed the ground before him, greeted him with a prayer for the endurance of his glory and prosperity, and for the attainment of his desires, the continuance of his beneficence, and the cessation of evil and punishments, and, addressing him in the best manner he was able, said, Peace be on thee, O Prince of the Faithful, and Protector of the congregation of the believers! Then he recited these two verses:—

May thy gate never cease to be repaired to as a Kaạbeh, and may its dust ever mark the foreheads of men!
That throughout all countries it may be proclaimed, This is the Maḳám, and thou art Ibráheem.[20]

And the Khaleefeh smiled in his face, returned his salutation, and, looking at him with the eye of respect, caused him to draw near and to seat himself before him, and said to him, O Moḥammad 'Alee, I desire of thee that thou relate to me what happened to thee this last night; for it was of a wonderful and surprising kind. The young man replied, Pardon, O Prince of the Faithful! Give me the handkerchief of indemnity,[21] that my terror may subside, and my heart be appeased. And the Khaleefeh said, Thou hast security from fear and sorrows.

So the young man began to relate to him the events which had happened to him from first to last. And the Khaleefeh, knowing that the young man was enamoured, and parted from the object of his passion, said to him, Dost thou desire me to restore her to thee?—This, answered the young man, will be an instance of the abundant beneficence of the Prince of the Faithful. And thereupon the Khaleefeh, looking towards the Wezeer, said to him, O Jaạfar, bring to me thy sister, the lady Dunyà, the daughter of the Wezeer Yaḥyà the son of Khálid. So Jaạfar replied, I hear and obey. He brought her immediately; and when she stood before him, the Khaleefeh said to her, Knowest thou who is this?—O Prince of the Faithful, she said, how should women have knowledge of men? And the Khaleefeh smiled, and said to her, O Dunyà, this is thy lover, Moḥammad 'Alee the son of the Jeweller: we have become acquainted with the case, and heard the story from its beginning to its end, and understood what was public and what was private of it; and the thing is not concealed, though it was veiled.—O Prince of the Faithful, she replied, it was written in the Book [of God's decrees], and I beg forgiveness of God the Great for the actions committed by me, and request of thy goodness that thou wilt pardon me. And upon this the Khaleefeh laughed, and, having summoned the Ḳáḍee and the witnesses, renewed the contract of her marriage to her husband Moḥammad 'Alee the son of the Jeweller; and there resulted to them the utmost felicity; and to the envious, mortification. The Khaleefeh also made the young man one of his boon-companions; and he and his wife continued in happiness and delight and cheerfulness until they were visited by the terminator of delights, and the separator of companions.[22]

NOTES TO CHAPTER THIRTEENTH.

NOTE 1. THIS story, and that in the next chapter of the present work, have, I believe, been translated into French, by M. Caussin, and published in the edition of the Thousand and One Nights mentioned in the first of the notes to my eleventh chapter.

NOTE 2. The kind of cresset here mentioned, called in Arabic "mesh'al," is a staff with a cylindrical frame (commonly of iron) at the top, filled with flaming wood, or having two, three, four, or five of these receptacles for fire. The mesh'al with a single receptacle for fire is the most common, and the entire length is generally about seven feet. Two different kinds are figured in my work on the Modern Egyptians, vol. i. ch. vi. They are borne in various nocturnal processions, and often before a horseman riding by night.

NOTE 3. The term "meezer" or "mi-zer" is properly applied to a cloth which is wrapped round the waist and reaches to the knees, or lower; and is now also used to signify a pair of drawers.

NOTE 4. What is here meant is doubtful. A cresset-bearer before a *horseman* might be properly described as having on his shoulder an embroidered saddle-cover, called in Arabic "gháshiyeh." This was usually borne before a King, and a less costly kind is now often seen on the shoulder of a groom preceding a horseman of the higher or middle rank.

NOTE 5. See Note 52 to Chapter ii.

NOTE 6. Literally, "the *second*, or the *other*, Khaleefeh." So also in the other instances in which I use the term "False Khaleefeh."

NOTE 7. "Sáj" is the name of an Indian tree, the wood of which is imported into Arabian countries; but our Orientalists disagree as to its species. De Sacy[1] thinks it likely that "sáj" is an Indian name adopted by the Arabs: if so, the tree so called is probably the teak (as he first supposed); this tree being termed in Sanscrit, "sáka."[2]

NOTE 8. In the original, "shádharwán." This word, which I here render in accordance with the manner in which my sheykh has explained it in several places, is

---

[1] See his Chrestomathie Arabe, vol. iii. pp. 473 *et seq.*, 2nd. ed.

[2] Johnson's edition of Richardson's Persian, Arabic, and English Dictionary, *voce* "sáj."

also written "shádarwán" and "shádirwán," and is, I believe, generally applied to a fountain, or jet d'eau, with pieces of glass, or glass bells, which, being put in motion by the water, produce a constant tinkling. The word is Persian.

NOTE 9. The "long mattresses" here mentioned are those described in Note 12 to Chapter iii.

NOTE 10. For a knowledge of the particular kind of round cushion here mentioned, by the term "mudowwarah," I am indebted to Mr. Salamé; for although I have one, which I purchased of an Arab at Gibraltar, I either did not inquire, or else forgot, the name. It is generally about fifteen inches in diameter, three or four inches thick, and covered with velvet or leather, embroidered or otherwise ornamented. Cushions of this kind I did not see in the East; but they are common among the Arabs in Western Africa, and have of late years been imported into England, where they are used as footstools. The Arabs use them generally to recline against, and sometimes as pillows for the head.

NOTE 11. Literally, "O full moons." The plural is used for the reason explained in Note 34 to Chapter x.

NOTE 12. Here again the plural is used in the original, to convey a superlative sense.

NOTE 13. It is a general custom among the Arabs, when a person is asked, "What is the news?" to reply, "Good" (kheyr), even when the news to be imparted is bad.

NOTE 14. I believe I have before mentioned El-'Abbás, as an uncle of the Prophet, and ancestor of the Khaleefehs of Baghdád, who were hence called the 'Abbásee Khaleefehs.

NOTE 15. See Note 8 to the Introduction.

NOTE 16. It is common with the Arabs to say that a day is like milk, or white as milk, to imply that it is fortunate; and that it is like mud, or black as mud, to signify the contrary.

NOTE 17. A money-changer is employed by Kings and grandees to pay and receive their money.[3]

NOTE 18. See Note 39 to Chapter ii.

NOTE 19. The action here mentioned is accompanied with a gentle rubbing. The object in this case was to awake the lady. See Note 55 to Chapter iii.

NOTE 20. These two verses may be explained by the following amplified paraphrase.—"May thy palace never cease to be an object of desire, a place where prayer will be answered, resorted to by multitudes, like the Temple of Mekkeh; and may men ever exhibit tokens of the honours or benefits that they have received there in paying their homage, as a person who has just prayed upon the bare ground exhibits a forehead marked with the dust: thus throughout every country it will be known, that thy palace is like the station of Ibráheem (or Abraham), a place within the inner enclosure of the Kaạbeh, where prayer is especially blessed,[4] and that thou art like Ibráheem himself." But my sheykh remarks, that these verses are not well applied except in praise of a person whose name is Ibráheem.

NOTE 21. See Note 95 to Chapter v.

NOTE 22. This story is followed by four anecdotes, ending with part of the two hundred and ninety-ninth night. The third and fourth of these are here subjoined.

---

[3] Marginal note by my sheykh.

[4] See the Ḳur-án, ch. ii. v. 119.

Anecdote of a Disinterested Lover.

It is related that Khálid the son of 'Abd-Allah El-Ḳusheyree[5] was Governor of El-Baṣrah; and there came to him a number of men grasping a young man of surpassing comeliness and evident good breeding and abundant intellect, of handsome figure, of sweet odour, and of a grave and dignified appearance; and they brought him forward unto Khálid. So Khálid inquired of them his story, and they said, This is a thief, whom we caught yesterday in our abode. And when Khálid looked at him, the beauty of his appearance, and his cleanliness, excited his admiration, and he said, Loose him. Then, approaching him, he asked him his story; and the young man answered, The people have spoken truth, and the case is as they have related.—And what, said Khálid, induced thee to do this, when thou hast so comely an appearance and so handsome a form? He answered, Covetousness of worldly goods, and the decree of God, whose perfection be extolled, and whose name be exalted! And upon this, Khálid said, May thy mother be bereft of thee! Hadst thou not in the comeliness of thy face, and the soundness of thy sense, and in thy good breeding, what would suffice to restrain thee from thieving?—Abstain from this language, O Emeer, replied the young man, and proceed to do what God (whose name be exalted!) hath ordained; for such is the recompense of that which my hands have done, and God is not tyrannical towards his servants. And Khálid remained a while silent, reflecting upon the affair of the young man; after which he desired him to draw near, and said to him, Thy confession before the witnesses hath perplexed me so that I know not what to do; and I do not think thee to be a thief. Probably thou hast some story to tell that is not one of theft. Acquaint me then with it.—But the young man replied, O Emeer, let nothing be imagined by thee, except that which I have confessed to thee; for I have no story to relate but this, that I entered the house of these people, and stole what I could, and they caught me, and took the property from me, and conveyed me unto thee. Upon this, therefore, Khálid gave orders to imprison him, and commanded a crier to proclaim throughout El-Baṣrah, Ho! whosoever desireth to witness the punishment of such-a-one, and the cutting off of his hand, let him come in the morning to such a place!

And when the young man had been a while in the prison, and they had put the irons upon his feet, he sighed heavily, shed copious tears, and recited these verses:—

Khálid hath threatened me with the cutting off of my hand if I reveal not to him her story;
But I said, Far be it from me that I should reveal the love for her which my heart entertaineth!
The cutting off of my hand for that which I have confessed is easier to my heart than disgracing her.

And the persons who were commissioned to guard him, hearing this, came to Khálid, and acquainted him with that which he had said. So when the night grew dark, he gave orders to bring him into his presence; and on his coming before him, he urged him to speak, and found him to be sensible, well-bred, intelligent, polite, and discreet. He gave orders to bring him food; and he ate, and conversed a while with him; after which, Khálid said to him, I know that thou hast a story to tell that is not one of theft: so when the morning cometh, and the people are present, with the Ḳáḍee, and he asketh thee respecting the theft, deny it, and assert that which may avert from thee the punishment of amputation; for the Apostle of God (may God bless and save him!) hath said, In cases of doubt, avert the punishments fixed by the law.—He then gave orders to take him back to the prison, where he remained that night.

And in the morning the people came to witness the amputation of the young man's

---

[5] "El-Ḳusheyree" is probably put by a mistake of a copyist for "El-Ḳasree." Khálid the son of 'Abd-Allah El-Ḳasree was a famous Governor of El-'Erák (in which El-Baṣrah is situate) for a period of nearly fifteen years, in the reign of the Khaleefeh Hishám the son of 'Abd-El-Melik, as related by Ibn-Khallikán.

hand, and there was not any one in El-Baṣrah, man or woman, who did not come to behold the punishment of that young man. Khálid mounted, attended by the chief persons of El-Baṣrah, and others, and, having summoned the Ḳáḍees, gave orders to bring the young man, who approached, jumping in the chains; and not one of the people beheld him without weeping for him, and the voices of the women rose in shrieks. So the [chief] Ḳáḍee commanded to silence the women, and then said to the young man, These people assert that thou enteredst their house, and stolest their property. Probably thou stolest less than the niṣáb.[6]—Nay, he replied, I stole a complete niṣáb.—Probably, rejoined the Ḳáḍee, thou art a partner of the people in some of the property. But the young man replied, Nay: the whole of it was theirs: I had no right in it. And upon this, Khálid was enraged, and came to him and struck him upon his face with the whip, repeating this verse as applicable to his own case:—

> Man desireth that his wish may be granted unto him; but God refuseth all save what Himself desireth.

He then called for the butcher, who came, and drew forth the knife, and, stretching forth the young man's hand, put the knife upon it.

But a damsel hastened forward from the midst of the women, clad in tattered and dirty garments,[7] and cried out, and threw herself upon the young man; after which she displayed a face like the moon; whereupon a great clamour arose among the people, and a fiery excitement of the passions of the spectators well nigh ensued in consequence of this spectacle. Then the damsel cried out with her loudest voice, I conjure thee by Allah, O Emeer, that thou hasten not the amputation until thou shalt have read this note. And she gave him a note, which Khálid opened and read, and, lo, in it were written these verses:—

> O Khálid, this person is a distracted slave of love, wounded by a glance shot from the bows of my eye-lashes.
> An arrow from my eye hath prostrated him; for he is wedded to the ardour of love, and recovereth not from his malady.
> He hath avowed a deed that he hath not committed, thinking this better than the disgrace of his enamoured.
> Have patience then with the afflicted lover; for he is one of the noble of mankind, not a thief.

When Khálid, therefore, read the verses, he withdrew, and separated himself from the people, and, having summoned the woman, inquired of her respecting the case. So she informed him that this young man was enamoured of her, and that she was enamoured of him; and that he had repaired to the house of her family with the desire of visiting her, and thrown a stone into the house to acquaint her with his arrival; but that her father and her brothers heard the sound of the stone, and came up to him; and when he perceived them, he collected all the linen of the house, making it appear to them that he was a thief, in order to protect the honour of his beloved. Therefore when they saw him thus engaged, they took him, and said, This is a thief,—and brought him to thee; whereupon he confessed that he had committed theft, and persisted in doing so, that he might not disgrace me. These things he did, making himself a thief, from the excess of his kindness, and the generosity of his mind.—And Khálid replied, Verily he is worthy of the accomplishment of his desire. Then having called the young man to him, he kissed him between the eyes; and he gave orders to bring before him the damsel's father, and said to him, O sheykh, we had determined upon the execution of the sentence upon this young man by the amputation of his hand; but God (to whom be ascribed might and glory!) hath preserved me from that act; and I have ordered that ten thousand pieces of silver be given to him, for his

---

[6] This term here means property amounting in value to a quarter of a deenár.—See Note 32 to Chapter v.

[7] It is probably meant that she had clad herself in this manner to testify her grief.

generous exposure of his hand in order to preserve thy honour and the honour of thy daughter, and to protect you both from reproach. I have ordered also that ten thousand pieces of silver shall be given to thy daughter, in consideration of her having informed me of the truth of the affair; and I beg that thou give me permission to marry her to him.—O Emeer, replied the sheykh, I give thee permission to do so. And Khálid praised God, and thanked Him, and recited an eloquent khuṭbeh;[8] after which he said to the young man, I marry to thee this damsel, such-a-one, who is here present, with her permission and consent, and with the permission of her father, for a dowry consisting of this money, the amount of which is ten thousand pieces of silver. And the young man replied, I accept from thee this offer of marriage. Then Khálid gave orders to carry the money to the house of the young man, borne in procession, upon trays; and the people dispersed, full of happiness.—I have not witnessed (says the narrator) a day more strange than that day, beginning with weeping and misfortunes, and ending with joy and happiness.

[In the following anecdote, mention is made of an event of a most melancholy nature, the knowledge of which has caused me to derive less pleasure than I should find, if ignorant of the fact, in many of the best stories in the present collection; and I therefore think that some of my readers may prefer passing it over unread.]

---

[8] See Note 39 to Chapter iv.

Anecdote of Jaạfar El-Barmekee.

A Bedawee of a distant desert[9] used, every year, to bring an ode to Jaạfar El-Barmekee, who used to give him a thousand pieces of gold as a largess for his ode; and the Bedawee took the money and departed, and remained expending from it upon his family until the close of the year. Now this Bedawee brought him the ode according to his custom, and, when he came, found Jaạfar hanged;[10] and he came to the place where he was hanged, and there, having made his camel lie down, wept violently, mourned greatly, and recited his ode, and slept. And in his sleep he saw Jaạfar El-Barmekee, who said to him, Thou hast wearied thyself, and come to us, and found us in the state thou seest: but repair to El-Baṣrah, and inquire for a man whose name is so-and-so, one of the merchants of El-Baṣrah, and say to him, Jaạfar El-Barmekee saluteth thee, and saith to thee, Give me a thousand pieces of gold, by the token of the bean.

When the Bedawee, therefore, awoke from his sleep, he repaired to El-Baṣrah, and inquired for that merchant; and, having met with him, he acquainted him with the words that Jaạfar had said in the dream; whereupon the merchant wept violently, so that his soul almost quitted the world. He then treated the Bedawee with honour, seating him by him, and making his stay pleasant; and the Bedawee remained with him three days, honourably entertained. And when he desired to depart, the merchant gave to him a thousand and five hundred pieces of gold, saying to him, The thousand are what I am commanded to give thee, and the five hundred are a present to thee from myself, and thou shalt receive every year a thousand pieces of gold.

And at his departure, the Bedawee said to the merchant, I conjure thee by Allah to acquaint me with the affair of the bean, that I may know its foundation. So the merchant replied, I was, at the commencement of my career, in a state of poverty, going about with hot beans[11] through the streets of Baghdád, and selling them as a means of subsistence. And I went forth on a cold and rainy day, without sufficient clothing on my body to preserve me from the bleakness of the air, now shivering from the severity of the cold, and now falling in the water of the rain, in so horrible a state that the skin quaketh at thinking upon it. Now Jaạfar was sitting that day in a pavilion overlooking the street, and with him were his chief attendants and concubines; and his eye fell upon me; whereupon he was moved with pity for my condition, and sent to me one of his servants, who took me and led me in to him; and when he saw me, he said to me, Sell the beans that thou hast with thee to my attendants. So I began to mete them with a measure that I had with me, and every one who took a measure of beans filled the measure with gold, until all that I had with me was exhausted, and there remained nothing in the basket [except one bean]. Then I collected together the gold that had accrued to me; and Jaạfar said to me, Doth aught of the beans remain with thee? I answered, I know not. And searching in the basket, I found in it nothing but one bean; whereupon Jaạfar took it from me, and split it in twain; and he took one half of it, and gave the other half to one of his concubines, saying, For what sum wilt thou buy the half of this bean? She answered, For twice the quantity of this gold. So I was confounded at my case, and said within myself, This is impossible. But while I was wondering, lo, the concubine gave orders to one of her female slaves, who brought a quantity of gold twice as much as that

---

9 In the original are a few introductory words, which I omit because they are inappropriate.

10 In the original, "maṣloob," which generally signifies "crucified." Jaạfar was first beheaded. I think it right to omit a description of the particulars of this case, respecting which there are various different assertions.

11 In the original, "el-fool el-ḥárr." These are beans soaked for a while in water, and then boiled. —Note by my sheykh.

which was already collected. Then Jaạfar saịd, And I will buy the half that I have taken for twice the quantity of the whole. And he said to me, Receive the price of thy bean. And he gave orders to one of his servants, who collected together the whole of the money and put it into my basket; and I took it and departed. After that, I came to El-Baṣrah, and trafficked with the money in my possession, and God gave me ample wealth. To God therefore be praise and thanks! So if I give thee every year a thousand pieces of gold, derived from the munificence of Jaạfar, it injureth me not at all.—Observe, then, the generous disposition of Jaạfar, and the praise bestowed upon him living and dead. The mercy of God (whose name be exalted!) be on him!

CHAPTER XIV.

COMMENCING WITH PART OF THE TWO HUNDRED AND NINETY-NINTH NIGHT, AND ENDING WITH PART OF THE THREE HUNDRED AND FIFTH.

THE STORY OF ABOO-MOHAMMAD THE LAZY.[1]

Hároon Er-Rasheed was sitting one day upon the imperial throne, when there came in to him a young man of the eunuchs, with a crown of red gold set with pearls and jewels, comprising all kinds of jacinths and jewels such as no money would suffice to procure. This young man kissed the ground before the Khaleefeh, and said to him, O Prince of the Faithful, the lady Zubeydeh kisseth the ground before thee, and saith to thee, Thou knowest that she hath made this crown, and it wanteth a large jewel to be affixed to its summit; and she hath searched among her treasures, but found not among them a large jewel such as she desireth. So the Khaleefeh said to the chamberlains and lieutenants, Search for a large jewel such as Zubeydeh desireth. They therefore searched, but found nothing that suited her; and they acquainted the Khaleefeh with this; in consequence of which his bosom became contracted, and he said, How is it that I am Khaleefeh, and King of the Kings of the earth, and am unable to procure a jewel? Wo unto you! Inquire of the merchants.—And they inquired of the merchants; but they answered them, Our lord the Khaleefeh will not find the jewel save with a man of El-Baṣrah, named Aboo-Moḥammad the Lazy. So they informed the Khaleefeh of this; and he ordered his Wezeer Jaạfar to send a note to the Emeer Moḥammad Ez-Zubeydee, the Governor of El-Baṣrah, desiring him to fit out Aboo-Moḥammad the Lazy, and to bring him before the Prince of the Faithful. The Wezeer, therefore, wrote a note to that effect, and sent it by Mesroor.

Mesroor immediately repaired with it to the city of El-Baṣrah, and went in to the Emeer Moḥammad Ez-Zubeydee, who rejoiced at seeing him, and treated him with the utmost honour. He then read to him the note of the Prince of the Faithful Háároon Er-Rasheed, and he said, I hear and obey. He forthwith sent Mesroor with a number of his retinue to Aboo-Moḥammad the Lazy, and they repaired to him, and knocked at his door; whereupon one of the pages came forth to them, and Mesroor said to him, Say to thy master, The Prince of the Faithful summoneth thee. So the page went in and acquainted him with this; and he came forth, and found Mesroor, the chamberlain of the Khaleefeh, attended by the retinue of the Emeer Moḥammad Ez-Zubeydee; upon which he kissed the ground before him, and said, I hear and obey the command of the Prince of the Faithful: but enter ye our abode. They replied, We cannot do so, unless to pay a hasty visit, as the Prince of the Faithful hath commanded us; for he is expecting thine arrival. But he said, Have patience with me a little, that I may arrange my business. And they entered the house with him, after excessive persuasion; and they beheld, in the passage, curtains of blue brocade embroidered with red gold. Then Aboo-Moḥammad the Lazy ordered some of his pages to conduct Mesroor into the bath which was in the house; and they did so. And he saw its walls and its marble pavements to be of extraordinary construction: it was decorated with gold and silver, and its water was mixed with rose-water. The pages paid all attention to Mesroor and those who were with him, and served them in the most perfect manner; and when they came forth from the bath, they clad them with honorary dresses of brocade interwoven with gold; after which, Mesroor and his companions entered, and found Aboo-Moḥammad the Lazy sitting in his pavilion. Over his head were hung curtains of brocade interwoven with gold, and adorned with pearls and jewels; the pavilion was furnished with cushions embroidered with red gold; and he was sitting upon his mattress, which was upon a couch set with jewels. When Mesroor came in to him, he welcomed him and met him, and, having seated him by his side, gave orders to bring the table; and when Mesroor beheld that table, he said, By Allah, I have never seen the like of this in the palace of the Prince of the Faithful! It comprised varieties of viands, all placed in dishes of gilt China-ware.—We ate, says Mesroor, and drank, and enjoyed ourselves until the close of the day, when he gave to each of us five thousand pieces of gold. And on the following day, they clad us in green dresses of honour, embroidered with gold, and treated us with the utmost honour.—Mesroor then said to Aboo-Moḥammad the Lazy, It is impossible for us to remain longer than this period, from our fear of the Khaleefeh. But Aboo-Moḥammad the Lazy replied, O our lord, have patience with us until to-morrow, that we may prepare ourselves, and then we will proceed with you. So they remained that day, and passed the night until the morning; when the pages equipped a mule for Aboo-Moḥammad the Lazy, with a saddle of

gold adorned with varieties of pearls and jewels; whereupon Mesroor said within himself, When Aboo-Moḥammad presenteth himself before the Khaleefeh with this equipage, I wonder whether he will ask him how he obtained such wealth.

After that, they took leave of Moḥammad Ez-Zubeydee, and, going forth from El-Baṣrah, journeyed on until they arrived at the city of Baghdád; and when they went in to the Khaleefeh, and stood before him, he ordered Aboo-Moḥammad to seat himself. So he sat, and, addressing the Khaleefeh with politeness, said, O Prince of the Faithful, I have brought with me a present in token of service: then may I produce it, with thy permission? Er-Rasheed answered, There will be no harm in that. Accordingly Aboo-Moḥammad gave orders to bring a chest, which he opened, and he took forth from it some rarities, among which were trees of gold, the leaves whereof were formed of white[2] emeralds, and its fruits of red and yellow jacinths, and white pearls; whereat the Khaleefeh wondered. Then he caused a second chest to be brought, and took forth from it a tent of brocade, adorned with pearls and jacinths, and emeralds and chrysolites, and varieties of other jewels: its poles were of new Indian aloes-wood; its skirts were adorned with emeralds; and upon it were represented the forms of all living creatures, as birds and wild beasts; all these designs being adorned with jewels, jacinths and emeralds, and chrysolites and balass rubies, and all kinds of minerals. And when Er-Rasheed beheld it, he rejoiced exceedingly. Aboo-Moḥammad the Lazy then said, O Prince of the Faithful, imagine not that I have brought to thee this, fearing any thing or coveting aught; for the truth is, that I saw myself to be a man of the common people, and saw that this was not suitable to any one but the Prince of the Faithful; and if thou give me permission, I will gratify thee with the sight of some of the feats that I am able to accomplish. To this, Er-Rasheed replied, Do what thou wilt, that we may see. And Aboo-Moḥammad said, I hear and obey. Then he moved his lips, and made a sign to the battlements[3] of the palace; whereupon they inclined towards him; and he made another sign to them, and they resumed their proper position. After this, he made a sign with his eye, and there appeared before him private chambers with closed doors; and he addressed some words towards them, whereat the voices of birds replied to him. And Er-Rasheed wondered at this extremely, and said to him, Whence obtainedst thou all this power, when thou art not known otherwise than by the appellation of Aboo-

Moḥammad the Lazy, and they have informed me that thy father was a cupper[4] serving in a public bath, and that he left thee nothing?—O Prince of the Faithful, he answered, hear my story; for it is wonderful and extraordinary: if it were engraven on the understanding, it would be a lesson to him who would be admonished. Er-Rasheed said, Relate what thou hast to tell, and acquaint me with it, O Aboo-Moḥammad. So he said,—

Know, O Prince of the Faithful (may God continue thy glory and power!), that the account of the people, that I am known by the surname of the Lazy, and that my father left me not any property, is true; for my father was no other than thou hast said: he was a cupper in a public bath. In my youth I was the laziest of all beings existing upon the face of the earth. My laziness was so great that when I was sleeping in the hot season and the sun came upon me, I was too sluggish to rise and remove from the sun to the shade. Thus I remained fifteen years, at the expiration of which period my father was admitted to the mercy of God (whose name be exalted!), and left me nothing. But my mother used to act as a servant to some people, and feed me and give me drink, while I lay upon my side. And it happened that my mother came in to me one day, bringing five pieces of silver; and she said to me, O my son, I have been told that the sheykh Abu-l-Muẓaffar hath determined to make a voyage to China. This sheykh loved the poor, and was one of the virtuous. And my mother said, O my son, take these five pieces of silver, and repair with us to him, and we will request him to buy for thee with it something from the land of China: perhaps a profit may thence accrue to thee, of the bounty of God, whose name be exalted! But I was too lazy to rise and go with her. And upon this she swore by Allah, that if I did not rise and accompany her she would not feed me nor give me to drink nor come in to me, but would leave me to die of hunger and thirst. So when I heard her words, O Prince of the Faithful, I knew that she would do so, on account of her knowledge of my laziness. I therefore said to her, Seat me. And she did so, while I wept.—Bring me my shoes, said I. And she brought them; and I said, Put them on my feet. And she put them on. I then said, Lift me up from the ground. And when she had done this, I said, Support me, that I may walk. So she supported me, and I continued walking, and stumbling upon my skirts, until we arrived at the bank of the river, when we saluted the sheykh, and I said to him, O uncle, art thou El-Muẓaffar? He answered, At thy service. And I said, Take these pieces of silver, and buy with them for me something from the land of China: perhaps God may give me a profit from it. And the sheykh Abu-l-Muẓaffar said to his companions, Do ye know this young man? They answered, Yes: this person is known by the name of Aboo-Moḥammad the Lazy; and we have never seen him to have come forth from his house except on this occasion. The sheykh Abu-l-Muẓaffar then said, O my son, give me the money, and may the blessing of God (whose name be exalted!) attend it. And he received the money from me, saying, In the name of God. After which, I returned with my mother to the house.

The sheykh Abu-l-Muẓaffar set forth on the voyage, and with him a company of merchants, and they proceeded without interruption until they arrived at the land of China; when the sheykh sold and bought, and set forth to return, he and those who were with him, after they had accomplished their desires. But when they had continued out at sea for three days, the sheykh said to his companions, Stay the vessel! The merchants asked, What dost thou want? And he answered, Know that the deposite committed to me, belonging to Aboo-Moḥammad the Lazy, I have forgotten: so return with us, that we may buy for him with it something by which he may profit. But

they replied, We conjure thee by Allah (whose name be exalted!) that thou take us not back; for we have traversed a very long distance, and in doing so we have experienced great terrors, and exceeding trouble. Still he said, We must return. They therefore said, Receive from us several times as much as the profit of the five pieces of silver, and take us not back. So he assented to their proposal; and they collected for him a large sum of money.

Then they proceeded until they came in sight of an island containing a numerous population, where they cast anchor; and the merchants landed to purchase thence merchandise consisting of minerals and jewels and pearls and other things. And Abu-l-Muẓaffar saw a man sitting, with a great number of apes before him; and among these was an ape whose hair was plucked off. The other apes, whenever their master was inadvertent, laid hold upon this plucked ape, and beat him, and threw him upon their master; who arose thereat, and beat them, and chained and tormented them, for doing this; and all these apes became enraged in consequence against the other, and beat him again. Now when the sheykh Abu-l-Muẓaffar saw this ape, he grieved for him, and shewed kindness to him, and said to his owner, Wilt thou sell me this ape? The man answered, Buy. And the sheykh said, I have with me, belonging to a lad who is an orphan, five pieces of silver. Wilt thou sell him to me for that sum?—He answered, I sell him to thee. May God bless thee in him!—Then the sheykh took possession of him, and paid the money to his owner; and the slaves of the sheykh took the ape, and tied him in the ship.

After this, they loosed the sails, and proceeded to another island, where they cast anchor. And the divers who dived for minerals and pearls and jewels and other things came down; and the merchants gave them money as their hire for diving. So they dived; and the ape, seeing them do this, loosed himself from his cord, leaped from the vessel, and dived with them; whereupon Abu-l-Muẓaffar exclaimed, There is no strength nor power but in God, the High, the Great! We have lost the ape, with the luck of this poor youth for whom we bought him!—They despaired of the ape; but when the party of divers came up, lo, the ape came up with them, having in his hands precious jewels; and he threw them down before Abu-l-Muẓaffar, who wondered at this, and said, Verily, there is a great mystery in this ape!

Then they loosed, and proceeded to an island called the Island of the Zunooj,[5] who are a people of the blacks, that eat the flesh of the sons of Adam. And when the blacks beheld them, they came to them in boats, and, taking all that were in the ship, bound their hands behind them, and conducted them to the King, who ordered them to slaughter a number of the merchants. So they slaughtered them, and ate their flesh. The rest of the merchants passed the night imprisoned, in great misery; but in the night the ape arose and came to Abu-l-Muẓaffar, and loosed his chains. And when the merchants beheld Abu-l-Muẓaffar loosed, they said, God grant that our liberation may be effected by thy hands, O Abu-l-Muẓaffar! But he replied, Know ye that none liberated me, by the will of God (whose name be exalted!), but this ape; and I have bought my liberty of him for a thousand pieces of gold. So the merchants said, And we in like manner: each of us buyeth his liberty of him for a thousand pieces of gold, if he release us. The ape therefore arose and went to them, and began to loose one after another, until he had loosed them all from their chains; and they repaired to the ship, and embarked in it, and found it safe; nothing being lost from it.

They loosed immediately, and continued their voyage, and Abu-l-Muẓaffar said, O merchants, fulfil the promise that ye have given to the ape. They replied, We hear and obey. And each of them paid him a thousand pieces of gold. Abu-l-Muẓaffar also took forth from his property a thousand pieces of gold; and a great sum of money was thus collected for the ape. They then continued their voyage until they arrived at the city of El-Baṣrah; whereupon their companions came to meet them; and when they had landed, Abu-l-Muẓaffar said, Where is Aboo-Moḥammad the Lazy? The news therefore reached my mother, and while I was lying asleep, my mother came to me and said, O my son, the sheykh Abu-l-Muẓaffar hath arrived, and come to the city: rise then, and repair to him and salute him, and ask him what he hath brought for thee: perhaps God (whose name be exalted!) hath blessed thee with something. So I replied, Lift me from the ground, and support me, that I may go forth and walk to the bank of the river. I walked on, stumbling upon my skirts, until I came to the sheykh Abu-l-Muẓaffar; and when he beheld me, he said to me, Welcome to him whose money was the means of my liberation and the liberation of these merchants, by the will of God, whose name be exalted! He then said to me, Take this ape; for I bought him for thee; go with him to thy house, and wait until I come to thee. I therefore took the ape before me,

and went, saying within myself, By Allah, this is none other than magnificent merchandise! I entered my house, and said to my mother, Every time that I lie down to sleep, thou desirest me to arise to traffic: see then with thine eye this merchandise. Then I sat down; and while I was sitting, lo, the slaves of Abu-l-Muẓaffar approached me, and said to me, Art thou Aboo-Moḥammad the Lazy? I answered them, Yes. And behold, Abu-l-Muẓaffar approached, following them. I rose to him, and kissed his hands, and he said to me, Come with me to my house. So I replied, I hear and obey. I proceeded with him until I entered the house, when he ordered his slaves to bring the money; and they brought it, and he said, O my son, God hath blessed thee with this wealth as the profit of the five pieces of silver. They then carried it in the chests upon their heads, and he gave me the keys of those chests, saying to me, Walk before the slaves to thy house; for all this wealth is thine.

I therefore went to my mother, and she rejoiced at this, and said, O my son, God hath blessed thee with this abundant wealth; so give over this laziness, and go down into the market-street, and sell and buy. Accordingly, I relinquished my lazy habits, and opened a shop in the market-street, and the ape sat with me upon my mattress: when I ate, he ate with me; and when I drank, he drank with me;

and every day he absented himself from me from morning until noon, when he came, bringing with him a purse containing a thousand pieces of gold, and he put it by my side, and sat down. Thus he ceased not to do for a long time, until abundant wealth had accrued to me; whereupon I bought, O Prince of the Faithful, possessions and rabạs,[6] and planted gardens, and purchased memlooks and male black slaves and female slaves.

And it happened one day that I was sitting, and the ape was sitting with me upon the mattress, and, lo, he looked to the right and left; whereat I said within myself, What is the matter with this ape? And God caused the ape to speak, with an eloquent tongue, and he said, O Aboo-Moḥammad! On hearing this, I was violently terrified; but he said, Fear not. I will acquaint thee with my condition. I am a Márid of the Jinn; but I came to thee on account of thy poverty, and now thou knowest not the amount of thy wealth; and I have a want for thee to perform, the accomplishment of which will be productive of good to thee.—What is it? I asked. He answered, I desire to marry thee to a damsel like the full moon.—And how so? said I.—To-morrow, he answered, attire thyself in thy rich clothing, mount thy mule with the saddle of gold, and repair with me to the market of the sellers of fodder: there inquire for the shop of the Shereef,[7] and seat thyself by him, and say to him, I have come to thee as a suitor, desiring thy daughter. And if he say to thee, Thou hast not wealth nor rank nor descent,—give him a thousand pieces of gold: and if he say to thee, Give me more,—do so, and excite his cupidity for money.—So I replied, I hear and obey: to-morrow I will do this, if it be the will of God, whose name be exalted!

Accordingly, when I arose in the morning, I put on the richest of my apparel, mounted the mule with the saddle of gold, and, having gone to the market of the sellers of fodder, inquired for the shop of the Shereef, and found him sitting in his shop. I therefore alighted and saluted him, and seated myself with him. I had with me ten of my black slaves, and memlooks; and the Shereef said, Perhaps thou hast some business with us which we may have the pleasure of performing. So I replied, Yes: I have some business with thee.—And what is it? he asked. I answered, I have come unto thee as a suitor, desiring thy daughter. He replied, Thou hast not wealth nor rank nor descent. And upon this I took forth and presented to him a purse containing a thousand pieces of red gold, saying to him, This is my rank and descent; and he whom may God bless and save hath said, An excellent rank is [that conferred by] wealth. How good also is the saying of the poet!—

Whoso possesseth two dirhems, his lips have learned varieties of speech, which he uttereth:
His brethren draw near and listen to him, and thou seest him haughty among mankind.
Were it not for his money, in which he glorieth, thou wouldst find him in a most ignominious state.
When the rich man erreth in speech, they reply, Thou hast spoken truly, and not uttered vanity:
But when the poor man speaketh truly, they reply, Thou hast lied,—and make void what he hath asserted.[8]
Verily money, in every habitation, investeth men with dignity and with comeliness:
It is the tongue for him who would be eloquent, and it is the weapon for him who would fight.

And when the Shereef heard these words, and understood the verses, he hung down his head for a while towards the ground; after which, he raised his head, and said to me, If it must be, I desire of thee three thousand pieces of gold besides. So I replied, I hear and obey. I immediately sent one of the memlooks to my house, and he brought me the money that the Shereef had demanded; and when the Shereef saw this come to him, he arose from the shop, and said to his young men, Close it. Then he invited his companions from the market to his house, and, having performed the contract of my marriage to his daughter, said to me, After ten days I will introduce thee to her.

I returned to my house, full of joy, and in privacy informed the ape of that which had happened to me; whereupon he said, Excellently hast thou done. And when the time appointed by the Shereef approached, the ape said to me, I have a want for thee to perform: if thou accomplish it for me, thou shalt obtain of me what thou wilt.—And what is thy want? said I. He answered, At the upper end of the saloon in which thou wilt pay thy first visit to the daughter of the Shereef is a closet, upon the door of which is a ring of brass, and the keys are beneath the ring. Take them, and open the door. Thou wilt find a chest of iron, at the corners of which are four talismanic flags; in the midst is a basin filled with money, and by its side are eleven serpents, and in the basin is tied a white cock with a cleft comb; and there is also a knife by the side of the chest. Take the knife, and kill with it the cock, tear in pieces the flags, and empty the chest; and after that, go forth to the bride. This is what I require of thee.—And I replied, I hear and obey.

I then went to the house of the Shereef, and, entering the saloon,

I looked towards the closet which the ape had described to me. And when I was left alone with the bride, I wondered at her beauty and loveliness, and her justness of stature and form; for she was such that the tongue cannot describe her beauty and loveliness. I was exceedingly delighted with her; and when midnight came, and the bride slept, I arose, took the keys, and opened the closet, and, taking the knife, I killed the cock, threw down the flags, and overturned the chest; whereupon the damsel awoke, and saw that the closet was opened, and the cock killed; and she exclaimed, There is no strength nor power but in God, the High, the Great! The Márid hath taken me!—And her words were not ended when the Márid encompassed the house, and snatched away the bride. Upon this, a clamour ensued; and, lo, the Shereef approached, slapping his face, and said, O Aboo-Moḥammad, what is this deed that thou hast done unto us? Is this the recompense that we receive from thee? I made this talisman in this closet through my fear for my daughter from this accursed wretch; for he was desirous of taking this damsel during a period of six years, and could not do so. But thou shalt no longer remain with us: so go thy way.

I therefore went forth from the house of the Shereef, and, having returned to my own abode, searched for the ape; but I found him not, nor saw any trace of him: so I knew that he was the Márid who had taken my wife, and that he had practised a stratagem against me so that I had acted thus with the talisman and the cock which prevented his taking her. I repented, and tore my clothes in pieces, and slapped my face. No region was wide enough for me; so I went forth immediately, seeking the desert, and stopped not until the evening overtook me; and I knew not whither to go. But while I was absorbed in meditation, lo, two serpents approached me; one, tawny-coloured; and the other, white; and they were contending together. I therefore took up a stone from the ground, and struck with it the tawny serpent, and killed it; for it was oppressing the white one. Then the white serpent departed, and was absent for a while; after which it returned, accompanied by ten other white serpents; and they came to the dead serpent, and tore it in pieces, so that there remained only its head; which having done, they went their way.

Thereupon I laid myself prostrate on my bosom in that place, through weariness; and while I was so lying, meditating upon my case, a being whose voice I heard, but whose form I saw not, uttered these two verses:—

Let destiny run with slackened reins, and pass not the night but with careless mind;
For between the closing of an eye and its opening, God effecteth a change in the state of affairs.

On hearing this, O Prince of the Faithful, I was vehemently affected, and inspired with the utmost trouble of mind; and I heard a voice behind me reciting this couplet:—

O Muslim, whose guide is the Ḳur-án, rejoice in it; for safety hath come to thee;
And fear not what Satan hath suggested; for we are people whose religion is the true one.

So I said to the person who addressed me, By the Object of thy worship, inform me who thou art! Whereupon the invisible speaker assumed the form of a man, and replied, Fear not; for thy kind conduct hath become known to us, and we are a tribe of the believing Jinn; if then thou hast any want, acquaint us with it, that we may have the pleasure of performing it. I therefore said to him, Verily I have a great want; for I have been afflicted with a heavy calamity. And unto whom hath happened the like of my calamity?—And he said, Perhaps thou art Aboo-Moḥammad the Lazy. I replied, Yes. And he said, O Aboo-Moḥammad, I am a brother of the white serpent, whose enemy thou killedst. We are four brothers by the same father and mother, and we are all thankful for thy kindness. And know that he who was in the form of an ape, and who practised this artifice with thee, is one of the Márids of the Jinn; and had he not employed this stratagem, he had never been able to take the damsel; for of a long time he hath been desirous of taking her, and this talisman prevented him; and had the talisman remained, he could not have obtained access to her. But fear not on account of this affair: we will convey thee to her, and we will slay the Márid; for thy kindness is not lost upon us.—He then uttered a great cry, with a terrible voice; and, lo, a troop approached him, and he inquired of them respecting the ape; upon which one of them answered, I know his abode. He said, Where is his abode? And he answered, In the City of Brass, upon which the sun riseth not. And he said, O Aboo-Moḥammad, take one of our slaves, and he will carry thee on his back, and will instruct thee how thou shalt take the damsel. But know that the slave is one of the Márids; and when he carrieth thee, mention not the name of God while he beareth thee; for if thou mention it, he will fly from thee, and thou wilt fall and perish.—So I replied, I hear and obey.

I took one of their slaves, and he stooped, and said, Mount. And I mounted. He then soared with me into the sky until he had ascended out of sight of the world; and I saw the stars resembling the firm mountains, and heard the Angels extolling the perfection of God in Heaven. All this while the Márid was conversing with me and amusing me, and diverting me from mentioning God, whose name be exalted! But while I was in this state, lo, a person clad in green garments,[9] and having long locks of hair, and a resplendent countenance, and in his hand a spear from which sparks flew forth, approached and said to me, O Aboo-Moḥammad, say, There is no deity but God: Moḥammad is God's Apostle—or I will smite thee with this spear. My heart was already rent in pieces by my abstaining from mentioning God (whose name be exalted!): so I said, There is no deity but God: Moḥammad is God's Apostle. And immediately that person smote the Márid with the spear; whereupon he dissolved, and became ashes; and I fell from his back, and continued descending to the earth until I dropped into a roaring sea, agitated with waves.

But, lo, there was a ship, containing five sailors; and when they saw me, they came to me, and took me up into the vessel, and began to speak to me in a language which I knew not. I therefore made a sign to them that I knew not their language. And they proceeded on their voyage until the close of the day, when they cast a net, and caught a large fish, which they broiled; and they gave me to eat. They continued their voyage until they had conveyed me to their city; upon which they took me in to their King, and placed me before him; and I kissed the ground, and he bestowed upon me a dress of honour. Now this King was acquainted with Arabic, and he said, I appoint thee to be one of my guards. And I said to him, What is the name of this city? He answered, Its name is Henád,[10] and it is in the land of China. Then the King delivered me to the Wezeer of the city, commanding him to shew me the city. The inhabitants of this city were originally infidels; in consequence of which, God (whose name

be exalted!) had turned them into stones. I amused myself by taking a view of it; and have beheld nowhere a greater abundance of trees and fruits than it possessed.

I resided there for the space of a month, after which I went to a river, and seated myself upon its banks; and while I was sitting, lo, a horseman came and said, Art thou Aboo-Moḥammad the Lazy? I answered him, Yes. And he said, Fear not; for thy kind conduct hath become known unto us. So I asked him, Who art thou? And he answered, I am a brother of the serpent, and thou art near unto the place of the damsel to whom thou desirest to obtain access. Then he took off his clothes, and, having clad me with them, said to me, Fear not; for the slave who perished beneath thee was one of our slaves. And after this, the horseman took me up behind him, and conveyed me to a desert, where he said to me, Alight from behind me, and proceed between these two mountains until thou seest the City of Brass: then stop at a distance from it, and enter it not till I return to thee, and instruct thee how to act. So I replied, I hear and obey. I alighted from behind him, and walked on until I arrived at the city, when I saw that its wall was of brass; and I went round about it, hoping to find a gate to it: but I found none. And while I was going round it, lo, the brother of the serpent approached me, and gave me a talismanic sword that would prevent any one from seeing me. He then went his way; and he had been but a short time absent from me when cries rose, and I beheld a number of persons whose eyes were in their breasts; and when they saw me, they said, Who art thou, and what cast thee into this place? So I acquainted them with the occurrence; and they replied, The damsel whom thou hast mentioned is with the Márid in this city, and we know not what he hath done with her; and we are brothers of the serpent. Then they added, Go to that spring, see by what channel the water entereth, and enter thou with it; for it will convey thee into the city.

I therefore did so. I entered with the water into a grotto beneath the earth, and, rising thence, beheld myself in the midst of the city, and found the damsel sitting upon a couch of gold, with a canopy of brocade over her, and round the canopy was a garden containing trees of gold, the fruits of which were of precious jewels, such as rubies and chrysolites, and pearls and coral. And when the damsel saw me, she knew me; and, having saluted me first, she said to me, O my master, who brought thee to this place? So I informed her of the events that had happened; and she replied, Know that this accursed wretch, from the excess of his affection for me, hath acquainted me with that which will injure him and that which will benefit him, and hath informed me that there is in this city a talisman with which, if he desired to destroy all who are in the city, he could destroy them; and whatsoever he should order his 'Efreets to do, they would comply with his command; and that talisman is upon a pillar.—And where, said I, is the pillar? She answered, In such a place.—And what is that talisman? I asked. She answered, It is the figure of an eagle, and upon it is an inscription which I know not. Take it, and place it before thee, and take a censer with fire, and throw into it a little musk, whereupon there will rise from it a smoke which will attract the 'Efreets. If thou do so, they will all present themselves before thee; not one of them will remain absent; and they will obey thy command, and do whatsoever thou shalt order them. Arise, therefore, and do that, and may the blessing of God (whose name be exalted!) attend the act.—So I replied, I hear and obey.

I arose, and went to that pillar, and did all that she desired me to do, and the 'Efreets came and presented themselves before me, each of them saying, At thy service, O my master! Whatsoever thou commandest us to do, we will do it.—I therefore said to them, Chain the Márid who brought this damsel from her abode. And they replied, We hear and obey. They repaired immediately to that Márid, and chained him, making his bonds tight; and returned to me, saying, We have done what thou hast commanded us. And I ordered them to return. I then went back to the damsel, and, having acquainted her with what had happened, said, O my wife, wilt thou go with me? She answered, Yes. And I went forth with her by the subterranean grotto by which I had entered; and we proceeded until we came to the party who had directed me to her; when I said to them, Direct me to a route that shall lead me to my country.

Accordingly they guided me and walked with me to the shore of the sea, and placed us on board a ship; and the wind was favourable, and the ship conveyed us on until we arrived at the city of El-Baṣrah. And when the damsel entered the house of her father, her family saw her, and rejoiced exceedingly at her return. I then fumigated the eagle with musk, and, lo, the 'Efreets approached me from every quarter, saying, At thy service, and what dost thou desire us to do? And I commanded them to transport all that was in the City of Brass, of money and minerals and jewels, to my house which was in El-Baṣrah; and they did so. After that, I commanded them to bring the ape; and they brought him in an abject and despicable state; whereupon I said to him, O accursed, why didst thou act perfidiously to me? And I ordered them to put him into a bottle of brass. So they put him into a narrow bottle of brass, and stopped it over him with lead. And I resided with my wife in joy and happiness. I have now, O Prince of the Faithful, of precious treasures, and extraordinary jewels, and abundant wealth, what cannot be expressed by numbers, nor confined by limits; and if thou desire any thing, of wealth or aught else, I will command the Jinn to bring it to thee immediately. All this I have received from the bounty of God, whose name be exalted!

And the Prince of the Faithful wondered at this story extremely. He gave him imperial presents in return for his gift, and treated him with the favour that was suitable to him.[11]

NOTES TO CHAPTER FOURTEENTH.

NOTE 1. THIS story I suppose to be the same as that which is entitled, in the list of the contents of Von Hammer's MS., as given by Trébutien, "Aboubekr Alkozlan;" the surname, or nickname, which I render "the Lazy," being in my original "El-Keslán."

NOTE 2. So in the two editions of Cairo and Breslau; but what a white emerald is I know not. Perhaps the word which I have rendered "white" may here signify "bright."

NOTE 3. The battlements here mentioned (in the original, "sharáreef," plural of "shurráfeh,") are in general merely ornamental, and of various different forms in different buildings.

NOTE 4. The Arab cupper is generally a barber, and shaving is a more common operation in the bath than bleeding.

NOTE 5. The "Zunooj," also called "Zinj" and "Zenj," are, properly speaking, an Ethiopian nation, the inhabitants of the country commonly called by us "Zanguebar."

NOTE 6. By the term "possessions" we may here understand property consisting of houses, &c., such being the general meaning of the word so rendered. "Rabạ" is a term commonly applied to a range of dwelling-rooms over shops or magazines.

NOTE 7. "Shereef" (signifying "noble"), and "seyd" or "seyyid" ("master," or "lord"), are titles given to any descendant of the Prophet, however low his station. Men and women of this caste often contract marriages with persons who are not members of the same; and as the title of shereef is inherited from either the father or the mother, the number of persons who enjoy this distinction has become very considerable. The men are privileged to wear the green turban; but not all of them do so. Many of the women wear a green face-veil.

NOTE 8. "It is related that a rich man informed his friends who were sitting with him, that the mice had eaten an iron utensil belonging to him, and they pronounced his assertion to be true: then a poor man told them that the mice had eaten his palm-stick [or staff], and they declared his assertion to be false. So he said to them, How is it that ye do not admit the truth of my assertion that the mouse ate the palm-stick, and ye admit its having eaten the iron?"[1]

---

[1] Marginal note by my sheykh.

NOTE 9. By this description, El-Khiḍr is evidently meant. See Note 2 to the Introduction (vol. i. p. 20). [The City of Brass mentioned just before the passage to which this note refers is not to be confounded with the city of the same name described in Chapter xxi. of this translation. See Note 1 to that chapter.—ED.]

NOTE 10. "Henád" I suppose to be an imaginary name, as the city so called is said to have been near to the regions of the Jinn.

NOTE 11. The three anecdotes here following occupy the next place to the story of Aboo-Moḥammad the Lazy, and end with part of the three hundred and eighth Night.

Anecdote of Yaḥyà *the Son of* Khálid El-Barmekee.

It is related that Hároon Er-Rasheed called for one of his guards, named Ṣáleḥ, before the period at which he became changed against the Barmekees, and when the man came before him he said to him, O Ṣáleḥ, go to Manṣoor, and say to him, Thou owest us a million pieces of silver, and we require that thou bring to us this sum immediately. I command thee also, O Ṣáleḥ, that if this sum be not paid to thee forthwith, before sunset, thou sever his head from his body, and bring it to me.—So Ṣáleḥ replied, I hear and obey. He repaired to Manṣoor, and informed him of that which the Prince of the Faithful had said; whereupon Manṣoor exclaimed, I perish, by Allah; for the price of all my property and all that my hand possesseth, if sold for its highest value, would not exceed a hundred thousand: how then, O Ṣáleḥ, can I procure the remaining nine hundred thousand pieces of silver? Ṣáleḥ therefore said to him, Contrive for thyself some stratagem by which thou mayest save thyself quickly, or thou perishest; for I cannot grant thee a moment's delay after the period which the Khaleefeh hath prescribed me, nor can I fail in aught of that which the Prince of the Faithful hath commanded me to do. Hasten then to employ a stratagem by which to save thy life before the period shall have expired.—Manṣoor replied, O Ṣáleḥ, I beg thee of thy kindness to take me to my house, that I may bid farewell to my children and my family, and give my directions to my relations.—Accordingly, says Ṣáleḥ, I went with him to his house, and he began to take leave of his family; and a clamour arose in his abode, with weeping and crying, and supplication for the aid of God, whose name be exalted!

Then Ṣáleḥ said to him, It hath occurred to my mind that God may effect thy relief by means of the Barmekees: so repair with us to the house of Yaḥyà the son of Khálid. And when they went to Yaḥyà the son of Khálid, he acquainted him with his case; whereat Yaḥyà grieved, and hung down his head for a while towards the ground; after which, he raised his head, and, having called his treasurer, said to him, How much money is in our treasury? He answered, The sum of five thousand pieces of silver. And Yaḥyà ordered him to bring it. He then sent a messenger to his son El-Faḍl, with a note, the purport of which was, There have been offered to me for sale some estates of great value, that will never be laid waste:[2] so send to us some money. And he sent to him a million pieces of silver. Then he sent another man to his son Jaạfar, with a note, of which the purport was this: We have an important affair to transact, and want for that purpose some money. And Jaạfar sent to him immediately a million pieces of silver. And Yaḥyà continued to send messengers to the Barmekees until he had collected from them for Manṣoor a great sum of money. Ṣáleḥ and Manṣoor, meanwhile, knew not of this proceeding; and Manṣoor said to Yaḥyà, O my lord, I have laid hold upon thy skirt, and I know not how to procure this money but from thee, agreeably with thy usual generosity: complete for me then the remainder of my debt, and make me thine emancipated slave. And Yaḥyà hung down his head and wept, and said, O page, the Prince of the Faithful presented to our slave-girl Denáneer[3] a jewel of great value. Repair then to her, and tell her to send to us this jewel.—So the page went, and brought it to him; and he said, O Manṣoor, I purchased this jewel for the Prince of the Faithful from the merchants for two hundred thousand pieces of gold,[4] and the Prince of the Faithful presented it to our slave-girl Denáneer, the lute-player; and when he seeth it with thee, he will know it, and will treat thee with honour, and spare thy life on our account, in honour of us; and thy money, O Manṣoor, is now complete.

So I carried the money and the jewel, says Ṣáleḥ, to Er-Rasheed, taking Manṣoor with me; but while we were on the way, I heard him repeat this verse, applying it to his own case:—

> It was not from love that my feet went towards them; but because I feared to be smitten by the arrows.

And I wondered at the wickedness of his disposition, and his worthlessness and depravity, and the baseness of his origin and birth; and I retorted and said to him, There is not upon the face of the earth any one better than the Barmekees, nor is there any more base or more evil than thyself; for they bought thee off from death, and saved thee from destruction, bestowing upon thee the means of thy deliverance, and thou hast not thanked them nor praised them, nor behaved in the manner of the ingenuous; but hast requited their kindness with these words.—I then went to Er-Rasheed, and related to him the story, acquainting him with all that had happened; and Er-Rasheed wondered at the generosity of Yaḥyà, and his munificence and kind disposition, and at the vileness of Manṣoor, and ordered that the jewel should be restored to Yaḥyà the son of Khálid, saying, Any thing we give unto him, it is not fit that we revoke. And Ṣáleḥ returned to Yaḥyà the son of Khálid, and related to him the story of Manṣoor, acquainting him with his evil conduct. But Yaḥyà replied, O Ṣáleḥ, when a man is in want, with a contracted heart and with a troubled mind, for whatsoever proceedeth from him he is not to be reproached; for it doth not come from his heart. And he sought excuses for Manṣoor. And upon this, Ṣáleḥ wept, and said, The revolutions of time will never bring about the existence of a person like thee. Alas, then, how can it be that one endowed with a nature like thine and generosity like thine shall be buried in earth!—And he recited these verses:—

> Hasten to accomplish any kind intention; for it is not always that generosity can be exercised.
> How many a man, when able, hath withheld himself from an act of generosity till poverty prevented him!

---

[2] By this, an allusion is meant to the thanks and praise which he would receive, and which would never cease. (Marginal note by my sheykh.)

[3] Plural of "deenár," "a piece of gold."

[4] Equivalent, at least, to four times the amount of Manṣoor's debt.

Another Anecdote of Yaḥyà *the Son of* Khálid El-Barmekee.

It is related also, that there existed, between Yaḥyà the son of Khálid, and 'Abd-Allah the son of Málik El-Khuzá'ee, a secret enmity, which neither of them manifested;[5] and the reason of this enmity between them was, that the Prince of the Faithful, Hároon Er-Rasheed, loved 'Abd-Allah the son of Málik so greatly as to occasion Yaḥyà the son of Khálid and his sons to say, that 'Abd-Allah enchanted the Prince of the Faithful. Thus they continued for a long time, with hatred in their hearts.

And it happened that Er-Rasheed bestowed the government of Irmeeneeyeh[6] upon 'Abd-Allah the son of Málik El-Khuzá'ee, and despatched him thither. And after he had established himself there in the seat of government, there came to him a man of the inhabitants of El-'Erák, of surpassing good breeding, and acuteness and intelligence; but his means had become contracted, and his wealth had passed away, and his prosperity had vanished: so he forged a letter in the name of Yaḥyà the son of Khálid to 'Abd-Allah the son of Málik, and journeyed to him in Irmeeneeyeh. On arriving at his door, he delivered the letter to one of his chamberlains, who took the letter and delivered it to 'Abd-Allah the son of Málik El-Khuzá'ee; and he opened it and read it, and, considering it, he knew that it was forged. So he gave orders to bring the man; and when he presented himself before him, he prayed for him and praised him and the members of his court; and 'Abd-Allah the son of Málik said to him, What induced thee to undergo this long toil, and to come to me with a forged letter? But be of good

---

5 In the Breslau edition, this anecdote is related somewhat differently: it is there said to have been founded upon an enmity between Jaafar El-Barmekee (the *son* of Yaḥyà) and a Governor of Egypt. So also in the works of some Arab historians: see, for instance, Fakhr-ed-Deen, in De Sacy's Chrestomathie Arabe, vol. i., page 26 of the Arabic text, 2nd. ed.

6 By this name may be understood either the whole or a part of Armenia.

heart; for we will not disappoint thy labour.—The man replied, May God prolong the life of our lord the Wezeer! If my coming be troublesome to thee, employ no pretext to repel me; for God's earth is wide, and the Bestower of the means of subsistence existeth: the letter that I have brought to thee from Yaḥyà the son of Khálid is genuine, not forged.—So 'Abd-Allah said, I will write a letter to my agent in Baghdád, and order him to inquire respecting this letter that thou hast brought to me; and if it prove to be true and genuine, not forged, I invest thee with the government of one of my districts, or I give thee two hundred thousand pieces of silver, with horses and excellent camels of high value, and an honorary gift besides, if thou desire a present: but if the letter prove to be forged, I give orders that thou shalt be beaten with two hundred blows of a staff, and that thy beard shall be shaven.—Then 'Abd-Allah commanded that he should be taken into a chamber; and that what he required should be put for him there until he should have ascertained his case. After this, he wrote a letter to his agent in Baghdád, the purport whereof was as follows:—

There hath come unto me a man with a letter which he asserteth to be from Yaḥyà the son of Khálid, and I have an evil opinion of this letter. It is therefore necessary that thou neglect not this affair; but go thyself and ascertain the case of this letter, and hasten to send me a reply, that we may know the truth or the falsity of the matter.

So when the letter was brought to him in Baghdád, he mounted immediately, and repaired to the mansion of Yaḥyà the son of Khálid. He found him sitting with his boon-companions and chief attendants, and he saluted him, and delivered to him the letter; and Yaḥyà the son of Khálid read it, and said to the agent, Return to me to-morrow, that I may write for thee the answer. Then looking towards his boon-companions, after the departure of the agent, he said, What shall be the recompense of him who beareth a letter forged in my name, and taketh it to mine enemy? And every one of the boon-companions offered some opinion, and each of them proposed some kind of punishment. But Yaḥyà said to them, Ye have erred in that which ye have proposed, and this advice which ye have given hath arisen from the baseness and meanness of your minds. Ye all know the close favour in which 'Abd-Allah is held by the Prince of the Faithful, and ye know the wrath and enmity that subsisteth between me and him. Now God (whose name be exalted!) hath made this man a means of effecting a reconciliation between us, and hath fitted him for that purpose, and appointed him to extinguish the fire of hatred in our hearts, which hath been increasing for a period of twenty years; and by his intervention our affairs shall be peaceably adjusted. It is incumbent on me to satisfy this man by verifying his opinions and amending his circumstances; and I will write for him a letter to 'Abd-Allah the son of Málik El-Khuzá'ee, to the effect that he shall treat him with increased honour, and continue to exalt and respect him.—And when the boon-companions heard this, they invoked blessings upon him, and wondered at his generosity and the abundance of his kindness. He then demanded the paper and the inkhorn, and wrote to 'Abd-Allah the son of Málik a letter in his own hand, of the following purport:—

In the name of God, the Compassionate, the Merciful. Thy letter hath arrived: may God prolong thy life! and I have read it, and rejoiced at thy safety, and been delighted at the tidings of thy well-being and thy general prosperity. Now thou imaginedst that that ingenuous man forged a letter as from me, and did not bear an epistle from me: but the case was not so; for the letter I myself wrote, and it was not forged; and I hope from thy liberality and kindness and excellence of disposition that thou wilt satisfy the hope and wish of that ingenuous and generous man, and regard him with the respect that he meriteth, and cause him to attain his desire, and make him a particular object of overflowing kindness and abundant favour; and whatsoever thou dost for him, I shall regard myself as the object of it, and shall be thankful to thee.

Then he directed the letter and sealed it and delivered it to the agent. So the agent sent it to 'Abd-Allah, who, when he read it, was delighted at its contents, and, having caused that man to be brought to him, said to him, Whichever of the two things that I promised thee is the more agreeable to thee I will present to thee. And the man replied, The gift will be more agreeable to me than any thing else. Accordingly, 'Abd-Allah gave orders to present him with two hundred thousand pieces of silver, and ten Arab horses, five of them with housings of silk, and five with jewelled saddles such as are used in processions of state, and with twenty chests of clothes, and ten memlooks, horsemen, together with what was appropriate of costly jewels. Then he bestowed upon him a dress of honour, and sent him to Baghdád magnificently equipped.

When he arrived, therefore, at Baghdád, he repaired to the door of the mansion of Yaḥyà the son of Khálid before he went to his family, and he begged permission to go in to him. So the chamberlain went in to Yaḥyà, and said to him, O our lord, at our door is a man of respectable appearance and comely form and good condition, with a number of pages, desiring to come in to thee. And he gave him permission to enter; and when he came in to him, he kissed the ground before him, and Yaḥyà said to him, Who art thou? The man answered, O master, I am he who was killed by the tyranny of fortune, and thou hast brought me to life from the grave of calamities, and raised me to the paradise of desires. I am he who forged a letter in thy name, and conveyed it to 'Abd-Allah the son of Málik El-Khuzá'ee.—And what, said Yaḥyà, hath he done with thee; and what hath he given to thee? He answered, He gave me of the benefits proceeding from thy liberality and benevolence, and thy comprehensive favours and universal generosity, and thy magnanimity and ample bounty, so that he enriched me, and he distinguished me by especial beneficence, and bestowed presents upon me; and I have brought all his gifts and his presents; they are at thy door, and the case is submitted unto thee, to decide upon it as thou wilt. Upon this, Yaḥyà replied, The action that thou hast done for me is better than that which I have performed for thee, and thou art entitled to abundant thanks from me, and great bounty, since thou hast changed the enmity that subsisted between me and that highly-revered man into sincere friendship and affection. I will therefore give thee the like of that which 'Abd-Allah the son of Málik hath given thee.—He then ordered that he should be presented with money and horses, and chests of clothing, such as 'Abd-Allah had bestowed upon him; and thus that man's original prosperity was restored to him by the kindness of these two generous men.

Anecdote of El-Ma-moon *and a Learned Man.*

It is said that there was not among the Khaleefehs of the descendants of El-'Abbás any more learned in all the sciences than El-Ma-moon. On two days in every week, he used to preside at discussions of the learned men; and the professors of religion and law, and the scholastic theologians, by whom the discussions were carried on, used to sit in his presence according to their several ranks and degrees. Now on one occasion, while he was sitting with them, there came in to his assembly a stranger, clad in white, tattered clothing, who seated himself at the lower end, behind the professors, in an obscure place. And when they began the discussion, and entered upon the consideration of the difficult propositions,—it being their custom to submit the proposition to the members of the assembly one after another, and for each who could offer some quaint addition to what others advanced, or some extraordinary, witty saying, to mention it,—the question was proposed to them by turns until it came to that stranger; whereupon he gave a reply better than the replies of all the professors; and the Khaleefeh approved it, and ordered that he should be raised from the place that he had taken to a higher one. Then, when the second question came to him, he gave a reply better than the first; and El-Ma-moon ordered that he should be raised to a place of higher dignity. And when the third question went round, he gave a reply better and more just than the two former replies; upon which El-Ma-moon ordered that he should sit near unto himself. And after the discussion was ended, the attendants brought the water, and the guests washed their hands; and they brought the repast, and they ate.

The professors then arose and went forth; but El-Ma-moon prevented the stranger from going out with them: he caused him to draw near unto him, and treated him with courtesy, promising him to bestow favours and benefactions upon him. And after this, the banquet of wine was prepared, the comely boon-companions came, and the wine circulated; but when it came round to that man, he rose upon his feet, and said, If the Prince of the Faithful give me permission, I will speak one word. El-Ma-moon replied, Say what thou wilt. And he said, The possessor of eminent judgment (whose eminence may God increase!) knoweth that the slave was to-day, in this noble assembly, one of the obscure among the people, and one of the mean among the company, and that the Prince of the Faithful hath raised him to a place near unto his own person, small as is the wisdom that he hath displayed, and hath elevated him to a rank above others, so that he hath attained to a goal to which his ambition did not aspire; and now he desireth to divest him of that small degree of wisdom which hath exalted him after his meanness, and enriched him after his poverty. But may God forbid, and by no means suffer, that the Prince of the Faithful should envy him for the small degree of wisdom and fame and excellence that he possesseth; for if the slave drink wine, wisdom will depart far from him, and ignorance will draw near to him, and he will be deprived of his politeness, and will return to his former contemptible station, and become despicable and obscure in the eyes of men. I therefore hope that the possessor of eminent judgment, of his bounty and generosity and princely qualities and excellent disposition, will not despoil him of this jewel.—And when the Khaleefeh El-Ma-moon heard these words from him, he praised him and thanked him, caused him to sit again in his place and treated him with respect, gave orders to present him with a hundred thousand pieces of silver and to mount him upon a horse, and gave him magnificent apparel. And in every assembly he exalted and favoured him above all the professors, so that he became the highest of them in rank and degree.—And God is all-knowing.[7]

---

[7] A similar anecdote has occurred in p. 196 of vol. i.—Ed.

CHAPTER XV.

COMMENCING WITH PART OF THE THREE HUNDRED AND EIGHTH NIGHT, AND ENDING WITH PART OF THE THREE HUNDRED AND TWENTY-SEVENTH.

THE STORY OF 'ALEE SHÉR AND ZUMURRUD.

THERE was, in ancient times, a certain merchant in the land of Khurásán,[1] whose name was Mejd-ed-Deen,[2] and he had great wealth, and black slaves, and memlooks and pages; but he had attained to the age of sixty years, and had not been blessed with a son. After this, however, God (whose name be exalted!) blessed him with a son, and he named him 'Alee Shér.[3]

When this boy grew up, he became like the full moon; and when he had attained to manhood, and was endowed with every charm, his father fell sick of a fatal disease. So he called his son, and said to him, O my son, the period of death hath drawn near, and I desire to give thee a charge.—And what is it, O my father? said the young man. He answered, I charge thee that thou be not familiar with any one among mankind, and that thou shun what may bring injury and misfortune. Beware of the evil associate; for he is like the blacksmith: if his fire burn thee not, his smoke will annoy thee. How excellent is the saying of the poet!—

There is none in thy time whose friendship thou shouldst covet; nor any intimate who, when fortune is treacherous, will be faithful.
Live then apart, and rely upon no man: I have given thee, in these words, good advice, and sufficient.[4]

And the saying of another:—

Men are as a latent disease: rely not therefore upon them.
Thou wilt find guile and artifice in them if thou examine them.

And that of another:—

Intercourse with men profiteth nothing, unless to pass time in idle conversation.
Then converse with them little, except for the purpose of acquiring knowledge or rectifying an affair.

And the saying of another:—

If a person of sagacity hath tried mankind, I have eaten them, when he hath but tasted;[5]
And I have seen their affection to be nought but deceit, and their religion I have seen to be nought but hypocrisy.

The young man replied, O my father, I hear and obey. Then what next dost thou counsel me to do?—His father answered, Do good when thou art able; persevere in comely conduct towards men, and avail thyself of opportunities to dispense kind actions; for a wish is not always of easy accomplishment; and how good is the saying of the poet!—

It is not at every time and season that acts of beneficence are easily performed.
When thou are able, then, hasten to do them, lest they should become difficult to execute.

And the son replied, I hear and obey. Then what more?—O my son, answered the father, Be mindful of God: He will then be mindful of thee. Guard also thy wealth, and be not prodigal of it; for if thou be prodigal of it, thou wilt become in need of the assistance of the least of mankind: and know that the estimation in which a man is held is according to that which his right hand possesseth. How excellent is the saying of the poet!—

> When my wealth becometh little, no friend consorteth with me; but when it increaseth, all men are my friends.
> How many enemies for the sake of wealth have borne me company! And how many friends for its loss have become my enemies.

—And what besides? said the young man. His father answered, O my son, consult him who is older than thyself, and hasten not to perform a thing that thou desirest to do: have compassion also upon him who is thine inferior; then he who is thy superior will have compassion upon thee; and oppress not any, lest God give power over thee to one who will oppress thee. How excellent is the saying of the poet!—

> Add to thy judgment another's, and ask counsel; for the truth is not concealed from the minds of two.
> A man's mind is a mirror, which sheweth him his face; but by means of two mirrors he will see his back.

And that of another:—

> Deliberate, and haste not to accomplish thy desire; and be merciful, so shalt thou meet with one merciful:
> For there is no hand but God's hand is above it; nor oppressor that shall not meet with an oppressor.

Beware of drinking wine; for it is the chief of every evil: it dispelleth the reason, and bringeth contempt upon the drinker: and how good is the saying of the poet!—

> By Allah, wine shall not disturb me while my soul is united with my body, and while words explain my thoughts;
> Nor ever will I childishly attach myself to it, nor choose any one as my associate but the sober.

This is my charge to thee, and do thou keep it before thine eyes; and may God supply my place to thee!—Then he fainted, and remained a while silent; after which he recovered his senses, and begged forgiveness of God, pronounced the professions of the faith, and was admitted to the mercy of God, whose name be exalted!

His son wept for him and lamented. He made becoming preparations for his burial; great and small walked in his funeral-procession, the reciters of the Ḳur-án recited around his bier, and his son omitted not the performance of any honour that was due to the deceased.

They then prayed over him and interred him, and inscribed upon his tomb these two verses:—

> Thou wast formed of dust, and camest to life, and learnedst eloquence of discourse;
> And to dust thou returnedst, and becamest a corpse, as though from the dust thou hadst never issued.

His son 'Alee Shér grieved for him violently, and observed the ceremonies of mourning for him in the manner usual at the death of persons of distinction. He remained mourning for his father until his mother died a short time after him; when he did with the corpse of his mother as he had done with that of his father. And after this, he sat in the shop to sell and buy, and associated with no one of the creatures of God (whose name be exalted!), conforming to the charge of his father.

Thus he continued to do for the space of a year; but after the expiration of the year, the sons of the licentious women obtained access to him by stratagems, and became his companions, so that he inclined with them unto wickedness, and declined from the path of rectitude; he drank wine by cupfuls, and to the beauties morning and evening he repaired; and he said within himself, My father hath amassed for me this wealth, and if I dispose not of it, to whom shall I leave it? By Allah, I will not do but as the poet hath said:—

> If during the whole of thy life thou collectest and amassest property,
> When wilt thou enjoy the wealth which thou hast thus acquired?

He ceased not to squander his wealth night and day until he had expended the whole of it and was reduced to poverty. Evil was his condition, and disturbed was his mind, and he sold the shop and the dwellings and other possessions; and after that, he sold his clothes, not leaving for himself more than one suit.

Now when intoxication had quitted him and reflection had come, he fell into grief; and he sat one day from dawn until the time of afternoon-prayers without breaking fast; whereupon he said within himself, I will go round to those upon whom I spent my wealth: perhaps one of them will feed me this day. He therefore went round to all of them; but on each occasion of his knocking at the door of one of them, the man denied himself, and hid himself from him; so hunger tortured him. And he went to the market of the merchants, and found there a ring of persons crowding together, and the people flocking thither; upon which he said within himself, What can be the reason of the assembling of these people? By Allah, I will not remove from this place until I have gratified myself with a sight of this ring.—Then advancing to it, he found there a damsel of quinary[6] stature, of just figure, rosy-cheeked, high-bosomed; she surpassed the people of her age in beauty and loveliness, and in elegance and every charm. The name of this damsel was Zumurrud;[7] and when 'Alee Shér beheld her, he wondered at her beauty and loveliness, and said, By Allah, I will not depart until I see to what sum the price of this damsel will amount, and know who will purchase her. So he stood among the merchants, and they imagined that he would buy, as they knew the abundance of wealth that he had inherited from his parents.

The broker, having stationed himself at the head of the damsel, then said, O merchants! O possessors of wealth! who will open the bidding for this damsel, the mistress of moon-like beauties, the precious pearl, Zumurrud the curtain-maker, the object of the seeker's wishes, and the delight of the desirer? Open the bidding; for the opener is not obnoxious to blame or reproach!—And one of the merchants said, Let her be mine for five hundred pieces of gold. Another said, And ten. And a sheykh, named Rasheed-ed-Deen,[8] who had blue eyes,[9] and a foul aspect, said, And a hundred. Another then said, And ten. And the sheykh said, For a thousand pieces of gold. And upon this, the tongues of the merchants were tied, and they were silent. The broker therefore consulted the damsel's owner; but he said, I am under an oath that I will not sell her save unto him whom she will choose: so consult her. The broker accordingly came to her and said, O mistress of moon-like beauties, this merchant desireth to purchase thee. And she looked at him, and, seeing him to be as we have described, she said to the broker, I will not be sold to a sheykh whom old age hath reduced to a most evil condition. Divinely gifted was he who said,—

I asked her for a kiss, one day; and she beheld my hoariness (but I was possessed of wealth and affluence),
And she turned away from me, saying, Nay: by Him who created mankind out of nothing,
I have no desire for hoary hairs. Shall my mouth while I am living be stuffed with cotton?[10]

And when the broker heard her words, he said to her, By Allah, thou art excused, and thy value is ten thousand pieces of gold. Then he informed her owner that she approved not of that sheykh; and he replied, Consult her respecting another. And another man advanced and said, Let her be mine for the sum that the sheykh of whom she approved not offered for her. But the damsel, looking at that man, found that he had a dyed beard; whereupon she said, What is this disgrace, and this dubious conduct, and blackening of hoary hairs! And after expressing great wonder, she recited these verses:—

A spectacle indeed did such-a-one present to me,—a neck, by Allah, to be beaten with shoes![11]
O thou who art fascinated by my cheek and my figure, dost thou thus disguise thyself, and care not;
Dyeing disgracefully thy hoary hairs, and concealing them for fraudulent purposes?[12]
Thou goest with one beard and returnest with another, as though thou wert one of the puppetmen.[13]

And the broker, when he heard her verses, said to her, By Allah, thou hast spoken truth. The merchant who had bidden for her asked, What was it that she said? So the broker repeated the verses to him; and he knew that he was in fault, and gave up the idea of purchasing her. Then another merchant advanced and said, Ask her if she will consent to be mine for the sum that thou hast heard. He therefore consulted her for him; and she looked at him, and saw that he was one-eyed, and replied, This man is one-eyed, and the poet hath said of such a person,—

Keep not company with the one-eyed for a single day; but beware of his malignity and falsehood;
For had there been any good in him, God had not caused the blindness in his eye.[14]

The broker then [pointing to another] said to her, Wilt thou be sold to that merchant? And she looked at him, and, seeing that he was a short man, with a beard descending to his girdle, she answered, This is he of whom the poet hath said,—

I have a friend with a beard which God hath made to grow to a useless length.
It is like unto one of the nights of winter, long and dark and cold.

The broker therefore said to her, O my mistress, see who among the persons here present pleaseth thee, and say which he is, that I may sell thee to him. So she looked at the ring of merchants, and as she examined their physiognomies, one after another, her eye fell upon 'Alee Shér. The sight of him occasioned her a thousand sighs, and her heart became enamoured of him; for he was of surprising loveliness, and more bland than the northern zephyr; and she said, O broker, I will not be sold to any but to this my master, with the comely face and surpassing figure, of whom one of his describers hath thus said:—

They displayed thy lovely face, and then blamed the person who was tempted.
If they had desired to protect me, they had veiled thy beautiful countenance.

None then shall possess me but he; for his cheek is smooth, and the moisture of his mouth is like Selsebeel,[15] a cure for the sick, and his charms perplex the poet and the prose-writer. He is as the poet hath said of him,—

His saliva is like wine; and his breath, like musk; and those his fore-teeth resemble camphor.
Riḍwán hath sent him forth from his abode in his fear that the Ḥooreeyehs might be tempted.[16]
Mankind reproach him for his pride; but for pride the full moon is to be excused.

The person with the curling hair, and the rosy cheek, and the enchanting glance, of whom the poet hath said,—

Oft a fawn-like person hath promised me a meeting, and my heart hath been restless and mine eye expectant.
His eyelids assured me of the truth of his promise; but how can they, languishing as they are, fulfil it?

—And when the broker heard the verses that she recited on the charms of 'Alee Shér, he wondered at her eloquence, as well as at the splendour of her beauty. But her owner said to him, Wonder not at her beauty, that putteth to shame the sun of day, nor at her having her memory stored with the elegant effusions of the poets; for she also reciteth the glorious Ḳur-án according to the seven readings,[17] and relateth the noble traditions as authentically transmitted, and writeth the seven different hands,[18] and knoweth of the sciences what the very learned sage knoweth not, and her hands are better than gold and silver; for she maketh curtains of silk, and selleth them, gaining, by every one, fifty pieces of gold; and she worketh a curtain in eight days.[19] So the broker said, O the good fortune of him in whose house this damsel shall be, and who includeth her among his choice treasures! Her owner then said to him, Sell her to whomsoever she chooseth.

Accordingly the broker returned to 'Alee Shér, and, having kissed his hands, said, O my master, purchase this damsel; for she hath made choice of thee. And he described her to him, telling him what she knew, and said to him, Happy will be thy lot if thou purchase her; for He who is not sparing of his gifts hath bestowed her upon thee. So 'Alee Shér hung down his head for a while towards the

ground, laughing at his case, and saying within himself, I am to the present hour without breakfast; but I am ashamed before the merchants to say that I have no money wherewith to purchase her. And the damsel, seeing him hanging down his head, said to the broker, Take me by the hand and lead me to him, that I may display myself to him, and excite his desire to possess me; for I will not be sold to any but him. The broker therefore took her and stationed her before 'Alee Shér, saying to him, What is thy good pleasure, O my master? But he returned him no answer. So the damsel said, O my master, and beloved of my heart, wherefore wilt thou not purchase me? Purchase me for what thou wilt, and I will be a means of good fortune to thee.—And he raised his head towards her, and said, Is a person to be made by force to purchase? Thou art dear at the price of a thousand pieces of gold.—She replied, O my master, purchase me for nine hundred. He said, No.—For eight hundred, she rejoined. He said, No. And she ceased not to abate the price until she said to him, For one hundred pieces of gold. But he said, I have not a hundred complete. And she laughed, and said to him, How much dost thou want of a hundred? He answered, I have not a hundred nor less than a hundred. By Allah, I possess not either white or red, either a piece of silver or a piece of gold. So see for thyself some other desirous customer.—And when she knew that he had nothing, she said to him, Take my hand, as though thou wouldst examine me in a by-lane. He therefore did so; and she took forth from her pocket a purse containing a thousand pieces of gold, and said to him, Weigh out from it nine hundred as my price, and retain the remaining hundred in thy possession, as it will be of use to us.

So he did as she desired him. He purchased her for nine hundred pieces of gold, and, having paid her price from that purse, repaired with her to the house. And when she arrived there, she found that the house presented plain, clear floors; having neither furniture nor utensils in it. She therefore gave him a thousand pieces of gold, saying to him, Go to the market, and buy for us, with three hundred pieces of gold, furniture and utensils for the house. And he did so. Then she said to him, Buy for us food and beverage with three pieces of gold. And he did this. Next she said to him, Buy for us a piece of silk, as much as will suffice for a curtain, and buy gold and silver thread, and silk thread of seven different colours. And this also he did. She then spread the furniture in the house, and lighted the candles, and sat eating and drinking with him; after which, they embraced each other, and presented the spectacle thus described by the poet:—

Eyes have not beheld a more beautiful sight than that of two lovers side by side,
Embracing each other, in the garments of content, pillowing themselves with wrist and arm.
When hearts have become united together, the censurers beat upon cold iron.
O thou who reproachest the lovers for their passion, canst thou reform a heart that is spoiled?
If in thy life one person delight thee, thou hast thy desire; then live with that one.

The love of each became fixed in the heart of the other; and on the following morning the damsel took the curtain, and embroidered it with the coloured silks, and ornamented it with the gold and silver thread. She worked a border to it, with the figures of birds, and represented around it the figures of wild beasts, and there was not a wild beast in the world that she omitted to portray upon it. She continued working upon it for eight days; and when it was finished, she cut it and glazed it, and then gave it to her master, saying to him, Repair with it to the market, and sell it for fifty pieces of gold to a merchant, and beware of selling it to any one passing along the street, because that would be a cause of separation between me and thee; for we have enemies who are not unmindful of us. And he replied, I hear and obey. He repaired with it to the market, and sold it to a merchant as she had desired him; after which he bought another piece of silk, together with the silk thread, and the gold and silver thread, as before, and what they required of food, and, having brought these things to her, gave her the rest of the money. And every eight days she gave him a curtain to sell for fifty pieces of gold.

Thus she continued to do for the space of a whole year. And after the expiration of the year, he went to the market with the curtain as usual, and gave it to the broker; and there met him a Christian, who offered him sixty pieces of gold. He refused to sell it to him; but the Christian ceased not to increase the sum until he offered him a hundred pieces of gold, and he bribed the broker with ten pieces of gold. So the broker returned to 'Alee Shér, informed him of the price that had been offered, and made use of artifice to induce him to sell the curtain to the Christian for that sum, saying to him, O my master, fear not this Christian; for no harm shall befall thee from him. The merchants also arose and urged him. So he sold it to the Christian, though his heart was full of fear, and, having taken the price, returned to the house. But he found the Christian walking behind him; and he said, O Christian, wherefore art thou walking behind me?—O my master, he answered, I have a want to accomplish at the upper end of the street: may God never cause *thee* to have any want! And 'Alee Shér arrived not at his abode without the Christian's overtaking him: so he said to him, O accursed, wherefore dost thou follow me whithersoever I go? The Christian replied, O my master, give me a draught of water, for I am thirsty, and thou wilt receive thy recompense from God, whose name be exalted! 'Alee Shér therefore said within himself, This is a tributary,[20] and he hath demanded of me a draught of water: so by Allah I will not disappoint him.

Then he entered the house, and took a mug of water; and his slave-girl Zumurrud, seeing him, said to him, O my beloved, hast thou sold the curtain? He answered, Yes. And she said, To a merchant or a passenger? For my heart is impressed with a presentiment of separation.—He answered, I sold it not but to a merchant. But she said, Acquaint me with the truth of the matter, that I may provide against my case. And wherefore, she added, tookest thou the mug of water?—To give drink to the broker, he answered. And she exclaimed, There is no strength nor power but in God, the High, the Great!—and recited these two verses:—

O thou who seekest separation, act leisurely, and let not the embrace of the beloved deceive thee!
Act leisurely; for the nature of fortune is treacherous, and the end of every union is disjunction.

—He then went forth with the mug, and found the Christian within the passage of the house. So he said, Hast thou come in hither, O dog? How is it that thou enterest my abode without my permission?—O my master, he answered, there is no difference between the door and the passage; and I shall not move from this my place but to go forth; yet thanks are due to thee for bounty and kindness, and liberality and obliging conduct. Then he took the mug of water, and drank what it contained; after which he handed it to 'Alee Shér, who took it, and expected that he would rise: but he rose not. So 'Alee Shér said to him, Wherefore dost thou not rise and go thy way? The Christian answered, O my lord, be not of those who confer favour and then make it a subject of reproach, nor of those of whom the poet hath said,—

They are gone who, if thou stoodest at their door, would give the most generous aid at thy petition;
And if thou stoodest at the door of any after them, they would reproach thee for a draught of water bestowed on thee.

O my lord, he added, I have drunk; but I desire of thee that thou give me to eat of any thing that is in the house: it will be equal to me if it be a morsel of bread or a biscuit and an onion.—'Alee Shér replied, Rise, without contention. There is nothing in the house.—But the Christian rejoined, O my lord, if there be nothing in the house, take these hundred pieces of gold, and bring us something from the market, though it be but a single cake of bread, that the bond of bread and salt may be established between me and thee.[21] So 'Alee Shér said within myself, Verily this Christian is mad: I will therefore take of him the hundred pieces of gold, and bring him something worth two pieces of silver, and laugh at him. And the Christian said to him, O my master, I only desire something that will banish hunger, though it be but a stale cake of bread and an onion; for the best of provision is that which dispelleth hunger; not rich food; and how excellent is the saying of the poet!—

Hunger is banished by a stale cake of bread. Why then are my grief and troubles so great?
Death is most just, since it acteth impartially both to the Khaleefeh and the miserable pauper.

'Alee Shér therefore said to him, Wait here while I lock the saloon and bring thee something from the market. And the Christian replied, I hear and obey. Then 'Alee Shér went away from him, and locked the saloon, putting a padlock upon it; and, taking the key with him, he repaired to the market, bought some fried cheese, and honey and bananas and bread, and brought them to him. And when the Christian saw this, he said, O my lord, this is a great quantity, sufficient for ten men, and I am alone: perhaps then thou wilt eat with me. 'Alee Shér replied, Eat thou alone; for I am satiated. But the Christian rejoined, O my lord, the sages have said, He who eateth not with his guest is baseborn. So when 'Alee Shér heard these words, he sat and ate with him a little; and was about to withdraw his hand, when the Christian took a banana, peeled it, and divided it in two, and put into one half of it some refined benj, mixed with opium, a dram of which would make an elephant to fall down. Then he dipped this half of the banana into the honey, and said to 'Alee Shér, O my lord, by thy religion thou shalt take this. And 'Alee Shér was ashamed to make him swear falsely: he therefore took it from him, and swallowed it, and scarcely had it settled in his stomach when his head fell before his feet, and he became as though he had been a year asleep.

So when the Christian beheld this, he rose upon his feet, as though he were a bald wolf, or empowered fate; he took with him the key of the saloon, and, leaving 'Alee Shér prostrate, went running to his brother, and acquainted him with what he had done. And the cause of his conduct was this:—The brother of this Christian was the decrepit old man who had desired to purchase Zumurrud for a thousand pieces of gold, and she accepted him not, but lampooned him with verses. He was an infidel in his heart, but a Muslim externally, and he named himself Rasheed-ed-Deen. And when Zumurrud lampooned him, and accepted him not as her master, he complained to his brother, the Christian who employed this stratagem to take her from her master 'Alee Shér, and whose name was Barsoom; and he replied, Grieve not on account of this affair; for I will employ a stratagem to take her without a piece of silver or of gold:—because he was a skilful, crafty, wicked magician. Then he ceased not to devise plots and stratagems until he practised the stratagem which we have described; and having taken the key, he repaired to his brother, and acquainted him with what had happened.

Upon this, Rasheed-ed-Deen mounted his mule, took his young men, and repaired with his brother to the house of 'Alee Shér, taking with him also a purse containing a thousand pieces of gold, that, if the Wálee met him he might give it to him. He opened the saloon, and the men who were with him rushed upon Zumurrud, and took her by force, threatening her with slaughter if she should speak; but the house they left as they found it, taking nothing from it, and they left 'Alee Shér lying in the passage. Then they closed the door upon him, having put the key of the saloon by his side; and the Christian Rasheed-ed-Deen took the damsel to his pavilion, where he put her among his female slaves and concubines, and said to her, O impudent wench, I am the sheykh whom thou wouldst not accept as thy master, and whom thou lampoonedst, and I have taken thee without expending a piece of silver or of gold. She replied, with her eyes filled with tears, God will sufficiently requite thee, O wicked old man, for thy separating me from my master.—O impudent wench! he rejoined, O thou inflamed with love! thou shalt see what torture I will inflict upon thee. By my faith, if thou do not comply with my command, and adopt my religion, I will inflict upon thee varieties of torture!—But she said, If thou cut my flesh in pieces, I will not abandon the faith of El-Islám; and perhaps God (whose name be exalted!) will send me speedy relief; for He is able to do whatsoever He willeth; and the wise have said, An evil in the body rather than an evil in religion. And upon this he called out to the eunuchs and female slaves, saying to them, Throw her down! So they threw her down. And he ceased not to inflict upon her cruel blows, while she called for aid; but she was not aided. Then she abstained from imploring aid, and began to say, God is my sufficiency, and He is indeed sufficient!—until her voice failed, and her groaning became inaudible. And when his heart was satisfied with punishing her, he said to the eunuchs, Drag her by her feet, and throw her into the kitchen, and give her nothing to eat. The accursed wretch then passed that night, and on the following morning he desired that she should be brought, and he repeated the beating; after which he ordered the eunuchs to throw her in her place; and they did so. And when the pain occasioned by the beating became alleviated, she said, There is no deity but God: Moḥammad is God's Apostle! God is my sufficiency, and excellent is the Guardian!—Then she implored aid of our lord Moḥammad,[22] may God bless and save him!—Such was her case.

Now as to 'Alee Shér, he continued lying asleep until the following day, when the intoxication occasioned by the benj quitted his head, and he opened his eyes, and called out, saying, O Zumurrud! But no one answered him. He therefore entered the saloon, and found the interior desolate, and the place of visitation distant: so he knew that this event had not happened unto him but through the Christian; and he yearned and wept, and sighed and complained, and recited verses. He repented when repentance was of no avail, weeping, and tearing his clothes; and he took two stones, and went round about the city, beating his bosom with them, and crying, O Zumur-

rud! The children therefore surrounded him, and said, A madman! A madman!—And every one who knew him wept for him, and said, This is such-a-one. What hath befallen him?—Thus he continued to do until the close of the day: and when the darkness of night came over him, he slept in one of the by-streets until the morning. And he went round about the city again with the stones till evening, when he returned to his saloon to pass the night there.

Then a female neighbour of his, who was an old woman, one of the virtuous, said to him, O my son, may God preserve thee! When becamest thou mad?—And he answered her with these two verses:—

They said, Thou ravest upon the person thou lovest. And I replied, The sweets of life are only for the mad.
Drop the subject of my madness, and bring her upon whom I rave. If she cure my madness, do not blame me.[23]

So his neighbour, the old woman, knew that he was a lover separated from his beloved; and she said, There is no strength nor power but in God, the High, the Great! O my son, I desire of thee that thou relate to me the story of thy calamity. Perhaps God may enable me to assist thee to overcome it, with his good pleasure.—He therefore told her all that had befallen him with Barsoom the Christian, the brother of the magician who called himself Rasheed-ed-Deen; and when she knew that, she said to him, O my son, verily thou art excused. Then she poured forth tears, and recited these two verses:—

Sufficient is the torment of lovers in this world. By Allah, Hell shall not torment them after it!
For they have perished of their passion, and chastely concealed it: and the truth of this the tradition attesteth.[24]

And after she had finished these verses, she said to him, O my son, arise now, and buy a crate, like the crates used by the goldsmiths, and buy bracelets and seal-rings and ear-rings, and other ornaments suited to women; and be not sparing of money. Put all those things into the crate; then bring the crate, and I will put it on my head, as a female broker, and I will go about and search for her in the houses until I obtain tidings of her, if it be the will of God, whose name be exalted!

'Alee Shér rejoiced at her words, and kissed her hands. He then went quickly, and brought her what she desired; and when the things were made ready for her, she arose and attired herself in a patched gown, put over her head a honey-coloured izár, and, taking in her hand a walking-staff, bore the crate about through the by-lanes and to the houses, and ceased not to go about from place to place, and from quarter to quarter, and from by-street to by-street, until God (whose name be exalted!) guided her to the pavilion of the accursed Rasheed-ed-Deen the Christian, within which she heard a groaning. So she knocked at the door; whereupon a slave-girl came down and opened to her the door, and saluted her. And the old woman said to her, I have with me these trifles for sale. Is there among you any one who will buy aught of them?—The girl answered her, Yes:—and she took her into the house, and seated her. The female slaves then seated themselves around her, and each of them took something from her; and the old woman began to address them with courtesy, and to make the prices of the goods easy to them; so that they were delighted with her, on account of her kindness, and the gentleness of her speech. Meanwhile, she looked round narrowly at the different quarters of the place, to discover the female whose groaning she had heard, and her eye fell upon her: so she treated the female slaves with additional favour and kindness; and, looking at the damsel whom she had heard groaning, she found her to be Zumurrud, laid prostrate. She recognised her, and wept, and said to the female slaves, O my children, wherefore is this damsel in this condition? And they related to her the whole story, adding, This affair is not of our choice; but our master commanded us to do thus; and he is now on a journey. And she said, O my children, I desire of you a favour, which is, that ye loose this poor damsel from her bonds, and leave her so until ye know of the return of your master, when ye shall bind her again as she was; and ye will gain a recompense from the Lord of all creatures. They replied, We hear and obey. And they loosed her and fed her and gave her to drink. The old woman then said, Would that my leg had broken and that I had not entered your abode! And after that, she went to Zumurrud, and said to her, O my daughter, God preserve thee! God will dispel from thee thine affliction.—And she told her that she had come from her master 'Alee Shér, and made an agreement with her, that she (Zumurrud) should, in the following night, listen for a sound; saying, Thy master will come to thee and stand by the maṣṭabah of the pavilion, and will whistle to thee; and when thou hearest him, do thou whistle to him, and let thyself down to him by a rope, and he will take thee and go. So the damsel thanked her for this.

The old woman then went forth, and, returning to 'Alee Shér,

informed him of what she had done, and said to him, Repair this next night, at midnight, to such a quarter; for the house of the accursed is there, and its appearance is of such and such a description. Station thyself beneath his pavilion, and whistle: she will thereupon let herself down to thee, and do thou take her and depart whither thou wilt. He therefore thanked her for this; and having waited till the night became dark, and the appointed time arrived, he went to that quarter which she had described to him, where he saw the pavilion, and he knew it. And he seated himself upon a maṣṭabah beneath it; but sleep overcame him, and he slept.—Glory be to Him who sleepeth not!—For a long time he had not slept, from the ecstasy of his passion: so he became like one intoxicated.

And while he was asleep, lo, a certain robber came forth that night, and went about the skirts of the city, to steal something; and destiny cast him beneath the pavilion of that Christian. So he went around it; but found no way of ascending and entering it; and he continued walking round it until he came to the maṣṭabah, when he beheld 'Alee Shér asleep. And he took his turban; and when he had done so, immediately Zumurrud looked forth, and, seeing him standing in the dark, imagined him to be her master. She therefore whistled to him, and the robber whistled to her; and she let herself down to him by the rope, having with her a pair of saddle-bags full of gold. So when the robber saw this, he said within himself, This is no other than a wonderful thing, occasioned by an extraordinary cause. He then took up the saddle-bags, and took Zumurrud upon his shoulders, and went away with both like the blinding lightning; whereupon the damsel said to him, The old woman told me that thou wast infirm on my account; but, lo, thou art stronger than the horse. And he returned her no answer. So she felt his face, and found that his beard was like the broom of the public bath;[25] as though he were a hog that had swallowed feathers, and their down had come forth from his throat. And she was terrified at him, and said to him, What art thou?[26] He answered her, O wench, I am the sharper Jawán the Kurdee,[27] of the gang of Aḥmad Ed-Denef: we are forty sharpers, all of whom will this night receive thee as their slave. And when she heard his words, she wept, and slapped her face, knowing that fate had overcome her, and that she had no resource but that of resignation to the will of God, whose name be exalted! She therefore endured with patience, and committed herself to the disposal of God (whose name be exalted!), and said, There is no deity but God! Each time that we are delivered from anxiety we fall into greater anxiety!

Now the cause of Jawán's coming to the place above mentioned was this:—He had said to Aḥmad Ed-Denef, O sharper, I entered this place before the present time, and know a cavern without the town, affording room for forty persons; and I desire to go before you to it, and to place my mother in that cavern. Then I will return to the city, and steal from it something for your luck, and keep it for you until ye come; so your entertainment on that day shall be of my supplying.—And Aḥmad Ed-Denef replied, Do what thou desirest. Accordingly he went before them to that place, and put his mother in the cavern; and when he went forth from it, he found a trooper lying asleep, with a horse tethered by him: so he slaughtered him, and took his clothes, and his horse and arms, and hid them in the cavern with his mother, tethering the horse there. He then returned to the

city, and walked on till he came to the pavilion of the Christian, where he did what we have described.

He ran on with the damsel without stopping until he deposited her with his mother, to whom he said, Take care of her till I return to thee in the morning. And having said this, he departed. So Zumurrud said within herself, Why am I thus careless about liberating myself by some stratagem? Wherefore should I wait until these forty men arrive?—Then she looked towards the old woman, the mother of Jawán the Kurdee, and said to her, O my aunt, wilt thou not arise and go with me without the cavern, that I may dress thy hair in the sun?—Yea, by Allah, O my daughter, answered the old woman; for of a long time I have been far from the public bath; these hogs incessantly taking me about from place to place. So Zumurrud went forth with her, and continued the operation until the old woman fell asleep; whereupon Zumurrud arose, and clad herself in the clothes of the trooper whom Jawán the Kurdee had killed, and, having bound his sword at her waist, and put on his turban, so that she appeared like a man, mounted the horse, and took the saddle-bags full of gold with her, saying, O kind Protector, protect me, I conjure Thee by the dignity of Moḥammad; God bless and save him! Then she said within herself, If I go to the city, perhaps some one of the family of the trooper may see me; and no good will happen unto me. So she refrained from entering the city, and proceeded over the bare desert, with the saddle-bags and the horse, eating of the herbs of the earth, and feeding the horse of the same, and drinking and giving him to drink of the waters of the rivers, for the space of ten days.

And on the eleventh day, she approached a pleasant and secure city, established in prosperity: the winter had departed from it with its cold, and the spring had come with its flowers and its roses; its flowers were gay and charming to the sight, its rivers were flowing, and its birds were warbling. Now when she came to this city, and approached its gate, she found there the troops and the emeers and the chiefs of its inhabitants; and she wondered when she saw them thus collected, and said within herself, The people of this city are all assembled at its gate, and there must be some cause for this. She then proceeded towards them; and when she drew near to them, the troops hastened forward to meet her, and, having alighted, kissed the ground before her, and said, God aid thee, O our lord the Sulṭán! The great officers arranged themselves in ranks before her, and the troops ranged the people in order, and exclaimed, God aid thee, and make thine arrival a blessing to the Muslims, O Sultán of all creatures! God establish thee, O King of the age, and incomparable one of the age and time!—So Zumurrud said to them, What is your story, O ye people of this city? The chamberlain answered, Verily He who is not sparing of his benefits hath bestowed favour upon thee, and made thee Sulṭán over this city, and ruler over the necks of all whom it containeth. Know that it is the custom of the inhabitants of this city, when their King dieth, and hath left no son, for the troops to go forth without the city, and to remain three days; and whatsoever man arriveth by the way by which thou hast come, they make him Sulṭán over them. And praise be to God who hath directed unto us a man of the sons of the Turks, of comely countenance; for had one of less consideration than thyself come unto us, he had been Sulṭán.—Now Zumurrud was a person of judgment in all her actions; so she said, Think me not one of the common people among the Turks: nay, I am of the sons of the great; but I was incensed against my family, and went forth from them and left them; and look ye at this pair of saddle-bags full of gold that I have brought beneath me, to give alms out of it to the poor and needy all the way. And on hearing this, they prayed for her, and were extremely rejoiced at her arrival; and she was also pleased with them. She then said within herself, Since I have attained to this, perhaps God will unite me with my master in this place; for He is able to do whatsoever He willeth. And she proceeded, accompanied by the troops, until they entered the city, when the troops alighted and walked before her till they had conducted her into the palace. She there alighted, and the emeers and grandees conveyed her with their hands beneath her arm-pits, and seated her upon the throne. Then all of them kissed the ground before her. And when she was seated on the throne, she gave orders to open the treasuries; and they were opened; and she bestowed presents upon all the troops; whereupon they offered up prayers for the continuance of her reign; and the people, and all the inhabitants of the provinces, acknowledged her authority.

She remained thus for some time, commanding and forbidding, and the hearts of the people were impressed with exceeding respect for her, on account of her generosity, and her abstinence from what is forbidden. She remitted the custom-taxes, liberated the persons confined in the prisons, and redressed the grievances of her subjects; so that all the people loved her. But whenever she thought upon her master, she wept, and supplicated God to effect her union with him. And thinking upon him one night, and upon her days that had passed, she poured forth tears, and recited these two verses:—

My desire for thee, though protracted, is fresh; and the tears have wounded my eye, and increase.
When I weep, I weep from the pain of ardent love; for separation, to the lover, is a fierce affliction.

And when she had ended these verses, she wiped away her tears, and went up into the pavilion. Then she entered the Ḥareem, and assigned separate apartments for the female slaves and concubines, appointing them allowances and supplies, and asserted that she desired to remain in a place alone, for the purpose of assiduously employing herself in devotion; and she betook herself to fasting and praying, so that the emeers said, Verily this Sulṭán is of exceeding piety. She retained of the eunuchs only two lads to serve her.

For a year she sat upon the throne of her kingdom, and heard no tidings of her master, nor discovered any trace of him. And upon this she was disquieted, and, her disquietude becoming excessive, she summoned the wezeers and chamberlains, and commanded them to bring to her the geometricians and builders, and gave orders that they should make for her, beneath the palace, a horse-course a league in length and a league in breadth. So they did as she commanded them in the shortest time, and the horse-course was agreeable to her desire.

And when it was finished, she descended into it. A great pavilion was pitched for her in it, chairs were arranged for the emeers, and she gave orders to spread in that horse-course a long table covered with all kinds of rich viands; and they did as she commanded. Then she ordered the lords of the empire to eat; and they ate; after which she said to the emeers, I desire, when the new month commenceth, that ye do thus, and proclaim in the city, that no one shall open his shop, but that all the people shall come and eat of the King's banquet; and that whosoever of them acteth contrary to this order shall be hanged at the door of his house.[28] So when the new month commenced, they did as she commanded them; and they continued to observe this custom until the commencement of the first month of the second year; when Zumurrud descended into the horse-course, and the crier proclaimed, O all ye companies of men, whosoever openeth his shop or his magazine or his house shall be hanged immediately at the door of his abode: for it is incumbent on you that ye all come to eat of the King's banquet! And when the proclamation was ended, the table having been prepared, the people came in companies, and she ordered them to seat themselves at the table, to eat until they were satisfied, of all the dishes. Accordingly, they sat and ate as she had commanded them, while she sat upon the throne of her kingdom looking at them; and every one at the table said within himself, The King is looking at none but me. They continued eating, and the emeers said to the people, Eat ye, and be not ashamed; for the King liketh your doing so. They therefore ate until they were satisfied, and departed praying for the King; and some of them said to others, In our lives we have not seen a Sulṭán that loveth the poor like this Sulṭán. They prayed for length of life for her; and she returned to her palace, full of joy at the plan which she had devised, and said within herself, If it be the will of God (whose name be exalted!), by this means I shall obtain tidings of my master 'Alee-Shér.

And when the second month commenced, she did the same, as usual. They prepared the table, and Zumurrud descended, and seated herself upon her throne, and ordered the people to sit and eat. And while she was sitting at the head of the table, and the people were seating themselves at it, company after company, and person after person, her eye fell upon Barsoom the Christian, who had bought the curtain of her master; and she knew him, and said, This is the commencement of the dispelling of my affliction, and the attainment of my desire. Then Barsoom advanced, and seated himself among the people to eat; and he looked at a dish of rice sweetened with sugar sprinkled over it; but it was far from him; so he pressed towards it, and, stretching forth his hand to it, reached it and put it before him. Upon this, a man by his side said to him, Why dost thou not eat of that which is before thee? Is not this a disgrace to thee? How is it that thou stretchest forth thy hand to a thing that is distant from thee? Art thou not ashamed?—But Barsoom replied, I will eat of none but it. So the man rejoined, Eat: may God not give thee enjoyment in it! And a man who was a ḥashshásh[29] said, Let him eat of it, that I too may eat with him. The man before mentioned, however, said to him, O most ill-omened of ḥashsháshes, this is not your food, but it is the food of the emeers; therefore leave it that it may return to those to whom it belongeth, that they may eat it. But Barsoom disobeyed him: he took from it a mouthful, and put it into his mouth, and was about to take the second, when Zumurrud, observing him, called out to certain of the soldiers, and said to them, Bring this man before whom is the dish of sweet rice, and let him not eat the mouthful that is in his hand; but throw it down from his hand. So four of the soldiers came to him, and dragged him along upon his face, after they had thrown down the mouthful from his hand; and they stationed him before Zumurrud. Upon this, the people refrained from eating; one of them saying to another, By Allah, he was unjust; for he would not eat of the food suited to persons of his own class. Another said, I was content with this kishk[30] that is before me. And the ḥashshásh said, Praise be to God, who prevented my eating aught

of this dish of sweet rice; for I was waiting for it to stop before him and for him to enjoy it, when I would have eaten with him; but what we have witnessed befell him. And the people said, one to another, Wait that we may see what will happen to him.

Now when they brought him before the Queen Zumurrud, she said to him, Wo to thee, O blue-eyed! What is thy name, and what is the reason of thy coming to our country?—And the accursed refused to give his true name, and, having a white turban,[31] he answered, O King, my name is 'Alee, and my business is that of a weaver, and I have come to this city for the sake of traffic. Zumurrud said, Bring ye to me a geomantic tablet, and a pen of brass. And they brought her what she demanded immediately; and she took the geomantic tablet and the pen, and performed an operation of geomancy, designing with the pen a figure like that of an ape; after which she raised her head, and looked attentively at Barsoom for a long time, and said to him, O dog, how is it that thou liest unto Kings? Art thou not a Christian, and is not thy name Barsoom, and hast thou not come to search for something? Tell me then the truth, or, by the glory of the Deity, I will strike off thy head!—And the Christian was agitated; and the emeers and others who were present said, This King is acquainted with geomancy. Extolled be the perfection of Him who hath endowed him with this knowledge!—Then she called out to the Christian, saying to him, Tell me the truth, or I destroy thee! And the Christian replied, Pardon, O King of the age! Thou art right in thy geomantic divination; for the most remote[32] is a Christian. So the emeers and others who were present wondered at the King's exactness in discovering the truth by geomancy, saying, Verily this King is an astrologer of whom there is not the like in the world! The Queen then ordered that the Christian should be flayed, that his skin should be stuffed with straw, and hung over the gate of the horse-course, and that a pit should be dug without the city, and his flesh and his bones should be burnt in it, and dirt and filth thrown upon his ashes. They replied, We hear and obey:—and did all that she had commanded them. And when the people saw what had befallen the Christian, they said, His recompense was that which hath befallen him: and what an unlucky mouthful was that unto him! One of them said, Divorcement shall be incumbent on the remote [if I break this vow]: in my life henceforth I will never eat of sweet rice![33] And the ḥashshásh said, Praise be to God who hath saved me from that which hath befallen this man, by his preserving me from eating that rice! Then all the people went forth; and they had become prohibited from sitting opposite to the sweet rice, in the place of that Christian.

Again, when the third month commenced, they spread the table as usual, and covered it with the dishes, and the Queen Zumurrud sat upon the throne, the troops standing in the customary manner, but fearing her awful power. The people of the city then entered as they were wont, and went around the table, looking for the place of the dish of rice; and one of them said to another, O ḥájj[34] Khalaf! The other replied, At thy service, O ḥájj Khálid! And the former said, Avoid the dish of sweet rice, and beware of eating of it; for if thou eat of it, thou wilt be hanged. Then they seated themselves around the table to eat; and while they were eating, and the Queen Zumurrud was sitting on the throne, a glance of her eye fell upon a man entering with a hurried pace from the gate of the horse-course, and, looking attentively at him, she found that he was Jawán the Kurdee, the robber who murdered the trooper: and the cause of his coming was this:—He had left his mother, and gone to his companions, and said to them, I obtained yesterday excellent booty: I murdered a trooper, and took his horse; and there fell to my lot the same night a pair of saddle-bags full of gold, and a damsel whose value is greater than the gold in the saddle-bags; and I have put all this booty in the cavern, with my mother. So they rejoiced at this, and repaired to the cavern at the close of the day. Jawán the Kurdee entered before them, and they followed him; and he desired to bring to them the things of which he had told them; but he found the place desolate. He therefore inquired of his mother the truth of the matter, and she acquainted him with all that had happened; on hearing which, he bit his hands in repentance,[35] and said, By Allah, I will search about for this impudent wench, and take her from the place in which she is, though she be within the shell of a pistachio-nut, and I will satisfy my malice upon her! Accordingly, he went forth to search for her, and ceased not to go about the surrounding districts until he came to the city of the Queen Zumurrud. And when he entered the city, he found no man in it: he therefore inquired of some of the women who were looking out from the windows,[36] and they informed him that on the first day of every month the Sulṭán made a banquet, and the people went and ate of it; and they directed him to the horse-course in which the table was spread.

So he came hurrying on, and, not finding a vacant place in

which to seat himself except one opposite the dish above mentioned, he seated himself there, and, as the dish was before him, stretched forth his hand to it. Upon this, the people called to him, saying, O our brother, what dost thou desire to do? He answered, I desire to eat of this dish until I am satiated. And one of them said to him, If thou eat of it, thou wilt be hanged. But he replied, Be silent, and utter not these words. Then he stretched forth his hand to the dish, and drew it before him. The ḥashshásh before mentioned was sitting by his side, and when he saw Jawán draw the dish before him, he fled from his place; the effect of the ḥasheesheh[37] instantly passed away from his head, and he seated himself afar off, saying, I have nothing to do with this dish. Jawán the Kurdee stretched forth his hand to the dish, and it resembled the foot of a raven; and he ladled the rice with it, and took it forth resembling the foot of a camel.[38] Then he compressed the handful into the form of a ball, so that it was like a great orange; he threw it rapidly into his mouth, and it descended into his throat, making a noise like thunder; and the bottom of the dish appeared in the place from which it was taken. So a man by his side said to him, Praise be to God, who hath not made me to be a dish of meat before thee; for thou hast exhausted the dish by a single mouthful! And the ḥashshásh said, Let him eat; for I imagine that I behold in him the figure of the hanged. Then looking towards him, he said to him, Eat: may God not give thee enjoyment! And Jawán stretched forth his hand to take the second mouthful, and was about to press it into the form of a ball like the first mouthful, when the Queen called to some of the soldiers, saying to them, Bring that man quickly, and suffer him not to eat the mouthful that is in his hand.

The soldiers therefore ran to him, while he was bending his head over the dish, and they seized him and took him and placed him before the Queen Zumurrud. Upon this, the people exulted over him, saying, one to another, Verily he deserveth it; for we gave him good advice, and he would not follow it. This place is predestined to occasion the slaughter of him who sitteth in it, and that rice is unfortunate to every one who eateth of it.—Then the Queen Zumurrud said to him, What is thy name, and what is thine occupation, and what is the reason of thy coming to our city?—O our lord the Sulṭán, he answered, my name is 'Osmán, and my occupation is that of a gardener, and the reason of my coming to this city is, that I am going about searching for a thing that I have lost. And the Queen said, Bring me the geomantic tablet. So they placed it before her; and she took the pen, and, having performed an operation of geomancy, meditated upon it a while; after which she raised her head, and said to him, Wo to thee, O wicked wretch! How is it that thou liest unto Kings? This geomantic experiment informeth me that thy name is Jawán the Kurdee, and thine occupation is that of a robber, that thou takest the property of men by iniquitous means, and slayest the soul that God hath forbidden to be slain unless for a just cause.—Then she called out to him and said, O hog, tell me thy true story, or I will cut off thy head! And when he heard her words, his complexion became sallow, and his teeth appeared, and, imagining that if he spoke the truth he would save himself, he replied, Thou hast spoken truth, O King; but I vow repentance unto thee from this time, and return unto God, whose name be exalted! The Queen, however, said to him, It is not lawful unto me to leave a viper in the path of the Muslims. And she said to some of her attendants, Take him and flay him, and do unto him as ye did unto the like of him last month. So they did as she commanded them. And when the ḥashshásh saw the soldiers seize that man, he turned his back to the dish of rice, and said, Verily, to present my face unto thee is unlawful! And as soon as they had finished eating, they dispersed, and went to their abodes: the Queen also went up into her palace, and gave permission to the memlooks to disperse.

And when the fourth month commenced, they descended into the horse-course as usual, and made ready the banquet, and the people sat waiting for permission. The Queen then approached, and sat upon the throne, looking at them; and she observed that the place opposite the dish of rice, affording room for four persons, was vacant; whereat she wondered. And while she was looking about, she beheld a man entering from the gate of the horse-course, with a quick pace, and he ceased not to hurry on until he stopped over the table, where he found no place vacant but that opposite the dish of rice. So he seated himself there; and she looked at him attentively, and found that he was the Christian who had named himself Rasheed-ed-Deen; whereupon she said within herself, How fortunate is this repast, by which this infidel hath been insnared!—Now the cause of his coming was wonderful; and it was this. When he returned from his journey, the people of his house informed him that Zumurrud was lost, together with a pair of saddle-bags full of money; on hearing which, he rent his clothes, and slapped his face, and plucked his beard. Then he sent his brother Barsoom to search for her through the surrounding districts; and when he was tired of waiting for news of him, he went forth himself to search through the provinces for his brother and Zumurrud, and destiny impelled him to Zumurrud's city. He entered that city on the first day of the month, and when he walked along its great thoroughfare-streets, he found them desolate, and saw the shops closed, and the women at the windows; so he inquired of some of them respecting this circumstance, and they told him that the King made a banquet for all the people on the first of every month, and all ate of it; none being able to sit in his house or in his shop; and they directed him to the horse-course.

On his entering the horse-course, he found the people crowding around the food, and found no place vacant except that opposite the well-known dish of rice. So he seated himself in it, and stretched forth his hand to eat of that dish; whereupon the Queen called to some of the soldiers, saying, Bring ye him who hath seated himself opposite the dish of rice. And they knew him from the former occurrences of the same kind, and seized him, and stationed him before the Queen Zumurrud, who said to him, Wo to thee! What is thy name, and what is thine occupation, and what is the reason of thy coming unto our city?—He answered, O King of the age, my name is Rustum,[39] and I have no occupation, for I am a poor darweesh. And she said to her attendants, Bring me the geomantic tablet, and the pen of brass. So they brought her what she demanded as usual: and she took the pen, and made some marks with it upon the tablet, and remained a while contemplating it: then raising her head and looking towards him, she said, O dog, how is it that thou liest unto the Kings? Thy name is Rasheed-ed-Deen the Christian, and thine occupation is, to practise stratagems against the female slaves of the Muslims, and to take them; and thou art a Muslim externally, but in heart a Christian. Declare then the truth; for if thou do not, I will strike off thy head.—And he hesitated to reply; but afterwards said, Thou hast spoken truth, O King of the age. So she gave orders that he should be stretched upon the ground, and receive upon each foot a hundred lashes, and upon his body a thousand lashes; and after that, that he should be flayed, and his skin stuffed with hards of flax; then, that a pit should be dug without the city, and his body be burnt in it, and dirt and filth thrown upon his ashes. And they did as she commanded them.

After this, she gave leave to the people to eat, and when they had finished, and gone their ways, the Queen Zumurrud went up into her palace, and said, Praise be to God who hath appeased my heart by the punishment of those who wronged me! And she thanked the Creator of the earth and the heavens. Then her master 'Alee Shér occurred to her mind, and she shed copious tears; after which, returning to her reason, she said within herself, Perhaps God, who hath given me power over mine enemies, may grant me the return of my beloved. She begged forgiveness of God (to whom be ascribed might and glory!), and said, Perhaps God will soon reunite me with my beloved 'Alee Shér; for He is able to do whatsoever He willeth, and is gracious

unto his servants, and acquainted with their states. She praised God again, continued her prayers for forgiveness, and resigned herself to the course of destiny, assured that every thing which hath a beginning must come to an end; and recited the saying of the poet:—

Endure thy state with an easy mind; for in the hand of God are the destinies of things;
And what is forbidden will not happen unto thee, nor will that which is appointed fail to befall thee.

She continued for the whole of that month occupying herself by day in judging the people, and commanding and forbidding, and by night weeping and lamenting for the separation of her beloved 'Alee Shér; and when the next month commenced, she gave orders to spread the table in the horse-course as usual, and sat at the head of the people. They were waiting for her permission to eat, and the place before the dish of rice was vacant; and as she sat at the head of the table, she kept her eye fixed upon the gate of the horse-course, to see every one who entered it. And she said within herself, O Thou who restoredst Yoosuf to Yaạḳoob, and removedst the affliction from Eiyoob, favour me by the restoration of my master 'Alee Shér, by thy power and greatness; for Thou art able to accomplish every thing! O Lord of all creatures! O Guide of those who go astray! O Hearer of cries! O Answerer of prayers! Hear my prayer, O Lord of all creatures!—And her supplication was not ended when there entered from the gate of the horse-course a person whose figure was like a branch of the Oriental willow; but he was of emaciated frame, and sallowness appeared in his countenance: he was the handsomest of young men, perfect in judgment and in polite accomplishments. When he entered, he found no place vacant but that which was before the dish of rice: he therefore sat in that place; and when Zumurrud beheld him, her heart palpitated. She looked at him with a scrutinizing glance, and it was evident to her that he was her master 'Alee Shér, and she was inclined to cry aloud for joy; but she stilled her mind, fearing to disgrace herself among the people: her bowels were moved with compassion, and her heart throbbed; yet she concealed what she felt.—And the cause of 'Alee Shér's coming was this:—

When he lay asleep upon the maṣṭabah, and Zumurrud descended, and Jawán the Kurdee took her, he awoke afterwards, and found himself with uncovered head; so he knew that some man had come upon him wrongfully, and taken his turban while he was asleep. He uttered the sentence which preserveth the person who pronounceth it

from being confounded; that is, Verily to God we belong, and verily unto Him we return! Then he went back to the old woman who had acquainted him with the situation of Zumurrud, and knocked at her door; whereupon she came forth to him; and he wept before her until he fell down in a fit. And when he recovered, he informed her of all that had befallen him; on hearing which, she blamed him, and severely reproved him for that which he had done, and said to him, Verily thy calamity and misfortune have arisen from thyself. She ceased not to blame him until blood ran from his nostrils, and he fell down again in a fit; and on his recovering from his fit, he beheld the old woman weeping on his account, pouring forth tears, and in a state of anguish; and he recited these two verses:—

How bitter unto lovers is separation, and how sweet unto them is union!
May God unite every separated lover, and preserve me, for I am of their number![40]

The old woman mourned for him, and said to him, Sit here while I ascertain the news for thee, and I will return quickly. And he replied, I hear and obey. Then she left him and went away, and was absent from him until midday, when she returned to him, and said, O 'Alee, I imagine nothing but that thou wilt die in thy grief; for thou wilt not again see thy beloved save on the Ṣiráṭ;[41] for the people of the pavilion, when they arose in the morning, found the window that overlooketh the garden displaced, and Zumurrud lost, and with her a pair of saddle-bags full of money belonging to the Christian; and when I arrived there, I found the Wálee standing at the door of the pavilion, together with his officers; and there is no strength nor power but in God, the High, the Great!—Now when 'Alee Shér heard these words from her, the light before his face became converted into darkness; he despaired of life, and made sure of death, and ceased not to weep until again he fell down in a fit; and after he recovered from his fit, love and separation so afflicted him that he was attacked by a severe sickness, and was confined to his house. The old woman, however, continued to bring the physicians to him, and to give him beverages, and make pottages for him, during the space of a whole year, until his soul returned to him. And when the second year commenced, the old woman said to him, O my son, this sadness and grief that thou sufferest will not restore to thee thy beloved: arise then, brace up thy nerves, and search for her through the surrounding districts; perhaps thou mayest meet with tidings of her. And she ceased not to encourage him and to strengthen his mind until she cheered him; and she conducted him into the bath, gave him wine to drink, and fed him with fowls. Thus she did every day for the space of a month, till he gained strength, and set forth on his journey, and he ceased not to travel until he arrived at the city of Zumurrud.

Having entered the horse-course, he seated himself at the table, and stretched forth his hand to eat; and upon this, the people grieved for him, and said to him, O young man, eat not of this dish; for affliction will befall him who eateth of it. But he replied, Suffer me to eat of it, and let them do unto me what they desire: perhaps I may be relieved from this wearying life. Then he ate the first morsel; and Zumurrud desired to have him brought before her; but it occurred to her mind that he might be hungry: so she said within herself, It is proper that I suffer him to eat until he satisfy himself. He therefore continued eating; and the people were confounded at his case, looking to see what would happen unto him. And when he had eaten, and satisfied himself, she said to certain of the eunuchs, Go to that young man who eateth of the rice, and bring him courteously, and say to him, Answer the summons of the King, to reply to a little question. So they said, We hear and obey:—and they went to him, and, standing over his head, said to him, O our master, have the goodness to answer the summons of the King, and let thy heart be dilated. He replied, I hear and obey:—and he went with the eunuchs; while the people said, one to another, There is no strength nor power but in God, the High, the Great! What will the King do with him?—But some of them said, He will do nought but good with him; for if he meant to do him harm, he had not suffered him to eat until he was satisfied.—And when he stood before Zumurrud, he saluted, and kissed the ground before her; and she returned his salutation, receiving him with honour, and said to him, What is thy name, and what is thine occupation, and what is the reason of thy coming unto this city? So he answered her, O King, my name is 'Alee Shér, I am of the sons of the merchants, and my country is Khurásán, and the reason of my coming unto this city is to search for a slave-girl whom I have lost: she was dearer to me than my hearing and my sight, and my soul hath been devoted to her ever since I lost her. This is my story.—Then he wept until he fainted; whereupon she gave orders to sprinkle some rose-water upon his face; and they did so until he recovered, when the Queen said, Bring to me the geomantic tablet, and the pen of brass. They therefore brought them; and she took the pen, and, having performed an operation of geomancy, considered it a while, after which she said to him, Thou hast spoken truly. God will unite thee with her soon: so be not uneasy.—She then ordered the chamberlain to take him to the bath, and to attire him in a handsome suit of the apparel of Kings, to mount him upon one of the most excellent of her horses, and after that, to bring him to the palace at the close of the day. The chamberlain replied, I hear and obey:—and led him away from before her, and departed. And the people said, one to another, Wherefore hath the King treated the young man with this courtesy? One said, Did I not tell you that he would do him no harm? for his appearance is comely; and from the King's waiting until he had satisfied himself, I knew that.—And every one of them said something. Then the people dispersed, and went their ways.

Zumurrud scarcely believed that the night was approaching when she should be alone with the beloved of her heart; and as soon as the night came, she entered her chamber, and sent to her beloved 'Alee Shér. And when they brought him, he kissed the ground before her, and prayed for her; and she said within herself, I must jest with him a while, without making myself known to him. So she said, O 'Alee, hast thou gone to the bath? He answered, Yes, O my lord. And she said, Arise, eat of this fowl and meat, and drink of this sherbet of sugar, and wine; for thou art tired; and after that, come hither. He replied, I hear and obey:—and he did as she commanded him; and when he had finished eating and drinking, she said to him, Come up unto me, and rub my feet.[42] He therefore began to rub her feet and her legs, and found them softer than silk. And after she had continued a while jesting with him, she said, O my master, hath all this happened, and dost thou not know me? He asked, And who art thou, O King? And she answered, I am thy slave-girl Zumurrud. So when he knew this, he kissed her, and embraced her, throwing himself upon her like the lion upon the sheep.

And on the following morning, Zumurrud sent to all the troops, and the lords of the empire, and summoned them, and said to them, I desire to journey to the city of this man. Choose for you therefore a viceroy to exercise authority among you until I return to you.—And they replied, We hear and obey. She then betook herself to preparing the necessaries for the journey, as food and money and other supplies, and rarities, and camels, and mules, and set forth from the city; and she continued her journey with him until she arrived at the city of 'Alee Shér, when he entered his abode, and gave gifts and alms and presents. He was blessed with children by her, and they both lived in the utmost happiness until they were visited by the terminator of delights and the separator of companions.—Extolled be the perfection of the Eternal; and praise be to God in every case!

NOTES TO CHAPTER FIFTEENTH.

NOTE 1. THOUGH the scenes of this story are Khurásán and some neighbouring country, in, or adjacent to, the north or north-east of Persia, its character throughout is Arabian.

NOTE 2. "Mejd-ed-Deen" signifies "the Glory of the Religion."

NOTE 3. On this first occasion of the mention of 'Alee Shér, the surname (Shér) is omitted in the edition from which I translate; namely, that of Cairo. As there afterwards written, this surname may be pronounced either "Shár" or (by what is termed "imáleh") "Shér:" but the latter is the preferable pronunciation; as the word is evidently the Persian "Shér," signifying "a Lion." In the edition of Breslau, it is "Sheer," or "Sheyr."

NOTE 4. This couplet has occurred before: so also have the sixth in the same paragraph, slightly varied, and the eighth, and one in my original which I omit because it is similar to the eighth, which it immediately follows. See vol. i. of the present work, pp. 240, 334; and (for the couplet that I omit) p. 57 in *this* volume. For this last also, a little varied, see vol. i. p. 240.

NOTE 5. A person who only tastes a thing may find sweetness in it, when it is bitter at the heart. "Dhaḳa," in the original, is put, by an error of the compositor, for "Dháḳa."[1]

NOTE 6. See Note 42 to Chapter x.

NOTE 7. "Zumurrud" signifies "Emerald."

NOTE 8. "Rasheed-ed-Deen" signifies, in this case, "Rightly directed in Religion," or "Orthodox."

NOTE 9. The Arabs in general entertain a prejudice against blue eyes; a prejudice said to have arisen from the great number of blue-eyed persons among certain of their northern enemies.

NOTE 10. She compares the old man's mustaches to cotton, with which the

[1] Marginal note by my sheykh.

nostrils, &c. of a corpse are stuffed. (See the second paragraph of Note 11 to Chapter vi.) From this it appears that the Arabs sometimes stuff the *mouth* of a corpse with cotton; but I have never heard of their doing so.

NOTE 11. Slapping the back of the neck is a common Arab custom, like slapping the face, or boxing the ears, in England; and beating with the shoe or slipper is one of the greatest insults that an Arab can offer.—The verse to which this note refers is, in my original, immediately followed by one too coarse to be translated.

NOTE 12. The Prophet forbade the dyeing of the hair black.—See Mishkát el-Maṣábeeḥ, vol. ii. pp. 360 and 362.

NOTE 13. The puppetmen here mentioned are the exhibiters of what we term "Chinese shadows," a show common in Arabian and other Eastern countries.

NOTE 14. See Note 81 to Chapter v.

NOTE 15. "Selsebeel" is the name of a fountain in Paradise.

NOTE 16. See Note 53 to Chapter viii.

NOTE 17. See Note 48 to Chapter iii.

NOTE 18. Seven different styles of writing are used by the Arabs in the present day. Herbin has given descriptions and specimens of them in an Essay on Oriental Caligraphy at the end of his "Développemens des Principes de la Langue Arabe Moderne."

NOTE 19.—*On the Occupations of the* Ḥareem. Next to the service of her husband or master, the care of her children, and attending to other indispensable domestic duties, the most important occupation of the wife or concubine-slave is that of spinning or weaving or needle-work. "Sitting for an hour employed with the distaff is better for women," said the Prophet, "than a year's worship; and for every piece of cloth woven of the thread spun by them they shall receive the reward of a martyr."—'Áïsheh, the Prophet's wife, thus declared the merit of spinning: "Tell the women what I say: There is no woman who spins until she hath clothed herself but all the angels in the Seven Heavens pray for forgiveness of her sins; and she will go forth from her grave on the day of judgment wearing a robe of Paradise, and with a veil upon her head, and before her shall be an angel, and on her right an angel who will hand her a draught of the water of Selsebeel;[2] and another angel will come to her, and carry her upon his wings, and bear her to Paradise. And when she enters Paradise, eighty thousand maidens will meet her, each maiden bringing a different robe; and she will have mansions of emeralds with three hundred doors, at each of which doors will stand an angel with a present from the Lord of the Throne."[3]—The arts above mentioned are pursued by the females in the ḥareems of the middle and higher classes. "Their leisure-hours are mostly spent in working with the needle; particularly in embroidering handkerchiefs, head-veils, &c., upon a frame called 'mensej,' with coloured silks, and gold. Many women, even in the houses of the wealthy, replenish their private purses by ornamenting handkerchiefs and other things in this manner, and employing a delláleh (or female broker) to take them to the market, or to other ḥareems, for sale."[4]

Thus it was in ancient Greece. We are told of Andromache, that—

> Far in the close recesses of the dome,
> Pensive she ply'd the melancholy loom;
> A growing work employ'd her secret hours,
> Confus'dly gay with intermingled flow'rs.[5]

---

[2] See above, Note 15 of the present series.

[3] Nuzhet el-Mutaämmil, &c., sect. 7.

[4] From my work on the Modern Egyptians, vol. i. ch. vi.

[5] Pope's Homer's Iliad, book xxii. lines 566-9.

Such also, until the decline of the Empire, was the habit of the Roman matrons. Of Augustus it is said, that his ordinary apparel was entirely of the manufacture of his wife, sister, daughter, and nieces.[6]

NOTE 20. The word which I render "a tributary" (namely, "dhimmee,") signifies a client of the state, or one who, by paying an annual tribute, is entitled to the protection of the Muslims and to most of the civil rights which the latter enjoy.

NOTE 21.—*On the Obligation imposed by eating Bread and Salt.* The obligation which is imposed by eating another person's bread and salt, or salt alone, or eating such things with another, is well known; but the following example of it may be new to some readers.—Yaaḳoob the son of El-Leys Eṣ-Ṣaffár,[7] having adopted a predatory life, excavated a passage one night into the palace of Dirhem the Governor of Sijistán, or Seestán; and after he had "made up a convenient bale of gold and jewels, and the most costly stuffs, was proceeding to carry it off, when he happened in the dark to strike his foot against something hard on the floor. Thinking it might be a jewel of some sort or other, a diamond perhaps, he picked it up and put it to his tongue, and, to his equal mortification and disappointment, found it to be a lump of rock-salt; for having thus tasted the salt of the owner, his avarice gave way to his respect for the laws of hospitality; and throwing down his precious booty, he left it behind him, and withdrew empty-handed to his habitation. The treasurer of Dirhem repairing the next day, according to custom, to inspect his charge, was equally surprised and alarmed at observing that a great part of the treasure and other valuables had been removed; but on examining the package which lay on the floor, his astonishment was not less, to find that not a single article had been conveyed away. The singularity of the circumstance induced him to report it immediately to his master: and the latter causing it to be proclaimed throughout the city, that the author of this proceeding had his free pardon, further announced, that on repairing to the palace, he would be distinguished by the most encouraging marks of favour." Yaaḳoob availed himself of the invitation, relying upon the promise, which was fulfilled to him; and from this period he gradually rose in power until he became the founder of a Dynasty.[8]

NOTE 22. The Prophet is often invoked as an *intercessor;* but not otherwise.

NOTE 23. Nearly the same couplet has occurred before: see page 104 in this volume. The idea expressed in the latter part of the first verse is found in a couplet in Dryden's Spanish Friar:—

> There is a pleasure sure in being mad
> Which none but madmen know:

and in Cowper's Task we have the following:—

> There is a pleasure in poetic pains
> Which none but poets know:

upon which Mr. Keightley remarks, "Though I think there is imitation here, I would not positively assert it."[9]

NOTE 24. This is, as my sheykh states in a marginal note, the tradition of the Prophet, namely, his saying, "Whoso is in love, and acteth chastely, and concealeth [his passion], and dieth, dieth a martyr."

NOTE 25. The kind of broom here mentioned, called "miḳashsheh," is short and

---

6 Suet. Aug. 73.

7 "Eṣ-Ṣaffár" signifies "the Brasier."

8 Price's "Mahommedan History," vol. ii. pp. 229 *et seq.*

9 "Tales and Popular Fictions," &c., p. 14.

flat, and is sometimes made of the thickest part of a palm-stick; the larger portion of which, being well soaked, is beaten until the fibres separate.

NOTE 26. From this question it seems that she feared he might be a Jinnee.

NOTE 27. "Kurdee" is the appellation of an individual of the nation called "El-Kurd," whose country, "Kurdistán," is on the south of Armenia. Ṣaláḥ-ed-Deen (commonly called by Europeans "Saladin") was of this nation.—"Jawán" is a Persian word, from the same root as the Latin "juvenis," and has the same meaning.

NOTE 28. On feasts of this kind, see Note 7 to Chapter viii.

NOTE 29. A "ḥashshásh" is a person addicted to the intoxicating hemp, called "ḥasheesh" and "ḥasheesheh."—See Note 46 to Chapter ii., and the fourth paragraph of Note 22 to Chapter iii.

NOTE 30. "Kishk" (as the word is commonly pronounced, but properly "keshik,") is prepared from wheat, first moistened, then dried, trodden in a vessel to separate the husks, and coarsely ground with a hand-mill: the meal is mixed with milk, and about six hours afterwards is spooned out upon a little straw or bran, and then left for two or three days to dry. When required for use, it is either soaked or pounded, and put into a sieve, over a vessel; and then, boiling water is poured on it. What remains in the sieve is thrown away: what passes through is generally poured into a saucepan of boiled meat or fowl, over the fire. Some leaves of white bete, fried in butter, are usually added to each plate of it.[10]

NOTE 31. See Note 55 to Chapter ii., and Note 98 to Chapter x.

NOTE 32. The narrator uses this expression fearing to say, "*I* am a Christian" even in repeating the words of another.—See Note 8 to Chapter ii.

NOTE 33. This expression again, like that just noticed, is worthy of remark. If a man, reading this work aloud, said, "Divorcement shall be incumbent upon *me* if henceforth I eat of sweet rice," some persons, having heard him say so, might swear that he applied the words seriously to himself, and had thereby bound himself to divorce his wife if ever he ate of that dish.—See Note 48 to Chapter viii.

NOTE 34. "Ḥájj" signifies "pilgrim," and is the usual Arab title of one who has performed the pilgrimage to Mekkeh and Mount 'Arafát. The Turks and Persians use, instead of it, the synonymous Arabic word "ḥájjee." [The Christians also give the title of Ḥájj to one who has performed the pilgrimage to Jerusalem.—ED.]

NOTE 35. See a note at the foot of page 61 in this volume.

NOTE 36. The streets being deserted by the *men* of the city, it was a fit opportunity for the women to look out from the windows, and for those who were neighbours thus to converse with each other.

NOTE 37. See above, Note 29.

NOTE 38. "His hand descends into the dish resembling the foot of a raven [with the thumb and first and second fingers nearly joined, and the other fingers turned up towards the palm of the hand], and comes up [so full that it is] like the foot of a camel," is a common proverb, applied to a coarse glutton.—See Burckhardt's "Arabic Proverbs," No. 756.

NOTE 39. Properly, "Rustam" (the name of the most celebrated of the Persian heroes); but pronounced by the Arabs, and generally, I believe, by the Turks, "Rustum."

---

[10] From my work on the Modern Egyptians, vol. ii. ch. xiii.

NOTE 40. The words here rendered "I am of their number" also signify, "I am at the point of death," or "—— in the agonies of death;" but the first is my sheykh's reading, and is more logical.

NOTE 41. The Ṣirâṭ is the bridge which all must pass on the day of judgment, extending over the midst of Hell, finer than a hair, and sharper than the edge of a sword.

NOTE 42. See Note 55 to Chapter iii.

CHAPTER XVI.

COMMENCING WITH PART OF THE THREE HUNDRED AND TWENTY-SEVENTH NIGHT, AND ENDING WITH PART OF THE THREE HUNDRED AND THIRTY-FOURTH.

THE STORY OF IBN-MANSOOR AND THE LADY BUDOOR AND JUBEYR THE SON OF 'OMEYR ESH-SHEYBÁNEE.

It is related that the Prince of the Faithful, Hároon Er-Rasheed, was restless one night, and sleep was difficult unto him: he ceased not to turn over from side to side, through the excess of his restlessness; and when this state wearied him, he summoned Mesroor, and said to him, O Mesroor, see for me some one who will divert me from this restlessness.[1] Mesroor said, O my lord, wilt thou enter the garden in the palace, and amuse thyself with the sight of the flowers it containeth, and look at the planets, and the beauty of their disposition, and the moon among them shining upon the water? He answered, O Mesroor, verily my soul inclineth not to any thing of that kind.—O my lord, rejoined Mesroor, there are in thy palace three hundred concubines, each of whom hath a separate apartment. Order, then, every one of them to retire into her apartment, and go thou about and amuse thyself by the sight of them while they know not.—The Khaleefeh replied, O Mesroor, the palace is mine, and the female slaves are my property; yet my soul inclineth not to any thing of that kind. Mesroor then said, O my lord, order the learned men and the sages and the poets to come before thee, and to enter into discussions, and recite verses to thee, and relate to thee tales and histories.—My soul, replied the Khaleefeh, inclineth not to any thing of that kind. Mesroor said, O my lord, order the pages and the boon-companions and the men of politeness to come before thee, and to entertain thee with strange witticisms. But the Khaleefeh replied, O Mesroor, my soul inclineth not to aught of that kind.—Then, said Mesroor, O my lord, strike off my head: perhaps that will put an end to thy restlessness, and dispel the uneasiness which thou sufferest. And Er-Rasheed laughed at his words, and said to him, O Mesroor, see who of the boon-companions is at the door. So Mesroor went forth, and returned saying, O my lord, he who is at the door is 'Alee the son of Manṣoor, the Wag, of Damascus. The Khaleefeh said, Bring him unto me. Mesroor therefore went and brought him; and when Ibn[2]-Manṣoor entered, he said, Peace be on thee, O Prince of the Faithful! And the Khaleefeh returned his salutation and said, O Ibn-Manṣoor, relate to us somewhat of thy stories.—O Prince of the Faithful, said he, shall I relate to thee a thing that I have actually witnessed, or a thing of which I have heard? The Prince of the Faithful answered, If thou have witnessed any thing extraordinary, relate it to us; for hearing a thing as reported by others is not like witnessing. So Ibn-Manṣoor said, O Prince of the Faithful, give up to me exclusively thy hearing and thy mind. Er-Rasheed replied, O Ibn-Manṣoor, see, I hear with mine ear, and look at thee with mine eye, and attend to thee with my mind. And Ibn-Manṣoor said,—

O Prince of the Faithful, know that I have an appointment every year from Moḥammad the son of Suleymán El-Háshimee, the Sulṭán of El-Baṣrah; and I went to him as I was wont, and when I came to him, I found him prepared to mount for the chase. I saluted him, and he saluted me, and said to me, O Ibn-Manṣoor, mount, and accompany us to the chase. But I replied, O my lord, I have not power to ride: seat me therefore in the mansion of entertainment, and give a charge respecting me to the chamberlains and lieutenants. And he did so; and then went to hunt. And they paid me the utmost honour, and entertained me in the best manner. And I said within myself, Allah! it is wonderful that for a long time I have been in the habit of coming from Baghdád to El-Baṣrah, and know not in this place aught but the way from the palace to the garden, and from the garden to the palace; and when shall I find such an opportunity to amuse myself with a sight of the quarters of El-Baṣrah as on this occasion? I will therefore arise immediately, and walk out alone to amuse myself, and let the food that I have eaten digest.

Accordingly I attired myself in the richest of my apparel, and walked through a part of El-Baṣrah. Now thou knowest, O Prince of the Faithful, that there are in it seventy streets, the length of each of which is seventy leagues by the measure of El-'Erák.[3] So I lost my way in its by-streets, and thirst overcame me; and while I was walking, O Prince of the Faithful, lo, a great door, with two rings of yellow brass, and with curtains of red brocade hung over it, and by the two sides of it were two maṣṭabahs, and above it was a trellis for grape-vines, which overshadowed that door. I stopped to divert myself with a sight of this mansion; and while I stood, I heard a voice of lamentation, proceeding from a sorrowful heart, warbling melodious sounds, and singing these verses:—

My body hath become the dwelling-place of diseases and afflictions,
On account of a fawn whose abode and home are distant.
O two zephyrs of the desert that have stirred up my anguish!
By Allah, your Lord, turn to my [heart's] abode,
And reproach him; perhaps reproach will change his conduct.

Five more stanzas like the above followed, and I said within myself, The person from whom these melodious sounds have proceeded, if comely, possesseth the united charms of comeliness and eloquence and sweetness of voice. I then approached the door, and began to raise the curtain by little and little; and, lo, I beheld a fair damsel, like the moon when it appeareth in its fourteenth night, with joined eye-brows, and languishing eyelids, and a bosom like two pomegranates; she had thin lips, like two pieces of carnelion,[4] a mouth like the seal of Suleymán,[5] and a set of teeth that would sport with the reason of

the poet and the prose-writer. Altogether she comprised all the charms of loveliness, and was a source of disturbance unto women and men. The beholder could not satisfy himself with gazing at her beauty; and she was as the poet hath said,—

When she approacheth, she killeth; and when she turneth her back, she maketh
all men to be enamoured of her.
She is like the sun, and like the full moon; but oppression and aversion are not in
her nature.
Paradise is opened when she exhibiteth herself, and the full moon is seen above her
neck-rings.

Now while I was looking at her through the interstice of the curtains, lo, she cast a glance, and beheld me standing at the door; whereupon she said to her slave-girl, See who is at the door. The slave-girl therefore arose and came to me, and said, O sheykh, hast thou no modesty; and do hoariness and disgraceful conduct exist together? I answered her, O my mistress, as to hoariness, we have experienced it; but as to disgraceful conduct, I do not think that I have been guilty of it. But her mistress said, And what conduct can be more disgraceful than thine intrusion upon a house that is not thine own, and thy looking at a ḥareem that is not thine? So I answered her, O my mistress, I have an excuse for doing so.—And what is thine excuse? she asked. I answered her, Verily I am a stranger, and thirsty; and thirst hath almost killed me. And upon this she said, We accept thine excuse. Then calling one of her female slaves, she said, O Luṭf,[6] give him a draught in the mug of gold. Whereupon she brought me a mug of red gold set with pearls and jewels, full of water perfumed with strong-scented musk, and covered with a napkin of green silk; and I began to drink, and prolonged my drinking, stealing glances at her in the mean while, until I had stood a length of time. I then returned the mug to the slave-girl, and remained standing. So she [the lady] said, O sheykh, go thy way. But I replied, O my mistress, I am troubled in mind.—Respecting what? said she. And I answered, Respecting the changes of fortune, and the vicissitudes of events. She replied, It becometh thee; for fortune giveth rise to wonders. But what (she added) hast thou witnessed of its wonders, that thou reflectest upon it?—I am reflecting, I answered, upon the owner of this house; for he was my sincere friend in his life-time. And she said to me, What was his name? I answered, Moḥammad the son of 'Alee the Jeweller; and he was possessed of great wealth.[7] But hath he, I asked, left children?—Yes, said she; he hath left a daughter, who is named Budoor,[8] and she hath inherited all his riches. So I said to her, It seemeth that thou art his daughter. She replied, Yes:—and laughed. Then she said, O sheykh, thou hast prolonged the discourse; therefore go thy way. I replied, I must go; but I see that thy charms are changed: acquaint me then with thy case: perhaps God may grant thee relief by means of me. And she said to me, O sheykh, if thou be of the number of those who are worthy of being intrusted with secrets, we will reveal to thee our secret. Inform me therefore who thou art, that I may know whether thou art a fit depositary for a secret, or not; for the poet hath said,—

None keepeth a secret but a faithful person: with the best of mankind it remaineth concealed.
I have kept my secret in a house with a lock, whose key is lost, and whose door is sealed.[9]

So I said to her, O my mistress, if thou desirest to know who I am, I

am 'Alee the son of Manṣoor, the Wag, of Damascus, the boon-companion of the Prince of the Faithful, Hároon Er-Rasheed.

And when she heard my name, she descended from her chair, and saluted me, and said to me, Thou art welcome, O Ibn-Manṣoor. Now I will acquaint thee with my state, and intrust thee with my secret. I am a separated lover.—O my mistress, said I, thou art comely, and lovest none but whomsoever is comely. Who then is he that thou lovest?—She answered, I love Jubeyr the son of 'Omeyr Esh-Sheybánee, the Emeer of the Benee-Sheybán.[10] And she described to me a young man than whom there was none more handsome in El-Baṣrah. I said to her, O my mistress, hath any interview or correspondence taken place between you?—Yes, she answered; but we have loved with the tongue; not with the heart and soul; since he hath not fulfilled a promise, nor performed a covenant. So I said to her, O my mistress, and what hath been the cause of the separation that hath occurred between you? She answered, The cause was this: I was sitting one day, and this my slave-girl was combing my hair; and when she had finished combing it, she plaited my tresses, and my beauty and loveliness charmed her; so she bent over me, and kissed my cheek; and just at that time he came in suddenly, and, seeing the slave-girl kiss my cheek, he drew back instantly in anger, determining upon a lasting separation, and recited these two verses:—

If another have a share in the object of my love, I abandon my beloved, and live alone.
My beloved is worthless if she desire aught of which her lover doth not approve.

And from the time of his withdrawing in aversion from me to the present day, neither letter nor reply hath come to us from him, O Ibn-Manṣoor.—And what, said I, dost thou desire? She answered, I desire to send to him a letter by thee; and if thou bring me his answer, thou shalt receive from me five hundred pieces of gold; and if thou bring me not his answer, thou shalt receive, as a compensation for thy walk, one hundred pieces of gold. So I replied, Do what seemeth fit unto thee. And she said, I hear and obey. Then she called one of her female slaves, and said, Bring to me an inkhorn, and a piece of paper. And she brought them to her; and she wrote these verses:—

My beloved, wherefore this estrangement and hatred? And when shall forgiveness and indulgence be granted?
Why dost thou abandon me in aversion? Thy face is not the face that I was wont to know.
Yes: the slanderers have falsified my words, and thou hast leaned to their report; so they have increased in their excesses.
If thou hast believed their tale, God forbid thou shouldst continue to do so; for thou knowest better.
By thy life inform me what is it thou hast heard; for thou knowest what hath been said, and wilt act justly.
If it be true that I have uttered the words, words admit of interpretation, and they admit of change.
Suppose that the words were revealed by God: people have changed and corrupted the Pentateuch.[11]
What falsehoods have been told of persons before us! Even Yoosuf was blamed in the presence of Yaạkoob!
For myself and the slanderer and thee together there shall be an awful day of judgment.

She then sealed the letter, and handed it to me; and I took it and went to the house of Jubeyr the son of 'Omeyr Esh-Sheybánee. I found that he was hunting; so I seated myself to wait for him; and while I sat, lo, he approached, returning from the chase; and when I beheld him, O Prince of the Faithful, upon his horse, my reason was confounded by his beauty and loveliness. Looking aside, he beheld me sitting at the door of his house; and as soon as he saw me, he alighted from his horse, and came to me and embraced and saluted me; and it seemed to me as though I held in my embrace the world and all that it containeth. Then he conducted me into his house, and seated me upon his couch, and gave orders to bring the table; whereupon they brought forward a table of khoolenj[12] of Khurásán, the feet of which were of gold; and upon it were all kinds of viands, varieties of meats, fried and roasted, and such like; and when I seated myself at the table, I looked at it, and found inscribed upon it these verses:—

Stay by the cranes that are lodged in the porringers, and alight among the tribe of fried meats and sikbájes;
And mourn over the daughters of the ḳaṭà—I have done so continually—and over the browned meat amid the chickens.[13]

Then Jubeyr the son of 'Omeyr said, Stretch forth thy hand to our food, and comfort our heart by eating of our provision. But I replied, By Allah I will not eat of thy food a single mouthful until thou perform my want. He said, And what is thy want? And I handed forth to him a letter; and when he had read it and understood its contents, he tore it in pieces and threw it upon the floor, saying to me, O Ibn-Manṣoor, whatsoever want thou hast, we will perform it, except this thing which concerneth the writer of this letter; for to her letter I have no reply to give. So I rose from his side in anger; but he laid hold upon my skirts, and said to me, O Ibn-Manṣoor, I will tell thee what she said to thee, though I was not present with you two. I asked him, What was it that she said to me? And he replied, Did not the writer of this letter say to thee, If thou bring me his answer, thou shalt receive from me five hundred pieces of gold; and if thou bring me not his answer, thou shalt receive from me, as a compensation for thy walk, one hundred pieces of gold?—I answered, Yes. And he said, Sit with me this day, and eat and drink, and enjoy thyself and be merry, and receive five hundred pieces of gold.

So I sat with him, and ate and drank, and enjoyed myself and was merry, and entertained him in the night by conversation; and afterwards I said, O my master, there is no music in thy house. He replied, Verily for a long time we have drunk without music. Then calling one of his female slaves, he said, O Shejeret-ed-Durr!—Whereupon a slave-girl answered him from her private chamber, bringing a lute of Indian manufacture enclosed in a bag of silk; and she came, and seated herself, and, having placed the lute in her lap, played upon it one and twenty airs; after which she returned to the first air, and, with exciting modulations, sang these verses:—

Whoso hath not tasted love's sweetness and its bitterness doth not distinguish between the company and the absence of the beloved:
And he who hath declined from love's right road doth not distinguish between the smoothness and the ruggedness of his path.
I ceased not to oppose the votaries of love until I experienced both its sweetness and its bitterness;

And I have drunk up the cup of its bitterness until I have abased myself both to the slave and the free.
How many a night hath the beloved caroused with me, and I have sipped the sweet draught that issued from her lips!
How short was each night when we were together! The nightfall and daybreak were simultaneous!
Fortune made a vow that she would disunite us; and now hath Fortune accomplished her vow.
Fate decreed, and the sentence cannot be reversed. Who is he that can oppose his Lord's command?

And when the slave-girl had finished her song, her master uttered a great cry, and fell down in a fit; upon which the slave-girl said, May God not punish thee, O sheykh; for of a long time we have drunk without music, fearing for our master, lest he should experience the like of this fit. But go to yon private chamber, and sleep there.—So I went to the private chamber to which she directed me, and slept there until the morning; when, lo, a page came to me, bringing a purse in which were five hundred pieces of gold; and he said, This is what my master promised thee; but return thou not to the damsel who sent thee, and let it be as though thou hadst not heard of this affair, and as though we had not heard. So I replied, I hear and obey.

I then took the purse, and went my way; but I said within myself, Verily the damsel hath been expecting me since yesterday. By Allah I must return to her, and acquaint her with that which hath taken place between me and him; for, if I return not to her, probably she will revile me, and will revile every one who cometh forth from my country.[14]—Accordingly, I went to her, and found her standing behind the door; and when she beheld me, she said, O Ibn-Manṣoor,

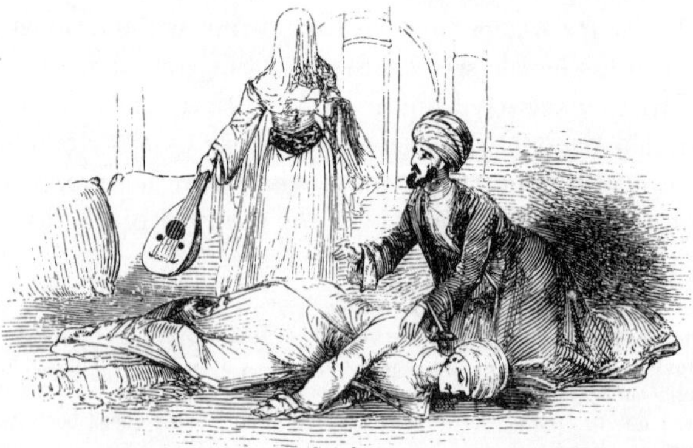

thou hast not accomplished for me any thing.—Who, said I, informed thee of this? She answered, O Ibn-Manṣoor, I have a further intuition; that, when thou handedst him the paper, he tore it in pieces and threw it down, and said to thee, O Ibn-Manṣoor, whatsoever want thou hast, we will perform it for thee, except the affair of her who wrote this letter; for to her I have no reply to give. Whereupon thou rosest from his side in anger; but he laid hold upon thy skirts, and said to thee, O Ibn-Manṣoor, sit with me this day; for thou art my guest, and eat and drink, and enjoy thyself and be merry, and receive five hundred pieces of gold. So thou sattest with him, and atest and drankest, and enjoyedst thyself and wast merry, and entertainedst him by night with conversation; and the slave-girl sang such an air and such verses; upon which he fell down in a fit.—So, O Prince of the Faithful, I said to her, Wast thou with us? She replied, O Ibn-Manṣoor, hast thou not heard the saying of the poet?—

The hearts of lovers have eyes, which see what spectators see not.

But, O Ibn-Manṣoor, she added, night and day succeed not one another during the course of an event without changing it.—Then she raised her eyes towards heaven, and said, O Object of my worship, and my Master, and my Lord, as Thou hast afflicted me by the love of Jubeyr the son of 'Omeyr, so do Thou afflict him by the love of me, and transfer the affection from my heart to his!—After this, she gave me a hundred pieces of gold, as a compensation for my walk, and I took it, and repaired to the Sulṭán of El-Baṣrah, whom I found returned from the chase; and I received from him my appointment, and returned to Baghdád.

And when the next year arrived, I went to the city of El-Baṣrah, to demand my appointment as usual, and the Sulṭán paid it to me; and when I was about to return to Baghdád, I reflected in my mind upon the case of the damsel Budoor, and said, By Allah I must repair to her, and see what hath taken place between her and her beloved. So I went to her house; and I found the ground before her door swept and sprinkled, and servants and dependants and pages there; whereupon I said, Probably anxiety hath overwhelmed the damsel's heart, and she hath died, and some one of the emeers hath taken up his abode in her house. I therefore left her house, and repaired to that of Jubeyr the son of 'Omeyr Esh-Sheybánee; and I found its maṣṭabahs demolished, and found not pages at its door as usual: so I

said within myself, Probably he hath died. Then I stood before the door of his house, and, pouring forth tears, bewailed its condition in these verses:—

O my lord, who hast departed, and whom my heart followeth, return, and so my festive days shall be renewed to me!
I pause at your house, bewailing your abode, with pouring tears, and with convulsed eyelids.
I ask the house with its mourning remains, Where is the dispenser of beneficence and favours?
Go thy way [it answereth]; for the friends have departed from the dwelling, and beneath the dust are buried.
May God not deprive us of the view of their merits in all their extent, and be their virtues never hidden!

And while I was bewailing the people of the house in these verses, O Prince of the Faithful, lo, a black slave came forth to me from the house, and said, O sheykh, be silent! May thy mother be bereft of thee! Wherefore do I behold thee bewailing this house in these verses?—So I answered him, I used to know it as the abode of one of my sincere friends. He said, And what was his name? I answered, Jubeyr the son of 'Omeyr Esh-Sheybánee. And he said, And what hath happened unto him? Praise be to God, he is still blest with his riches and prosperity and property; but God hath afflicted him with the love of a damsel named the lady Budoor, and he is overwhelmed by his love of her, and by the violence of his transport and torment, so that he is like a great rock overthrown: for when he is hungry, he saith not to his servants, Give me food;—and when he is thirsty, he saith not, Give me drink.—And I said, Ask permission for me to go in to him.—O my master, he asked, wouldst thou go in to him who understandeth, or to him who understandeth not? I answered, I must go in to him whatever be the case. So he entered the house and asked permission, and then returned giving it to me.

I therefore went in to him, and I found him like a mass of stone thrown down, understanding neither sign nor open speech. I spoke to him; but he answered me not; and one of his attendants said to me, O my master, if thou knowest any poetry, recite it to him, and raise thy voice in doing so; for thereupon he will be aroused. Accordingly, I recited these two verses:—

Hast thou relinquished the love of Budoor, or art thou stubborn? And dost thou pass the night wakeful, or do thine eyelids sleep?
If thy tears continue to flow in torrents, then know that thou wilt pass eternity in Paradise.[15]

And when he heard these verses, he opened his eye, and said to me, Welcome, O Ibn-Manṣoor. My emaciation hath become excessive.—And I asked him, saying, O my master, is there any thing that thou wouldst have me do for thee? He answered, Yes: I desire to write a letter to her, and to send it to her by thee; and if thou bring me her answer, thou shalt receive from me a thousand pieces of gold; and if thou bring me not her answer, thou shalt receive from me, as a compensation for thy walk, two hundred pieces of gold. So I replied, Do what seemeth fit to thee. And he called one of his female slaves, and said, Bring me an inkhorn and a paper. She therefore brought him what he demanded; and he wrote these verses:—

I conjure you by Allah, O my mistress, act gently towards me; for love hath deprived me of my reason!
My passion for you hath enslaved me, and clad me with the garment of sickness, and rendered me abject.

I was wont, before this, to think lightly of love, and regard it, O my mistress, as an easy matter;
But when it had shewn me the waves of its sea, I submitted to God's judgment, and excused the afflicted.
If you will, have mercy, and grant me a meeting; and if you will kill me, still forget not to shew favour.[16]

He then sealed the letter, and handed it to me, and I took it and repaired with it to the house of Budoor. I began to raise the curtain by little and little as before; and, lo, ten slave-girls, high-bosomed virgins, resembling moons; and the lady Budoor was sitting in the midst of them, like the full moon in the midst of the stars, or like the sun unobscured by clouds; and she was free from grief and pain. And while I was looking at her, and wondering at her being in this state, she cast a glance towards me, and saw me standing at the door; whereupon she said to me, A friendly and free and an ample welcome to thee, O Ibn-Manṣoor! Enter.—So I entered, and, having saluted her, handed to her the paper; and when she had read it, and understood its contents, she laughed, and said to me, O Ibn-Manṣoor, the poet lied not when he said,—

I will brook my love for thee resolutely till a messenger from thee come unto me.

O Ibn-Manṣoor, she added, I will now write for thee an answer, that he may give thee what he hath promised thee. And I replied, May God compensate thee well! Then she called one of her female slaves, and said, Bring me an inkhorn and a paper. And when she had brought her what she demanded, she wrote to him some harsh verses. I therefore said to her, By Allah, O my mistress, there remaineth not unto him before his death any more than the period that will expire on his reading this paper. I then tore it, and said to her, Write to him something different from these verses. And she replied, I hear and obey:—but she wrote to him some verses more severe than the former ones. So I said to her, By Allah, O my mistress, he will not read these verses without his soul's quitting his body. She replied, O Ibn-Manṣoor, my transport hath attained to such a pitch that I have said what I have said. I rejoined, Hadst thou said more than that, it had been just in thee; but a disposition to pardon is one of the qualities of the generous. And when she heard my words, her eyes filled with tears, and she wrote to him a note—by Allah, O Prince of the Faithful, there is not in thine assembly any one who can write the like of it. She wrote in it these verses:—

How long shall this coyness and aversion continue? Thou hast satisfied the malice which the enviers bore me.
Perhaps I did wrong, and was not aware of it: then inform me what thou hast been told concerning me.
I desire to welcome thee, O my beloved, as I welcome sleep to my eye and my eyelid:
And since *thou* hast drunk the pure cup of love, if thou see *me* intoxicated, do not blame me.

And when she had finished writing the letter, and sealed it, she handed it to me; and I said to her, O my mistress, verily this note will cure the sick, and satisfy the thirsty.

I took the letter, and went forth; and she called me after I had gone forth from her, and said to me, O Ibn-Manṣoor, say to him, She will be this night thy guest. So I rejoiced at this exceedingly. I repaired with the letter to Jubeyr the son of 'Omeyr; and when I went in to him, I found him with his eye fixed upon the door, waiting for the answer; and as soon as I handed to him the paper, he opened it and read it, and understood its meaning, and, uttering a great cry, fell down in a fit. And when he recovered, he said, O Ibn-Manṣoor, did she write this note with her hand, and did she touch it with her fingers?—O my master, said I, and do people write with their feet? —And by Allah, O Prince of the Faithful, my words to him were not ended when we heard the clinking of her anklets in the passage, as she entered. On beholding her, he rose upon his feet, as though he no longer felt any pain, and embraced her as the letter Lám embraces Alif,[17] and the disease of him who cannot escape from his ailment quitted him.[18] Then he seated himself; but she sat not: so I said to her, O my mistress, wherefore hast thou not sat down? She answered, O Ibn-Manṣoor, I will not sit down save on the condition that hath been made between us.—And what, I asked, is that condition between you two?—No one, she answered, knoweth the secrets of lovers. She then put her mouth to his ear, and said something privately to him; to which he replied, I hear and obey. And he arose, and whispered to one of his slaves; whereupon the slave absented himself for a while, after which he came back, accompanied by a Ḳáḍee and two witnesses. And Jubeyr arose, and, having brought a purse containing a hundred thousand pieces of gold, said, O Ḳáḍee, perform the ceremony of my contract of marriage to this damsel for this sum as a dowry. The Ḳáḍee therefore said to her, Say, I consent to that.—And she said so. So they performed the ceremony of the contract; and after that, the damsel opened the purse, filled her hand with part of its contents, and gave to the Ḳáḍee and the witnesses. Then she handed to him [Jubeyr] what remained in the purse, and the Ḳáḍee and witnesses departed.

I sat with them in joy and gladness until the greater part of the night had passed, when I said within myself, They are two lovers, and during a long period they have been separated; so I will arise immediately, that I may sleep in a place remote from them, and leave them together alone. Accordingly I arose; but the damsel laid hold upon my skirts, and said to me, What hath thy mind suggested to thee? I answered, Such and such things. And she replied, Sit, and when we desire thy departure, we will dismiss thee. I therefore remained sitting with them until the approach of the dawn, when she said, O Ibn-Manṣoor, go to yon private chamber; for we have furnished it for thee, and it is thy sleeping-place. And I arose, and slept in it until the morning; and when I got up, there came to me a page with a basin and ewer, and I performed the ablution, and recited the morning-prayers; after which I sat. And while I was sitting, lo, Jubeyr and his beloved came forth from a bath that was in the house, wringing their locks; and I bade them good morning, congratulating them on their safety and their reunion, and said to Jubeyr, What beginneth with stipulation endeth with content. He replied, Thou hast spoken truth, and thou art entitled to liberal treatment. Then calling his treasurer, he said to him, Bring to me three thousand pieces of gold. So he brought him a purse containing that sum, and Jubeyr said to me, Do us the favour to accept this. But I replied, I will not accept it until thou inform me what was the cause of the transition of the love from her to thee, after that excessive repulsion. And he said, I hear and obey. Know that we have a festival called the Festival of the New-year's-days, when the people go forth and embark in boats, and amuse themselves upon the river.[19] And I went forth to amuse myself with my companions, and saw a boat wherein were ten slave-girls like moons, and this lady Budoor was in the midst of them, having her lute with her; and she played upon it eleven airs; after which she returned to the first air, and sang these verses:—

Fire is cooler than the fires of my bosom; and rock is softer than the heart of my lord.
Verily I wonder at his composition, with a heart of rock in a body soft as water.

And I said to her, Repeat the two verses and the air. But she would not. So I ordered the boatmen to pelt her; and they pelted her with oranges until we feared that the boat in which she was would sink. Then she went her way: and this was the cause of the transition of the love from her heart to mine.—I therefore, says Ibn-Manṣoor, congratulated them on their reunion, and, taking the purse with its contents, repaired to Baghdád.

And the bosom of the Khaleefeh was dilated, and the restlessness, and the contraction of the heart that he suffered, ceased to trouble him.[20]

NOTES TO CHAPTER SIXTEENTH.

NOTE 1.—*Invention of the Air-bed.* HÁROON ER-RASHEED seems to have been, like many other Easterns, much troubled with sleeplessness. The usual means employed to relieve or divert a person thus suffering are story-telling, music, and a gentle kneading or pressing of the flesh; and for the same purpose, the air-bed was invented. El-Maḳreezee relates,[1] in his account of the constructions of Khumáraweyh (the Governor of Egypt),[2] the son of Aḥmad, the son of Ṭooloon, that upon his complaining of excessive sleeplessness, his physician advised him to make a pool of quicksilver. This pool he made in front of his palace, which was in the place now called the Rumeyleh:[3] it was fifty cubits in length and the same in breadth; and its construction, and the filling it with quicksilver, cost a great sum of money. At the corners of the pool were pegs of pure silver, to which were attached, by rings of silver, strong bands of silk; and a bed of skins, inflated with air, being thrown upon the pool and secured in the midst of it by the bands of silk, remained in a continual state of agreeable vacillation while the Prince lay upon it.

NOTE 2. "Ibn" signifies "son;" and "Ibn-Manṣoor," "*the* Son of Manṣoor."

NOTE 3. This is, of course, a monstrous exaggeration.

NOTE 4. So in the edition of Breslau. In the Cairo edition, "like two uḳ-ḥo-wánehs." This name is generally given to the chamomile.

NOTE 5. See Note 43 to Chapter x.

NOTE 6. "Luṭf" signifies "elegance," "delicacy," &c.

NOTE 7. We may suppose that he had learnt this of some passenger.

NOTE 8. See Note 34 to Chapter x.

NOTE 9. Nearly the same couplet has occurred before. See Note 19 to Chapter iii.

NOTE 10. "Benee-Sheybán" is the name of two tribes of Arabs.

---

1 In his "Khiṭaṭ."

2 In the latter part of the ninth century of our era. [Aḥmad the son of Ṭooloon was the founder of the virtually-independent dynasty of the Benee-Ṭooloon, which governed Egypt from the year of the Flight (*cir.*) 255 to 292. Khumáraweyh, the son and successor of Aḥmad, ruled from the year 270 to 282.—ED]

3 This is a large vacant space in front of the citadel of Cairo.

NOTE 11. See Note 112 to Chapter xi.

NOTE 12. "Khoolenj," also written "khalenj," is explained in dictionaries as the name of a tree from which wooden bowls are made.

NOTE 13. The word which I render "cranes" ("gharáneeḳ") may perhaps here signify some other kind of long-necked aquatic birds. That which I render "porringers" is "sekáreej," plural of "sukroojeh," also written "sukrujeh," and "sukurjeh," of Persian origin: the meaning which I have given to it (and which I find in a MS. dictionary of my own) appears to have been unknown to my sheykh. On the "sikbáj" see Note 98 to Chapter v.; but, I may add, there are other kinds of sikbáj than that which is there mentioned: vinegar, I believe, enters into the composition of all. Instead of "mourn over," we may read "call;" but I prefer the former sense, as it implies the celebration of the excellences of that which is mourned over. The "ḳaṭà" is a kind of grouse, and has been before mentioned. The "browned meat" (in the original, "moḥammar,") is meat cut into small pieces, and fried for a long time, till it becomes of a reddish-brown colour.—Four other verses follow in the original; but I have omitted them in my text, as I consider them inappropriate, and of little merit. I however insert them here:—

O the sighing of my heart for two dishes[4] of fish that were placed by a cake of new bread on the stairs![5]
God be praised for the supper! How excellent it was, with the pulse steeped in the vinegar of the jars,[6]
And the rice dressed with buffalo's milk, in which hands were plunged even to the armlets!
O my soul, be patient; for God is bountiful: if thy means be narrow, He will give thee relief.

NOTE 14. "Such is the custom of men: when any one acteth ill towards them, they revile both him and every one who cometh from his country."[7]

NOTE 15. He who dieth of love will enjoy Paradise. See Note 24 to Chapter xv.

NOTE 16. That is, forget not to beg mercy for me.

NOTE 17. Lám and Alif, when not united with any other letter, generally have the form of two nearly upright strokes, crossing each other obliquely, and connected at the feet.

NOTE 18. This phrase (in the original, "zálet 'anhu 'illetu-lledhee lá yenṣarif"), which I have freely rendered, bears another meaning, and conveys an allusion to a rule of grammar, with which the Arabic scholar is acquainted, and of which others will not require an explanation.

NOTE 19.—*On the Festival of the New-year's-days.* The Festival of the New-year's-days, commencing at the Vernal Equinox, is generally said to have been of Persian origin; but I think it not improbable that it originated from the Jewish Passover. It was the principal festival among the ancient Persians, and continued six days. "On the first, [called by them 'Now-róz,' and by the Arabs 'Nórooz,'] the King gave his chief attention to promote the happiness of the body of the people; on the second, he entertained the doctors and astrologers; on the third, the priests, and counsellors of state; on the fourth, the princes of the blood, and grandees; on the fifth, the royal children; and on the sixth, which was considered as the King's particular day, his sub-

---

[4] Literally "two colours" ("lóneyn"). Several different dishes are commonly called so many "lóns," or "colours."

[5] The words which I render "on the stairs" ("fi-l-ma'áreeji") may perhaps admit of some better interpretation.

[6] The word rendered "jars" is "dekákeej," plural of "dekkoojeh," or perhaps "dukkoojeh" (for I am doubtful as to the first vowel). It is applied to a small kind of jar, and I find it in the dictionary above mentioned, and in Boethor's and Caussin de Perceval's "Dictionnaire Français-Arabe."

[7] Marginal note by my sheykh.

jects made him free gifts agreeable to their rank. On the eve of the Now-róz, a young man of an elegant figure, personating the new year, was stationed at the door of the royal bedchamber, which he entered without ceremony the moment the sun appeared above the horizon. The King, immediately addressing him, said, 'What art thou? Whence dost thou come? Whither dost thou go? What is thy name? Wherefore dost thou approach? And what dost thou bring?' To which he answered, 'I am the fortunate and the blessed: I am sent hither by God, and bring with me the new year.' Then sitting down, another appeared with a large silver dish, in which were wheat, barley, pease, vetches, sesame, and rice (seven ears and nine grains of each), with a lump of sugar, and two new-coined pieces of gold, which, as an offering, were placed before the King. Then entered the prime-minister, the general of the forces, the lord high treasurer, and the superintendent of war; after whom followed the nobles and people, according to their dignity and respective classes. A large loaf, made of the above-mentioned grains, being then presented to the King, after eating part of it he offered some to those who were around him, saying, 'This is the new day, of the new month, of the new year, of the new time; when all things consistent with time must be renewed.' Then investing his nobles with rich robes, he blessed and distributed amongst them the presents which had been brought. The origin of this solemnity is carried up to one of their ancient Kings, called Jemshéd, who then made his first public entry into Istakhr (Persepolis), which he had just finished; and, amongst other regulations, ordered that the Persian era should commence from that day."[8]

A custom similar to that described in the passage to which this note refers prevails at the present day in Egypt. It is termed "Shemm en-Neseem" (or "the Smelling of the Zephyr"), and is observed on the first day of the Khamáseen, which is a period of forty-nine days (when hot southerly winds are of frequent occurrence), commencing on the day immediately following the Coptic festival of Easter Sunday, and terminating on the Day of Pentecost, or Whit Sunday. Early in the morning of the first day of this period, many persons, especially women, break an onion, and smell it; and in the course of the forenoon, many of the citizens of Cairo ride or walk a little way into the country, or go in boats, generally northwards, to take the air, or, as they term it, *smell* the air, which, on that day, they believe to have a wonderfully-beneficial effect. The greater number dine in the country, or on the river.—The 'ulamà (or learned), however, have their Shemm en-Neseem at a fixed period of the solar year; the first three days of the spring-quarter, corresponding with the Persian Now-róz.

Having mentioned the period of the Khamáseen, I may add that I believe it has been called by all European writers who have mentioned it, except myself, "el-Khamseen," or by the same term differently expressed, signifying "the Fifty;" i. e. "the Fifty Days;" but it is always termed by the Arabs "el-Khamáseen," which signifies "the Fifties," being a vulgar *plural* of "Khamseen." In like manner, the Arabs call the corresponding period of the Jewish calendar by a term exactly agreeing with "el-Khamáseen;" namely "el-Khamseenát;" only its *last day* being termed "el-Khamseen;" as may be seen in an extract from El-Maḳreezee, given by De Sacy.[9] This eminent orientalist, however, appears to have had no authority but that of Europeans for the name of the above-mentioned period of the Coptic calendar; for he has followed the travellers, and written it "khamsin."

NOTE 20. This story is followed by sixteen anecdotes, ending with part of the three hundred and fifty-seventh night; eleven of which I translate, and here insert.

---

[8] Richardson's Persian, Arabic, and English Dictionary, Johnson's edition, *voce* "máh."

[9] See his Chrestomathie Arabe, 2nd ed., vol. i., page 98 of the Arabic text. See also pp. 292 and 320 of his translation and notes.

Instances of the Vicissitudes of Fortune.

It is related that a man was burdened with numerous debts, and his circumstances became strait unto him; so he left his people and his family, and went forth wandering in perplexity and at random. He ceased not to proceed until he approached, after a length of time, a city with lofty walls, and great buildings, and he entered it in a state of abasement and despondency. His hunger had become violent, and the journey had wearied him; and as he walked through one of its great thoroughfare-streets, he saw a company of the great passing along; whereupon he proceeded with them until they entered an abode resembling the abode of Kings, and he entered with them, and they went in until they came to a man sitting at the upper end of the mansion. He was of magnificent appearance, and great dignity, and surrounded by pages and servants, as though he were of the sons of the wezeers; and when he saw the party, he rose to them, and treated them with respectful hospitality. So trouble of mind overcame the man above mentioned at witnessing this thing, and he was confounded at that which he beheld of the beauty of the building, and the servants and dependants. He therefore drew back, in perplexity and distress, fearing for himself, until he seated himself in a place alone, remote from the people, that no one might see him. And while he was sitting, lo, there approached a man with whom were four dogs, of the dogs of the chase, decked with varieties of silk and brocade, and having, upon their necks, collars of gold with chains of silver; and he chained each of them in a separate place. Then he went away, and returned bringing to each dog a dish of gold full of rich food, and he put before each of them his separate dish, and departed and left them. This man therefore began to look at the food, on account of the violence of his hunger, and desired to advance to one of the dogs and to eat with him; but his fear of them prevented him. Presently, however, one of the dogs looked at him, and God (whose name be exalted!) inspired him with a knowledge of his case: so he drew back from the dish, and made a sign to the man, who thereupon approached, and ate until he was satisfied, when he would have departed; but the dog made a sign to him that he should take the dish, with the food remaining in it, for himself, and pushed it towards him with his fore-paw. He therefore took it, and went forth from the house, and proceeded without any one following him.

He then journeyed to another city, where he sold the dish, and, having purchased merchandise with its price, returned with it to his own town. There he sold what he had brought, and discharged the debts that he owed, and his wealth increased so that he became in a state of abundant affluence and perfect prosperity; and he ceased not to reside in his town for a length of time; after which, he said within himself, I must journey to the city of the owner of the dish, and take for him a handsome and suitable present, and pay him the price of the dish which one of his dogs bestowed upon me. Then he took a present befitting that person, and took with him the price of the dish, and set forth on his journey.

He ceased not in his journey days and nights until he arrived at that city, and he entered it, desiring to meet with the man; and he walked along its great thoroughfare-streets until he approached his abode. But he saw nothing of it save mouldering ruins, and a raven uttering its lamentable cry, and dwelling-places rendered desolate, and circumstances changed, and a state of things so altered as not to be recognised; whereupon his heart and soul were agitated, and he recited the words of the poet:—

> The recesses are devoid of their hidden treasures, as hearts are devoid of sciences and piety;
> And the valley is changed altogether, and its gazelles are not those antelopes, nor is its sand-heap that sand-heap.

And the saying of another:—

> The phantom of Soạdà[10] came by night to rouse me, towards morning, while my companions were sleeping in the desert:
> But when we awoke to behold the nightly phantom, I saw the air vacant, and the place of visitation distant.

And when that man beheld those mouldering ruins, and saw what the hands of fortune had openly done unto them, and found of the substance nothing but traces, knowledge rendered it needless for him to ask information. He then looked aside, and saw a miserable man, in a state that made the skin to quake at it, and rock to be moved with sympathy for it; and he said, O thou![11] what have fortune and time done with the master of this place, and where are his shining full moons and brilliant stars,[12] and what hath been the cause of the event that hath happened unto his structures, that there remaineth of them naught save the walls? He answered, He is this miserable wretch whom thou seest, sighing on account of that which hath come upon him. But knowest thou not (he added) that in the saying of the Apostle is a lesson to him who would follow it, and an admonition to him who would be directed aright,—his saying (God bless and save him!), Verily it is the way of God (whose name be exalted!) not to

---

10 "Soạdà" is a female proper name, and often used as a fictitious name, applied to a beautiful woman.

11 The expression thus rendered is generally used as one of slight contempt.

12 That is, "Where are his beautiful damsels, like full moons and stars?"

elevate any thing of this world without afterwards bringing it down? If thou inquire respecting the cause of this event, there is nothing in the vicissitudes of fortune wonderful. I was the master of this place, and its founder and proprietor and builder, and the possessor of its shining full moons and magnificent appurtenances and splendid rarities and beautiful slave-girls: fortune however hath turned from me, and taken away the servants and the wealth, and reduced me to this present condition, and brought upon me events that it before kept concealed. But there must be a cause for this thine inquiry. Acquaint me then with it, and cease to wonder.—So the man acquainted him with the whole affair, being the while in grief and distress, and said to him, I have brought thee a present such as souls desire, and the price of thy dish of gold that I took; for it was the cause of enriching me after my poverty, and of the replenishment of my abode after it was desolate, and of the dissipation of the anxiety and straitness that I suffered. But the other man shook his head, and wept and sighed and lamented, and said, O thou! I imagine thou art a madman: for this conduct proceedeth not from a man of sense. How should one of our dogs make thee a present of a dish of gold, and I take it back? My taking back that which my dog hath presented would be wonderful; and were I in the severest anxiety and disease, by Allah there should not find acceptance with me, from thee, any thing of the value of a nail-paring. So go to the place whence thou camest, in health and safety.—The man therefore kissed his feet, and went forth on his return, praising him; and on parting with him, and taking leave of him, recited this verse:—

The men and the dogs are gone together; and on the men and the dogs be peace!

—And God is all-knowing.[13]

---

[13] In Trébutien's translation, this anecdote is briefly related. The owner of the dogs is there described as complaining of the injustice of fortune, and the other man is said to have replied, You are wrong in accusing destiny of injustice: if you are ignorant of the cause of your ruin, I will acquaint you with it. You have fed the dogs in dishes of gold, and left the poor to die of hunger.

Ḥosám-ed-Deen *the* Wálee, *and a Sharper.*

There was, in the fortified coast-town of Alexandria, a Wálee named Ḥosám-ed-Deen;[14] and as he was sitting in his seat of office one night, there came to him a trooper, who said to him, Know, O our lord the Wálee, that I entered this city in the present night, and took up my lodging in such a Khán, and slept there until a third of the night had passed; and when I awoke, I found my pair of saddle-bags cut open, and there had been stolen from it a purse containing a thousand pieces of gold. And his words were not ended when the Wálee sent, and caused the Muḳaddams[15] to come before him, and ordered them to bring all who were in the Khán, commanding them also to imprison those persons till the morning. So when the morning came, he gave orders to bring the instruments of punishment.[16] He then caused those men to be brought before him in the presence of the trooper, the owner of the money, and was about to punish them.

But, lo, a man approached, forcing his way among the people until he stood before the Wálee and the trooper; and he said, O Emeer, release all these people; for they are unjustly treated: I am the person who took the property of this trooper, and here is the purse that I took from his saddle-bags. Then he produced it from his sleeve, and placed it before the Wálee and the trooper. So the Wálee said to the trooper, Receive thy property and take possession of it, and thou hast nothing further to demand of the people. And those people, and all who were present, began to praise that man, and to pray for him. But the man said, O Emeer, there was no cleverness in my presenting myself before thee, and bringing this purse: rather there would be cleverness in taking this purse a second time from this trooper.—And how, said the Wálee, didst thou do, O sharper, when thou tookest it?

O Emeer, he answered, I was standing in Cairo in the market of the money-changers, and saw this trooper when he took this gold in change and put it into the purse; and I followed him from by-street to by-street without finding any way of taking the property from him. Then he set forth on his journey, and I followed him from town to town, trying stratagems against him on the way; but could not take it from him. And when he entered this city, I followed him until he entered this Khán; whereupon I took my lodging next to him, and watched him until he slept and I heard his snoring; when I walked gently towards him, cut open the saddle-bags with this knife, and took the purse thus:—So saying, he stretched forth his hand, and took the purse from before the Wálee and the trooper, both of whom, with the rest of the people, drew back, looking at him, and believing that he would only shew them how he took the purse from the saddle-bags: but, lo, he

---

14 "Ḥosám-ed-Deen" signifies "the Sharp Sword of the Religion."

15 His chief officers.

16 Whips or sticks.

ran, and threw himself into a pool of water.[17] So the Wálee cried out to his dependants and said, Overtake him, and descend after him. They however had not pulled off their clothes and descended the steps before the sharper had gone his way; and they searched for him; but found him not; for the by-streets of Alexandria all communicate one with another. The men therefore returned without catching the sharper; and the Wálee said to the trooper, Thou hast no claim upon the people; for thou hast known thine offender, and taken possession of thy property, and not guarded it. And the trooper arose, his money was lost, and the people were saved from his hands and from those of the Wálee, entirely through the favour of God, whose name be exalted!

The Three Wálees.

El-Melik en-Náṣir[18] summoned one day the three Wálees, the Wálee of El-Ḳáhireh,[19] the Wálee of Booláḳ,[20] and the Wálee of Miṣr el-Ḳadeemeh,[21] and said, I desire that each of you acquaint me with the most wonderful thing that hath happened to him during the period of his holding the office of Wálee. And they replied, We hear and obey.

Accordingly, the Wálee of El-Ḳáhireh said, Know, O our lord the Sulṭán, that the most wonderful thing that hath happened to me during the period of my holding the office of Wálee was as follows:—There were, in this city, two legal witnesses,[22] who gave testimony respecting blood and wounds; but they were addicted to the love of [disreputable] women, and the drinking of wine, and iniquity; and I could succeed in no stratagem to revenge myself upon them. So being unable to do this, I charged the vintners, and the sellers of dried fruits, and those of fresh fruits, and the dealers in candles, and the keepers of houses prepared for vicious practices, that they should inform me of these two witnesses whenever they might be in a place drinking, or committing any act of iniquity, whether they should be together or separate, and if they bought, or either of them bought, any thing of these persons that was designed for the purpose of carousing; and that they should not conceal it from me. They replied, that they heard and obeyed. And it happened that a man came to me one night, and said, O our lord, know that the two witnesses are in such a place, in such a by-street, in the house of such-a-one, and that they are engaged in abominable iniquity. So I arose and disguised myself, I and my young man, and I repaired to them without any one accompanying me save my young man, and stopped not on the way until I stood before the door and knocked; whereupon a female slave came to me and opened to me the door, and said, Who art thou? So I entered without answering her; and I beheld the two witnesses and the master of the house sitting, with common women, and with abundance of wine. But when they saw me, they rose to me, treated me with honour, seated me at the upper end of the apartment, and said to me, Welcome to thee, as an excellent guest, and a polite boon-companion! They met me without fearing me or being alarmed; and after that, the master of the house arose from them, and, having been absent a while, returned bringing three hundred pieces of gold, without the least fear; and they said, Know, O our lord the Wálee, that thou canst do more than disgrace us, and that it is in thy power to chastise us; but naught save fatigue would

---

17 The Egyptian thieves are notorious for their dexterity, and often escape by plunging with their booty into the Nile. Of this trick I experienced an instance.

18 There were several Sulṭáns of Egypt thus surnamed.

19 Cairo; now commonly called by its inhabitants "Maṣr," for "Miṣr."

20 Booláḳ is the principal port of Cairo.

21 That is, "Old Miṣr;" now commonly called by the Egyptians "Maṣr el-'Ateeḳah," which has the same meaning; and by Europeans, improperly, "Old Cairo."

22 The word rendered "two legal witnesses" is the dual of "'adl," which literally signifies "just;" but is a term applied to a legal or unobjectionable witness. The two men here mentioned were legal witnesses because their immoral practices could not be proved against them.

accrue to thee from doing so. It is advisable, therefore, that thou receive this sum, and protect us; for God (whose name be exalted!) is named the Excellent Protector, and He loveth of his servants such as are liberal of protection; and thou wilt receive a reward and recompense.—So I said to myself, Receive this gold from them, and protect them this time; and if thou have them in thy power another time, take thy revenge upon them. I coveted the money, and took it from them, and left them and departed, no one knowing what I had done. But suddenly on the following day a sergeant of the Ḳáḍee came to me, and said, O Wálee, have the goodness to answer the summons of the Ḳáḍee; for he citeth thee. I arose, therefore, and went with him to the Ḳáḍee, not knowing the cause of this; and when I went in to him, I saw the two witnesses and the master of the house who gave me the three hundred pieces of gold sitting with him; and the master of the house arose and sued me for three hundred pieces of gold. It was not in my power to deny it; and he produced a written obligation, and those two legal witnesses testified against me that I owed the money. So it was established with the Ḳáḍee by the testimony of the two witnesses, and he ordered me to pay that sum. I therefore went not forth from them until they had received from me the three hundred pieces of gold; and I was enraged, purposing every kind of mischief against them, and repenting that I had not tormented them; and I departed in a state of the utmost confusion.

Then arose the Wálee of Booláḳ, and said, As to myself, O our lord the Sulṭán, the most wonderful thing that hath happened to me since I have been Wálee was this:—I had debts to pay amounting to three hundred thousand[23] pieces of gold; and, being distressed thereby, I sold what was behind me and what was before me and what was in my hand,[24] and thus collected one hundred thousand pieces of gold and no more.

[23] In the Breslau edition, three thousand; a more probable sum. [24] That is, all that I possessed.

I therefore remained in great perplexity; and while I was sitting in my house one night, in this state, a person knocked at the door; upon which I said to one of the young men, See who is at the door. And he went forth, and then returned to me with sallow countenance, changed in complexion, and with the muscles of his side quivering. So I said to him, What hath befallen thee? And he answered, Verily at the door is a man stripped of his proper clothing, and clad in apparel of leather, and with a sword, and in his girdle is a knife, and with him is a party of men equipped in the same manner, and he asketh for thee. I therefore took my sword in my hand, and went forth to see who these were; and, lo, they were as the young man had said. I asked them, What is your affair? And they answered, We are robbers, and we have acquired this night vast booty, and assigned it to thee, that thou mayest thereby help thyself to manage the affair on account of which thou art in anxiety, and pay the debt that thou owest. I said to them, And where is the booty? And they brought before me a great chest full of vessels [apparently] of gold and silver. So when I beheld it, I rejoiced, and said within myself, I will pay the debt that I owe from this, and there will remain to me as much again as the amount of that debt. I therefore took it, and entered the house, and said within myself, It would not be consistent with humanity in me to let them go without any thing. Accordingly, I took the hundred thousand pieces of gold that were in my possession, and gave it to them, thanking them for what they had done; and they took the pieces of gold and went their way under the covering of night, without any one's knowing of their coming. But when the morning arrived, I saw that the contents of the chest were gilded brass, and tin, the whole of them worth but five hundred pieces of silver; and the thing afflicted me: the pieces of gold that I had were lost; and my grief was increased.

Then the Wálee of Miṣr el-Ḳadeemeh arose and said, O our lord the Sulṭán, with regard to myself, the most wonderful thing that hath happened to me during the period of my holding the office of Wálee was this:—I hanged ten robbers, each on a separate gallows, and charged the guards to watch them, and not to suffer the people to take away any one of them. But on the morrow I came to see them, and beheld two men hanged upon one gallows: so I said to the guards, Who did this, and where is the gallows on which was the second of these hanged men? They however denied the fact; and I was about to beat them, when they said, Know, O Emeer, that we slept last night, and when we awoke, we found that one hanged man had been stolen, together with the gallows on which he was suspended; whereupon we feared thee; and, lo, a peasant on a journey approached us, having with him an ass; and we seized him and killed him, and hanged him instead of the one that was stolen, on this gallows. And I wondered at this, and said to them, What was with the peasant? They answered, With him was a pair of saddle-bags on the ass.—And what, said I, was in them? They answered, We know not. And I said to them, Bring me the saddle-bags. So they placed them before me; and I gave orders to open them; and, lo, in them was a murdered man, cut in pieces; and when I saw this, I wondered at it, and said within myself, Extolled be the perfection of God! The cause of the hanging of this peasant was naught but the crime that he had committed against this murdered man; and thy Lord is not tyrannical towards his servants![25]

The Money-changer and the Sharper.

It is related that a man of the money-changers had with him a purse full of gold, and he had passed by the robbers; whereupon one of the sharpers said, I am able to take this purse. The others said to him, How wilt thou do? And he replied, See ye. Then he followed the money-changer to his abode, and the latter entered, and, having

[25] The last anecdote in this volume, told of the prophet Moses, presents an illustration of the justice of Providence, similar to that related by the Wálee of Miṣr el-Ḳadeemeh.—Ed.

thrown down the purse upon the ṣuffeh,[26] called to a slave-girl to bring a ewer of water for ablution; and the slave-girl took the ewer to him, and followed him into a private chamber, leaving the street-door open. So the robber entered, took the purse, and repaired with it to his companions, whom he told what had happened to him with the money-changer and the slave-girl. They replied, By Allah, that which thou hast done was a clever exploit, and not every man is capable of performing such; but (they added) immediately the money-changer will come forth from the private chamber, and, not finding the purse, will beat the slave-girl, and inflict upon her a painful punishment; and it seemeth that thou hast not done any thing for which thou art to be praised. If then thou be a clever sharper, save the slave-girl from the beating and punishment.—So he said to them, If it be the will of God (whose name be exalted!), I will save the slave-girl and the purse.

Then the robber returned to the house of the money-changer, and found him punishing the slave-girl on account of the purse; and he knocked at his door; whereupon the money-changer said to him, Who is this? And he answered him, I am the young man of thy neighbour in the Ḳeysáreeyeh.[27] The money-changer therefore came forth to him, and said to him, What is thy business? And he answered him, My master saluteth thee, and saith to thee, thy habits are all changed. How is it that thou throwest down such a thing as this purse at the door of the shop, and goest and leavest it? Had any stranger found it, he had taken it and gone away.—And had not my master seen it and taken care of it, thou hadst lost it.—He then took forth the purse, and shewed it to him; and when the money-changer saw it, he said, This is my purse itself. And he stretched forth his hand to take it from the sharper; but the latter said to him, By Allah I will not give it to thee until thou write a paper to my master stating that thou hast received the purse from me; for I fear he may not believe me that thou hast taken the purse and received it safely unless thou write for me a paper and seal it with thy seal. So the money-changer entered to write for him a paper acknowledging the safe arrival of the purse as he had told him, and the robber went his way with the purse, and the slave-girl was saved from the punishment.

[The next anecdote describes a trick exactly of the same kind as that related by the second of "the Three Wálees;" and therefore I omit it.]

Anecdote of Ibráheem *the Son of* El-Mahdee.[28]

It is related that the Prince of the Faithful, El-Ma-moon, said to Ibráheem the son of El-Mahdee, Tell us the most wonderful thing that thou hast witnessed. And he replied, I hear and obey, O Prince of the Faithful.

---

[26] The term "ṣuffeh" is generally applied in Egypt to a shelf of marble or of common stone, about four feet high, supported by two or more arches, or by a single arch, under which are placed utensils in ordinary use, such as perfuming-vessels, and the basin and ewer which are used for washing before and after meals, and for the ablution preparatory to prayer. Water-bottles, coffee-cups, &c., are placed *upon* the ṣuffeh.—This term is also applied to a bench, or *sofa;* and to a porch, or roofed vestibule, or the like.

[27] See Note 18 to Chapter v.

[28] This anecdote differs little from one before inserted in this work (vol. i. p. 202); but I hope the differences, though slight, are such as will render it acceptable to the reader.—Respecting Ibráheem the son of El-Mahdee, see a note at the foot of page 298 in this volume.—My sheykh remarks, in a marginal note, "The author of the 'Eḳd has related this anecdote more fully, and says that its narration was thus occasioned. A spunger found ten criminals, and followed them, imagining that they were going to a feast; but, lo, they were going to slaughter. And when they were put to death, and he remained, he was brought before the Khaleefeh; and Ibráheem the son of El-Mahdee related this anecdote to obtain the liberation of that man: whereupon the Khaleefeh pardoned him."—Here then we have the origin of "the Barber's story of himself," in page 342 of the first volume of this work.—The 'Eḳd above-mentioned is a very celebrated miscellany, the author of which was Ibn 'Abd Rabbuh, or, more properly, ——— Rabbihi, of Cordova: he died in the year of the Flight 328 (A. D. 940), in the 82nd year of his age.

Know that I went forth one day to divert myself, and my course led me to a place where I smelt the odour of food, and my soul longed for it. I stopped, O Prince of the Faithful, in perplexity, unable to depart from the spot or to enter that dwelling; and I raised my eyes, and, lo, there was a lattice-window, behind which were a hand and wrist, than which I had never beheld any more beautiful. My reason fled at the sight of them, and I forgot the odour of the food on account of that hand and wrist, and began to devise a stratagem by means of which to obtain access to that dwelling. And, lo, there was a tailor near unto that place: so I advanced to him and saluted him, and he returned my salutation. I then said to him, To whom belongeth this house? He answered, To a man of the merchants. And I said, What is his name?—His name, he answered, is such-a-one the son of such-a-one, and he carouseth with none but the merchants. And while we were speaking, lo, there approached two comely, intelligent men, and he informed me that they were his most particular associates, and acquainted me with their names.

I therefore urged on my beast until I met them, when I said to them, May I be your ransom! The father of such-a-one[29] hath thought you tardy.—And I proceeded with them till we arrived at the door; whereupon I entered, and the two men entered also; and when the master of the house saw me with them, he doubted not that I was their associate: so he welcomed me, and seated me in the highest of the places. Then the servants brought the table, and I said within myself, God hath granted me the attainment of my desire with respect to these viands, and there remain the hand and the wrist. And after this, we removed for the purpose of carousal to another apartment, which I found decked all over with elegant objects; and the master of the house busied himself in shewing me courtesy, addressing his conversation to me, as he imagined me to be a guest of his guests, while they in like manner treated me with the utmost courtesy, imagining me to be a companion of the master of the house. They all continued incessantly their politeness to me until we had drunk several cups, when there came forth to us a damsel like a willow-branch, of the utmost elegance and comeliness of appearance, and she took a lute, and, with exciting modulations, sang these verses:—

Is it not wonderful that one house should contain us, and yet thou drawest not near, nor speakest?
Only eyes reveal the secrets of souls, and the breaking of hearts by love's fire inflamed.
We have only signals with the eyes and eyebrows, and sidelong glances, and the hand saluting.

Disquieting feelings were excited in me, O Prince of the Faithful, and I was moved with delight by the excess of her beauty, and the elegance of her verses that she sang, and envied her for the excellence of her performance; but I said, Thou wantest one thing, O slave-girl. And upon this, she threw the lute from her hand in anger, and said, When were ye wont to bring impertinent dolts into your assemblies?

So I repented of that which I had done, and I saw that the party were displeased with me; wherefore I said, All that I hoped for hath eluded me, and I see no resource by which to avert reproach from me save this: I demanded a lute, and said, I will shew what was omitted by her of the air that she played. And the party replied, We hear and obey. They immediately brought me a lute, and I tuned its strings, and sang these verses:—

This is thy lover, prostrated in his passion; the enamoured, whose tears are running down upon his body:
He hath one hand raised in supplication to the Compassionate, for the attainment of his hope, and the other on his heart.
O thou who beholdest one perishing of his love, his death is occasioned by his eye and by his hand.

---

29 He calls the master of the house by a surname, such as "Abu-l-Ḥasan," or "the Father of Ḥasan."

And upon this the slave-girl sprang up, and threw herself upon my feet, kissing them, and said, It is thine to excuse, O my master! By Allah I knew not thy dignity, nor have I ever heard the like of this performance.—Then the party began to honour and exalt me, after they had been moved with extreme delight; and each of them requested me to sing. I therefore sang an exciting piece, and the party became intoxicated, their reason quitting them, so that the two guests were carried away to their houses, and the master of the house alone remained with the slave-girl. And after he had drunk some cups with me, he said, O my master, my life hath passed unprofitably, since I have not known such a person as thyself before the present time. By Allah, then, O my master, tell me who thou art, that I may know my cup-companion with whom God hath favoured me this night.—And I began to give ambiguous hints, without telling him plainly my name. But he conjured me: so I informed him. And when he knew my name, he sprang upon his feet, and said, I wondered to think that this excellence could belong to any but thyself; and fortune hath granted me a favour for which I am unable to render due thanks: but perhaps this is a dream; for when did I hope that one connected with the Khaleefeh would visit me in my abode, and pass this night carousing with me.

I conjured him to sit; and he sat, and began to inquire of me the cause of my visiting him, in the most polite manner. So I acquainted him with the affair from first to last, concealing nothing of it, and said, With regard to the food, I have attained what I sought; but with regard to the hand and wrist, I have not attained my desire. He replied, With regard to the hand and wrist, thou shalt attain thy desire, if it be the will of God, whose name be exalted! Then he said, O such-a-one [mentioning a female name], tell such-a-one that she is to come down. And he proceeded to call for his female slaves, one after another, and to shew them all unto me; but I saw not the object of my affection, until he said, By Allah, O my master, there remain none save my mother and my sister; but, by Allah, they must be brought down to thee and shewn to thee, that thou mayest see them. And I wondered at his generosity, and his frankness of mind; and I said, May I be thy ransom! Begin then with the sister.—He replied, With pleasure. Then his sister came down, and he shewed me her hand, and, lo, she was the person whose hand and wrist I had seen. So I said, May I be thy ransom! This damsel is she whose hand and wrist I saw.—And he ordered the young men to bring the witnesses immediately. They therefore brought them; and he produced two myriads [30] of pieces of gold, and said to the witnesses, This our lord, Seyyidee [31] Ibráheem the son of El-Mahdee, the uncle of the Prince of the Faithful, demandeth in marriage my sister such-a-one, and I call you to witness that I have married her to him, and he hath given her as her dowry a myriad. And after this he said, I marry to thee my sister such-a-one for the said dowry. I replied, I accept that offer, and approve of it. Then he paid one of the two myriads to his sister, and the other to the witnesses; and said, O our lord, I desire to furnish one of the chambers for thee and thy wife. But I was abashed at that which I had experienced of his generosity, and was ashamed to accept his proposal: so I said, Equip her and send her to my abode.—And by thy existence, O Prince of the Faithful, there were brought to me, of her paraphernalia, such things that our rooms were too small to contain them, spacious as they were. Then I had by her this boy who is standing before thee.

And El-Ma-moon wondered at the generosity of this man, and said, Divinely was he gifted! I have never heard of the like of him!—He ordered Ibráheem the son of El-Mahdee to bring the man that he might see him. So he brought him before the

---

[30] The word here signifying "a myriad," or "ten thousand [pieces of money]," namely "bedreh," is employed in the vulgar Arabic to signify "a sum of money which an Emeer or some such person throws to the people, as the Báshà does at certain festivals, or in visiting [the mosque of] our lord El-Ḥoseyn." (Marginal note by my sheykh.)

[31] "Seyyidee" signifies "my master."

Khaleefeh, who desired him to speak, and his politeness and good breeding so pleased him that he made him one of his chief attendants.—And God is the Giver, and the Liberal Bestower.

Anecdote of a Charitable Woman.

It is related that a certain King said to the people of his dominions, If any one of you give aught in alms, I will assuredly cut off his hand. So all the people refrained from alms-giving, and none could bestow upon another. And it happened that a beggar came to a woman one day, and hunger tormented him, and he said to her, Give me somewhat as an alms.—How, said she, can I bestow an alms upon thee when the King cutteth off the hand of every one who doth so? But he rejoined, I conjure thee by God (whose name be exalted!) that thou give me an alms. So when he conjured her by God, she was moved with pity for him, and bestowed upon him two cakes of bread. And the news reached the King; whereupon he gave orders to bring her before him; and when she came, he cut off her hands. And she returned to her house.

Then the King, after a while, said to his mother, I desire to marry: therefore marry me to a comely woman. And she replied, There is, among our female slaves, a woman than whom none more beautiful existeth; but she hath a grievous defect.—And what is it? he asked. She answered, She is maimed of the two hands. The King however said, I desire to see her. Wherefore she brought her to him, and when he saw her, he was tempted by her beauty, and married her. And that woman was she who bestowed upon the beggar the two cakes of bread, and whose hands were cut off on that account. But when he had married her, her fellow-wives envied her, and wrote to the King, telling him that she was unchaste: and she had given birth to a

son. And the King wrote a letter to his mother, in which he commanded her to go forth with her to the desert, and to leave her there, and return.

His mother therefore did so: she took her forth to the desert, and returned. And that woman began to weep for the misfortune that had befallen her, and to bewail violently, with a wailing not to be exceeded. And while she was walking, with the child upon her neck, she came to a river, and kneeled down to drink, because of the violence of the thirst that had affected her from her walking and fatigue and grief; and when she stooped her head, the child fell into the water. So she sat weeping violently for her child; and while she wept, lo, there passed by her two men, who said to her, What causeth thee to weep? She answered, I had a child upon my neck, and he fell into the water. And they said, Dost thou desire that we rescue him, and restore him to thee? She answered, Yes. And upon this they supplicated God (whose name be exalted!), and the child came forth to her safe and unhurt. Then they said to her, Dost thou desire that God should restore to thee thy hands as they were? She answered, Yes. And they supplicated God (whose perfection be extolled, and whose name be exalted!); whereupon her hands returned to her in the most perfect state. After this they said to her, Knowest thou who we are?—God, she replied, is all-knowing. And they said, We are thy two cakes of bread which thou gavest as an alms to the beggar, and which alms occasioned the cutting off of thy hands.[32] Therefore praise God (whose name be exalted!) that He hath restored to thee thy hands and thy child.—And she praised God (whose name be exalted!), and glorified Him.

Anecdote of a Charitable Israelite.

There was, among the Children of Israel,[33] a devout man, having a family who spun cotton; and he used every day to sell the thread that they spun, and to buy fresh cotton; and with the profit that arose he bought, for his family, food, which they ate that day. And he went forth one day, and sold the thread which they had spun, and there met him one of his brethren, who complained to him of his need; whereupon he gave him the price of his thread, and returned to his family without either cotton or food. So they said to him, Where is the cotton and the food? And he answered them, Such-a-one met me, and complained to me of his need; wherefore I gave him the price of the thread. They said, And what shall we do; for we have nothing to sell? But they had a broken wooden bowl, and a jar; and he took them to the market. No one, however, would buy them of him; but while he was in the market, there met him a man with a stinking, swollen fish, which no one would buy of him; and the owner of the fish said to him, Wilt thou sell to me thy unmarketable property for mine? He answered, Yes:—and gave the man the wooden bowl and the jar, receiving from him the fish, which he brought to his family. They said, What shall we do with this fish? He answered, We will broil it and feed upon it until God (whose name be exalted!) please to supply us with sustenance. They therefore took it, and ripped open its belly, and they found in it a pearl. So they informed the sheykh [the devotee]; and he said, See if it be pierced; for if so, it belongeth to some one of the people; but if it be not

---

[32] "That is, God (whose name be exalted!) made her action to assume the forms of two men, like as He causeth the virtuous action to assume the form of a man who cheereth the dead in his sepulchre." (Marginal note by my sheykh.)

[33] Such of the descendants of Jacob as held the true faith the Muslims call "the Children of Israel;" but the deniers of the Messiah they do not honour with this appellation; calling them "Yahood," i. e. "Jews." [The Muslims believe that the Israelites held the true religion until the time of the Messiah, asserting that Moḥammad restored the religion of the patriarchs. They also say that the coming of Moḥammad was prophesied in the Gospel. On the subject of the pretended prophecy of his mission, see Note 112 to Chapter xi.—Ed.]

pierced, it is a gift which God (whose name be exalted!) hath bestowed upon you. And they looked, and, lo, it was not pierced. And when the morning came, he went with it to one of his brethren, of those who were acquainted with pearls; and this person said, O such-a-one, whence gottest thou this pearl? He answered, It is a gift which God (whose name be exalted!) hath bestowed upon us. And the man said, Verily it is worth a thousand pieces of silver, and I will give thee that sum; but take it to such-a-one; for he is of more wealth and knowledge than myself. So he took it to him, and he said, Verily it is worth seventy thousand pieces of silver: not more than that. Then he paid him seventy thousand pieces of silver; and the sheykh called the porters, who carried for him the money until he arrived at the door of his dwelling; when a beggar came to him, and said to him, Give me of that which God (whose name be exalted!) hath given unto thee. And he said to the beggar, We were yesterday like thee. Take half of this money.—And when he had divided the money into two equal portions, and each of them had taken his half, the beggar said to him, Keep thy money, and take it: may God bless thee in it: for verily I am a messenger of thy Lord, who hath sent me to thee to try thee. And the sheykh said, To God be praise and thanks!—And he ceased not to pass a most comfortable life, he and his family, until death.

Anecdote of Aboo-Ḥassán Ez-Ziyádee.

Aboo-Ḥassán Ez-Ziyádee saith, My circumstances one day became severely straitened, so that the grocer and the baker and the rest of the tradesmen importuned me, and my affliction became violent, and I found no resource. But while I was in this state, not knowing what to do, lo, there came in to me a young man belonging to me, and he said, At the door is a man on pilgrimage, who desireth to come in to thee. So I said, Give him permission. And he came in; and, behold, he was a man of Khurásán. He saluted me, and I returned his salutation; and he said, Art thou Aboo-Ḥassán Ez-Ziyádee? I answered, Yes. And what, said I, dost thou want?—I am a stranger, he answered, and am desirous of performing the pilgrimage, and I have with me a sum of

money, the carrying of which is a burden to me: wherefore I desire to deposit with thee these ten thousand pieces of silver until I accomplish my pilgrimage and return: and if the caravan return and thou see me not, know that I have died, and the money is a present from me unto thee; but if I return, it is mine. I replied, Thy desire shall be complied with, if it be the will of God, whose name be exalted! And he took forth a leathern bag; and I said to the young man, Bring me a pair of scales. So he brought a pair of scales, and the man weighed the money, and, having delivered it to me, went his way. I then summoned the tradesmen, and paid my debts, and expended and made ample purchases, saying within myself, Ere he returneth, God will aid me with somewhat of his gifts.

But after a day, the young man came in to me, and said to me, Thy acquaintance the man of Khurásán is at the door. I replied, Give him permission. And he entered, and said, I had determined on performing the pilgrimage; but news hath been brought to me of the death of my father; and I have resolved to return; therefore give me the money that I entrusted to thee yesterday. Now when I heard from him these words, excessive anxiety overcame me, such as none hath ever experienced; and I was perplexed, and returned him not a reply; for if I denied, I knew that he would require me to swear, and ignominy would have been my lot in the world to come; and if I informed him that I had expended it, he would [I imagined] have cried out, and disgraced me. So at last I said, God preserve thee in health! This my abode is not a strong nor a secure place of custody for that money; and when I received thy leathern bag, I sent it to him with whom it now is: therefore return to us to-morrow to receive it, if it be the will of God, whose name be exalted!—Accordingly he departed from me; and I passed the night in perplexity on account of the return of the man of Khurásán to me, and sleep came not to me that night, nor could I close my eye. So I arose and went to the young man, and said to him, Saddle for me the mule.—O my lord, he replied, it is now the first third of the night, and indeed nought of the night hath passed. I therefore returned to my bed; but sleep was forbidden me, and I ceased not to rouse the young man, who continued to turn me back from my purpose, until the dawn rose, when he saddled for me the mule, and I mounted. I knew not whither to go: so I threw the mule's bridle upon her shoulders, and became occupied with reflection and anxieties, while she proceeded to the eastern side of Baghdád.

And while I was passing on, lo, I beheld a company; and I turned from them, and went out of their way to another way; but they followed me; and when they saw me with a ṭeylesán,[34] they hastened towards me, and said to me, Dost thou know the abode of Aboo-Ḥassán Ez-Ziyádee? I answered them, I am he. And they said, Answer the summons of the Prince of the Faithful. I therefore proceeded with them until I went in to El-Ma-moon; and he said to me, Who art thou? I answered, A man of the companions of the Ḳáḍee Aboo-Yoosuf, one of the professors of the law and of the traditions. He asked, By what surname of relationship art thou called? I answered, By the surname of Aboo-Ḥassán Ez-Ziyádee. And he said, Explain to me thy case. So I explained to him my story, and he wept violently, and said, Wo to thee! The Apostle of God (may God bless and save him!) suffered me not to sleep this last night because of thee; for when I slept in the beginning of the night, he said to me [in a dream], Aid Aboo-Ḥassán Ez-Ziyádee.[35] And I awoke, and knew thee not. Then a

[34] I have never had an opportunity of examining the ṭeylesán, so as to be enabled to describe it exactly. I believe it to be a simple kind of scarf, which is thrown over the head and shoulders, or sometimes over the shoulders only. It is peculiar to faḳeehs (or professors of religion and law); and I am inclined to think that it is similar, not only in this respect, but also in its origin, to our academical scarfs and hoods.

[35] "Whoso seeth me in his sleep," said the Prophet, "seeth me truly; for Satan cannot assume the similitude of my form."—Hence various points of dispute among the Muslims have been settled by dreams. I have given an instance in my work on the Modern Egyptians, vol. i. ch. ix.

second time I slept, and he came to me, and said to me, Wo to thee! Aid Aboo-Ḥassán Ez-Ziyádee.—And I awoke, and knew thee not. Then I slept again, and he came to me, and still I knew thee not. And again I slept, and he came to me, and said to me, Wo to thee! Aid Aboo-Ḥassán Ez-Ziyádee.—So I dared not sleep after that. I remained awake the whole of the remainder of the night, and roused the people, and sent them to seek for thee in every quarter.—He then gave to me ten thousand pieces of silver, saying, This is for the man of Khurásán. And after that, he gave me ten thousand more pieces of silver, and said, Make, with this, ample purchases, and reform thy circumstances with it. Then he gave me thirty thousand pieces of silver, saying, Equip thyself with this, and when the day of the state-procession arriveth, come to me, that I may invest thee with an office.

So I went forth, taking the money with me, and, having returned to my house, performed there the morning-prayers; and, lo, the man of Khurásán came. I brought him into the house, and produced to him ten thousand pieces, saying to him, This is thy money. But he replied, This is not my very money. I said, Yes. And he asked, What is the cause of this? I therefore related to him the story; whereupon he wept, and said, By Allah, hadst thou told me the truth in the beginning of the affair, I had not demanded the money of thee; and now, by Allah, I will not accept aught of this money: thou art absolved of responsibility with respect to it. And he departed from me. I then arranged my affairs, and repaired on the day of the state-procession to the gate of El-Ma-moon, and I went in to him as he sat. And when I presented myself before him, he called me near to him, and produced unto me a written appointment from beneath his prayer-carpet, saying, This is an appointment conferring the office of Ḳáḍee of the Noble City,[36] from the western side [of the mosque], from the Báb es-Selám,[37] to an extent unlimited; and I have assigned thee such and such allowances every month. Then fear God (to whom be ascribed might and glory!), and be mindful of the solicitude of the Apostle of God (may God bless and save him!) respecting thee. —And the people wondered at his words, and asked me their meaning: so I acquainted them with the story from beginning to end, and the report spread among the people.

And Aboo-Ḥassán Ez-Ziyádee ceased not to be Ḳáḍee in the Noble City until he died, in the days of El-Ma-moon. The mercy of God be on him!

A Friend in Need.

It is related that a man possessed great wealth, and it departed from him, and he became destitute of every thing; whereupon his wife advised him to seek of one of his friends something wherewith to repair his condition. So he betook himself to a friend of his, and mentioned to him his necessity; and this friend lent him five hundred pieces of gold, that he might traffic with them. Now he was originally a jeweller. He therefore took the gold, and went to the market of jewels, where he opened a shop to buy and sell. And when he sat in the shop, there came to him three men, who inquired of him respecting his father; and he told them of his death; upon which they said to him, Hath he left any offspring? He answered, He hath left the slave[38] who is before you.—And who, said they, knoweth that thou art his son? He answered, The people of the market. And they said to him, Bring them together to us, that they may testify that thou art his son. He therefore collected them, and they testified to that fact. And the three men produced a pair of saddle-bags containing the sum of thirty thousand pieces of gold, together with jewels and precious minerals; and they

---

[36] "El-Medeeneh esh-Shereefeh." This is a common honourable appellation of the city in which the Prophet is buried; commonly called by European writers "Medina."

[37] This is the name of the principal gate (at the south-west corner) of the mosque in which the Prophet is buried.

[38] This is a common expression of humility.

said, This was deposited with us in trust for thy father. Then they departed; and there came to him a woman, who demanded of him some of those jewels worth five hundred pieces of gold, and bought them of him for three thousand pieces of gold. And he sold them to her, and took the five hundred pieces of gold that he had borrowed of his friend, and carried them to him, and said to him, Receive the five hundred pieces of gold that I borrowed of thee; for God hath aided me and prospered me. But his friend replied, I presented thee with them, and gave them up for the sake of God: therefore take them; and take this paper, but read it not until thou art in thy house, and act agreeably with its contents: so he took the money and the paper, and repaired to his house; and when he opened the paper, he found written in it these verses:—

The men who came to thee were my relations, my father and my paternal uncle and my maternal uncle Ṣáleḥ the son of 'Alee.
In like manner, what thou soldest for cash, to my mother thou soldest it; and the money and jewels were sent from me.
I desired not, by doing so, any detriment to thee; but to spare thee the embarrassment of bashfulness before me.

A Dream.

It is related also, that a man of Baghdád was possessed of ample riches and great wealth; but his wealth passed away, and his state changed, and he became utterly destitute, and could not obtain his sustenance save by laborious exertion. And he slept one night, overwhelmed and oppressed, and saw in his sleep a person who said to him, Verily thy fortune is in Cairo: therefore seek it and repair to it. So he journeyed to Cairo; and when he arrived there, the evening overtook him, and he slept in a mosque. Now there was, adjacent to the mosque, a house; and as God (whose name be exalted!) had decreed, a party of robbers entered the mosque, and thence passed to that house; and the people of the house, awaking at the disturbance occasioned by the robbers, raised cries; whereupon the Wálee came to their aid with his followers, and the robbers fled. The Wálee then entered the mosque, and found the man of Baghdád sleeping there: so he laid hold upon him, and inflicted upon him a painful beating with miḳra'ahs, until he was at the point of death, and imprisoned him; and he remained three days in the prison; after which, the Wálee caused him to be brought, and said to him, From what country art thou? He answered, From Baghdád.—And what affair, said the Wálee, was the cause of thy coming to Cairo? He answered, I saw in my sleep a person who said to me, Verily thy fortune is in Cairo: therefore repair to it. And when I came to Cairo, I found the fortune of which he told me to be those blows of the miḳra'ahs that I have received from thee.—And upon this the Wálee laughed so that his grinders appeared, and said to him, O thou of little sense, *I* saw three times in my sleep a person who said to me, Verily a house in Baghdád, in such a district, and of such a description, hath in its court a garden, at the lower end of which is a fountain, wherein is wealth of great amount: therefore repair to it and take it. But I went not; and thou, through the smallness of thy sense, hast journeyed from city to city on account of a thing thou hast seen in sleep, when it was only an effect of confused dreams.—Then he gave him some money, and said to him, Help thyself with this to return to thy city. So he took it and returned to Baghdád. Now the house which the Wálee had described, in Baghdád, was the house of that man; therefore when he arrived at his abode, he dug beneath the fountain, and beheld abundant wealth. Thus God enriched and sustained him; and this was a wonderful coincidence.[39]

El-Mutawekkil *and* Maḥboobeh.

There were, in the palace of the Prince of the Faithful, El-Mutawekkil 'ala-lláh, four hundred[40] concubines, two hundred Greeks, and two hundred muwelledehs[41] and Abyssinians; and 'Obeyd the son of Ṭáhir gave to El-Mutawekkil four hundred slave-girls, two hundred white, and two hundred Abyssinians and muwelledehs. Among these was a slave-girl of the muwelledehs of El-Baṣrah, named Maḥboobeh.[42] She was preeminent in beauty and loveliness, and in elegance and amorous manners; she played upon the lute, and sang well, composed verses, and wrote an excellent hand; and El-Mutawekkil in consequence became captivated by her, and could not bear to be

[39] This anecdote is also related by El-Is-ḥáḳee (reign of El-Ma-moon). [I have also found it in a MS. (in Mr. Lane's possession) entitled Murshid ez-Zoowár ilà Ḳuboor el-Abrár (before cited); with the difference that it is there related of an Egyptian saint who travelled to Baghdád, and was, in the same manner as above described, directed to his house in El-Fusṭáṭ.—Ed.]

[40] In my original, "four thousand;" but this appears, from what follows, to be a mistake. [This alteration is necessary to give consistency to the anecdote, but the mistake in the original appears to be rather in the enumeration of the several classes of which El-Mutawekkil's female slaves were composed, than in their total number, for I find in the Mir-át ez-Zemán (reign of El-Mutawekkil) the number stated to be five thousand, and in Es-Suyooṭee's History of the Khaleefehs (ed. Lees, Calcutta, 1857), four thousand. The two works here mentioned contain the anecdote, though differing from each other and from the text of it in the Thousand and One Nights.—El-Mutawekkil was the tenth Khaleefeh of the house of El-'Abbás; and he reigned from the year of the Flight 232 to 247. I refrain from any comment on his character. Maḥboobeh is included among the female poets in the Kitáb el-Aghánee. See Alii Ispahanensis Liber Cantilenarum (Proem. p. 32), ed. Kosegarten, Gripesvold: 1840.—Ed.]

[41] A person born a slave in an Arabian country is called, if a male, "muwelled," and if a female, "muwelledeh."

[42] Maḥboobeh signifies "beloved."

absent from her a single hour. But when she saw his affection for her, she behaved arrogantly towards him, and was ungrateful for his favours: so he became violently incensed against her, and deserted her, forbidding the inmates of the palace to speak to her.

She remained in that state some days; but El-Mutawekkil still had an affection for her; and he arose in the morning one day, and said to his usual associates, I dreamed this last night that I became reconciled to Maḥboobeh. They replied, We beg of God (whose name be exalted!) that such an event may happen when thou art awake. And while he was speaking, lo, a maid-servant came, and communicated some information to him; upon which he arose from the assembly, and entered the abode of the Ḥareem. And the communication that she made to him was this: she said to him, We heard from the chamber of Maḥboobeh the sounds of singing, and playing upon the lute, and we know not the cause of this. And when he arrived at her chamber, he heard her singing to the lute, striking it sweetly, and singing these verses:—

> I wander through the palace and behold not any one unto whom to complain, nor any one to speak to me;
> As though I had committed an act of rebellion, of which no repentance could avail to acquit me.
> Is there any intercessor to plead for me with a King who hath paid me a visit in sleep and made peace with me,
> And who, when the daybreak appeared unto us, resumed his desertion, and severed me from him?

So when El-Mutawekkil heard her words, he wondered at these verses, and at this strange coincidence; at Maḥboobeh's seeing a dream agreeing with his dream. He therefore went in to her in the chamber; and when he entered and she was sensible of his presence, she hastened to rise to him, and threw herself upon his feet, kissing them, and saying, By Allah, O my lord, I saw this event in my sleep last night; and when I awoke, I composed these verses.—By Allah, replied El-Mutawekkil, I beheld in my sleep the like of this. Then they embraced each other, and became reconciled; and he remained with her seven days with their nights. And Maḥboobeh had written upon her cheek, with musk, the name of El-Mutawekkil; and his name was Jaạfar; and when he beheld his name so written, he composed and recited these verses:—

> She wrote Jaạfar with musk on her cheek. With my soul would I ransom her who wrote on the cheek what I see.
> If her fingers have inscribed one line upon her cheek, she hath deposited many lines in my heart.
> O thou whom Jaạfar among mankind possesseth, may God fill Jaạfar[43] with the draught of thy love!

And when El-Mutawekkil died, all the female slaves that had belonged to him dismissed him from their minds, except Maḥboobeh; for she ceased not to mourn for him until she died, and she was buried by his side.—The mercy of God be on them all!

---

[43] "Jaạfar" signifies "a river."

CHAPTER XVII.

COMMENCING WITH PART OF THE THREE HUNDRED AND FIFTY-SEVENTH NIGHT, AND ENDING WITH PART OF THE THREE HUNDRED AND SEVENTY-FIRST.

THE STORY OF THE MAGIC HORSE.

THERE was, in ancient times, in the country of the Persians,[1] a mighty King, of great dignity, who had three daughters, like shining full moons and flowery gardens; and he had a male child, like the moon. He observed two annual festivals, that of the New-year's-day, and that of the Autumnal Equinox;[2] and it was his custom, on these occasions, to open his palaces, and give his gifts, and make proclamation of safety and security, and promote the chamberlains and lieutenants: the people of his dominions also used to go in to him and salute him, and congratulate him on the festival, offering him presents and servants: and he loved philosophy and geometry. And while the King was sitting on the throne of his dominions, on a certain day, during one of these festivals,[3] there came in to him three sages: with one of them was a peacock of gold; and with the second, a trumpet of brass; and with the third, a horse of ivory and ebony: whereupon the King said to them, What are these things, and what is their use? The owner of the peacock answered, The use of this peacock is, that whenever an hour of the night or day passeth, it will flap its wings, and utter a cry.[4] And the owner of the trumpet[5] said, If this trumpet be placed at the gate of the city, it will be as a defender of it; for if an enemy enter the city, this trumpet will send forth a sound against him; so he will be known and arrested. And the owner of the horse said, O my lord, the use of this horse is, that if a man mount it, it will convey him to whatever country he desireth. Upon this the King said, I will not bestow any favour upon you until I make trial of the uses of these things. Then he made trial of the peacock, and found it to be as its owner had said. And he made trial of the trumpet, and found it as its owner had said. He therefore said to the two sages (the owners of the peacock and the trumpet), Request of me what ye will. And they replied, We request of thee that thou marry to each of us one of thy daughters. Whereupon the King bestowed upon them two of his daughters. Then the third sage, the owner of the horse, advanced, and, having kissed the ground before the King, said to him, O King of the age, bestow upon me like as thou hast bestowed upon my companions. The King replied, When I shall have made trial of that which thou hast brought. And upon this, the King's son advanced and said, O my father, I will mount this horse, and make trial of it, and obtain proof of its use.[6] So the King replied, O my son, try it as thou desirest.

The King's son accordingly arose, and mounted the horse, and urged it with his feet; but it moved not from its place. He therefore said, O sage, where is its rapidity of pace of which thou boastedst? And on hearing this, the sage came to him, and shewed him a turning-pin, by which to make it ascend; saying to him, Turn this pin. And the King's son turned it, and, lo, the horse moved, and soared with him towards the upper region of the sky, and ceased not its flight with him until he was out of sight of the people; whereupon the prince was perplexed at his case, and repented of his having mounted the horse. He said, The sage hath made use of a stratagem to destroy me, and there is no strength nor power but in God, the High, the Great! Then he began to examine all the members of the horse; and while he was doing so, he saw a thing like the head of a cock, on the horse's right shoulder, and the like on the left shoulder: so he said, I see not any indication except these two buttons. And he turned the button that was on the right shoulder; upon which the horse bore him upwards with increased velocity into the sky: so he took off his hand from that button, and, looking at the left shoulder, and seeing the button that was there, he turned it; and the movements of the horse became lessened in velocity, and changed from ascending to descending. It ceased not to descend with him towards the earth by little and little, while he continued to exercise caution for his safety; and when he saw this, and knew the uses of the horse, his heart was filled with joy and happiness, and he thanked God (whose name be exalted!) for the favour that He had shewn him in saving him from destruction. He ceased not to descend for the whole of the remainder of the day; for in his ascent, the earth had become distant from him; and he turned about the face of the horse as he desired, while it descended with him: when he would, he was carried downwards by it; and when he would, he was borne by it upwards.

Now when he had obtained what he desired with respect to the horse, he proceeded on it towards the earth, and began to look at its countries and cities, which he knew not; for he had never seen them before during the whole of his life. And among the objects that he beheld was a city constructed in the most excellent manner, in the midst of a land beautifully verdant, with trees and rivers: upon which he meditated in his mind, and said, Would that I knew what is the name of this city, and in what region it is. He then made a circuit around the city, viewing it attentively, right and left. The day had nearly departed, and the sun was about to set: so he said within himself, I have not found any place in which to pass the night better than this city: I will therefore pass this night in it, and in the morning I will return to my family and my royal residence, and acquaint my family and my father with that which hath happened to me, and inform him of the things that mine eyes have seen. Accordingly he began to search for a place in which he might feel secure of the safety of himself and his horse, and where no one might see him; and while

he was thus engaged, lo, he beheld, in the midst of the city, a palace rising high into the air, surrounded by a large wall with high battlements; whereupon he said within himself, This place is agreeable.

He turned the button that caused the horse to descend, and ceased not to be carried downwards on it until he descended steadily on the flat roof of the palace, when he alighted from the horse, praising God (whose name be exalted!), and began to go round about the horse, and to examine it, and said, By Allah, he who made thee thus was an expert sage; and if God (whose name be exalted!) extend the term of my life, and restore me to my country and my family in safety, and reunite me with my father, I will assuredly bestow every favour upon this sage, and treat him with the utmost beneficence. He then sat upon the roof of the palace until he knew that the inmates had betaken themselves to sleep. Hunger and thirst pained him; for since he had parted from his father he had not eaten food; and he said within himself, Verily such a palace as this is not devoid of the necessaries of life. He therefore left the horse in a place alone, and walked down to see for something to eat; and finding a flight of steps, he descended by them to the lower part of the building, where he found a court paved with marble; and he wondered at this place, and at the beauty of its construction; but he heard not in the palace any sound, nor the cheering voice of an inhabitant. So he paused in perplexity, and looked to the right and left, not knowing whither to go. Then he said within himself, there is no better course for me than to return to the place in which is my horse, and to pass the night by it; and when the morning cometh, I mount and depart.

But while he was addressing himself with these words, he beheld a light approaching the place where he stood, and, looking attentively at that light, he found that it was with a party of female slaves, among whom was a beautiful damsel, of a stature like the letter Alif,[7] resembling the splendid full moon, as the poet hath said:—

> She came without appointment, in the gloom of nightfall, like the full moon in the dark horizon;
> Slender-formed; there is none among the creation like her in excellence of beauty or the charms of disposition.
> I exclaimed, when my eye beheld her beauty, Extolled be the perfection of the Creator of mankind!
> I guard her from the eyes of every person by seeking refuge with the Lord of Men and of the Daybreak.[8]

That damsel was the daughter of the King of this city; and her father loved her with so great an affection that he built for her this palace; and whenever her heart was contracted, she used to come hither, together with her female slaves, and to remain here a day, or two days, or more; after which she returned to the palace where she generally resided. It happened that she came that night for the sake of diversion and dilatation of the mind, and she walked among the female slaves, attended by a eunuch armed with a sword; and when they entered the palace, they spread the furniture, and gave vent to the odours from the perfuming-vessels, and sported and rejoiced. Now while they were thus engaged, the King's son rushed upon that eunuch, struck him a blow which laid him prostrate, and, taking the sword from his hand, ran upon the female slaves who were with the King's daughter, and dispersed them to the right and left. And when the King's daughter saw his beauty and loveliness, she said, Perhaps thou art he who demanded me in marriage yesterday of my father, and whom he rejected, and whom he asserted to be of hideous aspect. By Allah, my father lied in saying those words; for thou art none other than a handsome person.

Now the son of the King of India had requested her of her father, and he had rejected him, because he was disagreeable in aspect; and she imagined that the prince now before her was he who had demanded her in marriage. She then came to him, and embraced and kissed him, and seated herself with him. The female slaves, however, said to her, O our mistress, this is not the person who demanded thee in marriage of thy father; for that person was hideous, and this is handsome; and he who demanded thee of thy father, and whom he rejected, is not fit to be a servant to this person: but, O our mistress, verily this young man is one of high dignity. And after this, the female slaves went to the prostrated eunuch, and roused him; whereupon he sprang up in alarm, and searched for his sword, not finding it in his hand. So the female slaves said to him, He who took thy sword, and laid thee prostrate, is sitting with the King's daughter.—Now the King had charged this eunuch with the office of guarding his daughter, in his fear for her from misfortunes and evil accidents.—The eunuch therefore arose, and went to the curtain, and when he raised it, he saw the King's daughter sitting with the King's son, and they were conversing together; and as soon as he beheld them, he said to the King's son, O my master, art thou a human being or a Jinnee? To which the King's son replied, Wo to thee, O most ill-omened of slaves! How is it that thou regardest the sons of the royal Kisràs[9] as of the unbelieving devils?—Then, taking the sword in his hand, he said to him, I am the son-in-law of the King, and he hath married me to his daughter, and commanded me to introduce myself to her. So when the eunuch heard these words from him, he said to him, O my master, if thou be of the human species, as thou hast asserted, she is suited to none but thee, and thou art more worthy of her than any other.

The eunuch then went shrieking to the King; and he had rent his clothes, and thrown dust upon his head. And when the King heard his crying, he said to him, What hath befallen thee; for thou hast agitated my heart? Acquaint me quickly, and be brief in thy words.—He therefore answered him, O King, go to the assistance of thy daughter; for a devil of the Jinn, in the garb of human beings, and having the form of the sons of the Kings, hath got possession of her: therefore seize him. And when the King heard these words from him, he thought to slay him, and said to him, How came it to pass that thou wast neglectful of my daughter, so that this event befell her? He then went to the palace wherein was his daughter, and on his arrival he found the female slaves standing there, and said to them, What is it that hath happened to my daughter? They answered him, O King, while we were sitting with her, suddenly there rushed upon us this young man, who resembleth the full moon, and than whom we have never seen any one more handsome in countenance, with a drawn sword in his hand; and we inquired of him respecting his business, and he asserted that thou hadst married to him thy daughter: we know nothing more than this; and we know not whether he be a human being or a Jinnee; but he is chaste and well bred, and doth not addict himself to that which is disgraceful. So when the King heard their words, his rage was cooled. He then raised the curtain by little and little, and looked, and beheld the King's son sitting with his daughter, conversing; and he was of most comely form, with a face like the shining full moon.

The King could not control himself, through his jealousy for his daughter. He therefore raised the curtain and entered, with a drawn sword in his hand, and rushed upon them as though he were a Ghool.[10] The King's son, on seeing him, said to her, Is this thy father? She answered, Yes. And upon this, he sprang upon his feet, and, taking his sword in his hand, shouted at the King with an amazing cry which terrified him, and was about to attack him with the sword; but the King, perceiving that the prince was stronger than he, sheathed his sword, and stood until the King's son came up to him, when he met him with courtesy, and said to him, O young man, art

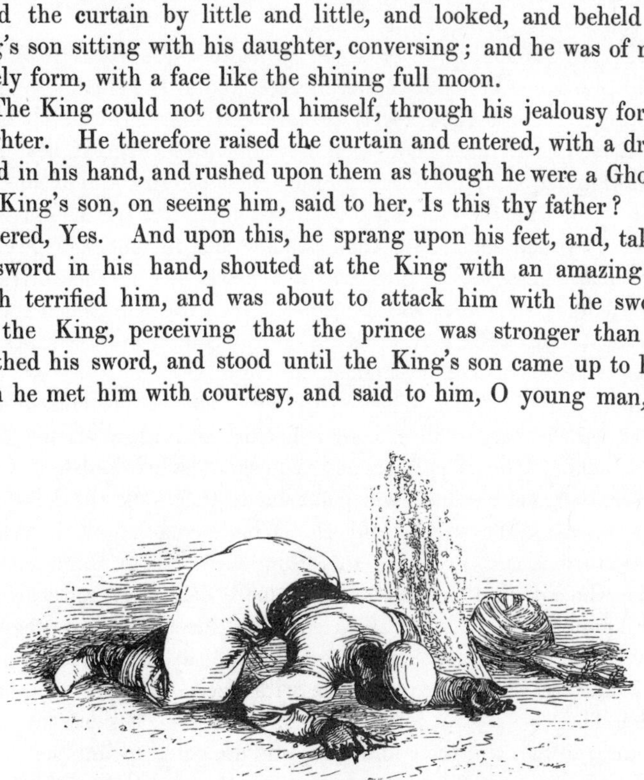

thou a human being or a Jinnee? The King's son replied, Were it not that I respect thy right and the honour of thy daughter, I had shed thy blood. How is it that thou derivest me from the devils, when I am of the sons of the royal Kisràs, who, if they desired to take thy kingdom, would make thee totter from thy glory and dominion, and despoil thee of all that is in thy dwellings?—So the King,[11] on hearing his words, dreaded and feared him; but said to him, If thou be of the sons of the Kings, as thou hast asserted, how is it that thou hast entered my palace without my permission, and dishonoured me, and come unto my daughter, asserting that thou art her husband, and pretending that I had married thee to her, when I have killed the Kings and the sons of the Kings on their demanding her of me in marriage? And who will save thee from my power, when, if I cried out unto my slaves and my young men and commanded them to slay thee, they would slay thee immediately? Who then can deliver thee from my hand?

The King's son, however, when he heard these words from him, said to the King, Verily I wonder at thee, and at the smallness of thy penetration. Dost thou covet for thy daughter a husband better than myself; and hast thou seen any one more firm of heart, and superior in requital, and more glorious in authority and troops and guards than I am?—The King answered him, No, by Allah: but I would, O young man, that thou demand her in marriage publicly, that I may marry her to thee; for if I marry her to thee privately, thou wilt disgrace me by so taking her. And the King's son replied, Thou hast said well: but, O King, if thy slaves and servants and troops were to assemble against me and slay me, as thou hast imagined, thou wouldst disgrace thyself, and the people would be divided with respect to thee, some believing, and others accusing thee of falsehood. It is my opinion that thou shouldst relinquish this idea, and adopt the course that I will point out to thee.—So the King said, Propose what thou wilt. And the King's son rejoined, What I propose to thee is this: either that thou meet me in single combat, and he who killeth the other shall be more deserving and worthy of the kingdom; or else, that thou leave me this night, and when the morning cometh, that thou send forth to me thy soldiers and troops and young men; and acquaint me with their number. The King replied, Their number is forty thousand horsemen, besides the slaves belonging to me, and their followers, who are equal in number. And the King's son said, When the day beginneth, send them forth to me, and say to them, This person hath demanded of me my daughter in marriage on the condition that he will meet you all in combat; and he hath pretended that he will overcome and subdue you, and that ye cannot prevail against him. Then leave me with them to combat them; and if they kill me, the result will be more proper for the concealment of thy secret and the preserving of thine honour; but if I overcome and subdue them, then am I such a person as the King should desire for his son-in-law.—And when the King heard his words, he approved of his advice and accepted it, notwithstanding that he wondered at his saying, and was struck with terror at his determination to meet in combat all his army that he had described unto him. Then they sat conversing.

And after this, the King called the eunuch, and commanded him to go forth immediately to his Wezeer, and to desire him to collect all the troops, and order them to equip themselves with their arms, and to mount their horses. So the eunuch went to the Wezeer, and acquainted him with that which the King had commanded. And upon this the Wezeer summoned the chiefs of the army, and the grandees of the empire, and ordered them to mount their horses, and to go forth equipped with the weapons of war.—Meanwhile, the King continued to converse with the young man, being pleased with his conversation and sense and good breeding; and as they were talking together, the morning arrived. The King therefore arose, and went to his throne, ordered his troops to mount, and caused an excellent horse, one of the best that he possessed, to be brought before the King's son, commanding that it should be equipped for him with handsome saddle and trappings. But the young man said to him, O King, I will not mount until I take a view of the troops, and observe them. And the King replied, It shall be as thou desirest. Then the King proceeded, with the young man before him, until they arrived at the horse-course, when the young man looked at the troops and their number. And the King called out, O companies of men, a young man hath come unto me demanding in marriage my daughter, and I have never beheld any handsomer than he, nor any stronger in heart, nor any greater in intrepidity than he: and he hath asserted that he alone will overcome you and subdue you, and pretendeth that ye, even if your number amounted to a hundred thousand, would be in his estimation but few. But when he cometh forth to combat you, receive him upon the points of your spears, and the edges of your swords; for he hath undertaken a great enterprise.

The King then said to the young man, O my son, do as thou desirest with them. But he replied, O King, thou hast not treated me equitably. How shall I go forth to combat them when I am on foot and thy people are mounted on horses?—So the King said to him, I desired thee to mount, and thou refusedst. Take then of the horses and choose of them that which thou wilt.—He replied, None of thy horses pleaseth me, and I will mount none but the horse on which I came. The King therefore said to him, And where is thy horse? He answered him, It is on the top of thy palace.—In what place in my palace? asked the King. He answered, On the roof of the palace. And when the King heard his words, he said to him, This is the first instance that hath appeared of thine insanity. O, wo to thee! How can the horse be upon the roof? But now will thy veracity be distinguished from thy lying.—Then the King looked towards one of his chief officers, and said to him, Go to my palace, and bring what thou shalt find upon the roof. And the people wondered at the words of the young man; one saying to another, How can this horse descend the stairs from the roof? Verily this is a thing the like of which we have never heard!—Now the person whom the King had sent to the palace ascended to its roof, and beheld the horse standing there; and he had seen none more handsome than it; and he approached it and examined it, and found it to be of ebony and ivory. Some others of the chief officers of the King also went up with this person; and when they beheld the horse, they laughed together, and said, Did the young man speak of such a horse as this? We imagine that he is no other than a madman: but his case will soon appear to us; and perhaps he may be a person of great importance.—They then raised the horse upon their hands, and carried it without stopping until they came before the King, when they placed it before him; and the people assembled around it, gazing at it, and wondering at the beauty of its make, and at the beauty of its saddle and bridle. The King also admired it, and wondered at it extremely; and he said to the King's son, O young man, is this thy horse? He answered, Yes, O King, this is my horse, and thou shalt see a wonder performed by it. The King said to him, Take thy horse and mount it. But he replied, I will not mount it unless the troops retire to a distance from it. So the King commanded the troops that were around him to retire from it as far as an arrow might be shot.

Then said the young man, O King, I am going to mount my horse, and charge upon thine army, and disperse them to the right

and left, and split their hearts. The King replied, Do what thou desirest, and pity them not; for they will not pity thee. And the King's son went to the horse and mounted it. The troops were arranged in ranks before him; and one said to another, When the young man arriveth between the ranks, we will receive him with the points of the spears, and the edges of the swords. But one of them said, By Allah, it is a calamity! How shall we kill this young man with the comely face and the surpassing figure?—And another said, By Allah, ye shall by no means reach him unless after a great event; and the young man hath not done these deeds but from his knowledge of his own valour and preeminence.—And when the King's son had seated himself firmly upon his horse, he turned the pin of ascent. The eyes of the spectators were strained to see what he would do; and his horse bestirred itself, and moved about with violent action, until it had performed the most extraordinary of the motions of horses, and its body became filled with air. Then it rose, and ascended into the sky. So when the King saw that he had risen, and ascended aloft, he called out to his troops, and said, Wo to you! Take him before he escape from you.—But his Wezeer and lieutenants replied, O King, can any one catch the flying bird? This is none other than a great enchanter. God hath saved thee from him: therefore praise God (whose name be exalted!) for thine escape from his hand.

The King therefore returned to his palace, after he had witnessed these acts of the King's son; and when he arrived at his palace, he went to his daughter, and acquainted her with that which had happened to him with the King's son in the horse-course; but he found her greatly lamenting for him, and for her separation from him; and she fell into a violent sickness, and took to the pillow. So when her father saw her in this state he pressed her to his bosom, kissed her between the eyes, and said to her, O my daughter, praise God (whose name be exalted!) and thank Him for our escape from this crafty enchanter. He began to repeat to her the account of the deeds of the King's son that he had witnessed, describing to her how he had ascended into the air. But she listened to nought of her father's words; her weeping and wailing increased in violence, and afterwards she said within herself, By Allah, I will not eat food, nor drink any beverage, until God reunite me with him. Therefore exceeding anxiety overcame her father the King on account of this; the state of his daughter afflicted him, and he mourned in heart for her; and every time that he addressed her with soothing words, she only increased in her passion for the young man.—Such was her case.[12]

Now, as to the King's son, when he had ascended into the sky, being alone, he reflected upon the beauty of the damsel, and her loveliness. He had inquired of the King's people respecting the name of the city, and the name of the King, and that of his daughter; and that city was the city of Ṣan'à.[13] He then prosecuted his journey with diligence until he came in sight of the city of his father; and after he had made a circuit around the city, he bent his course to his father's palace, and descended upon the roof. Having left his horse there, he descended to his father, and went in to him; and he found him mourning and afflicted on account of his separation: therefore, when his father saw him, he rose to him and embraced him, pressing him to his bosom, and rejoicing exceedingly at his return. And the Prince inquired of his father respecting the sage who made the horse, saying, O my father, what hath fortune done with him? His father answered him, May God not bless the sage nor the hour in which I beheld him; for he was the cause of thy separation from us, and he hath been imprisoned, O my son, since thou absentedst thyself from us. He gave orders, however, to relieve him, and take him forth from the prison, and bring him before him; and when he came before him, he invested him with an honorary dress in token of satisfaction, and treated him with the utmost beneficence; but would not marry his daughter to him. So the sage was violently enraged at this, and repented of that which he had done, knowing that the King's son had become acquainted with the secret of the horse and the mode of its motion. Then the King said to his son, It is my opinion that thou shouldst not approach this horse henceforth, nor mount it after this day; for thou knowest not its properties, and thou art deceived respecting it. The King's son had related to his father what had happened to him with the daughter of the King, the lord of the city, and what had happened to him with her father; and his father said to him, Had the King desired to slay thee, he had slain thee; but the end of thy life was delayed.

After this,[14] they ate and drank and were merry; and there was with the King a handsome slave-girl, who played upon the lute; and she took the lute, and began to play upon it, singing of absence, before the King and his son; and she sang these verses:—

> Think not that absence hath made me forget: for if I forget you, what shall I remember?
> Time passeth; but never shall our love for you end: in our love for you we will die and be raised.

Then anxious thoughts were aroused in the mind of the King's son by his love of the damsel, the daughter of the King of Ṣan'à: so he rose and went to the horse and mounted it, and turned the pin of ascent; whereupon it soared with him into the air, and rose with him towards the upper region of the sky. And in the morning, his father missed him, and found him not: he therefore went up to the top of the palace, in a state of affliction, and he beheld his son mounting into the air; and upon this he grieved for his separation, and repented extremely that he had not taken the horse and concealed it. He said within himself, By Allah, if my son return to me, I will not preserve this horse, that my heart may be at rest respecting my son. And he resumed his weeping and wailing.—But as to his son, he ceased not his course through the sky until he came to the city of Ṣan'à, when he descended in the place where he descended the first time, and he walked down stealthily until he came to the chamber of the King's daughter; but he found neither her nor her female slaves, nor the eunuch who was her guard; and the event greatly afflicted him. Then he went about searching for her through the palace, and at last he found her in a different chamber from that in which he had been with her. She had taken to the pillow, and around her were the female slaves and nurses. And he went in to them and saluted them; and when the damsel heard his speech, she rose to him and embraced him, and began to kiss him between his eyes, and to press him to her bosom. He said to her, O my mistress, thou hast rendered me desolate during this period. And she replied, Thou hast rendered *me* desolate, and had thine absence from me continued longer, I had perished without doubt.—O my mistress, he

rejoined, what thoughtest thou of my conduct with thy father, and his actions to me? Were it not for my love of thee, O temptation to all creatures, I had slain him, and made him an example to beholders: but I love him for thy sake.—And she said to him, How couldst thou absent thyself from me? Can my life be pleasant after thy departure? —He then said to her, Wilt thou comply with my desire, and listen to my words? She answered him, Say what thou wilt; for I will consent to that which thou requirest me to do, and will not oppose thee in any thing. And he said to her, Journey with me to my country and my kingdom. She replied, Most willingly.

So when the King's son heard her words, he rejoiced exceedingly, and, taking her by her hand, he made her swear by God (whose name be exalted!) that she would do so. Then he led her up to the roof of the palace, mounted his horse, and placed her on it behind him, and after he had bound her firmly, he turned the pin of ascent in the shoulder of the horse, and it ascended with them into the sky. Upon this the female slaves cried out, and informed the King her father, and her mother, who thereupon came up in haste to the roof of the palace; and the King, looking up into the sky, beheld the ebony horse soaring with them in the air. The King was agitated, and his agitation increased, and he called out and said, O son of the King, I conjure thee by Allah that thou have mercy upon me, and have mercy upon my wife, and that thou make not a separation between us and our daughter! The King's son, however, answered him not; but he imagined that the damsel repented of parting from her mother and her father; so he said to her, O temptation of the age, dost thou desire that I restore thee to thy mother and thy father?—O my master, she answered, by Allah that is not my desire: my desire is rather to be with thee wherever thou shalt be; for I am drawn off by my love of thee from every thing else, even from my father and my mother. And when the King's son heard her reply, he rejoiced exceedingly, and began to make the horse proceed gently with them, that it might not disquiet her; and he ceased not to journey on with her until he beheld a green meadow, in which was a spring of water. There they alighted, and ate and drank; after which, the King's son mounted his horse again, took her up behind him, and bound her, in his fear for her. He then proceeded with her, and ceased not in his course through the air until he arrived at the city of his father. His joy thereat was great; and he desired to shew to the damsel the seat of his power and the dominion of his father, and to inform her that the dominion of his father was greater than that of her father. He therefore deposited her in one of the gardens in which his father diverted himself, put her in a private chamber that was furnished for his father, and placed the ebony horse at the door of that chamber, charging the damsel to guard it, and saying to her, Sit here until I send to thee my messenger; for I am going to my father, to prepare for thee a palace, and to display to thee my dominion. And the damsel rejoiced when she heard from him these words, and replied, Do what thou desirest. Then it occurred to her mind that she was not to enter [the city] but with respect and honour, as was suitable to persons of her rank.

So the King's son left her, and proceeded until he arrived at the city, and went in to his father; and when his father saw him, he rejoiced at his coming, and met him and welcomed him; and the King's son said to his father, Know that I have brought the King's daughter of whom I informed thee, and I have left her without the city, in one of the gardens, and come to acquaint thee with her arrival, that thou mayest prepare the procession of state, and go forth to meet her, and display to her thy dominion and thy troops and guards. The King replied, Most willingly. And immediately he commanded the people of the city to decorate the city in the most handsome manner, and rode forth in a procession equipped in the most perfect manner and with the most magnificent decorations, with all his soldiers and the grandees of his empire, and all his memlooks and servants. The King's son also took forth, from his palace, ornaments and apparel and such things as Kings treasure up, and prepared for the damsel a camel-litter of green and red and yellow brocade, in which he seated Indian and Greek and Abyssinian female slaves, and he displayed wonderful treasures. Then he left the camel-litter, with the persons that were in it, and went on before to the garden; and he entered the private chamber in which he had left the damsel, and searched for her; but found her not, nor did he find the horse. Upon this he slapped his face and rent his clothes, and began to go round about through the garden, with a mind confounded; after which, he returned to his reason, and said within himself, How did she learn the secret of this horse when I did not acquaint her with aught of it? But perhaps the Persian sage who made the horse hath found her, and taken her, as a requital for that which my father hath done unto him.—Then the King's son sought the keepers of the garden, and asked them who had passed by them, saying, Have ye seen any one pass by you and enter this garden? And they answered, We have not seen any one enter this garden except the Persian sage; for he entered to collect useful herbs. So when he heard their words, he was convinced that the person who had taken the damsel was that sage.

Now it happened, in accordance with destiny, that, when the King's son left the damsel in the private chamber that was in the garden, and repaired to the palace of his father to make his preparations, the Persian sage entered the garden to collect some useful herbs, and smelt the odour of musk and other perfumes with which the air was impregnated; and this sweet scent was from the odour of the King's daughter. The sage therefore proceeded in the direction of this odour until he came to the private chamber, when he saw the horse that he had made with his hand standing at the door of the chamber. So when the sage saw the horse, his heart was filled with joy and happiness; for he had mourned after it greatly since it had gone from his possession. He approached it, and examined all its members, and found it sound; but when he was about to mount it and depart, he said within himself, I must see what the King's son hath brought and left here with the horse. Accordingly he entered the private chamber, and found the damsel sitting there, resembling the shining sun in the clear sky. As soon as he beheld her, he knew that she was a damsel of high dignity, and that the King's son had taken her, and brought her upon the horse, and left her in that private chamber while he repaired to the city to prepare for her a stately procession, and to conduct her into the city with respect and honour. The sage therefore went in to her, and kissed the ground before her; and she raised her eyes towards him, and, looking at him, found him to be of most hideous aspect and disagreeable form; and she said to him, Who art thou? He answered her, O my mistress, I am the messenger of the King's son, who hath sent me to thee, and commanded me to remove thee to another garden, near unto the city. And when the damsel heard from him these words, she said to him, And where is the King's son? He answered her, He is in the city, with his father, and he will come to thee immediately with a grand procession. But she said to him, O thou! could not the King's son find any one to send to me but thee?—And the sage laughed at her words, and replied, O my mistress, let not the hideousness of my face and the disagreeableness of my aspect deceive thee; for hadst thou experienced of me what the King's son hath, thou wouldst approve of me. Verily the King's son hath especially chosen me to send to thee on account of the hideousness of my aspect and the horrible nature of my form, through his jealousy of thee, and his love of thee; for were it otherwise, he hath of memlooks and black slaves, and pages and servants and dependants, an abundance that cannot be calculated.

So when the damsel heard his reply, it appeared reasonable to her, and she believed it, and arose and went with him, putting her hand in his. She then said to him, O my father, what hast thou brought with thee for me to ride?—O my mistress, he answered, the horse on which thou camest thou shalt ride. She replied, I cannot ride it by myself. And when he heard this reply from her, the sage smiled, and knew that he had got possession of her; and he said to her, I myself will ride with thee. Then he mounted, and mounted the damsel behind him, and, pressing her to him, bound her tightly, while she knew not what he desired to do with her. And after this, he turned the pin of ascent, whereupon the body of the horse became filled with air, and it moved and bestirred itself, and ascended into the sky, and continued incessantly bearing them along until it was out of sight of the city. So the damsel said to him, O thou! what meant that which thou saidst respecting the King's son, when thou assertedst that he sent thee to me?—The sage replied, May Allah keep the King's son from every thing good; for he is base and vile!—O, wo to thee! she exclaimed; how is it that thou disobeyest thy lord in that which he hath commanded thee to do? He replied, He is not my lord. And knowest thou, he added, who I am? She answered him, I know thee not but as thou hast informed me of thyself. And he said to her, Verily my telling thee this was a stratagem that I made use of against thee and against the King's son. I was lamenting constantly for this horse that is beneath thee, for it is of my making, and he had made himself master of it; but now I have obtained possession of it and of thee also, and have tortured his heart as he hath tortured mine, and he will never have it in his power henceforth. But be of good heart and cheerful eye; for I shall be more useful to thee than he.—And when the damsel heard his words, she slapped her face, and cried out, O my grief! I have neither obtained my beloved nor remained with my father and my mother!—And she wept violently for that which had befallen her, while the sage incessantly proceeded with her to the country of the Greeks,[15] until he descended with her in a verdant meadow with rivers and trees.

This meadow was near unto a city, in which was a King of great dignity; and it happened on that day that the King of the city went forth to hunt, and to divert himself, and, passing by that meadow, he saw the sage standing there, with the horse and the damsel by his side. And the sage was not aware of their approach when the slaves of the King rushed upon him, and took him, together with the damsel and the horse, and placed all before the King, who, when he beheld the hideousness of his aspect, and the disagreeableness of his appearance, and beheld the beauty of the damsel, and her loveliness, said to her, O my mistress, what relation is this sheykh to thee? The sage hastily answered and said, She is my wife, and the daughter of my paternal uncle. But the damsel declared that he was a liar, as soon as she heard his words, and said, O King, by Allah I know him not, and he is not my husband; but he took me away by force and stratagem. And when the King heard what she said, he gave orders to beat the sage; and they beat him until he almost died. Then the King commanded that they should carry him to the city, and cast him into the prison; and so they did with him; and the King took the damsel and the horse from him; but he knew not the property of the horse, nor the mode of its motion.—Thus did it befall the sage and the damsel.

As to the King's son, he put on the apparel of travel, and, having taken what money he required, journeyed forth in a most evil state, and quickly endeavoured to trace them, seeking them from town to town and from city to city, and inquiring respecting the ebony horse; and every one who heard his mention of the ebony horse wondered at it, and was greatly astonished at his words. Thus he continued to do for a long period; but notwithstanding his frequent questions and his searching for them, he met with no tidings of them. Then he journeyed to the city of the damsel's father, and there inquired for her, but he heard no tidings of her, and he found her father mourning for her loss. So he returned, and repaired to the country of the Greeks, endeavouring to trace them, and inquiring respecting them. And it happened that he alighted at one of the Kháns, and saw a party of the merchants sitting conversing; and he seated himself near them, and heard one of them say, O my companions, I have met with

a wonderful thing.—And what was it? they asked. He answered, I was in a certain district, in such a city (and he mentioned the name of the city in which was the damsel), and I heard its inhabitants talking of a strange story, which was this:—The King of the city went forth one day to hunt, attended by a party of his associates and the grandees of his empire, and when they went forth into the desert, they passed by a verdant meadow, and found there a man standing, and by his side a woman sitting, and with him a horse of ebony. As to the man, he was of hideous aspect, very horrible in form; and as to the woman, she was a damsel endowed with beauty and loveliness, and elegance and perfect grace, and justness of stature; and as to the ebony horse, it was a wonderful thing: eyes have not beheld its superior in beauty or in comeliness of make.—The persons present said to him, And what did the King with them? He answered, As to the man, the King took him, and asked him respecting the damsel, and he pretended that she was his wife, and the daughter of his paternal uncle. But as to the damsel, she declared that he lied in his assertion. So the King took her from him, and gave orders to beat him, and to cast him into the prison. And as to the ebony horse, I know not what became of it.—When the King's son therefore heard these words from the merchant, he approached him, and proceeded to question him with mildness and courtesy until he acquainted him with the name of the city and the name of its King; and when he knew the name of the city and that of its King, he passed the night happy; and in the morning he went forth on his journey.

He ceased not to prosecute his journey until he arrived at that city; but when he desired to enter it, the gate-keepers took him, and would have conducted him into the presence of the King, that he might inquire of him respecting his condition, and of the cause of his coming into that city, and as to what art or trade he was skilled in; for so was the King's custom to question the strangers respecting their conditions and their arts or trades. But the arrival of the King's son at that city happened to be at eventide; and that was a time at which it was not possible to go in to the King or to consult respecting him. So the gate-keepers took him and conducted him to the prison, to put him in it. When the jailers, however, saw his beauty and loveliness, they could not bear to put him in the prison: on the contrary, they seated him with themselves, outside the prison; and when the food was brought to them, he ate with them until he was satisfied; and after they had finished eating, they sat conversing, and, addressing the King's son, they said to him, From what country art thou? He answered, I am from the country of Persia, the country of the Kisràs. And when they heard his answer, they laughed, and one of them said to him, O Kisrawee,[16] I have heard the sayings of men, and their histories, and have observed their conditions; but I have neither seen, nor heard of, a greater liar than this Kisrawee who is with us in the prison. And another said, Nor have I seen any one more hideous than he in person, or more disagreeable than he in form.

So the King's son said to them, What instance of his lying hath appeared unto you? They answered, He pretendeth that he is a sage, and the King saw him as he was going to hunt, and with him a woman of surprising beauty and loveliness, and elegance and perfect grace, and justness of stature, and there was with him also a horse of black ebony, than which we have never seen any more handsome. As to the damsel, she is with the King, and he loveth her; but the woman is mad; and if that man were a sage as he pretendeth, he had cured her; for the King is striving to find her remedy, desiring to recover her of her malady. As to the ebony horse, it is in the King's treasury; and as to the man of hideous aspect, who was with it, he is with us in the prison; and when the night overshadoweth him, he weepeth and waileth in his grief for himself, and suffereth us not to sleep.

Now when the keepers of the prison acquainted the King's son with these circumstances, it occurred to his mind that he might contrive a plan by means of which to attain his desire. And when the gate-keepers desired to sleep, they put him into the prison, and closed the door upon him; and he heard the sage weeping and lamenting for himself in the Persian language, and saying in his lamentation, Wo unto me for the injustice that I have committed against myself and against the King's son, and for that which I did unto the damsel, since I neither left her nor accomplished my desire. All this arose from my ill management; for I sought for myself that which I deserved not, and which was not suited to me; and he who seeketh that which is not suited to him falleth into a calamity like that into which I have fallen.—And when the King's son heard these words of the sage, he spoke to him in the Persian language, saying, How long wilt thou continue this weeping and lamentation? Dost thou think that such a misfortune hath befallen thee as hath not befallen any beside thee?—And the sage, on hearing his words, was cheered by him, and complained to him of his case, and of the distress he experienced.

Then, when the morning came, the gate-keepers took the King's son, and conducted him to the King, and informed him that he had arrived at the city on the preceding day, at a time when it was impossible to go in unto the King. So the King questioned him, and said to him, From what country art thou, and what is thy name, and what thy art or trade, and what the reason of thy coming unto this city? And the King's son answered, As to my name, it is, in the Persian language, Ḥarjeh;[17] and as to my country, it is the country of Persia; and I am of the men of science, especially the science of medicine; for I cure the sick and the mad; and for this purpose I travel about through the regions and cities, to profit myself by adding science to my science; and when I see a sick person, I cure him. This is my occupation.—And when the King heard his words, he rejoiced at them exceedingly, and said to him, O excellent sage, thou hast come to us at a time when we need thee. Then he acquainted him with the case of the damsel, and said to him, If thou cure her, and recover her of her madness, thou shalt receive from me all that thou shalt desire. And the King's son, on hearing this, replied, May God confirm the power of the King! Describe to me every thing that thou hast observed of her madness, and inform me how many days ago this madness attacked her, and how thou tookest her and the horse and the sage.—He therefore acquainted him with the matter from beginning to end, and said to him, The sage is in the

prison. And the King's son said, O happy King, and what hast thou done with the horse that was with them? The King answered him, It remaineth with me to the present time, preserved in one of the private chambers. So the King's son said within himself, It is my opinion that I should examine the horse before every thing else, and if it be sound, and no accident have happened to it, all that I desire is accomplished; but if I see that its motions are destroyed, I will yet devise some stratagem to save my life. Then looking towards the King, he said to him, O King, it is requisite that I see the horse which thou hast mentioned. Perhaps I may find in it something that will aid me to recover the damsel.—The King replied, Most willingly. And he arose, and, taking him by the hand, led him in to the horse; whereupon the King's son began to go round about the horse, and to examine it and observe its condition; and he found it sound, without any defect. He therefore rejoiced at it exceedingly, and said, May God confirm the power of the King! I desire to go in to the damsel, that I may see how she will act; and I beg of God that her recovery may be effected by me, by means of the horse, if it be the will of God, whose name be exalted!

He gave orders to take care of the horse, and the King conducted him to the chamber in which was the damsel. And when the King's son went in to her, he found her beating herself, and falling down prostrate as usual; but she was affected by no madness, and only did thus that no one might approach her. So the King's son, on seeing her in this state, said to her, No harm shall befall thee, O temptation to all creatures! Then he began to address her gently and courteously until he acquainted her with himself; and when she knew him, she uttered a great cry, and fell down in a fit through the violence of the joy that she experienced; and the King imagined that this fit was occasioned by her fear of him. And the King's son put his mouth to her ear, and said to her, O temptation to all creatures, spare my life and thine, and be patient and firm; for this is a place wherein we stand in need of patience and good management in devising stratagems to make our escape from this tyrannical King. A part of my stratagem shall be, that I go forth to him and say to him, The disease that she suffereth ariseth from her being possessed by a Jinnee,[18] and I promise thee her recovery. And I will make a condition with him that he shall loose thy bonds, and will assure him that this Jinnee which hath afflicted thee[19] will be dispelled from thee. Therefore if he come in to thee, address him with pleasant words, that he may see that thou hast recovered through my means, and so shall all that we desire be accomplished.—And she replied, I hear and obey.—He then went forth from her, and, returning to the King, full of joy and happiness, said, O fortunate King, I have discovered, through thy good fortune, her remedy and cure, and I have cured her for thee. Arise then and go in to her, and speak gently and mildly to her, and promise her that which shall rejoice her; for all that thou desirest of her shall be accomplished for thee.—The King therefore arose and went in to her; and when she saw him, she rose to him, and kissed the ground before him, and welcomed him; whereat the King rejoiced exceedingly. He ordered the female slaves and eunuchs to betake themselves to serve her, to conduct her into the bath, and to prepare for her the ornaments and apparel. So they went in to her and saluted her, and she returned their salutation with the most courteous utterance and the most pleasant words. Then they attired her in royal apparel, put upon her neck a necklace of jewels, conducted her to the bath, served her, and brought her out from the bath, resembling the full moon. And when she came to the King, she saluted him, and kissed the ground before him.

The King therefore was greatly rejoiced at seeing her thus, and said to the King's son, All this is occasioned by the blessings attendant upon thee! May God increase to us thy benefactions!—And the King's son replied, O King, the perfection of her recovery and the completion of her affair must be effected by thy going forth with all thy guards and thy soldiers to the place where thou foundest her, and the ebony horse that was with her must be taken with thee, that I may there confine from her the Jinnee that hath afflicted her, and imprison him and kill him, so that he may never return to her. The King said, Most willingly. Accordingly he sent forth the ebony horse to the meadow in which he had found the damsel with the horse and the Persian sage, and the King mounted with his troops, taking the damsel with him; and they knew not what he desired to do. And when they arrived at that meadow, the King's son who feigned himself a sage ordered that the damsel and the horse should be placed as far from the King and the troops as the eye could reach, and said to the King, With thy permission and leave, I desire to burn perfumes, and to recite a form of exorcism, and imprison the Jinnee here, that he may never return to her. After which, I will mount the ebony horse, and mount the damsel behind me; and when I have done that, the horse will move about with violent action, and walk forward

until it cometh to thee, when the affair will be finished, and thou shalt do with her what thou wilt.—And when the King heard his words, he rejoiced exceedingly. Then the King's son mounted the horse, and placed the damsel behind him, while the King and all his troops looked at him. And he pressed her to him, and bound her firmly, and turned the pin of ascent; whereupon the horse rose with them into the air. The troops continued gazing at him until he disappeared from before their eyes; and the King remained half a day expecting his return to him; but he returned not: so he despaired of him, and repented greatly, and grieved for the separation of the damsel. Then he took his troops, and returned to his city.

But as to the King's son, he bent his course to the city of his father, full of joy and happiness, and ceased not in his journey until he descended upon his palace, when he took down the damsel into the palace, and felt secure of her. He then repaired to his father and his mother, and saluted them, and acquainted them with the arrival of the damsel; whereat they rejoiced exceedingly.—Meanwhile, the King of the Greeks, when he returned to his city, secluded himself in his palace, mourning and afflicted. So his wezeers went in to him, and began to console him, saying to him, Verily he who took the damsel is an enchanter; and praise be to God who hath saved thee from his enchantment and craftiness. And they ceased not until he was consoled for the loss of her.—And as to the King's son, he made magnificent banquets for the people of the city, and they continued the rejoicings for a whole month; after which, he took the damsel as his wife, and they were delighted with each other exceedingly. And his father broke the ebony horse, and destroyed its motions. Then the King's son wrote a letter to the father of the damsel, and in it described to him his state, informing him that he had married the damsel, and that she was with him in the most happy condition. He sent it to him by a messenger, bearing precious presents and rarities; and when the messenger arrived at the city of the damsel's father, which was Ṣan'à of El-Yemen, he transmitted the letter, with the presents, to that King, who, on reading the letter, rejoiced exceedingly, accepted the presents, and treated the messenger with honour. He then prepared a magnificent present for his son-in-law, the King's son, and sent it to him by that messenger, who returned with it to the King's son, and informed him of the joy which the King, the father of the damsel, experienced when he brought him the news of his daughter. At this the King's son was affected with great happiness; and every year he wrote to his father-in-law, and sent him a present.

Thus they continued until the King, the father of the young man, was taken from the world; and the young man reigned after him over his dominions. He ruled his subjects with equity, and conducted himself among them in a laudable manner; the country was subject to him, and the people obeyed him: and thus they remained, passing the most delightful and most agreeable and most comfortable and most pleasant life, until they were visited by the terminator of delights and the separator of companions, the devastator of palaces and the replenisher of the graves.—Extolled then be the perfection of the Living who dieth not, and in whose hand is the dominion that is apparent and the dominion that is hidden![20]

NOTES TO CHAPTER SEVENTEENTH.

NOTE 1. The words "in the country of the Persians" are not in my original. In the Breslau edition, the King mentioned immediately after is called "a King of the Persians, named the King Sáboor," an Arabic corruption of "Shápoor," which was a name borne by several Kings of Persia. In the old version, the court of this monarch is said to have been at Sheeráz.—On the origin of the tale of the Magic Horse some remarks will be made in the last note of the present series.

NOTE 2.—*On the Persian Festival of the Autumnal Equinox.* The sentence to which this note refers I have taken from the Breslau edition, correcting some errors. Of the first of the two festivals here mentioned, I have already given some account.[1]

The festival of the Autumnal Equinox, called "Mihrgán," "Mihrján," and "Mahraján" (the last of which terms is that by which the Arabs call it), was one of the greatest of those celebrated by the ancient Persians. It began on the 16th of Mihr, the seventh month. "Many traditional motives are assigned for the origin of this solemnity, which was held for six days; but the most rational conjecture leads us to conclude that it was instituted at this season of the autumnal equinox in honour of their great ostensible deity, the Sun; as the other high festival of the Now-róz was, on the same principles, intended to celebrate the sun's entering the constellation Aries. The sixteenth was more particularly distinguished than the rest; all who could afford the purchase anointing themselves then with the oil of bán,[2] sprinkling themselves with rose-water, and eating of various fruits, from an idea that such observances would defend them from a number of evils which might otherwise distress them in the course of the year. The King, on the first day of this festival, after anointing himself with the oil of bán, dressed in a superb robe of many colours, his head adorned with the royal táj (or diadem), on which was a splendid figure of the Sun, seated himself on his throne; when the high priest, entering alone, with a large silver dish, filled with sugar, peaches, quinces, apples, citrons, pomegranates, the jujube, the lote, a bunch of white grapes, and seven myrtle-berries, muttered over them a prayer, and presented them to the King, who ate of them all; after which, the nobility and others, approaching according to their rank, followed their sovereign's example; when a variety of

---

[1] In Note 19 to Chapter xvi.

[2] Generally called by English writers "ben."

robes and other rich furniture, from the royal wardrobes, were distributed amongst them in proportion to their degree. On this day it was esteemed fortunate to wean or name children; and if a son was then born to the King, he was immediately, with great solemnity, consecrated high priest of the Sun."[3]

NOTE 3. The words "during one of these festivals" I have inserted from the Breslau edition.

NOTE 4. In the Breslau edition, the peacock is described as being in the middle of a basin of silver, and surrounded by four and twenty young ones of gold; and the owner of it explains that at the expiration of each hour, the peacock would peck one of its young ones; then, at the end of another hour, a second of them; and so on; and that at the termination of the month, it would open its beak, and that the new moon would be seen in it.

NOTE 5. Instead of a mere trumpet, the Breslau edition describes "a figure of gold set with fine and precious stones and jewels, with a trumpet of gold in its hand;" but "naḳeer" is put for "nefeer," a trumpet.

NOTE 6. In the Breslau edition, the sage is said to have first mounted the ebony horse, and ascended on it, and descended. Afterwards, the King's youngest daughter, whom he had granted in marriage to the owner of the horse, disgusted with the hideous aspect of this person, implores the assistance of her brother, who remonstrates with the King, and is induced by him to try the wonderful properties of the horse in order that he may consent to the marriage, nearly as in the tale of Cleomades and Claremond, with which, in some other particulars, the story of the Magic Horse in the Breslau edition agrees more nearly than that in the edition of Cairo; as also does the story in each of these editions more than that in Galland's version. To the tale of Cleomades and Claremond I shall have occasion to revert.

NOTE 7. See Note 15 to Chapter iii.

NOTE 8. Literally, "by 'Say, I seek refuge with the Lord of Men' and 'the Day-break:'" that is, by repeating the last Chapter, and the last but one, of the Ḳur-án; which are called "the Two Preventives." See Note 18 to Chapter x, and Note 58 to Chapter viii.

NOTE 9. See Note 50 to Chapter x.—This would refer the story to a period antecedent to the conquest of Persia by the Muslims; but such is evidently not the idea of the Arab narrator.

NOTE 10. That is, as though he would eat the Prince. See Note 21 to the Introduction.

NOTE 11. In the Breslau edition, this King is called "Ḳeyṣar;" that is, Cæsar: but in the edition from which I translate, his kingdom is El-Yemen, or Arabia Felix.

NOTE 12. This princess is called, in the Breslau edition, "Shems-en-Nahár," which signifies "the Sun of Day."

NOTE 13. Ṣan'à is the capital of El-Yemen, and a very ancient city. It is celebrated for its trees and waters, and hence compared to Damascus.

NOTE 14. From the commencement of this paragraph to the end of the two verses, I have taken from the Breslau edition, correcting some obvious errors.

NOTE 15. In the original, "Bilád er-Room." This name is applied by some of the Arab geographers to the territories constituting Modern Greece and European Turkey; but by others, to the greater part of Asia Minor. The latter I suppose to be

---

[3] Richardson's Persian, Arabic, and English Dictionary, Johnson's edition, *voce* "máh."

here meant. Instead of "the country of the Greeks," we have in the Breslau edition, China; and in Galland's version, Kashmeer.

NOTE 16. "Kisrawee" here signifies "a subject of Kisrà;" i. e. of the Persian Monarch.

NOTE 17. This name, I fancy, has been altered by a copyist.

NOTE 18. It is the general belief of the Arabs, that furious or dangerous madness is occasioned by the patient's being possessed by a devil, or evil Jinnee; and the usual term applied to it (namely "junoon") signifies this.

NOTE 19. Literally, "this accident," or "— misfortune," &c. My sheykh, by a note on a later passage, authorizes the rendering which I have adopted.

NOTE 20. This story differs so little from that of Cleomades and Claremond that it is evident that one of these was derived, immediately or mediately, from the other, or that both of them are derived from a common origin. Of the latter story, Mr. Keightley has given a copious extract,[4] to which he has subjoined several notices of the mention of magic horses of wood, the brazen horse of King Cambuscan, and enchanted horses of flesh and blood. He shews that "Cleomades and Claremond" was written in the thirteenth century of our era, and remarks, "The story, as every one must see, is that of the Enchanted Horse in the Thousand and One Nights; and it is a very remarkable instance of the transmission of fictitious narratives, little altered, from distant regions. . . . The Enchanted Horse," he adds, "is in my opinion an ancient Persian tale, from the time of the Shápoors and Yezdejirds." I agree with him in regarding it as an old Persian tale, and think that it is probably derived from the "Hezár Afsáneh."

[4] In his "Tales and Popular Fictions," ch. ii.

CHAPTER XVIII.

COMMENCING WITH PART OF THE THREE HUNDRED AND SEVENTY-FIRST NIGHT, AND ENDING WITH PART OF THE THREE HUNDRED AND EIGHTY-FIRST.

THE STORY OF UNS-EL-WUJOOD AND EL-WARD FI-L-AKMÁM.[1]

There was, in ancient times, a King of great dignity, possessed of glory and absolute power, and he had a Wezeer named Ibráheem, who had a daughter of surprising beauty and loveliness, surpassing in elegance and in every grace, endowed with abundant sense and eminent polite accomplishments; but she loved carousing and wine, and comely faces, and pretty verses, and strange histories. The delicacy of her charms enticed the minds of mankind to love. Her name was El-Ward fi-l-Akmám;[2] and the reason of her being so named was her excessive delicacy of beauty, and her perfect elegance; and the King was fond of carousing with her, on account of her accomplished manners.

Now it was the custom of the King, every year, to collect the chief men of his dominions, and to play with the ball.[3] And on one of those days when he did so, the daughter of the Wezeer sat at a lattice-window to amuse herself; and while they were engaged in the game, she cast a glance, and beheld among the soldiers a young man, than whom there was none more handsome in aspect, nor any more beautiful in appearance; bright in countenance, with laughing teeth, generous, wide-shouldered. She looked at him again and again, and was not satiated with gazing at him; and she said to her nurse, What is the name of this young man of comely qualities, who is among the soldiers? The nurse replied, O my daughter, all of them are comely. Who then among them?—Wait, rejoined the damsel, until I point him out to thee. And she took an apple, and threw it upon him. So he raised his head, and beheld the Wezeer's daughter at the window,[4] resembling the full moon in the darkness of night; and he withdrew not his eye without his heart's being engrossed by love for her; and he recited the saying of the poet:—

Hath the archer shot me, or have thine eyes? Thou hast destroyed the heart of the enamoured on his looking at thee.
Hath the notched arrow been suddenly[5] lanced at me from the midst of an army or from a window?

And when the game was ended, the damsel said to her nurse, What is the name of this young man whom I have shewn to thee? She answered, His name is Uns-el-Wujood.[6] And upon this, she shook her head, and laid herself down upon her mattress; her mind was fired, and she uttered groans, and recited these verses:—

He hath missed not who named thee the Delight of the World, O thou who impartest both delight and liberality![7]
O thou whose countenance resembleth the full moon, and whose face diffuseth light over all the creation!
Thou art without an equal among mankind, the sovereign of beauty, and I have witnesses to prove it.
Thine eyebrow is like a well-formed Noon; and thine eye, like Ṣád, the work of the Benevolent.[8]

Thy figure resembleth a fresh, slender branch; and if asked, thou givest every thing liberally.
Thou surpassest the horsemen of the world in assault, and in imparting delight, and in beauty and beneficence.

She then wrote these verses on a paper, which she wrapped in a piece of silk embroidered with gold, and put beneath the pillow. And one of her nurses was looking at her; so this nurse came to her, and proceeded to engage her with conversation until she slept, when she stole the paper from beneath the pillow, and read it. She therefore knew that she was affected with a violent passion for Uns-el-Wujood; and after she had read the paper, she put it again in its place. And when her mistress awoke, she said to her, O my mistress, I am an admonisher unto thee, and one who pitieth thee. Know that love is difficult, and the concealment of it would melt iron, and occasioneth diseases and infirmities; and the person who revealeth love is not obnoxious to reproach.—Upon this, El-Ward fi-l-Akmám said to her, O my nurse, and what is the remedy for desire?—Its remedy, answered the nurse, is an interview.—And how can that be obtained? said the damsel. The nurse answered, O my mistress, it may be obtained by means of letters, and gentle words, and by many compliments and salutations; for this mode of proceeding bringeth lovers together, and by it things that are difficult are rendered easy; and if thou have any affair to be performed, O my lady, I am most fit to conceal thy secret, and to accomplish thy business, and bear thy letter. And when El-Ward fi-l-Akmám heard these words from her, her reason fled, through joy; but she withheld herself from replying, that she might see the result of her affair, and said within herself, Verily this thing no one hath known from me, and I will not reveal it to this woman until after I shall have tried her. Then the woman said to her, O my mistress, I saw in my sleep as though a man came to me and said to me, Thy mistress and Uns-el-Wujood love each other: therefore manage their affair, and carry their letters, and accomplish their wants, and conceal their case and their secrets: so wilt thou experience abundant good fortune. Now I have related to thee what I saw, and it is thine to decide.—And El-Ward fi-l-Akmám said to her nurse, when she had thus informed her of the dream that she had (as she pretended) seen, Wilt thou conceal secrets, O my nurse? The nurse replied, How should I not conceal secrets when I am of the choicest of the ingenuous?

Upon this, therefore, the damsel produced to her the paper upon which she had written the verses, saying to her, Repair with this my note to Uns-el-Wujood, and bring me an answer to it. So she took it, and went with it to Uns-el-Wujood; and when she went in to him, she kissed his hands, complimented him with the most courteous words, and gave him the paper; and after he had read it, and understood its meaning, he wrote upon the back of it these verses:—

I soothe my heart in my passion, and conceal it; but my state interpreteth and sheweth my love.
When my tears flow, I say, My eye is sore—lest the censurer should see and understand my condition.
I was free from care, and knew not what was love; but have become enamoured, and with enslaved heart.
I submit to you my case, complaining of my passion and my ecstasy, in the hope that you will pity, and shew mercy:
I have written it with the tears of my eye, that perchance it may explain to you the love with which you have affected me.
God guard a face that is veiled with loveliness! The full moon is its slave, and the stars are its servants.
In beauty, I have never beheld her equal; and from her motions, the branches might learn to wave.
I beg, without imposing on yourself a trouble, that you will pay us a visit; for we should highly esteem it.
I give you my soul—perhaps you will accept it—for to me, union will be Paradise, and aversion will be Hell.

Then he folded the letter, kissed it, and gave it to her, saying to her, O nurse, conciliate the favour of thy mistress. She replied, I hear and obey. And she took from him the letter, and returned to her mistress, and gave it to her; and she kissed it, and put it on her head; after which, she opened it and read it, and understood its meaning; and she wrote beneath it these verses:—

O thou whose heart is enamoured by our beauty, have patience in thy love, and perhaps thou wilt obtain us.
When we knew that thine affection was true, and that the passion that hath afflicted our heart had afflicted thine,
We would have granted thee the union thou desirest, and more; but were prevented doing so by our chamberlains.
When the night becometh dark, through the excess of our love, fires are kindled within our bosoms,
And sleep is driven away from our beds, and often are our bodies afflicted by our passion.
An imperative law in love's code is concealment. Raise not the curtains that are lowered over us.
My bosom is filled with love of the gazelle. Would that he were never distant from our home!

And when she had finished her verses, she folded the paper, and gave it to the nurse, who took it, and went forth from her; but the chamberlain met her, and said to her, Whither art thou going? She answered, To the bath. And she was alarmed at him, and the paper fell from her as she went forth from the door in her alarm, and one of the eunuchs, seeing it lying in the way, took it. Then the Wezeer came forth from the Ḥareem, and seated himself upon his couch, and the eunuch who had picked up the paper repaired to him. So while the Wezeer was sitting upon his couch, lo, that eunuch approached him, with the paper in his hand, and said to him, O my lord, I found this paper thrown down in the house, and I took it. The Wezeer therefore took it from his hand, folded as it was, and opened it, and saw written upon it the verses above mentioned. He read them, and understood their meaning; and then, examining the writing, he found it to be that of his daughter; whereupon he went in to her mother, weeping violently, so that his beard was wetted. His wife said to him, What hath caused thee to weep, O my lord? And he replied, Take this paper, and see its contents. So she took the paper, and read it, and found it to be a letter from her daughter El-Ward fi-l-Akmám to Uns-el-Wujood; upon which she was affected with an inclination to weep; but she subdued her mind, and restrained her tears, and said to the Wezeer, O my lord, there is no profit in weeping. The right opinion is this: that we consider a plan by which to protect thy honour, and to conceal the affair of thy daughter.—And she proceeded to console him, and to alleviate his sorrows. But he said to her, Verily I am in fear for my daughter on account of her passion. Knowest thou not that the Sulṭán loveth Uns-el-Wujood with a great affection? There are two causes for my fear. The first is, with respect to myself; she being my daughter. And the second is, with respect to the Sulṭán; Uns-el-Wujood being a favourite with the Sulṭán; and probably an affair of great moment may hence ensue. What then dost thou see fit to be done in this case?—She replied, Have patience with me until I shall have performed the prayer for direction in the right course. Then she performed the prayers of two rek'ahs, the prophetic ordinance for seeking to be directed aright;[9] and when she had finished her prayers, she said to her husband, In the midst of the Sea of the Kunooz[10] is a mountain called the Mountain of the Bereft Mother (and the cause of its being so named will be mentioned hereafter), and to that mountain none can obtain access, unless with difficulty: therefore make for her a place there.

So the Wezeer agreed with his wife that he should build there an impregnable palace, and place her in it, and put with her the provisions necessary for her year after year, and place with her such attendants as should cheer her and serve her. He collected the carpenters and builders and architects, and sent them to that mountain; and they built for her an impregnable palace, such as eyes had never beheld. Then he prepared the provisions for the journey, and the caravan to accompany her; and, going in to his daughter at night, commanded her to set forth on the journey. So her heart felt the pangs of separation, and when she went forth, and saw the preparation for travel, she wept violently, and wrote some words on the door to acquaint Uns-el-Wujood with the transport of passion that she experienced, which was such as would make the flesh to quake, and melt the heart of rock, and make tears to flow: and what she wrote consisted of these verses:—

By Allah, O house, if the beloved pass by, in the morning, saluting with the signals of lovers,
Give him from us a pure and fragrant greeting; for he knoweth not where we pass the evening;
And I know not whither they have journeyed with us, proceeding quickly, and lightly equipped,
By night, when the birds of the thicket, perched upon the branches, bewail us and announce our fate;
The tongue of their condition saying, Alas, for the bereavement effected by the disjunction of the lovers!
When I saw that the cups of separation were filled, and fate would by force make us drink them undiluted,
I mixed them with becoming patience, to excuse myself; but now patience consoleth us not for the loss of you.

And when she had finished her verses, she mounted, and they journeyed with her, crossing the deserts and wastes, and the plain and rugged tracts, until they arrived at the Sea of the Kunooz, when they pitched the tents upon the shore, and built for her a great vessel, in which they embarked the damsel and her household. The Wezeer had commanded them, that, when they had arrived at the mountain, and had taken her into the palace, together with her household, they should return with the vessel, and, after they had landed, that they should break it up. So they went and did all that he had commanded them, and returned weeping for that which had happened.—Such was their case.

But as to Uns-el-Wujood, he rose from his sleep, and, having performed the morning-prayers, mounted, and repaired to attend upon the Sulṭán. And he passed in his way by the door of the Wezeer, as he was wont to do, in the hope that perhaps he might see some one of

the Wezeer's dependants whom he was accustomed to see; and he looked at the door, and beheld the verses above-mentioned written upon it. On seeing them he became unconscious of his existence; a fire was kindled in his vitals, and he returned to his house. He could not rest, nor be patient, and he ceased not to suffer agitation of mind, and transport, until the night came; when he concealed his case, and disguised himself; and he went forth in the middle of the night, wandering at random, and not knowing whither to go. He journeyed on during the whole of the remainder of that night, and the next day until the heat of the sun became fierce, and the mountains were of a burning heat, and thirst violently oppressed him; but he beheld a tree, and found by the side of it a stream of water. So he went to that tree, and seated himself in its shade, on the bank of that stream, and desired to drink; but he found that the water had no taste in his mouth. His complexion had changed, his face had become sallow, and his feet were swollen by walking and toil; and he wept violently, pouring forth tears, and recited these verses:—

The lover is intoxicated by his passion; but when his desire increaseth, he recovereth.
Distracted in his love, ardent, bewildered, he findeth no abode nor food that pleaseth him.
How can life be agreeable to the enamoured who is parted from the object of his love? Were it so, it were wonderful.
I melt when I burn with transport for her, my tears flowing down upon my cheek in torrents.
Shall I see her, or see any one from her abode by whom the afflicted heart may be cured?

And when he had ended his verses, he wept until he wetted the ground. Then rising forthwith he proceeded from that place; and as he journeyed on through the deserts and wastes, there came forth upon him a lion, whose neck was closely covered with his hair, and his head was as large as a cupola, and his mouth wider than a door, with teeth like the tusks of the elephant. When Uns-el-Wujood beheld him, he made sure of destruction, and, turning his face towards the Ḳibleh,[11] he pronounced the two professions of the faith, and prepared for death. But he had read in books, that, if any one attempt to beguile the lion, he may be beguiled by him with kind words, and be rendered gentle by praise. So he began to say to him, O lion of the forest and the plain! O bold lion! O father of the generous! O Sulṭán of the wild beasts! verily I am a longing lover, whom passion and separation have consumed, and when I became severed from the beloved I lost my reason: hear then my words, and pity my ardour and desire.—And when the lion heard what he said, he drew back from him, and sat upon his tail; then raising his head towards him, he began to make playful motions to him with his tail

and fore-paws; and Uns-el-Wujood, on seeing him do thus, recited these verses:—

Lion of the desert, wilt thou kill me before I meet with her who hath enslaved me?
I am not game; nor am I fat: the loss of my beloved hath wasted me away,
And estrangement from her hath so consumed me that I am like a phantom wrapped in grave-clothes.
O Abu-l-Ḥárith![12] O lion of strife! make not the censurers to rejoice at my anguish.
I am burning with love, my tears have drowned me, and the absence of the beloved hath troubled my mind,
And my thoughts of her in the darkness of night have made me unconscious of my existence.

And as soon as he had finished his verses, the lion arose and walked gently towards him, with his eyes filled with tears; and when he came to him he licked him with his tongue, and then walked before him, making a sign to him, as though he would say, Follow me. So he followed him, and the lion proceeded, with Uns-el-Wujood behind him, for some time, until he had ascended to the summit of a mountain. Then he descended from that mountain, and Uns-el-Wujood beheld the track of travellers in the desert, and knew it to be that of the people who accompanied El-Ward fi-l-Akmám. He therefore followed this track; and when the lion saw that he did so, and that he knew it to be the track of the attendants of his beloved, he returned, and went his way.

Uns-el-Wujood proceeded along the track for days and nights, until he approached a roaring sea, agitated with waves; and the foot-marks reached to the shore of the sea, and there ended. So he knew that the people had embarked in a vessel on the sea and pursued their course over it; in consequence of which, his hope of finding them was then cut off, and he poured forth tears, and recited these verses:—

Distant is the place I seek, and my patience hath failed. How can I advance to her over the abyss of the sea?
Or how can I be patient when my vitals are consumed by love of her, and I have exchanged sleep for wakefulness?
Since the day when she journeyed forth from her home, my heart hath been inflamed with a vehement fire.
Like Seyḥoon and Jeyḥoon[13] and Euphrates are my tears: they form a flood more copious than deluge and rain.
My eyelids are sore from continual weeping, and my heart is tortured with fire and sparks.

And after reciting some more verses, he fell down in a fit, and he remained in it a long time. Then, recovering, he looked to the right and left; but saw no one in the desert; and he feared for himself on account of the wild beasts.

So he ascended a high mountain, and while he was upon it, he heard the voice of a human being, speaking in a cave; and he listened to him, and, lo, he was a devotee, who had forsaken the world, and occupied himself with devotion. He knocked at the door of the cave three times; but the devotee answered him not, nor came forth to him; and upon this, he uttered groans, and recited these verses:—

How can I find means to attain my desire, and be relieved from anxiety and trouble and weariness?
All terrors have united to render me aged in heart and head in the time of my youth,
And I find not any to aid me in my passion, nor a friend to alleviate my transport and toil.
How great are the troubles that I have suffered! Fortune seems turned entirely against me.
Oh, for mercy on the ardent and agitated lover, who hath drunk the cup of separation and abandonment!
Fire is in his heart, and his bowels are destroyed, and the pain of disjunction hath deprived him of reason.
How terrible was the day when I came to her abode, and beheld what was written upon the door!
I wept in my anguish till I wetted the ground; but concealed my case from the near and the distant.
O thou devotee who art idle in thy cave, as though thou hadst tasted and been captivated by love!
After all that I have suffered, if I gain my object, I shall not remember anxiety or fatigue.

And when he had ended his verses, lo, the door of the cave was opened, and he heard a person saying, Alas! Mercy!—So he entered the door, and saluted the devotee, who returned his salutation, and said to him, What is thy name? He answered, My name is Uns-el-Wujood. And the devotee said to him, What is the cause of thy coming unto this place? He therefore related to him his story from beginning to end, acquainting him with all that had befallen him. And on hearing it, the devotee wept, and said to him, O Uns-el-Wujood, verily I have been in this place twenty years without seeing in it any one, until lately, when I heard weeping and clamour, and, looking in the direction of the sounds, I saw many people, and tents pitched on the shore of the sea, and they built a vessel, in which a party of them embarked, and they proceeded in it over the sea. Then some of those who had embarked in the vessel returned with it, and broke it up, and went their way: and I imagine that those who passed over the sea and returned not are the people whom thou seekest, O Uns-el-Wujood. In that case, thine anxiety must be great, and thou art excused: but there existeth no lover who hath not endured griefs.—Then the devotee recited these verses:—

Uns-el-Wujood, dost thou think me free from care, when desire and transport kill me and resuscitate me?
I have known love and passion from my early years, since I was an infant nourished by milk.
Long I struggled with Love, till I became notorious: if thou ask respecting me, he will know me.
Lovesick and pining, I drank the cup of passion, and well nigh perished by the wasting of my body.
I was strong; but my strength became impaired, and the army of my patience fell beneath the swords of the eyes.
Hope not for union with the beloved without torment; for opposites are ever leagued together.
Love hath decreed against all its votaries, that relinquishment is forbidden as a wicked heresy.

Then the devotee arose and came to Uns-el-Wujood, and embraced him, and they both wept so that the mountains resounded with their cries. They ceased not to weep until they both fell down senseless; and when they recovered, they made a vow to be brothers in God (whose name be exalted!); after which, the devotee said to Uns-el-Wujood, I will this night pray, and beg of God to be rightly directed as to the course which thou shouldst pursue. And Uns-el-Wujood replied, I hear and obey.

Meanwhile, when the people had arrived with El-Ward fi-l-Akmám at the mountain, and taken her into the palace, and she beheld it, and beheld its order, she wept, and said, By Allah, thou art a beautiful place; but thou wantest the presence of the beloved in thee. And she saw birds in that island: so she ordered one of her attendants to set a snare for them, and catch some of them, and whenever he caught any, to put them in cages within the palace: and he did as she commanded him. Then she sat at a lattice-window of the palace, and, reflecting upon the events that had befallen her, her desire and transport and distraction increased; and she shed tears, and recited these verses:—

O, to whom shall I complain of the desire that I suffer, and my grief, and my disjunction from my beloved,
And the flame that rageth within my bosom; but which I shew not, in my fear of the watcher?
I have become extenuated like a tooth-pick, by estrangement and ardour and lamentation.
Where is the eye of the beloved to see how my state hath become like that of the distracted?

They tyrannized over me when they confined me in a place to which he can never come.
I beg the sun to give a thousand salutations, at the time of its rising, and again at its setting,
To the loved-one who shameth the full moon in beauty, and surpasseth in figure the slender branch.
If the rose be compared to his cheek, I say of it, Thou resemblest it not if thou be not of my portion.[14]
The moisture of his mouth is like pleasant wine that would cool me when a fire flameth within me.
How can I give him up who is my heart and my soul, a cause of wasting and sickness to me, but my beloved and my physician!

And when the darkness of night overshadowed her, her desire became more violent, and again she reflected upon past events, and recited some verses commencing thus:—

It is dark, and my transport and disease are excited, and desire provoketh my usual pain.
The torment of separation is constant in my bosom, and trouble of mind hath rendered me destitute.

Now to return to Uns-el-Wujood:—the devotee said to him,

Descend into the valley, and bring me, from the palm-trees, some of their fibres.[15] So he descended, and brought him some of the fibres of the palm-trees; and the devotee took them and twisted them, and made of them a kind of net,[16] like those used for carrying straw; after which he said, O Uns-el-Wujood, in the midst of the valley is a kind of gourd[17] that groweth up and drieth upon its roots: go down then to it, fill this net with the gourds, and tie it, and throw it into the sea: then place thyself upon it, and proceed upon it into the midst of the sea: perhaps thou wilt attain thy desire; for he who risketh not himself will not gain his object. To this, Uns-el-Wujood replied, I hear and obey. And he bade him farewell, and departed from him to do as he had directed him, after the devotee had prayed for him. He proceeded, without stopping, to the midst of the valley, and did as the devotee had said to him; and when he arrived, upon the net, in the midst of the sea, there came upon him a wind which propelled him with the net until he disappeared from before the eyes of the devotee. He ceased not to traverse the surface of the deep, one wave raising him and another depressing him, while he beheld the wonders and terrors of the sea, until destiny cast him upon the Mountain of the Bereft Mother, after three days. He landed like a giddy young bird, distressed by hunger and thirst; but he found, in that place, rivers flowing, and birds warbling upon the branches, and fruit-bearing trees of the same and of different kinds; and he ate of the fruits, and drank of the water of the rivers.

Then he arose and walked; and he beheld something white in the distance; so he proceeded thither until he arrived at it, when he found it to be an impregnable palace. He came to its gate, and found it closed; and he sat at it for three days: but at length, as he was sitting there, the gate of the palace was opened, and there came forth from it one of the eunuchs, who, seeing Uns-el-Wujood sitting, said to him, Whence hast thou come, and who brought thee hither? He answered, From Iṣpahán, and I was on a voyage with merchandise, and the vessel that I was in was wrecked, and the waves threw me upon this island. And the eunuch wept, and embraced him, saying, God prolong thy life, O chief of friends! Verily, Iṣpahán is my native place, and I have there a cousin, the daughter of a paternal uncle, whom I loved in my youth, and I was passionately attached to her; but a people stronger than we made war upon us, and took me with their spoil, while I was yet a youth, and sold me: thus have I become reduced to my present condition.—And after he had saluted him and wished him long life, he led him into the court of the palace, where, when he entered, he beheld a great pool surrounded by trees with spreading branches, and in it were birds in cages of silver with doors of gold: these cages were hung to the branches, and the birds within them were warbling, and singing the praises of the Requiting King. On his coming to the first of them, he looked at it; and, lo, it was a turtle-dove; and when it saw him, it raised its voice, crying, O Bountiful![18] Whereupon Uns-el-Wujood fell down in a fit; and on his recovering, he uttered groans, and recited these verses:—

O turtle-dove, art thou enamoured like me? Pray then to the Lord, and warble, O Bountiful!
Is this thy cry occasioned by merriment, or is it by desire dwelling in the heart?
If thou moanest from transport on account of the beloved that hath gone, and left thee wasted and pining,
And like me thou hast lost the object of affection, disjunction must manifest long-felt rapture.
O, may Allah guard a faithful lover! I will not relinquish her though my bones decay.

And when he had finished these verses, he wept until again he fell down in a fit; and after he had recovered, he went on to other cages, and addressed, in a similiar manner, a ring-dove, a hezár,[19] a nightingale, and a wood-pigeon, which last appeared as though it would utter these verses in reply:—

O thou lover, thou hast brought to my remembrance the time when my early strength failed,
And an object of love, of whose form I was enamoured, endowed with surpassing and tempting beauty,
Whose voice, as he sat upon the branches on the sand-hill, diverted me from listening to the sounds of the flute.
A fowler set for him a snare, and took him, while he cried, O, that he would leave me at large!
I hoped that he might be a man of compassion; or that, seeing me to be a lover, he would pity me.
But God overthrew him after he had thus with cruelty parted me from my beloved.
My desire for him hath become excessive, and hath tortured me with the fire of disjunction.
May Allah guard an impassioned lover, who hath struggled with love and hath known my sadness,
And, seeing me so long imprisoned in my cage, will in mercy loose me that I may fly to my beloved.

He then looked towards his friend, the man of Iṣpahán, and said to him, What is this palace, and what doth it contain, and who built it? The man answered him, The Wezeer of such a King built it for his daughter, fearing for her from misfortunes and calamities, and hath lodged her in it, together with her dependants, and it is not opened save once in every year, when their provisions are brought to them.—So he said within himself, My desire is accomplished; but the time to wait is long.

Now during this period, El-Ward fi-l-Akmám found neither drink nor food agreeable to her, nor sitting nor sleeping. Her desire and transport and distraction of love had increased; and she searched about in the corners of the palace, but found no way of escape for her; and she poured forth tears, and recited these verses:—

They have cruelly confined me from my beloved, and made me to taste of anguish in my prison.
They have tortured my heart with the fires of love, by preventing my beholding him.
In a lofty palace have they imprisoned me, on a mountain placed in the midst of the sea.
If they would have me forsake him, their wish is vain, for my love is become more trying.
How can I forsake him, when the origin of all that I suffer hath been the beholding his face?
The whole of my day is passed in sorrow, and the night I spend in thinking upon him.
Remembrance of him cheereth me in my solitude, while I find myself destitute of his presence.
Would that I knew if, after all this, fortune will consent to my heart's desire!

She then went up to the roof of the palace, and, taking some garments of the stuff of Baạla-bekk, tied herself by them, and let herself down until she came to the ground. She was attired in the most magnificent of her apparel, and on her neck was a necklace of jewels. And she proceeded over the adjacent deserts and wastes until she came to the shore of the sea, when she saw a fisherman going about in his vessel upon the sea to fish. The wind had cast him towards that island, and he looked, and saw there El-Ward fi-l-Akmám; but when he beheld her, he was frightened at her, and steered away his boat in flight. So she called him, making many signs to him, and recited some verses, informing him that she was a human being (not a Jinneeyeh, as he feared), and explaining her case; on hearing which, the fisherman wept and sighed and lamented, remembering what had happened to himself in the days of his youth, when love overpowered him, and his desire was violent, and his transport and distraction were excessive, the fires of passion burning him; and he replied to her in verse, telling her that he had been afflicted by love from his youth.

He then made fast his vessel to the land, and said to her, Embark in the vessel, that I may transport thee to whatsoever place thou desirest. So she embarked in the vessel, and he set it afloat with her, and when it had proceeded a little way from the land, there blew upon it a favourable wind, and the vessel advanced rapidly until the land disappeared from before their eyes. The fisherman then knew not whither to steer; and the wind continued violent for the space of three days; after which it subsided by the permission of God (whose name be exalted!), and the vessel bore them on until it came to a city on the shore of the sea, where the fisherman desired to make it fast.

In this city was a King of great power, named Dirbás.[20] He was at that time sitting with his son in his palace, and they were looking from a window, and, casting their eyes towards the sea, they saw that vessel; and on their observing it attentively, they found that there was in it a damsel like the full moon in the sky, having, in her ears, earrings of costly balass rubies, and on her neck, a necklace of precious jewels. The King therefore knew that she was of the daughters of the grandees or of the Kings, and he descended from his palace, and went forth from a door opening upon the sea; whereupon he saw the vessel made fast to the shore; and the damsel was sleeping, while the fisherman was busy in attaching the vessel. The King roused her from her sleep, and she awoke weeping; and the King said to her, Whence comest thou, and whose daughter art thou? and what is the cause of thy coming hither? So she answered him, I am the daughter of Ibráheem, the Wezeer of the King Shámikh,[21] and the cause of my coming hither is a wonderful event and an extraordinary affair. And she related to him her whole story, from beginning to end, hiding from him nothing; after which, she uttered groans, and recited some verses; and the King, on hearing them, was convinced of her transport and desire, and was moved with compassion for her; and he said to her, Thou hast no cause of fear nor of terror. Thou hast attained thy wish; for I must accomplish for thee what thou desirest, and procure for thee what thou seekest: and hear from me these words.—Then he recited these verses:—

Daughter of the noble, thou hast gained thine object. Receive good tidings, and fear not here fatigue.
This day will I collect wealth, and I will send it to Shámikh, attended by horsemen and heroes:
I will send to him bags of musk, and brocade, and white silver also will I send, and gold.
Yea; and my letters shall inform him for me that I am desirous of alliance with him;
And to-day will I use endeavours to aid thee, that what thou wishest for may be hastened.
I have tasted of love long, and known it, and excuse the person who hath drunk the same cup.

And when he had ended his verses, he went forth to his troops, and, having summoned his Wezeer, caused wealth incalculable to be packed up for him, and commanded him to repair with it to the King Shámikh, saying to him, Thou must without fail bring to me a person who is with him, named Uns-el-Wujood; and do thou say to him, The King desireth to form an alliance with thee by marrying his daughter to Uns-el-Wujood, thy dependant,[22] and he must be sent with me, that the ceremony of the contract of his marriage to her may be performed in the kingdom of her father.—Then the King Dirbás wrote a letter to the King Shámikh, to the effect above mentioned, and gave it to his Wezeer, strictly charging him to bring Uns-el-Wujood, and saying to him, If thou bring him not to me, thou shalt be displaced from thy station.

The Wezeer therefore replied, I hear and obey,—and repaired with the present to the King Shámikh. And when he came to him, he delivered to him the salutation of the King Dirbás, and gave him the letter and the present that he had brought. But when the King Shámikh saw them, and read the letter, and saw the name of Uns-el-Wujood, he wept violently, and said to the Wezeer who was sent to him, And where is Uns-el-Wujood? For he hath gone away, and we know not where he is. Bring him then to me, and I will give to thee double the presents thou hast brought.—Then he wept and sighed and lamented, poured forth tears, and recited these verses:—

Restore unto me my favourite: I am not in want of wealth;
Nor do I wish for presents of jewels or of pearls.
I brought him up an infant, upon the bed of fondness,
And verily I am mourning and troubled for him in mind.

And after this, he looked towards the Wezeer who had brought the present and the letter, and said to him, Repair to thy lord, and inform him that Uns-el-Wujood hath been absent for a year, and his lord knoweth not whither he hath gone, nor hath he any tidings of him. But the Wezeer replied, O my lord, verily my sovereign said to me, If thou bring him not to me, thou shalt be displaced from the post of Wezeer, and shalt not enter my city. How then can I go to him without him?—So the King Shámikh said to his Wezeer Ibráheem, Go thou with him, accompanied by a party of men, and search for Uns-el-Wujood in every quarter. And he replied, I hear and obey.

Accordingly he took a party of his dependants, and, accompanied by the Wezeer of the King Dirbás, they proceeded in search of Uns-el-Wujood; and whenever they passed by Arabs[23] or any people, they inquired of them respecting Uns-el-Wujood, saying to them, Hath there passed by you a person of such a name, and of such and such a description? To which they answered, We know him not. They ceased not to inquire in the cities and villages, and to search in the plain and rugged tracts, and the deserts and wastes, until they arrived at the shore of the sea; when they sought a vessel, and embarked in one, and proceeded in it until they approached the Mountain of the Bereft Mother. Upon this, the Wezeer of the King Dirbás said to the Wezeer of the King Shámikh, On what account is this mountain so named? And the latter answered, For this reason:—A Jinneeyeh sojourned upon it in ancient times, and that Jinneeyeh was of the Jinn of China. She loved a man, and became passionately attached to him; but she was in fear of her family; and, her desire becoming

excessive, she searched in the earth for a place wherein to conceal him from them, and found this mountain to be cut off from mankind and from the Jinn, so that no one of either of these races (herself excepted) found the way to it. She therefore carried off her beloved, and placed him there, and used to repair to her family, and to come to him privately; and thus she ceased not to do for a long time, until she bore him, on that mountain, a number of children. And those merchants who passed by this mountain in their voyages over the sea used to hear the weeping of the infants, like the weeping of a woman bereft of her children; whereupon they said, Is there here a bereft mother?—And the Wezeer of the King Dirbás wondered at these words.

Then they proceeded until they came to the palace, and they knocked at the door; upon which the door was opened, and there came forth to them a eunuch, who, knowing Ibráheem, the Wezeer of the King Shámikh, kissed his hands. And the Wezeer Ibráheem entered the palace, and found in its court a poor man among the servants; and he was Uns-el-Wujood. So he said to them, Whence is this man? And they answered him, He is a merchant: his property was lost at sea, and he saved himself; and he is a person abstracted from the world.[24] He therefore left him, and went on into the interior of the palace; but found no trace of his daughter; and he inquired of the female slaves who were there, and they answered him, We know not how she went, and she stayed not with us save for a short time. And upon this, he poured forth tears, and recited these verses:—

O thou mansion, the birds of which were singing, and the thresholds whereof were fortunate,
Until the enamoured came to thee bewailing his desire, and beheld the doors opened![25]
Would that I knew where my soul is gone, that was lately in a mansion whose mistress now is distant!
It was stored with every thing magnificent, and its chamberlains were happy and exalted,
And they clothed it with draperies of brocade. O, whither hath its mistress departed?

Then he wept and sighed and lamented, and said, There is no resource against that which God hath ordained, nor any escape from that which He hath predestined and decreed! And he ascended to the roof of the palace, and found the garments of the stuff of Baạla-bekk tied to the battlements and reaching to the ground. So he knew that she had descended from that place, and gone like one distracted and confounded. And he looked aside, and saw there two birds, a raven and an owl, from the sight of which he augured evil; and he uttered groans, and recited these verses:—

I came to the abode of the beloved, hoping, by beholding her, to assuage my transport and affliction;
But I found her not in it, nor found I there aught save an ill-omened raven and owl;
And the scene seemed to tell me, Thou hast acted cruelly, in severing the two desirous lovers:
So taste thou the grief which they have tasted, and live in sorrow, weeping and burning.

He then descended, weeping, from the roof of the palace, and ordered the servants to go forth upon the mountain to search for their mistress; and they did so; but found her not.—Meanwhile, Uns-el-Wujood, when he was assured that El-Ward fi-l-Akmám had gone, uttered a great cry, and fell down in a fit, in which he remained long; and they imagined that a state of abstraction from the world had overcome him, and that he was drowned in the contemplation of the beauty of the majesty of the Requiter.[26]

Now when they despaired of finding Uns-el-Wujood, and the heart of the Wezeer Ibráheem was troubled by the loss of his daughter El-Ward fi-l-Akmám, the Wezeer of the King Dirbás desired to return to his country, though he had not attained his desire by his journeys. So the Wezeer Ibráheem began to bid him farewell; and the Wezeer of the King Dirbás said to him, I desire to take this poor man with me: perhaps God (whose name be exalted!) may incline the heart of the King to me by the blessing attendant upon him; for he is a person abstracted from the world; and after that, I will send him to Iṣpahán, since it is near unto our country. The Wezeer Ibráheem replied, Do as thou desirest. And each of the Wezeers departed to his own country. The Wezeer of the King Dirbás took with him Uns-el-Wujood, still insensible, and proceeded with him three days, during which he continued in his fit, carried on mules, and not knowing whether he was carried or not. So when he recovered from his fit, he said, In what place am I? And they answered him, Thou art with the Wezeer of the King Dirbás. Then they went to the Wezeer, and informed him that he had recovered; whereupon he sent to him rose-water, and sherbet of sugar, and they gave him to drink, and revived him. And they continued their journey until they approached the city of the King Dirbás, when the King sent to the Wezeer, saying to him, If Uns-el-Wujood be not with thee, come not to me ever. When, therefore, he read the order of the King, it afflicted him. Now the Wezeer knew not that El-Ward fi-l-Akmám was with the King, nor did he know the reason of the King's sending him to Uns-el-Wujood, nor the reason of his desiring the alliance with him; and Uns-el-Wujood knew not whither they were going with him, nor that the Wezeer was sent to seek for him; nor did the Wezeer know that this was Uns-el-Wujood. And when the Wezeer saw that he was recovered, he said to him, Verily the King hath sent me on a business, and it is not accomplished; and when he knew of my approach, he sent to me a letter, saying to me in it, If the business be not accomplished, enter not my city.—And what, said Uns-el-Wujood, is the business of the King? The Wezeer therefore related to him the whole story; and Uns-el-Wujood said to him, Fear not; but go to the King, and take me with thee; and I will be surety to thee for the coming of Uns-el-Wujood.

So the Wezeer rejoiced at this, and said to him, Is it true that thou sayest? He answered, Yes. And thereupon he mounted, taking him with him, and conducted him to the King; who, when they came to him, said to the Wezeer, Where is Uns-el-Wujood? To which Uns-el-Wujood replied, O King, I know where Uns-el-Wujood is. And the King called him near to him, and said, In what place is he? He answered, In a place very near: but inform me what thou desirest of him, and then will I bring him before thee. The King replied, Most willingly: but this affair requireth privacy. Then he commanded the people to retire, and, having gone with him into a closet, acquainted him with the story from first to last; whereupon Uns-el-Wujood said to him, Supply me with rich apparel, and cause me to be clad in it, and I will bring to thee Uns-el-Wujood quickly. The King therefore brought to him a rich suit, and he put it on, and said, I am Uns-el-Wujood, and a cause of grief to the envious. Then he smote the hearts of beholders by his glances, and recited these verses:—

The mention of the beloved cheereth me in my solitude, and dispelleth my desolate feelings in estrangement.
I know no fountain but that of tears, which, flowing from mine eye, assuage my anguish.
My longing is violent: none like it existeth; and the story of my love and affection is wonderful.
I pass my night with sleepless eyelid, and walk in my passion between Hell and Paradise.
I possessed becoming patience; but have lost it; and love's only gift to me is affliction.
I am wasted by the pain of separation from her, and longing hath changed my aspect and form,
And mine eyelids are wounded by my tears, the flowing of which I cannot prevent.
My strength is impaired, and I have lost my heart; and how many griefs in succession have I suffered?
And my heart and my head are alike aged by the loss of a mistress, the most beautiful of mistresses.
In spite of her our disjunction took place, and her only desire is to find and meet me.
Will fortune, after separation and distance, grant me the enjoyment of union with my beloved,
Close the book of estrangement after opening it, and efface my trouble by the comforts of meeting?
And shall my beloved be my cup-companion, and my griefs be exchanged for pure delights?

And when he had finished his verses, the King said to him, By Allah, ye are two sincere lovers, and in the heaven of beauty two shining stars; and your case is wonderful, and your affair extraordinary.

Uns-el-Wujood then said to the King, Where is El-Ward fi-l-Akmám, O King of the age? He answered, She is now with me. And he summoned the Ḳáḍee and witnesses, performed the ceremony of the contract of her marriage to him, and treated him with honour and beneficence; and he sent to the King Shámikh, informing him of all that had happened to him with respect to Uns-el-Wujood and El-Ward fi-l-Akmám.

On hearing this, the King Shámikh rejoiced exceedingly, and sent to the King Dirbás a letter, the purport of which was this:—Since the ceremony of the contract hath taken place at thy residence, it is fit that the festival and the conclusion of the marriage be at mine.—He prepared the camels and horses and men, and sent for them; and when his letter was brought to the King Dirbás, he aided them with a great sum of money, and sent them with a party of his soldiers, who proceeded with them until they entered their city; and it was a noted day: none more remarkable had ever been witnessed. The King Shámikh collected all the mirth-exciting instruments of music, and made banquets; and thus they continued seven days; on each of which the King conferred upon the people costly robes of honour, and bestowed favours upon them. And after this, Uns-el-Wujood went to El-Ward fi-l-Akmám, and embraced her; and they sat weeping from the excess of joy and happiness; and El-Ward fi-l-Akmám recited these verses:—

Happiness hath come, dispelling care and grief. We are united, and have mortified our enviers.
The fragrant zephyr of union hath blown, and revived the heart and the bowels and the body;
And the beauty of delight hath appeared with perfumes, and our drums of glad tidings have been beaten around us.[27]
Do not imagine that we are weeping from grief; for it is from joy that our tears have flowed.
How many terrors have we seen! but they have passed; and we have borne with patience what roused up anguish.
One hour of union hath made me forget what rendered us gray from excess of terror.

Then they embraced each other, and continued to do so until they fell down senseless from the delight of finding themselves together; and when they recovered, Uns-el-Wujood recited these verses:—

O how sweet are the nights of the fulfilment of promise, when the beloved is just to me,
And when we are uninterruptedly united, and an end is put to our estrangement,
And fortune cometh with favours to us, after turning away from us in aversion!

Prosperity hath set up her standards for us, and we have drunk from her hand a cup of pleasure;
And we have met, and complained to each other of sorrow, and of nights during which we have suffered oppression;
But now we have forgotten our griefs, O my mistress; and may the Compassionate pardon what is past!
How delightful is life, and how sweet is it! Union hath only increased my passion.

And after this, they embraced again, and continued carousing, and reciting verses and pleasant tales and histories, until they were drowned in the sea of love; and there passed over them seven days while they knew not night from day, through the excess of their delight and happiness and pleasure and joy. It was as though the seven days were one day not succeeded by another; and they knew not the seventh day but by the coming of the musical instruments.[28] They then went forth from their chamber, and bestowed upon the people money and dresses. And they continued together in the most delightful of joys until they were visited by the terminator of delights and the separator of companions.—Extolled be the perfection of Him who changeth not nor ceaseth, and to whom every thing returneth![29]

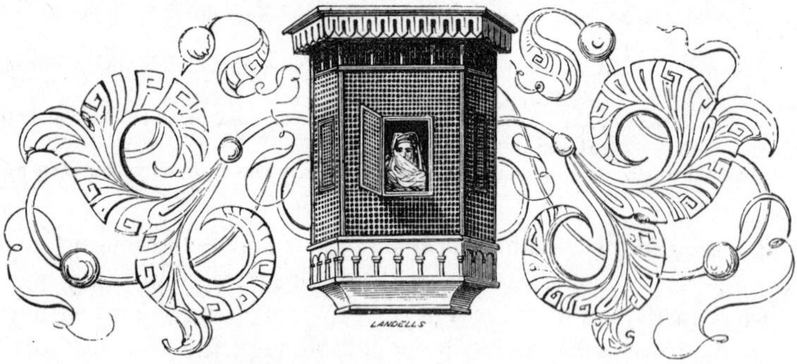

NOTES TO CHAPTER EIGHTEENTH.

NOTE 1. THIS story has been given in French, but greatly abridged, by Trébutien; and in English, still more abridged, by Dr. Scott. I have felt that I could not convey a fair notion of the original without translating not only the whole of the prose (with the exception of a very few words), but also considerably more than half of the poetry. The latter, whatever may be thought of it in other respects, has the merit of being characteristic; and though specimens of the amatory poetry of the Arabs are not wanting in other parts of the present work, I hope that the reader will excuse their abundance in this story as it is entirely one of love.

The story is evidently Arabian; but the couutries in which its scenes are laid are doubtful. In one part (as will be shewn in a subsequent note), we seem to have an exaggerated description of a part of the Nile, and of a small island there situate, namely that of Philæ. In another, a country is mentioned as near to Iṣpahán.

NOTE 2. "El-Ward fi-l-Akmám" signifies "the Rose in the Calyx," or, literally, "—— in the segments of the Calyx:" i. e. "the Rose-bud," or "the Unblown Rose."

NOTE 3. The game here mentioned appears to be that of goff.

NOTE 4. The lattice-windows in the East generally have small frames opening upon hinges.

NOTE 5. I read "baghtatan" instead of "burhatan," as recommended by my sheykh.

NOTE 6. My sheykh explains the meaning of "Uns-el-Wujood" (vulgarly pronounced "Anas-el-Wujood") by the words "Lezzet (or Ledhdhet) ed-Dunyà," which signify "the Delight of the World." "Uns" is here used, and in many other cases, as synonymous with "eenás" (infinitive noun of "ánasa," fourth conjugation), though I do not know that it is so interpreted in any published dictionary; and "el-wujood" often signifies "the world;" as in "Ḥosn-el-Wujood" (a female name), "the Beauty of the World."

NOTE 7. In this verse, in the original, there is a play upon the name of Uns-el Wujood, which I have not attempted to imitate.

NOTE 8. "Noon" and "Ṣád" are two letters of the Arabic alphabet. The former, lengthened, as it often is, forms an elegant curve; and the latter, without the curve, which is added to it when it occurs alone or at the end of a word, resembles the outline of a human eye, almond-shaped.—"The Benevolent" is one of the many epithets of the Deity.

NOTE 9. The prayers of two rek'ahs, here mentioned, are not the only practice observed by Muslims with the view of obtaining a right direction: several others I have described in my work on the Modern Egyptians, towards the close of Chapter xi. in the First Volume.

NOTE 10. The words which I render "the Sea of the Kunooz" are "Baḥr el-Kunooz." The term "baḥr" is applied to "a large river" as well as "a sea," and "Kunooz" may be rendered "Treasures:" but I prefer retaining the latter of these two Arabic words untranslated, for the following reasons:—The people who inhabit the banks and islands of the Nile from a considerable distance north of Aswán as far as Wádee es-Subooạ are called "the Kunooz;" therefore that portion of the Nile which flows through their country may be properly called "Baḥr el-Kunooz;" and Philæ, which is in this part of the Nile, near the northern limits of Nubia, is now called "the Island of Anas- (or more properly Uns-) el-Wujood." Hence it appears to me most probable that the author of this story founded it upon some tradition that was preserved in Philæ and its neighbourhood; and without having heard any exaggerated description of that picturesque island, he may have taken the liberty of magnifying it, as well as giving it a new name (which the story required him to do), and of converting a great river into a sea. Burckhardt[1] renders "Anas-el-Wujood" "the social pleasures of Wujood;" and adds, "Wujood, say the Arabs, was the name of the mighty King who built the temples of Philæ." But, if my memory deceive me not, I was there told that "Anas-el-Wujood," not simply "Wujood," was the name of the builder of those temples; and of his history I could learn nothing; the tradition relating to him being lost.

NOTE 11. This is commonly done in expectation of immediate death.

NOTE 12. "Abu-l-Ḥárith" is a surname of the lion, given to him on account of his abundant acquisitions.[2]

NOTE 13. Seyḥoon and Jeyḥoon are the rivers anciently called Jaxartes and Oxus, which flow into the sea of Aral.

NOTE 14. That is, because *he* is of my portion, according to my sheykh. But may not the meaning be, because *his* cheek cannot be rosy if *mine* be not?

NOTE 15. Of these fibres, which grow at the top of the trunk, and which are called in Arabic "leef," are made most of the ropes used by the Arabs.

NOTE 16. The kind of net here mentioned (in the original "shinf") has the form of a large sack.

NOTE 17. So in the Breslau edition. In the edition of Cairo, by the omission of a dot, the word signifies "branch" instead of "gourd."

NOTE 18. See Note 30 to the Introduction.

NOTE 19. The "hezár" is a species of nightingale, and is so called from the great variety of its notes; the word "hezár" (which is Persian) signifying "a thousand."

NOTE 20. "Dirbás" is one of the many Arabic words signifying "a lion."

NOTE 21. "Shámikh" signifies "high," "lofty," and "proud."

NOTE 22. This deception is accounted for by the information which El-Ward fi-l-

---

[1] Travels in Nubia, p. 5.

[2] Marginal note by my sheykh.

Akmám had given to the King, respecting the obstacles that had been raised against her marriage to Uns-el-Wujood.

Note 23. By "Arabs," we are here to understand Bedawees, or Arabs of the Desert.

Note 24. In illustration of this passage, see Note 63 to Chapter iii., particularly pp. 211 *et seqq.*

Note 25. The Wezeer Ibráheem, it seems, inferred that Uns-el-Wujood had come to this palace, and, seeing the doors opened, had carried off his beloved.

Note 26. "The Requiter" is one of the epithets of the Deity.

Note 27. The words rendered "around us" literally signify "in the four quarters of the horizon," or, "among the flapping [standards]," as my sheykh explains in a marginal note. Perhaps these words, with those immediately connected with them, may be also meant to convey an allusion to the palpitating of the heart occasioned by the hearing of glad tidings. The word which bears the significations above mentioned also signifies "palpitating" or "throbbing;" and that rendered "our drums of glad tidings" may with equal propriety be applied to any things announcing such news.

Note 28. "On the seventh day after a marriage, the wife receives her female relations and friends during the morning and afternoon; and sometimes, the husband entertains his own friends in the evening; generally hiring persons to perform a khatmeh or a zikr."[3] Professional vocal and instrumental performers are also often hired on this occasion, as on others of a similar kind, to amuse each party of guests. In the case to which the present note refers, we may suppose the musicians to have been sent by the King.

Note 29. Next follows a long series of forty-eight anecdotes, ending with part of the four hundred and twenty-fourth Night. Twenty-two of these I have selected for translation, and here insert.

Anecdote of a Man and his Slave-girl.

It is related that a man of the inhabitants of El-Baṣrah purchased a slave-girl, whom he educated and instructed well; and he loved her extremely, and expended all his property in diversion and amusement while he lived with her, so that nothing remained in his possession, and excessive poverty afflicted him. The slave-girl therefore said to him, O my master, sell me; for thou art in need of my price, and I am moved with pity for thee by the state of poverty into which thou hast fallen. If thou sell me, and employ my price for thy support, it will be better for thee than my remaining with thee; and perhaps God (whose name be exalted!) will make thy means of subsistence ample.—So he assented to her proposal, on account of the straitness of his circumstances. He took her and went down with her to the market, and the broker offered her for sale to the Governor of El-Baṣrah, whose name was 'Abd-Allah Ibn-Maạmar Et-Teymee; and she pleased him, and he bought her for five hundred pieces of gold, which sum he paid to her master. But when her master had received the money, and was about to depart, the slave-girl wept, and recited this couplet:—

May the money which thou hast collected delight thee! But for me, nought remaineth save sorrow and anxiety.
I say to my grievously-oppressed soul, Mourn little or much: the beloved is separated.[4]

---

[3] From my work on the Modern Egyptians, vol. ii. ch. xiv.
[4] That is, my mourning will not profit me.

On hearing which, her master uttered groans, and thus replied:—

> If thou have not any resource in this case, and find not aught but death, yet excuse me.
> Eve and morn the remembrance of you will console me, and comfort a heart severely troubled.
> Peace be on thee! Henceforth shall no visit nor meeting take place between us unless Ibn-Maạmar willeth.

And when 'Abd-Allah Ibn-Maạmar heard their verses, and witnessed their sorrow, he said, By Allah, I will not be a means of separating you. It hath become evident to me that ye love one another: so take the money and the slave-girl, O man. May God bless thee in them both! for the separation of two lovers is painful to them.—They both, therefore, kissed his hand, and departed; and they ceased not to live together until death parted them.—Extolled be the perfection of Him whom death doth not overtake!

Anecdote of Two Victims of Love.

There was a graceful man of the tribe of 'Odhrah, who was never free from the passion of love for a single day. And it happened that he loved a beautiful woman of his tribe, and he sent messages to her during the space of some days; but she ceased not to treat him with cruelty and aversion until desire and transport and distraction afflicted him, and he fell into a violent sickness. He confined himself to the pillow, and relinquished sleep; his case became manifest to the people, and his passion notorious; his infirmity increased, and his pain became severe, so that he almost died. His family and the family of his beloved incessantly begged her to visit him; but she refused, until he was at the point of death, when they acquainted her with this, and at length she was moved with compassion for him, and granted him the favour of a visit.

And upon his beholding her, his eyes poured forth tears, and, with a broken heart, he recited these words:—

By thy life, when my corpse passeth by thee, borne upon the necks of four men,
Wilt thou not follow the bier, to salute the grave in which that corpse shall be laid?

And when she heard his words, she wept violently, and said to him, By Allah, I did not imagine that thy desire had risen to such a pitch as to cast thee into the arms of death. Had I known that, I had aided thee in thine affair, and thou hadst enjoyed the union thou desirest.—And on his hearing what she said, his tears became like rain; and he repeated the saying of the poet:—

She drew near at the time when death was parting us, and favoured me with union when it would not profit me.

Then he uttered a groan, and died. And upon this, she threw herself upon him, kissing him and weeping, and she ceased not to weep until she fell down by him in a fit. And when she recovered, she charged her family that they should bury her in his grave when she should have died. Then she poured forth tears, and recited these two verses:—

We lived upon the earth a life of comfort, and the tribe and abode and home were proud of us;
But fortune, with its changes, hath parted us from each other, and now the grave-clothes will unite us.

And after she had ended her verses, she wept violently, and ceased not to weep and wail till she fell down in a fit, in which she remained three days; and then she died, and was buried in his grave.—This was one of the strange coincidences that have happened in love.

Love in a School.

A boy and a slave-girl learned in one school, and the boy became affected with a violent passion for the slave-girl: so, one day, when the other boys were inadvertent, he took her tablet,[5] and wrote upon it these two verses:—

[5] A wooden tablet, painted white, upon which the schoolboy writes his lesson.

What sayest thou of him whom disease hath wasted by excessive love of thee, and who hath become perplexed;
Who in transport and pain complaineth of his passion, unable to conceal the feelings of his heart?

When the slave-girl, therefore, took the tablet, she saw these verses written upon it; and after she had read them, and understood their meaning, she wept in compassion for the boy, and wrote, beneath his lines, this couplet:—

If we behold a lover whom desire hath afflicted, we will confer favours upon him;
And that which he requireth of us he shall obtain, whatever happen to us in consequence.

And it happened that the teacher came in to them, and, finding the tablet at a moment when it was lying unheeded, took it, and read what was upon it; whereat he was moved with pity for their state, and wrote these two verses (addressed to the girl) beneath those which they had written:—

Receive thy lover, and fear not punishment; for he hath become perplexed in his passion.
As to the teacher, fear not his authority; for he hath long been afflicted by love.

Then the master of the slave-girl happened to enter the school, and he found the girl's tablet; so he took it, and read the words of the slave-girl, and those of the boy, and those of the teacher; and beneath the verses of them all, he wrote this couplet:—

May God never cause a separation between you; and may your slanderer be perplexed and wearied!
As to the teacher, never, by Allah, have my eyes beheld a greater fosterer of intrigues.

The master of the slave-girl then sent for the Ḳáḍee and witnesses, and performed the ceremony of her contract of marriage to the youth in their presence. He made for them also a feast, and treated them with great beneficence; and they continued together in joy and happiness until they were overtaken by the terminator of delights and the separator of companions.

Anecdote of a Faithless Wife.

There was a man who had a mill, and an ass which turned it; and he had a wicked wife, whom he loved; but she hated him, and loved a neighbour of hers, who detested her, and withheld himself from her. And her husband dreamt that a person said to him, Dig in such a spot in the ass's circuit in the mill: thou wilt find a treasure. And when he awoke, he told his wife of his dream, commanding her to conceal the secret. But she acquainted with it her neighbour whom she loved, for the purpose of ingratiating herself with him, and he promised to come to her at night. Accordingly he came to her in the night, and dug in the circuit of the mill, and they found the treasure, and took it forth. He then said to her, What shall we do with this? She answered, We will divide it into two equal portions, and thou shalt part thyself from thy wife, and I will devise a stratagem to separate myself from my husband: then thou shalt marry me; and when we are united, we will put all the money together, and it shall be in our possession. Her neighbour however replied, I fear that the Devil will seduce thee, and that thou wilt take some other man in my stead; for gold in the house is like the sun in the world; and the right opinion is, that the money be all in my keeping, in order that thou mayest eagerly study to effect thy release from thy husband and to come to me. But she rejoined, I also fear the like of that which thou fearest, and I will not give up to thee my share of this money; for I was the person who gave thee information of it. And when he heard these words from her, covetousness incited him to kill her: so he killed her, and threw her into the place of the treasure; after which, daylight overtook him, and prevented his concealing her. And the miller awoke, and found not his wife; and he went into the mill, attached the ass there, and urged it with his voice; whereupon it walked on, and then stopped. The miller beat it violently; but every time that he did so, it drew back; for it took fright at the dead woman, and could not advance. All this while, the miller knew not the cause of the stopping of the ass; and he took a knife, and goaded it many times; yet still it would not move from its place; and upon this, he was enraged at it, and stabbed it in the side, and the ass fell down dead. Then, when day came, the miller saw the ass dead, and his wife dead, and found her in the place of the treasure; and his rage increased at discovering the loss of the treasure and the slaughter of his wife and the ass, and great sorrow came upon him.—All this happened in consequence of his revealing his secret to his wife, and not concealing it.

Anecdote of a Simpleton and a Sharper.

A certain simpleton was walking along, holding the halter of his ass, which he was dragging after him; and two sharpers saw him; whereupon one of them said to his companion, I will take this ass from this man.—How wilt thou take it? said the other. The first replied, Follow me, and I will shew thee. So he followed him; and that sharper, advancing to the ass, unloosed from it the halter, and gave the ass to his companion; after which, he put the halter upon his own head, and walked on behind the simpleton until he knew that his companion had gone away with the ass. Then he stopped: so the simpleton dragged him by the halter; but he advanced not. The man therefore looked back at him, and, seeing the halter upon the head of a man, he said to him, What art thou? The sharper answered, I am thy ass, and my story is wonderful; and it is this:—I had a mother, a virtuous old woman, and I went to her one day in a state of intoxication; whereupon she said to me, O my son, turn with repentance unto God (whose name be exalted!) from these sins. But I took a staff, and beat her with it; and she uttered an imprecation against me; upon which God (whose name be exalted!) transformed me into an ass, and caused me to fall into thy possession, and I remained with thee all this time. To-day, however, my mother remembered me, and God inclined her heart towards me; so she prayed for me, and God restored me to the human shape as I was.—And the simpleton said, There is no strength nor power but in God, the High, the Great! By Allah, O my brother, absolve me of responsibility for that which I have done unto thee, in riding thee and in other things.—Then he left the sharper to go his way, and he himself returned to his house intoxicated with anxiety and grief. His wife therefore said to him, What hath afflicted thee, and where is the ass? He said to her, Hast thou no knowledge of the case of the ass? Then I will acquaint thee with it.—And he related to her the story; on hearing which, she exclaimed, Alas for the punishment that we shall receive from God, whose name be exalted! How hath it happened that all this time hath passed over us and we have been making a son of Adam to labour for us!—Then she gave alms,[6] and prayed for the

[6] As an atonement.

forgiveness of God. And the man remained a long time in the house without work. So his wife said to him, How long wilt thou remain in the house without work? Go to the market and buy for us an ass with which to work.—He therefore went to the market, and stopped by the asses; and, lo, he beheld his own ass for sale. And when he recognised it, he advanced to it, and, putting his mouth to its ear, said to it, Wo to thee, O unlucky! Doubtless thou hast returned to intoxication, and beaten thy mother again. By Allah, I will never again buy thee!—Then he left it, and departed.

Anecdote of El-Ḥákim bi-amri-lláh *and a Merchant of Cairo.*

It is related that El-Ḥákim bi-amri-lláh[7] was riding in his state-procession one day, and he passed by a garden, where he saw a man surrounded by slaves and servants; and he demanded of him a draught of water. The man therefore gave him to drink; after which he said, Perhaps the Prince of the Faithful will honour me by alighting and paying me a visit in this garden. So the King alighted, and his troops also, and entered that garden; and the man above mentioned caused a hundred carpets to be brought out, and a hundred skins,[8] and a hundred pillows, and a hundred dishes of fruits, and a hundred bowls full of sweets, and a hundred saucers full of sherbet of sugar. El-Ḥákim bi-amri-lláh was amazed at this, and he said, O man, verily thy case is wonderful. Didst thou know of our coming, and prepare for us this?—The man answered, No, by Allah, O Prince of the Faithful: I knew not of your coming. I am a merchant, of the number of thy subjects, and I have a hundred concubines; and when the Prince of the Faithful honoured me by alighting and paying me a visit, I sent to each of them, desiring her to send me the dinner in the garden; and each of them sent somewhat of her furniture and the surplus of her food and her drink. Each of them sendeth to me every day a dish of meat, and a dish of something cooling, and a dish of fruit, and a bowl full of sweetmeat, and a saucer of sherbet; and this is my dinner every day: I have not added to it any thing for thee.—And the Prince of the Faithful prostrated himself, offering up thanks to God (whose name be exalted!), and said, Praise be to God, who hath made to be of the number of our subjects one upon whom He hath bestowed such affluence that he feedeth the Khaleefeh and his troops without preparing for them, but only of the surplus of his food! Then he gave orders to present to him all that the government-treasury contained of coins struck during that year; and they amounted to three millions and seven hundred thousand; and he mounted not until he had caused them to be brought, and had given them to that man, saying to him, Make use of them as thy case may require; for thy generosity is worthy of a greater recompense. Then the King mounted and departed.

Anecdote of Anooshirwán.

The just King, Kisrà Anooshirwán,[9] rode forth one day to the chase, and separated himself from his troops, pursuing a gazelle; and as he proceeded after it, he saw a tract of cultivated land near unto him. He was exceedingly thirsty; so he repaired thither, and, going to the door of the house of a family, he asked for some water to drink; whereupon there came forth to him a damsel, who looked at him, and then returned to the house, and pressed for him a single sugar-cane, mixed its juice with water, poured it into a cup, and put into it some sweet-scented substance resembling dust. Then she gave it to Anooshirwán, who looked into the cup, and saw in it something

---

7 El-Ḥákim bi-amri-lláh was the third Khaleefeh of the house of Fáṭimeh, in Egypt. He was celebrated for tyranny and insanity, and was the founder of the religion of the Druses. He reigned from the year of the Flight 386 to 411.—Ed.

8 Either to place the food upon or to sit upon; but in this case, I suppose, for the former purpose.

9 Anooshirwán, or Nooshirwán, was the famous Persian monarch in whose reign Moḥammad was born, and whose justice has been a theme of countless Oriental writers.

like dust. He therefore drank it slowly, until he came to the end of it, when he said to the damsel, O damsel, excellent was the water, and how sweet had it been but for those particles swimming upon the surface; for they rendered it turbid. The damsel replied, O guest, I purposely threw into it those particles which rendered it turbid.—And why didst thou that? said the King. She answered, Because I saw thee to be violently thirsty, and feared that thou wouldst drink it at a single draught, and it would have been injurious to thee; and had there not been in it those particles upon the surface, thou wouldst have drunk it up quickly at once, and thy doing so would have been hurtful to thee. So the just King, Anooshirwán, wondered at her words and her intelligence, knowing that what she had said had proceeded from intelligence and acuteness and excellence of understanding; and he said to her, From how many canes didst thou press that juice? She answered, From one cane. And Anooshirwán wondered, and demanded the register of the taxes that arose from the village there; and he saw that its taxes were little; wherefore he purposed in his mind, when he should return to his seat of government, to increase those taxes; saying, Wherefore should the taxes of a village from a single sugar-cane of which this juice proceedeth be so little?

Then he departed from that village to the chase; and at the close of the day he returned to it, and, passing alone by that door again, he asked a second time for water to drink; upon which that same damsel came forth to him; and, seeing and knowing him, she returned to bring him the water. But she was long absent from him. So Anooshirwán hastened her, and said, Wherefore hast thou been tardy? She answered, Because there proceeded not from one cane as much as thou wantest; therefore I pressed three canes; and there came not from them as much as before came from one cane. The King said, What is the cause of that? And she answered, The cause of it is, that the purpose of the Sulṭán hath become changed. He therefore asked her, Whence learnedst thou this? She answered, We have heard from the wise, that, when the purpose of the Sulṭán becometh changed against a people, their prosperity ceaseth, and their blessings are diminished. And Anooshirwán laughed, and dismissed from his mind that which he had purposed against the people; and forthwith he married that damsel, being pleased with the excess of her intelligence and acuteness, and the excellence of her speech.

Anecdote of Khusrow *and* Sheereen *and a Fisherman.*

Khusrow,[10] who was one of the Kings [of Persia], was fond of fish; and he was one day sitting in his saloon, with Sheereen, his wife, when there came a fisherman with a large fish, which he gave to Khusrow. And the King was pleased with that fish, and gave orders to present the man with four thousand pieces of silver. But Sheereen said to him, Evil is that which thou hast done!—And why? he asked. She answered, Because if, after this, thou give any one of thy dependants this sum, he will despise it, and say, He hath given me the like of the sum which he gave to the fisherman. And if thou give him less than that, he will say, He hath despised me, and given me less than he gave to the fisherman.—So Khusrow replied, Thou hast spoken truth; but it is disgraceful in Kings to take back their gifts, and this hath passed. Sheereen however rejoined, I will contrive for thee a means of getting back the present from him.—And how so? said he. She answered, If thou desire that, call the fisherman, and ask him of what species is this fish. And if he say to thee, Of such a species,—reply, We desired one of another kind.—He therefore sent after the fisherman, who returned; and this fisherman was a person of intelligence and acuteness; and the King Khusrow asked him, of what species was the fish which he had brought; whereupon the fisherman kissed the ground, and said, This fish is of a mixed kind, and of no one particular species. And Khusrow laughed at his words, and gave orders to present him with four thousand more pieces of silver.

The fisherman therefore went to the treasurer, and received from him eight thousand pieces of silver, which he put into a leathern bag that he had with him; and he raised it upon his neck, and was about to go forth, when there fell from him one piece of silver; upon which he set down the leathern bag from his shoulders, and stooped to pick up the piece of silver, and took it. Now the King and Sheereen were looking at him; and Sheereen said, O King, hast thou seen the vileness of this man, and his meanness, in that when there fell from him a piece of silver, it was not easy for him to leave it for one of the pages of the King to take it? And when the King heard her words, he was enraged at the fisherman, and said, Thou hast spoken truth, O Sheereen. Then he gave orders to bring back the fisherman, and said to him, O thou devoid of spirit! Thou art not a man! How was it that thou puttest down this money from thy shoulders, and stoopedst for a piece of silver, and wast too covetous to leave it in its place?—But the fisherman kissed the ground, and answered, May God prolong the life of the King! I took not up that piece of silver from the ground on account of its value in my estimation; but I did so because upon one of its faces is the effigy of the King, and upon its other face his name, and I feared that some person might put his foot upon it unknowingly, and that would be dishonouring the name of the King, and his effigy; and I should be the one to be blamed for this offence. And the King won-

---

[10] Khusrow Parwéz, or Parvéz, was a very famous monarch, grandson of Anooshirwán, and contemporary with Moḥammad. Having been driven from his country by his uncle, he "took refuge with the Greek Emperor Maurice, by whose assistance he defeated the usurper, and recovered his crown. Khusrow, whilst at Maurice's court, married his daughter Irene [called by the Persians 'Sheereen,' signifying 'Sweet',] who is highly celebrated in the East for her singular beauty. . . . The throne of this prince is celebrated by many Eastern historians. It is said to have been of such vast extent, that it was supported by forty thousand columns of silver; and that, among other magnificent ornaments, a thousand globes, suspended in the dome, shewed, by various movements, the motions of the heavenly bodies; thirty thousand pieces of embroidered tapestry adorned the walls; and underneath were vaults containing immense treasures in gold, silver, and precious stones." (Richardson's Persian, Arabic, and English Dictionary, Johnson's edition, *voce* parwéz.)

dered at his words, and approved what he said, and gave orders to present him with four thousand more pieces of silver. He also commanded a crier to proclaim and say, It is not fit that any one should follow the counsel of women; for he who followeth their counsel will lose with his piece of silver two pieces of silver beside.

Anecdote of Yaḥyà El-Barmekee.

It is related that Yaḥyà the son of Khálid El-Barmekee went forth from the palace of the Khaleefeh to return to his house, and saw, at the door of the house, a man, who, when he approached, rose and saluted him, and said to him, O Yaḥyà, I am in need of that which is in thy hand, and I beg of God to conciliate thy favour for me. And Yaḥyà gave orders to appropriate to him a place in his house, and commanded his treasurer to take to him every day a thousand pieces of silver, and directed that he should be fed with the choicest of his food. Thus the man remained a whole month; at the expiration of which, he had received thirty thousand pieces of silver; but he feared that Yaḥyà would take from him the money, on account of its large amount: so he departed privily. And they informed Yaḥyà of this. He however replied, By Allah, had he remained with me for his life, and for all his days, I had not withheld my gifts, nor deprived him of the honours of my hospitality.—And the excellencies of the Barmekees were incalculable, and their virtues cannot be fully described: especially those of Yaḥyà the son of Khálid; for he chiefly abounded in illustrious actions, as the poet hath said of him:—

I asked Liberality, Art thou free? He answered, No; but I am the slave of Yaḥyà the son of Khálid.
By purchase? said I.—God forbid! he answered; for he had me by inheritance from father after father.

Moḥammad El-Emeen *and the Slave-girl* El-Bedr el-Kebeer.

Jaạfar the son of Moosà El-Hádee[11] had a slave-girl, a lute-player, whose name was El-Bedr el-Kebeer,[12] and there was not in her time any more beautiful in face, or of more just figure, or more graceful, or more skilful in the art of singing, and striking the chords: she was endowed with the utmost loveliness and elegance, and every charm. And Moḥammad El-Emeen[13] the son of Zubeydeh heard of her, and besought Jaạfar to sell her to him: but he replied, Thou knowest that it becometh not such a person as myself to sell female slaves and to set prices upon concubines; and were she not brought up in my house, I would send her as a present to thee, and not covetously withhold her from thee. Then Moḥammad El-Emeen repaired one day, for the purpose of exhilaration, to the house of Jaạfar, who thereupon shewed him the hospitality suitable to friends, and ordered his slave-girl El-Bedr el-Kebeer to sing to him and make him merry. She therefore tuned the instruments, and sang with the sweetest of melodious tones. And Moḥammad El-Emeen betook himself to drinking and making merry, and ordered the cup-bearers to give abundance of wine to Jaạfar, that they might intoxicate him. He then took the slave-girl with him, and repaired to his residence; but he extended not his hand towards her. And in the morning he gave orders to invite Jaạfar; and when he came he placed the wine before him, and commanded the slave-girl to sing to him within the curtain. When Jaạfar, therefore, heard her voice, he knew her; and he was enraged at this; but he shewed not his rage, by reason of the nobleness of his nature, and his magnanimity; and he manifested no

---

[11] El-Hádee was the brother and immediate predecessor of Hároon Er-Rasheed.

[12] Literally, "the Great Full Moon."

[13] The son and next successor of Hároon Er-Rasheed.

change in his convivial converse. And as soon as the carousal was ended, Moḥammad El-Emeen gave orders to one of his dependants to fill the skiff in which Jaạfar had come to him with pieces of gold and silver, and varieties of jewels and jacinths, and rich apparel, and exceeding wealth. So he did as he commanded him, putting into the skiff a thousand myriads of pieces of money, and a thousand large pearls, each pearl of the value of twenty thousand pieces of silver; and he ceased not to put in it varieties of rarities, until the boatmen called out for aid, and said, The skiff cannot carry any thing more. And he ordered them to convey the wealth to the house of Jaạfar.—Such are the noble actions of the great. May God have mercy on them!

Anecdote of El-Faḍl *and* Jaạfar *the* Barmekees.

Sa'eed the son of Sálim El-Báhilee saith, My circumstances became difficult in the time of Hároon Er-Rasheed; many debts were accumulated upon me, burdening my back, and I was unable to discharge them. My means were contracted, and I became perplexed, not knowing what to do; for payment was vehemently urged upon me, the persons to whom I was indebted surrounded my door, those who had demands to make crowded upon me, and the creditors constantly importuned me. Thus my invention of expedients was straitened, and my trouble of mind was excessive. So when I saw my affairs involved in difficulty, and my circumstances changed, I repaired to 'Abd-Allah the son of Málik El-Khuzá'ee, and besought him to aid me by his advice, and direct me to the door of relief by his good counsel; and he said, No one can save

thee from thy trouble and anxiety, and straitness and grief, except the Barmekees. I replied, And who can bear their pride, and endure their haughtiness?—Thou wilt bear that, he rejoined, for the sake of amending thy circumstances. I therefore rose from his presence, and went to El-Faḍl and Jaạfar, the sons of Yaḥyà the son of Khálid, related to them my case, and shewed them my condition. And they said, May God give thee his aid, and render thee independent of his creatures by his beneficence, and liberally bestow on thee abundant prosperity, and grant thee sufficiency above any being beside Him; for He is able to do whatsoever He willeth, and is gracious unto his servants, and acquainted with their wants.

So I departed from them, and returned to 'Abd-Allah the son of Málik with contracted bosom, perplexed mind, and broken heart, and repeated to him what they had said; and he replied, It is expedient that thou remain to-day with us, that we may see what God (whose name be exalted!) will decree. I therefore sat with him a while; and, lo, my young man approached and said, O my master, at our door are many mules, with their loads, and with them is a man who saith, I am the agent of El-Faḍl the son of Yaḥyà, and Jaạfar the son of Yaḥyà. Upon this, 'Abd-Allah the son of Málik said, I hope that relief hath approached thee: rise then, and see what is the affair. Accordingly, I rose from his presence, and hastened running to my house, and saw at my door a man with a note, in which was written,—

When thou hadst been with us, and we had heard thy words, we repaired, after thy departure, to the Khaleefeh, and informed him that thou hadst been reduced to the ignominious necessity of begging; whereupon he commanded us to convey to thee, from the government-treasury, a million pieces of silver. But we said to him, This money he will disburse to his creditors, and he will pay with it his debts; and whence is he to sustain himself? So he gave orders to present thee with three hundred thousand pieces of silver besides. And each of us also hath sent to thee, of his proper wealth, a million pieces of silver. The whole sum, therefore, is three millions and three hundred thousand pieces of silver, wherewith thou shalt amend thy circumstances and affairs.

See then this generosity evinced by these noble persons. May God (whose name be exalted!) have mercy on them!

Anecdote of a Deceitful Wife.

It is related that a woman practised a stratagem against her husband; and it was this:—Her husband brought her a fish, on a Friday, and desired her to cook it and make it ready by the time that the congregational prayers should be ended. He then went forth to his work; and her friend came to her, and invited her to attend a wedding in his house; to which she assented. She put the fish into a water-jar in her abode, and went with him, and remained absent from her house until the next Friday; while her husband was searching in other houses, and inquiring for her; but no one gave him any tidings of her. Then she came on the following Friday, and took forth to him the fish alive, and, having collected a number of people before him, related to them her tale; whereupon they pronounced the man a liar, and said to him, It is impossible that the fish should remain alive all this time. They made it appear evident that he was mad, and imprisoned him and laughed at him.

Anecdote of a Homicide.

The shereef Ḥoseyn the son of Reiyán hath related, that the Prince of the Faithful, 'Omar the son of El-Khaṭṭáb, was sitting one day to judge the people, and to exercise jurisdiction among his subjects, attended by the chiefs of his companions, of those possessed of judgment and just perception. And as he sat, there approached him a young man, of the most comely of young men, of clean apparel, upon whom two of the most comely of young men had laid hold; and they dragged him by the upper edge of his vest, and stationed him before the Prince of the Faithful. So the Prince of the Faithful looked at the two young men, and at the other, and, having ordered them to withdraw from him, caused him to draw near unto him, and said to the two young men, What is your affair with him?—O Prince of the Faithful, they answered, we are two brothers by the same mother, and suited to follow the truth. We had a father, a very old man, prudent, honoured among the tribes, free from meannesses, well known for virtues, who reared us from infancy, and bestowed on us great favours, a person of abundant virtues and illustrious actions, deserving of the praise of the poet:—

They said, Is Aboo Saḳr of Sheybán? I answered them, Nay, by my life; but Sheybán is of him:[14]
For how many a father hath derived eminence from a noble son, as did 'Adnán from God's Apostle!

And he went forth to an orchard belonging to him, to recreate himself among its trees, and to pluck its ripe fruits, and this young man slew him, swerving from the path of rectitude. We therefore request thee to retaliate his offence, and to pass sentence upon him in accordance with the command of God.

So 'Omar cast a terrifying glance at the young man, and said to him, Thou hast heard what these two young men have stated. What then sayest thou in reply?—Now that young man was of firm heart and bold tongue; he had cast off the garments of dastardy, and divested himself of the apparel of fear: so he smiled, and spoke with a most eloquent tongue, complimenting the Prince of the Faithful with elegant language. Then he said, By Allah, O Prince of the Faithful, I have retained in my mind their charge, and they have spoken truth in that which they have said in relating what happened; and the command of God is a determinate decree. But I will state my case before thee, and it is thine to decide upon it. Know, O Prince of the Faithful, that I am of the choicest of the genuine Arabs, who are the most noble of the races under heaven. I grew up in the dwellings of the desert, and gloomy times of oppressive sterility afflicted my people; wherefore I came to the environs of this town, with my family and wealth and children. I followed one of the roads around it leading amid its gardens of trees, with she-camels of high estimation and dear unto me, among which was a male camel of high breed and of numerous offspring and beautiful form, whereby they bore abundantly, and he walked among them like a king wearing a crown. Now one of the she-camels ran away to the orchard of the father of these two young men, and its trees appeared above the wall, and she reached them with her lips: so I drove her away from that orchard. But, lo, a sheykh appeared through an interstice of the wall, the flame of his rage casting forth sparks, and with a stone in his right hand; and he walked like the lion that swayeth[15] in his pace, and, smiting the male camel with that stone, he killed it; for the stone struck its eye. Therefore when I saw that the male camel had fallen down by my side, I felt the burning coals of anger lighted in my heart, and I took up that same stone, and smote

[14] "Sheybán" is the name of a tribe.
[15] I read "khaṭara," as recommended by my sheykh, instead of "ḥaḍara" or "ḥaḍira."

him with it, and it was the cause of his destruction. Thus he found an evil result to his action; the man being killed with that wherewith he had killed. And when he was struck with the stone, he uttered a great cry and a painful shriek; whereupon I hastened from my place; but these two young men hastened after me, and laid hold upon me; and they brought me unto thee, and placed me before thee.

On hearing this, 'Omar (may God, whose name be exalted, be well pleased with him!) said, Thou hast confessed the crime that thou hast committed: liberation hath become difficult, retaliation is necessary, and there is no opportunity of escape. The young man replied, I hear and obey the sentence which the Imám hath passed, and consent to that which the law of El-Islám requireth. But I have a young brother, and he had an old father, who, before his death, assigned him abundant wealth, and a great sum of gold, and committed the care of him to me, calling God to witness against me, and saying, This is in trust with thee for thy brother: keep it then carefully. I therefore received that money from him, and buried it; and no one knoweth of it but myself. So if thou now pass sentence of death upon me, the wealth will be lost, and thou wilt be the cause of its loss, and the child will sue thee for his right on the day when God will judge his creatures. But if thou grant me three days' delay, I will appoint some one to act as guardian to the boy, and I will return to discharge my obligation; and I have one who will be my surety for the fulfilment of this promise.—And upon this, the Prince of the Faithful hung down his head. Then he looked at those who were present, and said, Who will be surety unto me for his return to his place?—And the young man looked at the faces of those who composed the assembly, and, pointing to Aboo-Dharr[16] in preference to the rest of the persons present, said, This will be my guarantee and my surety. So 'Omar (may God, whose name be exalted, be well pleased with him!) said, O Aboo-Dharr, hast thou heard this saying, and wilt thou be surety unto me for the return of this young man? He answered, Yes, O Prince of the Faithful: I will be surety for him for three days. 'Omar, therefore, consented to this, and gave permission to the young man to depart.

And when the period of delay had drawn towards its close, and the time had almost expired, or had expired, the young man had not come unto the assembly of 'Omar, whom the Companions[17] were surrounding like the stars around the moon. Aboo-Dharr was present, and the plaintiffs were waiting, and they said, Where is the delinquent, O Aboo-Dharr? How shall he who hath fled return? But we will not move from our place until thou bring him to us, that our blood-revenge may be taken.—Aboo-Dharr replied, By the Omniscient King, if the three days expire and the young man shall not have come, I will discharge the obligation of surety, and surrender myself to the Imám! And 'Omar (may God be well pleased with him!) said, By Allah, if the young man delay his coming, I will assuredly pass sentence upon Aboo-Dharr according as the law of El-Islám requireth! And upon this, the tears of the persons present flowed, and the sighs of the spectators rose, and great was the clamour. The chiefs of the Companions proposed to the two young men to take the pecuniary compensation, and obtain the thanks of the people. But they refused, and would admit nothing but the taking of the blood-revenge.

While the people, however, were in a state of tumult and clamour in their lamentation for Aboo-Dharr, lo, the young man approached, and stood before the Imám, and greeted him with the most courteous salutation. His face was shining brightly, and glistening with perspiration; and he said to the Imám, I have committed the youth unto his maternal uncles, and acquainted them with all his affairs, and informed them of what had been done with his wealth: then I rushed into the sultry mid-day heat, and fulfilled my promise with the fidelity of the ingenuous. And the people wondered at his veracity and good faith, his ready offering of himself

---

16 A celebrated and highly-esteemed relater of the sayings and actions of the Prophet.

17 The Companions of the Prophet.

to death, and his boldness. And some of them said, How generous a young man art thou, and how faithful in the performance of thy promise and duty! But the young man replied, Are ye not convinced that when the period of death hath come, no one can escape from it? Verily I fulfilled my promise that it might not be said, Fidelity hath departed from among men.—And Aboo-Dharr said, By Allah, O Prince of the Faithful, I became surety for this young man and knew not of what tribe he was, nor had I seen him before that day. But when he turned from all else who were present, and desired me, and said, This will be surety and guarantee for me,—I deemed it not right to reject him, and humanity refused to disappoint his desire; for there is no evil in complying with a desire, that it may not be said, Virtue hath departed from among men.—And upon this, the two young men said, O Prince of the Faithful, we give up to this young man the blood of our father, since he hath converted sadness into a cause of cheerfulness, that it may not be said, Kindness hath departed from among men. And the Imám rejoiced at the pardon granted to the young man, and at his veracity and his fidelity in the performance of his duty, and he highly extolled the humanity of Aboo-Dharr above his companions, and approved of the resolution of the young men in the shewing of kindness: he bestowed upon them grateful thanks, and recited, as applicable to their case, the saying of the poet:—

> He who acteth kindly among men will be requited for it. Kindness is not lost with God nor with men.

Then he offered to pay them the fine for their father's blood from the government-treasury. But they said, Verily we pardoned him from a desire of seeing the face of God, the Bountiful, the Exalted; and he whose intention is of this nature doth not make his kindness to be followed by reproach for his benefits, nor by detriment.

Anecdote of an Impudent Thief.

A man, who was a robber, turned with repentance unto God (whose name be exalted!), and his repentance was sincere, and he opened for himself a shop in which to sell stuffs. This life he led for a length of time; and it happened, one day, that he locked his shop, and went to his house; and one of the artful robbers came, and, having disguised himself in the garb of the owner of the shop, took forth from his sleeve some keys. This was in the night; and he said to the watchman of the market, Light for me this candle. So the watchman took it from him, and went to light it;[18] and the robber opened the shop, and lighted another candle that he had with him; and when the watchman came again, he found him sitting in the shop, with the account-book in his hand, and he was looking at it, and calculating with his fingers. Thus he continued to do until the first appearance of daybreak, when he said to the watchman, Bring me a camel-driver with his camel, to convey for me some of the merchandise. Accordingly he brought him a camel-driver with his camel, and the robber took and gave him four bales of stuffs, which he placed upon the camel. Then he locked the shop, gave to the watchman two pieces of silver, and followed the camel-driver; the watchman believing that he was the owner of the shop.

And when the morning arrived, and daylight appeared, the owner of the shop came, and the watchman began to greet him with prayers for his prosperity, on account of the two pieces of silver. So the owner of the shop disavowed what he said, and wondered at it; and when he opened the shop, he found the wax that had run down from the candles, and the account-book thrown down, and, examining the shop, he found four bales of stuffs missing; whereupon he said to the watchman, What hath happened? He therefore told him of that which had been done in the night, and of

[18] See Note 7 to Chapter v.

what had been said to the camel-driver respecting the bales; and the owner of the shop said, Bring to me the camel-driver who took up the bales with thee at daybreak. The watchman replied, I hear and obey;—and brought him. And the owner of the shop said to him, Whither conveyedst thou the stuffs at daybreak? He answered, To such a landing-place, and I stowed them in the vessel of such-a-one. And the merchant said to him, Go with me thither. He accordingly went thither with him, and said to him, This is the vessel, and this is her owner. So he said to the boatman, Whither conveyedst thou the merchant and the stuffs? He answered, To such a place, and he brought to me a camel-driver, who placed the stuffs upon his camel, and departed, and I know not whither he went. The owner of the shop said to him, Bring me the camel-driver who conveyed the stuffs from thee. And he brought him; and he said to him, Whither conveyedst thou the stuffs from the vessel, with the merchant?—To such a place, he answered. And he said to him, Go with me thither, and shew it to me. And the camel-driver went with him to a place distant from the bank of the river, acquainted him with the Khán in which he had deposited the stuffs, and shewed him the magazine of the [pretended] merchant. So he advanced to the magazine and opened it, and found the four bales of stuffs in their original state, unopened; and he gave them to the camel-driver. The robber had placed his cloak upon the stuffs; and the owner of the stuffs handed it also to the camel-driver, who placed the whole upon his camel. Then he closed the magazine, and departed with the camel-driver. And, lo, the robber confronted him, and followed him until he had embarked the stuffs in the boat; when he said to him, O my brother, mayest thou be in the keeping of God! Thou hast taken thy stuffs, and nought of them is lost: so give me the cloak.—And the merchant laughed at him, and gave him the cloak, and did not molest him; and each of them went his way.

Compact of Mesroor *with* Ibn-El-Ḳáribee.

The Prince of the Faithful, Hároon Er-Rasheed, was troubled one night with an exceeding restlessness; so he said to his Wezeer Jaafar the son of Yaḥyà El-Barmekee, I am sleepless this night, and my heart is contracted, and I know not what to do. Now his eunuch Mesroor was standing before him, and he laughed. The Khaleefeh therefore said to him, At what dost thou laugh? Dost thou laugh in contempt of me, or because thou art mad?—He answered, No, by Allah, O Prince of the Faithful, by thy relationship to the chief of Apostles, I did it not willingly; but I went forth yesterday to walk without the palace, and proceeded until I came to the bank of the Tigris, where I saw a crowd of people collected together: so I stopped, and I saw a man making the people laugh. He is named Ibn-El-Ḳáribee. And I remembered just now his words, and laughter overcame me; for which I beg thy pardon, O Prince of the Faithful.—Upon this, the Khaleefeh said, Bring him unto me immediately. Mesroor therefore went forth and hastened until he came to Ibn-El-Ḳáribee; and he said to him, Answer the summons of the Prince of the Faithful.—I hear and obey, replied Ibn-El-Ḳáribee. And Mesroor said to him, But on the condition that, if thou go in to him and he bestow upon thee any thing, the quarter of it shall be thine, and the rest be mine.—Nay, replied Ibn-El-Ḳáribee; thou shalt have half, and I half. But Mesroor said, No. And Ibn-El-Ḳáribee said, I will have a third, and thou shalt have two thirds.[19] And to this, Mesroor assented, after excessive striving.

Then Ibn-El-Ḳáribee arose and went with him, and when he came into the presence of the Prince of the Faithful, he greeted him with the salutation usually given to Khaleefehs, and stood before him; and the Prince of the Faithful said to him, If thou do not make me laugh, I beat thee three times with this leathern bag. So Ibn-El-Ḳáribee said within himself, And it will be no great matter if three blows be inflicted with this leathern bag, when beating with whips hurteth me not. For he imagined that the leathern bag was empty. He then uttered sayings that would make the enraged to laugh, with varieties of drolleries; but the Prince of the Faithful laughed not, nor even smiled; and Ibn-El-Ḳáribee wondered at him, and was vexed, and feared; and the Prince of the Faithful said to him, Now thou hast deserved the beating. Accordingly, he took the leathern bag, and beat him once; and there were in it four pebbles, each pebble of the weight of two pounds; and the blow fell upon his neck: so he uttered a great cry, and, remembering the agreement made between him and Mesroor, he said, Pardon, O Prince of the Faithful! Hear from me two words!—The Khaleefeh replied, Say what thou wilt. And he said, Verily Mesroor imposed on me a condition, and I agreed with him respecting it; and it was, that of whatsoever the Prince of the Faithful should bestow upon me, one third of it should be for me, and two thirds for him; and he consented not to this my proposal save after excessive striving. Now thou hast not bestowed on me aught save beating, and this blow is my share, and the remaining two blows are his share; for I have received my share, and here he is standing, O Prince of the Faithful; therefore pay him his.—And when the Prince of the Faithful heard his words, he laughed until he fell backwards; and, having called Mesroor, he gave him a blow, whereupon he cried out, and said, O Prince of the Faithful, the third sufficeth me, and do thou give him the two thirds. And the Khaleefeh laughed at them, and gave orders to present each of them with a thousand pieces of gold, And they departed, rejoiced at that which he had bestowed upon them.

---

19 In the original, "*thou* shalt have a third, and *I* will have two thirds;" but this is inconsistent both with what precedes and what follows.

Anecdote of a Devotee, Son of Hároon Er-Rasheed.[20]

The Prince of the Faithful, Hároon Er-Rasheed, had a son who had attained the age of sixteen years, and he was averse from the world, following the course of the abstinent and the devotees. He used to go forth to the burial-grounds, and to say, Ye were in possession of the world; but that saved you not; and ye have gone unto your graves. Would then that I knew what ye said,[21] and what was said unto you!—And he wept as the fearful and the dreading, and recited the saying of the poet:—

The funerals constantly terrify me, and the weeping of the wailing women grieveth me.

And it happened that his father passed by him one day, proceeding in state, surrounded by his wezeers and the great men of his empire and of the people of his dominions, and they saw the son of the Prince of the Faithful with a woollen jubbeh[22] upon his body, and a piece of woollen stuff (as a turban) upon his head. So one of them said to another, This youth hath disgraced the Prince of the Faithful among the Kings, and if he reproved him, he would relinquish his present course. And the Prince of the Faithful, hearing their words, spoke to him on that subject, and said to him, O my child, thou hast disgraced me by thy present life. But his son looked at him, and answered him not. Then he looked at a bird upon one of the battlements of the palace, and said to it, O bird, by Him who created thee, drop upon my hand. Whereupon the bird darted down upon the youth's hand. And he said to it, Return to thy place. And it returned. He then said to it, Drop upon the hand of the Prince of the Faithful. But it refused to do so. And the youth said to his father, Thou hast disgraced *me* among the Welees[23] by thy love of the world, and I have resolved to part from thee, never to return unto thee save in the world to come. Then he went down the river to El-Baṣrah, where he employed himself in working with the labourers in mud;[24] and he worked not each day save for a piece of silver and a sixth:[25] with the sixth, he fed himself; and with the piece of silver, he gave alms.

Aboo-'Ámir of El-Baṣrah hath related as follows:—A wall having fallen in my house, I went forth to the station of the labourers, to see for a man to repair it; and my eye fell upon a comely youth, of beautiful countenance; whereupon I went to him and saluted him and said to him, O my friend, dost thou desire service? He answered, Yes. And I said, Arise and come with me to build a wall. He replied, On certain conditions which I will impose upon thee.—O my friend, said I, what are they? He answered, The hire shall be a piece of silver and a sixth; and when the Muëddin

[20] This anecdote seems to be founded upon one which I have before related, of 'Alee the son of El-Ma-moon. See vol. i. p. 210.

[21] This, as my sheykh explains, alludes to the questions put by the two Angels, Munkar (vulgarly called Nákir) and Nekeer, who examine the dead, and torture the wicked, in the grave.—When the dead has been deposited in the grave, a person (called a Mulaḳḳin) is generally employed to instruct him how to answer these questions, and usually addresses him thus:—"O servant of God! O son of a handmaid of God! know that, at this time, there will come down to thee two angels commissioned respecting thee and the like of thee. When they say to thee, 'Who is thy Lord?' answer them, 'God is my Lord,' in truth; and when they ask thee concerning the Prophet, or the man who hath been sent unto you, say to them, 'Moḥammad is the Apostle of God,' with veracity; and when they ask thee concerning thy religion, say to them, 'El-Islám is my religion;' and when they ask thee concerning thy book of direction, say to them, 'The Ḳur-án is my book of direction, and the Muslims are my brothers;' and when they ask thee concerning thy Ḳibleh, say to them, 'The Kaạbeh is my Ḳibleh; and I have lived and died in the assertion, that there is no deity but God, and Moḥammad is God's Apostle:' and they will say, 'Sleep, O servant of God, in the protection of God.'" (From my work on the Modern Egyptians.)

[22] See Note 29 to Chapter vi.

[23] The favourites of God, or saints.

[24] That is, in building, in which mud is largely used, with, or instead of, lime.

[25] The name of the sixth of the dirhem (which latter, as it was the standard of silver coin, I call "a piece of silver,") is "dániḳ."

chanteth the call to prayer, thou shalt let me go to pray with the congregation. I replied, Well. Then I took him and went with him to the house, and he worked in a manner of which I have not seen the like. And I mentioned to him the dinner; but he said, No :—so I knew that he was fasting. And when he heard the call to prayer, he said to me, Thou knowest the condition. I replied, Yes. And he loosed his girdle, and applied himself to the ablution, performing it in a manner that I have not seen surpassed.[26] He then went forth to prayer, and, having prayed with the congregation, he returned to his work. And when the afternoon-call to prayer was chanted, he performed the ablution again and went to prayer, and returned to his work. Upon this I said to him, O my friend, the period of work is ended; for the work of the labourers is until the time of afternoon-prayers. But he replied, Extolled be the perfection of God! Verily my work is until night.—And he ceased not to work till night, when I gave him two pieces of silver; on seeing which, he said, What is this? I answered, By Allah, this is but a portion of thy hire, on account of thy diligence in my service. But he threw them back to me, saying, I desire not any addition to that for which we agreed together. I urged him; but could not prevail upon him. So I gave him a piece of silver and a sixth, and he went away.

And when the next morning came, I went early to the station; but found him not. I therefore inquired respecting him; and it was told me, He cometh not hither save on Saturday only. And when the next Saturday arrived, I repaired to that place, and found him; and I said to him, In the name of Allah, do me the favour to come to work. He replied, On the conditions which thou knowest. I said, Yes. And I went with him to my house, and stood and looked at him without his seeing me. And he took a handful of mud, and placed it upon the wall, and, lo, the stones ranged themselves, one upon another. So I said, Thus are the Welees of God! He worked that day, and exceeded what he had done before; and when the night came, I paid him his hire, and he took it and departed.

Again, on the third Saturday, I went to the station; but found him not; wherefore I asked respecting him, and was answered, He is sick, and lying in the booth of such a woman. This was an old woman well known for devotion, and she had a booth of reeds in the burial-ground. And I went to the booth, and entered it; and, lo, he was lying upon the ground, with nothing under him: he had placed his head upon an unburnt brick, and his face was beaming with light. I saluted him, and he returned my salutation; and I seated myself at his head, weeping on account of his youth, and his absence from his native place, and his aptness to the obedience of his Lord. Then I said to him, Hast thou any want? He answered, Yes.—And what is it? I asked. He answered, To-morrow come to me, at the mid-time between sunrise and noon, and thou wilt find me dead. Wash me, and dig my grave, without acquainting any one with it; and shroud me in this jubbeh that is upon me; and after unsewing it, search its breast, take forth what is within it, and keep it in thy possession. Then, when thou hast prayed over me, and deposited my body in the earth, repair to Baghdád, and watch for the Khaleefeh, Hároon Er-Rasheed, until he cometh forth, and give him what thou shalt find in the breast of my jubbeh, with my salutation.—Having said this, he repeated the professions of the faith, and praised his Lord with the most eloquent words, and recited these verses:—

> Convey the deposite of him whom death awaiteth to Er-Rasheed; for thou wilt be rewarded for that act;
> And say to him, A stranger, desirous of beholding thee, long loving and distant, hath offered thee his homage.

---

[26] Numerous ejaculations (short prayers) are uttered by the more strict Muslims in the performance of the ablution; but most persons more or less neglect these.—See my "Modern Egyptians," vol. i. ch. iii.

Neither hatred nor weariness hath removed him from thee; for by kissing thy right hand,[27] he is brought near to God:
But that which hath estranged him from thee, O my father, is a soul which forbeareth to share thy worldly pleasures.

Then he employed himself in begging God's forgiveness, and in prayer, and invoking blessings upon the Chief of the Just,[28] and reciting some verses of the Ḳur-án, and repeated these lines:—

O my father, be not thou deceived by enjoyment; for life will pass away, and enjoyment will end.
When thou art informed that a people are oppressed, know that thou wilt be inquired of respecting them;[29]
And when thou conveyest a corpse unto the tombs, know that thou likewise wilt be borne after it.

And when the youth had ended his charge and his recitations, I departed from him, and went to my house. And on the following morning I repaired to him again, at the mid-time between sunrise and noon, and found that he had died. May the mercy of God be on him! So I washed him, and unsewed his jubbeh, and I found in its breast a ruby worth thousands of pieces of gold; whereupon I said within myself, By Allah, this young man hath abstained from worldly pleasures with the extreme of abstinence!

Then, after I had buried him, I repaired to Baghdád, and, arriving at the palace of the Khaleefeh, I watched for Er-Rasheed's coming forth until he came; when I presented myself before him in one of the streets, and gave to him the ruby. As soon as he saw it, he knew it, and fell down in a fit; upon which the servants laid hold upon me; but when he recovered, he said to them, Loose him, and send him with courtesy to the palace. So they did as he commanded them; and on his entering his palace, he summoned me, and took me into his chamber, and said to me, What did the owner of this ruby? I answered him, He is dead. And I described to him his case; whereupon he wept, and said, The son hath profited, and the father hath been disap-

[27] That is, by honouring thee as his father.
[28] The Prophet.
[29] On the day of judgment.

pointed! Then he called out, O such-a-one! (naming a female);—and a woman came forth; but when she saw me, she was about to return: so he said to her, Come hither. Thou needest not mind him.—She therefore entered and saluted, and he threw to her the ruby; on seeing which she uttered a great cry, and fell down in a fit. And when she recovered from her fit, she said, O Prince of the Faithful, what hath God done with my son? He said to me, Acquaint her with his case. And weeping overcame him. Accordingly I informed her of his case; and she began to weep, and to say with a faint voice, O, how I longed to meet thee! O delight of mine eye! Would that I had given thee to drink when thou foundest not any to do so! Would that I had cheered thee when thou foundest not a cheerer!—Then she poured forth tears, and recited these verses:—

I weep for a stranger who died in solitude, with no friend unto whom to complain of his misery.
After glory, and union with those who loved him, he became lone and desolate, seeing no one.
What fortune concealeth a while will be manifest. Death never spareth any one among us.
O absent! my Lord decreed thine absence; and after nearness thou becamest remote from me!
Though death makes me hopeless of meeting thee now, O my son, we shall meet on the day of account.

And I said, O Prince of the Faithful, was he thy son? He answered, Yes; and before I held this office he used to visit the learned men, and keep company with the just; and when I assumed this office he avoided me, and estranged himself from me. So I said to his mother, This youth is devoted unto God (whose name be exalted!), and probably adversities may befall him, and he may be afflicted with trials; therefore give to him this ruby, that he may find it in the time of his wanting it. Accordingly, she gave it to him, conjuring him to retain it, and he complied with her desire and took it from her. Then he left our worldly enjoyments to us, and absented himself from us, and ceased not to remain absent from us until, pious and pure, he met God, to whom be ascribed might and glory!

And after this, the Khaleefeh said to me, Arise, and shew me his tomb. I therefore went forth with him, and journeyed on until I shewed it to him; whereupon he wept and lamented until he fell down in a fit; and when he recovered from his fit, he begged forgiveness of God, and said, Verily to God we belong, and verily unto Him we return! And he invoked blessings on his son. After which, he asked me to become his associate; but I replied, O Prince of the Faithful, I have, in the case of thy son, the most momentous of admonitions.[30]

Anecdote of an Illiterate Schoolmaster.[31]

It is related that a certain man among the collegians,[32] neither acquainted with writing nor with reading, practised stratagems upon the people for the purpose of obtaining his bread. And it occurred to his mind one day that he should open for himself a school, and teach boys in it to read. So he collected writing-tablets and written papers, and hung them up in a place, and he enlarged his turban,[33] and seated

[30] The first of the next two anecdotes in my original (both of which I omit) is that of a schoolmaster mentioned (on the authority of the "Kitáb el-'Onwán &c.") in vol. i. p. 468. See a foot-note (No. 29) in p. 294 of this volume.

[31] I have related an anecdote almost exactly similar to this, as descriptive of a late occurrence, in my work on the Modern Egyptians (vol. i. ch. ii.). It appears therefore that my informant's account was not true as to time, or that the man alluded to by him was, in the main, an imitator. The latter is not improbable, as I have been credibly informed of several similar imitations, and of one which I know to be a fact.

[32] In the original, "mujáwireen." This appellation is given to persons who reside in or near a collegiate mosque, for the purpose of study, attending lectures, &c.

[33] Most of the professors of religion and law used to wear, and many do still, a very large and formal turban; and a great turban is generally regarded by the vulgar as an indication of great learning.

himself at the door of the school. The people therefore, passing by him, and looking at his turban, and at the writing-tablets and papers, imagined that he was an excellent faḳeeh,[34] and brought to him their children. And he used to say to this one, Write;—and to this, Read;—and thus the boys taught one another. But as he was sitting one day at the door of the school as usual, lo, a woman approached from a distance, with a letter in her hand; whereupon he said within himself, Without doubt this woman is coming to me, that I may read to her the letter that she holdeth; and how shall I manage with her, when I know not how to read writing? He meditated upon descending to flee from her; but she came up to him before he had descended, and said to him, Whither goest thou? He answered her, I desire to perform the noon-prayers, and to return.—Noon, she replied, is yet distant: therefore read for me this letter. And he took it from her, and turned it upside down, and began to look at it; and one moment he shook his turban, and another moment moved about his eyebrows, and manifested rage. Now the husband of the woman was absent, and the letter was sent to her from him. So when she saw the faḳeeh in this state, she said within herself, No doubt my husband is dead, and this faḳeeh is ashamed to tell me that he is dead. She therefore said to him, O my master, if he be dead, tell me. And he shook his head, and was silent. And the woman said to him, Shall I rend my clothes?—Rend, he answered.—Shall I slap my face? she asked. He answered her, Slap.

So she took the letter from his hand, and returned to her abode; and she and her children began to weep; whereupon some of her neighbours, hearing the weeping, inquired respecting her state; and were answered, A letter hath come to her acquainting her with the death of her husband. But a man among them replied, Verily this assertion is false; for her husband sent me a letter yesterday informing me in it that he was well, in prosperity and health, and that after ten days he will be with her. And he arose immediately, and, coming to the woman, said to her, Where is the letter that hath come to thee? She therefore brought it to him, and he took it from her and read it, and, lo, it contained these words:—To proceed, I am well, in prosperity and health, and after ten days I shall be with you; and I have sent unto you a quilt and a mekmarah.[35]—So she took the letter, and returned with it to the faḳeeh, and said to him, What induced thee to act as thou hast done with me? And she acquainted him with that which her neighbour had said, respecting the safety of her husband, and his having sent to her a quilt and a mekmarah; whereupon he replied, Thou hast spoken truth; but, O respectable woman, excuse me; for I was at that time enraged, troubled in mind, and, seeing the mekmarah wrapped up in the quilt, I imagined that he had died, and that they had shrouded him. And the woman knew not the trick: so she said to him, Thou art excused. And she took the letter from him, and departed.

The Rukh'.[36]

A man of the people of Western Africa[37] had travelled in various regions, and traversed the wastes and the seas, and destiny cast him upon an island, where he remained a long time. Then he returned to his country, bringing with him the quill-

---

[34] This appellation is now usually given only to a person versed in religion and law; the term "fiḳee," which is a corruption of "faḳeeh," being commonly applied to a man who merely recites the Ḳur-án &c. professionally, or who teaches children.

[35] The term "mekmarah" is interpreted by my sheykh, but rather vaguely. I believe it to be a belt or girdle containing a purse for money, commonly called "kamar."

[36] Or Rukhkh; but an accent very well denotes what the Arabs call "teshdeed," and should, I think, be always employed in a case of this kind, to avoid the combination of four consonants without a vowel following them.

[37] Called by the Arabs "El-Maghrib." This name is generally given to the districts of Northern Africa west of Egypt. The inhabitants of those parts are called "Maghrabees."

part of a feather from the wing of a young rukh', which was in the egg, and had not come forth from it into the world; and that quill held as much as a goat's skin of water. It is said that the length of the wing of the young rukh', at the time of its coming forth from the egg, is a thousand fathoms; and the people wondered at that quill when they saw it. This man was named 'Abd-Er-Raḥmán El-Maghrabee; and he became commonly known by the surname of the Chinese, on account of his long residence in China; and he used to relate wonders.[38]

Result of Restraint upon two Lovers.

El-Ḳásim the son of 'Adee hath related that a man of the tribe of the Benee-Temeem said, I went forth to seek a stray beast, and, coming to the waters of the tribe of Ṭeiyi, I saw two parties of people, near unto each other, and among one of them words were passing like as among the people of the other. And I looked attentively, and saw among one of the parties a young man whom disease had emaciated, so that he was like a worn-out, dried-up water-skin; and while I was looking at him, he recited these verses:—

Wherefore doth the beauteous damsel not return? Is it from niggardness in her, or aversion?
I fell sick, and each member of my family visited me. Then wherefore wast thou not seen among them?
Hadst thou been sick, I had come unto thee, and threats would not have prevented my doing so.
I missed thee among them, and became desolate. Grievous was thy loss, O my heart's abode!

And a damsel of the other party heard his words, and hastened towards him. Her family followed her; but she encountered them with blows; and the young man, perceiving her, sprang towards her, while the people of his party quickly followed him. He however dragged himself from them, and she in like manner dragged herself from her party until she liberated herself, and each of them ran to the other till they met between the two parties, and embraced each other: then they fell down upon the ground, dead. Upon this, an old man came forth from one of the adjacent tents, and, standing over them, exclaimed, Verily to God we belong, and verily unto Him we return!—and wept violently; after which he said, May God (whose name be exalted!) have mercy on you both! By Allah, if ye were not united in your lives, I will assuredly unite you after death!—Then he gave orders to prepare them for burial; and they were washed, and shrouded in the same grave-clothes; one grave was dug for them, and the people prayed over them, and buried them in that grave; and there was not a male nor a female among the two parties that I did not see weeping for them, and slapping [the face]. So I inquired of the old man respecting them; and he answered me, This was my daughter, and this was the son of my brother. Their love hath brought them to the issue which thou beheldest.—I said to him, May God give thee reparation! Didst thou not marry them to each other?—He answered, I feared reproach and disgrace, and now I have fallen into both.—This is one of the wonders in the histories of lovers.

---

38 One of his wonderful stories, related in the original, I here omit, that I may not anticipate incidents in the voyages of Es-Sindibád; in my notes on which, I shall have occasion to revert to it. (See Notes 22 and 62 to Chapter xx.)—The above anecdote is followed in the original by four which I omit. One of these (an adventure of Is-ḥáḳ the son of Ibráheem) I should translate were it not nearly the same as that of Mukháriḳ, in vol. i. p. 202; and similar also to that of Ibráheem the son of El-Mahdee, in the present volume, p. 452.

Anecdote of a Distracted Lover.

Abu-l-'Abbás El-Mubarrad[39] saith, I repaired to El-Bereed,[40] with a party of men, on some business, and, passing by the Convent of Heraclius,[41] we alighted in its shade; and there came to us a man who said to us, There are in the convent some madmen, among whom is one that uttereth wisdom; and if ye saw him, ye would wonder at his words. So we all arose and entered the convent, and we saw a man sitting in a private chamber, upon a skin, with his head uncovered, and his eye fixed upwards towards the wall. We saluted him, and he returned our salutation without looking at us; and a man said, Recite to him some poetry; for when he heareth poetry, he will speak. I therefore recited these two verses:—

O thou best of all men to whom Eve[42] hath given birth! but for thee, the world were not beautiful nor pleasant.
The man whom God sheweth thy form[43] hath obtained immortality, and will grow neither decrepit nor hoary.

And when he heard me say this, he turned towards us, and recited thus:—

God knoweth that I am in affliction. I cannot make manifest the pain that I feel.
Two souls have I: one place containeth one soul; and another place, the other.
I imagine that my absent soul is like my present, and that she experienceth what I do.

Then he asked, Have I said well or ill? We answered him, Thou hast not said ill; but well and admirably. And he stretched forth his hand to a stone that was by him, and took it. So we imagined that he would smite us with it, and we fled from him. But he began to beat with it his own bosom, with violent blows, and said, Fear ye not. Draw near to me, and hear from me something: receive it from me.—We therefore approached him; and he recited these verses:—

When they made their white camels kneel down, near daybreak, they mounted, and the camel departed with the beloved.
My eye, through the interstice of the prison, beheld them, and I said, in my anguish, with tears overflowing,
O camel-driver turn, that I may bid her farewell; for in parting, and in bidding her farewell, I shall die.
I am faithful to the vow of love, and have not broken it. Would that I knew how she hath[44] acted with regard to it!

He then looked towards me, and said, Hast thou any knowledge of what the beloved hath done? I answered, Yes she hath died. May God (whose name be exalted!) have mercy on her!—And upon this, his countenance changed, and he sprang upon his feet, and said, How knewest thou her death? I answered, Had she been alive, she had not left thee thus. And he replied, Thou hast spoken truth, by Allah: but I also love not life after the loss of her. Then the muscles of his side quivered, and he fell upon his face; whereat we hastened to him, and moved him, and found him dead. The mercy of God (whose name be exalted!) be on him! And we wondered at this, and grieved for him violently; and we prepared his body for the grave, and buried him. And when I returned to Baghdád, and went in to El-Mutawekkil, he saw the traces of tears upon my face; whereupon he said, What is this? So I related to him the story; and it distressed him, and he said, What induced thee to act so? By Allah, if I knew that thou mournedst not for him, I should reprove thee for it.—And he mourned for him all the rest of the day.

---

[39] A famous grammarian and rhetorician. He died at the age of 80, in the year of the Flight 286, or 285: El-Muzhir, MS. in my possession.

[40] Name of a place.

[41] Called by the Arabs "Hiraḳl."

[42] In Arabic, "Ḥowwà."

[43] For "aráka" and "ṣooretahu" in the Cairo edition, I read "aráhu" and "ṣooretaka" as in the Breslau edition, vol. viii. p. 271.

[44] Literally, "they have."

The Converted Prior.

Aboo-Bekr the son of Moḥammad El-Ambáree saith, I went forth from El-Ambár,[45] on one of my journeys, to 'Ammooriyeh,[46] in the country of the Greeks,[47] and alighted, on the way, at the Convent of the Lights, in a village near 'Ammooriyeh, whereupon there came forth to me the chief of the convent, the Prior, whose name was 'Abd-El-Meseeḥ;[48] and he conducted me into the convent. I found in it forty monks; and they honoured me that night with a hospitable entertainment. Then, on the morrow, I departed from them, after I had seen, of their exceeding diligence in their exercises, and of their devotion, what I had not seen exhibited by others; and I returned to El-Ambár. And in the following year, I performed the pilgrimage to Mekkeh; and while I was compassing the House,[49] lo, I beheld 'Abd-El-Meseeḥ the monk compassing also, and with him five persons of his companions, the monks. Therefore when I was sure that I knew him, I advanced to him, and said to him, Art thou 'Abd-El-Meseeḥ the monk? He answered, Rather I am 'Abd-Allah the suppliant. So I began to kiss his hoary hairs, and to weep; and, taking him by the hand, I turned to a side of the Temple, and said to him, Acquaint me with the cause of thy conversion to El-Islám. And he replied, It was one of the most wonderful of wonderful events; and it was this.

A party of Muslim devotees passed by the village in which is our convent, and sent a young man to buy for them food, and he beheld in the market a Christian damsel selling bread; and she was of the most beautiful of women in form. On beholding her, he was fascinated by her, and fell down upon his face in a fit; and when he recovered, he returned to his companions, and informed them of that which had befallen him, and said to them, Depart ye to your business; for I go not with you. They reproved him and admonished him; but he paid no regard to them: so they departed from him; and he entered the village, and seated himself at the door of the shop of that woman. She therefore asked him what he wanted, and he informed her that he was enamoured of her; whereupon she turned from him. He remained in his place three days, without tasting food; keeping his eye fixed upon her face; and when she saw that he would not depart from her, she went to her family, and told them of him; and they set upon him the boys, who pelted him with stones until they fractured his ribs and broke his head; notwithstanding which, he would not depart. The people of the village, therefore, resolved to kill him; but a man of them came to me, and acquainted me with his case; upon which I went forth to him, and beheld him laid prostrate; and I wiped the blood from his face, and conveyed him to the convent, where I applied remedies to his wounds, and he remained with me fourteen days. As soon, however, as he was able to walk, he went forth from the convent to the door of the damsel's shop, and sat again gazing at her. And when she saw him, she rose to him, and said to him, By Allah, I am moved with compassion for thee. Wilt thou then adopt my religion, that I may marry thee?—But he answered, God preserve me from abandoning the religion of the Unity, and adopting the religion of Polytheism!—Then depart from me, said the damsel.—My heart, he replied, will not consent to my doing so. And she turned her face from him. And the boys, seeing him again, came to him and pelted him as before with stones, and he fell upon his face, saying, Verily my helper is God, who sent down the Book,[50] and He taketh charge of the just!—I therefore went forth from the convent, and drove from him the boys, and, lifting up his head from the

---

[45] A city on the Euphrates.

[46] The ancient Amorium, in Phrygia.

[47] Er-Room.

[48] "The Servant of the Messiah."

[49] The Kaạbeh, which the pilgrims compass seven times.

[50] The Ḳur-án.

ground, I heard him say, O my Lord, unite me with her in Paradise!—I conveyed him to the convent; but he died before I had arrived there with him; and I took him forth from the village, dug a grave for him, and buried him.

And in the following night, when half of it was spent, that woman shrieked out as she lay in her bed; whereupon the people of the village came together to her, asking her what had happened to her; and she answered, While I was asleep, this Muslim came in to me, and, taking me by my hand, went away with me to Paradise. But when he arrived with me at its gate, its Guardian prevented my entering it, saying, It is denied unto the infidels. So I made profession of El-Islám to him, and entered with him; and I beheld in it pavilions and trees such as I cannot describe to you. Then he took me to a pavilion of jewels, and said to me, Verily this pavilion is for me and thee. I will not enter it but with thee; and after five nights thou wilt be with me in it, if it be the will of God, whose name be exalted!—And thereupon he stretched forth his hand to a tree at the door of that pavilion, and plucked from it two apples, which he gave to me, saying, Eat this, and conceal the other, that the monks may see it. I therefore ate one; and I have tasted nothing more sweet than it. He then took me by my hand, and went forth with me until he conducted me to my house; and when I awoke, I found the taste of the apple in my mouth, and the other apple with me.—Having said this, she produced the apple, and it shone in the darkness of night as though it were a glistening star. So they brought the woman to the convent, and the apple with her; and she related to us the vision, and produced to us the apple. We had seen nothing like it among all the fruits of the world; and I took a knife, and divided it in pieces according to the number of my companions; and we had not tasted any thing more delicious than its flavour, nor smelt any thing more sweet than its odour. But we said, Perhaps this was a devil who presented himself to her to seduce her from her religion. And her family took her and departed. And she abstained from eating and drinking; and when the fifth night arrived, she rose from her bed, went forth from her house, and repaired to the grave of that Muslim; and she threw herself upon it, and died; her family not knowing what she had done.

Then, in the morning, there came to the village two Muslim sheykhs, attired in apparel of hair-cloth, and accompanied by two women in the like garb; and they said, O people of the village, ye have among you a Weleeyeh[51] of God; she hath died a Muslimeh, and we will take charge of her in preference to you. So the people of the

[51] A female saint.

village sought that woman, and they found her upon the grave, dead. But they said, This was our friend: she died in our religion, and we will take charge of her. The two sheykhs said, Nay: she died a Muslimeh, and we will take charge of her. And the altercation and dispute between them became violent. Therefore one of the two sheykhs said, The sign of her having embraced El-Islám shall be this: the forty monks of the convent shall come together, to drag her from the grave; and if they be able to lift her from the ground, she died a Christian; but if they cannot do so, one of us shall advance and drag her; and if she come with him, she died a Muslimeh. And to this the people of the village consented. The forty monks assembled, and encouraged one another, and came to her to lift her; but they could not do so; and we tied to her waist a great rope, and attempted to drag her; but the rope broke, and she moved not. The people of the village also advançed and did the like: yet she moved not from her place. So when we were unable to lift her by any means that we adopted, we said to one of the two sheykhs, Advance thou, and lift her. Accordingly one of them advanced to her, and wrapped her in his cloak, and saying, In the name of God, the Compassionate, the Merciful, and through the religion of the Apostle of God, may God favour and preserve him!—he carried her in his bosom. The Muslims conveyed her to a cavern there, and put her in it; and the two women came, and washed her and shrouded her. Then the two sheykhs carried her, and prayed over her, and buried her by the side of his grave, and departed; we having witnessed all this.

And when some of us were in private with others of our associates, we said, Verily the truth is most deserving of being followed, and the truth hath become manifest to us by ocular witness, and we can have no proof of the truth of El-Islám more manifest to us than what we have beheld with our eyes. Then I embraced El-Islám, and so also did all the monks of the convent, and the people of the village. After this, we sent to the people of El-Jezeereh,[52] supplicating for a professor of religion and law, to teach us the ordinances of El-Islám, and the precepts of the religion; and a professor, a just man, came to us, and taught us the rites of divine worship, and the precepts of El-Islám; so that we are now enjoying abundant happiness; and to God be praise and thanks!

Aboo-'Eesà *and* Ḳurrat-el-'Eyn.

'Amr the son of Mes'adah hath related, that Aboo-'Eesà the son of Er-Rasheed and brother of El-Ma-moon was enamoured of Ḳurrat-el-'Eyn,[53] the slave-girl of 'Alee the son of Hishám, and she also was enamoured of him; but Aboo-'Eesà concealed his love, and revealed it not, nor complained of it to any one, nor acquainted any one with his secret. Thus he did from his magnanimity and generosity. He endeavoured, however, to purchase her of her lord by every expedient. But he could not attain his object; and when his patience failed him, and his transport of love became violent, and he found no means of obtaining her, he went in to El-Ma-moon on a festival-day, after the departure of the people from him, and said, O Prince of the Faithful, if thou wouldst try thy heart this day and pay unexpected visits, thou wouldst distinguish the people of generosity from others, and wouldst know the place of each of them, and the quality of his mind. Aboo-'Eesà desired, by these words, to get an opportunity of sitting with Ḳurrat-el-'Eyn in the house of her lord. And El-Ma-moon replied, Verily this advice is right. He gave orders to prepare a bark which was named the Flyer:[54] so they brought it forward to him, and he embarked in it, together with a party of his chief officers; and the first pavilion that he entered was that of Ḥomeyd

[52] Mesopotamia.

[53] "The Delight of the Eye."

[54] "Eṭ-Ṭeiyár." Perhaps this is put for the feminine, "ṭeiyárah," the name of a kind of swift vessel.

Eṭ-Ṭaweel, of Ṭoos. They went in to him in the pavilion when he expected them not, and found him sitting upon a mat, with the singers before him, having lutes and flutes and other instruments of music in their hands; and after El-Ma-moon had sat a while, there were brought to him dishes of the flesh of beasts, without any of the flesh of birds; and El-Ma-moon paid no regard to any of those viands. So Aboo-'Eesà said, O Prince of the Faithful, we entered this place unexpected, and its owner knew not of thine approach. Arise then and go with us to a place prepared for thee and suited to thee.

The Khaleefeh accordingly arose, with his chief officers and his brother Aboo-'Eesà, and they repaired to the house of 'Alee the son of Hishám. And when he knew of their coming, he received them in the most honourable manner, kissing the ground before the Khaleefeh. Then he conducted them into the pavilion, and opened a chamber, such as none had seen surpassed in beauty. Its floor and columns and walls were of varieties of marbles, it was decorated with various kinds of Greek paintings,[55] and its floor was spread with mats of Es-Sind,[56] and furniture of El-Baṣrah, made to suit the length and breadth of the chamber. El-Ma-moon sat a while contemplating the apartment and the roof and the walls; after which he said, Give us some food. And there were brought to him immediately nearly a hundred dishes of fowls, besides other birds, and thereeds[57] and fries and cold things; and when he had eaten, he said, Give us something to drink, O 'Alee. And there was brought to him aromatic wine, prepared with fruits and fragrant spices, in vessels of gold and silver and crystal; and those who brought in that wine were pages like moons, attired in garments of stuff of Alexandria interwoven with gold, and before their bosoms were bottles of crystal containing rose-water infused with musk. El-Ma-moon wondered exceedingly at that which he beheld, and said, O Abu-l-Ḥasan.[58] Whereupon he sprang to the carpet and kissed it, and then, standing before the Khaleefeh, replied, At thy service, O Prince of the Faithful. And the Khaleefeh said, Let us hear some mirth-exciting songs. His host replied, I hear and obey, O Prince of the Faithful. Then he said to one of his servants, Bring the singing slave-girls. So the eunuch replied that he heard and obeyed; and, after he had been absent a moment, returned with ten eunuchs bringing ten chairs of gold. And when they had placed the chairs, there came ten maids like shining full moons and flowery gardens, attired in black brocade, and with crowns of gold upon their heads; and they walked forward until they seated themselves upon the chairs, when they sang varieties of melodies. Then those slave-girls departed, and ten others came, and sang; and after these, came ten others; and again, after them, ten others.

El-Ma-moon then said, Bring forward the boat. And he was about to embark and go. But 'Alee the son of Hishám arose and said, O Prince of the Faithful, I have a slave-girl whom I purchased for ten thousand pieces of gold, and who hath captivated my whole heart, and I desire to shew her to the Prince of the Faithful. If she please him, and he approve of her, she shall be his; and if not, let him hear from her something.—So the Khaleefeh said, Bring her unto me. And there came forth a damsel like a twig of the Oriental willow, with fascinating eyes, and eyebrows like two bows, and upon her head was a crown of red gold set with large pearls and with jewels, beneath which was a bandage whereon was worked with chrysolites this verse:—

A Jinneeyeh, and she hath Jinn who teach her to smite hearts by means of a stringless bow.

This damsel walked forward like a fugitive gazelle; and she would have fascinated a devotee. She continued to advance till she seated herself upon a chair; and when El-

---

[55] Or carvings.

[56] Western India.

[57] Crumbled or sliced bread, with broth, &c.

[58] A surname, I suppose, of 'Alee the son of Hishám.

Ma-moon beheld her, he wondered at her beauty and loveliness; and Aboo-'Eesà was pained in heart; his complexion became sallow, and his whole state changed. El-Ma-moon therefore said to him, What is the matter with thee, O Aboo-'Eesà, that thy state hath changed? He answered, O Prince of the Faithful, it is by reason of a malady that cometh upon me sometimes. And the Khaleefeh said to him, Hast thou known this slave-girl before the present day?—Yes, O Prince of the Faithful, he answered. And can the moon (he added) be hidden?—Then El-Ma-moon said to her, What is thy name, O damsel? She answered, My name is Ḳurrat-el-'Eyn, O Prince of the Faithful. And he said to her, Sing to us, O Ḳurrat-el-'Eyn. So she sang; and the Khaleefeh said to her, Divinely art thou gifted! By whom are these verses?—She answered, By Deạbil El-Khuzá'ee, and the air is by Zurzoor Eṣ-Ṣagheer. And Aboo-'Eesà looked at her, and weeping choked him, so that the company wondered at him.

Then the damsel looked towards El-Ma-moon, and said to him, O Prince of the Faithful, wilt thou give me permission to change the words of my song? He answered, Sing what thou wilt. And, with exciting modulations, she sang these verses:—

If thou please one and he also please thee publicly, be more careful of preserving thy love in secret;
And reject the assertions of the slanderers; for seldom do they wish for aught but the estrangement of the lover.
They have averred that whenever the lover approacheth, he is wearied; and that absence is the remedy for passion.
We have tried both remedies, and not been cured; but nearness of abode is better than distance:
Yet nearness of abode is of no advantage when the person thou lovest doth not love thee.

And when she had finished her song, Aboo-'Eesà said, O Prince of the Faithful, if we be disgraced,[59] we shall be at ease. Wilt thou give me permission to reply to her?—The Khaleefeh answered him, Yes: say to her what thou wilt. And he restrained his tears, and sang these two verses:—

I was silent, and said not that I was a lover; but concealed my affection from my own heart.
If my love, notwithstanding, appear in my eye, 'tis because it is near to the shining moon.

Then again the damsel took the lute and sang; and again Aboo-'Eesà sang in reply to her; and when he had ended, 'Alee the son of Hishám sprang to his feet and kissed them, saying to him, O my master, God hath answered thy prayer, and heard thy secret, and consented to thy taking her with all her appurtenances of rarities and beautiful things, if the Prince of the Faithful have no desire for her. And El-Ma-moon said, If we had a desire for her, we had given Aboo-'Eesà the preference to ourself, and aided him in the attainment of his desire. Then El-Ma-moon arose, and embarked in the boat. Aboo-'Eesà remained behind to take Ḳurrat-el-'Eyn, and he took her and departed with her to his abode, with a dilated heart.—Consider then the generosity of 'Alee the son of Hishám.

---

[59] By revealing our love.

CHAPTER XIX.

COMMENCING WITH PART OF THE FOUR HUNDRED AND TWENTY-FOURTH NIGHT, AND ENDING WITH PART OF THE FOUR HUNDRED AND THIRTY-FOURTH.

THE STORY OF 'ALEE OF CAIRO.

THERE was, in the city of Cairo, a merchant who had abundance of wealth and ready money, and jewels and minerals, and possessions incalculable, and his name was Ḥasan the Jeweller of Baghdád. God had also blessed him with a son, of handsome countenance, of just stature, rosy-cheeked, endowed with elegance and perfection, and beauty and loveliness;

and he named him 'Alee of Cairo. He had taught him the Ḳur-án and science, and eloquence and polite literature; and he became excellent in all the sciences, and was employed by his father in commerce.

Now a disease attacked his father, and so increased that he felt sure of death. So he summoned his son 'Alee of Cairo, and said to him, O my son, verily this world is transitory, and the world to come is everlasting; every soul must taste of death, and now, O my son, my decease hath drawn near, and I desire to give thee a charge. If thou act according to it, thou wilt not cease to be safe and prosperous until thou shalt meet God (whose name be exalted!); but if thou act not according to it, excessive trouble will befall thee, and thou wilt repent of thy neglecting my charge.—O my father, said 'Alee, how should I refuse to attend, or to act according to thy charge, when obedience to thee is an obligation divinely imposed upon me, and the attending to thy words is absolutely incumbent upon me? And his father rejoined, O my son, I leave to thee dwelling-places and mansions and goods and wealth incalculable; so that if thou expend of that wealth every day five hundred pieces of gold, nought of it will be missed by thee. But, O my son, be mindful of holding the fear of God, and obeying the ordinances which He hath appointed thee, and following the precepts of El-Muṣṭafà[1] (may God bless and save him!) in the things that he is related to have commanded and forbidden in his traditional laws. Be assiduous in the performance of acts of beneficence, and the dispensing of kindness, and associating with the good and just and learned; and mind that thou care for the poor and the needy, and shun avarice and niggardness, and the company of the wicked, and those who are objects of suspicion. Regard thy servants and thy family with benignity, and thy wife also; for she is of the daughters of the great, and she is now likely to bear thee issue: perhaps God will bless thee with virtuous offspring by her.—He ceased not to admonish him, and to weep, and say to him, O my son, I beg of God, the Bountiful, the Lord of the magnificent throne, that He save thee from every difficulty that may befall thee, and grant thee his ready relief. And his son wept violently, and said, O my father, by Allah I am dissolved by these words: it seemeth that thou utterest the language of him who biddeth farewell. His father replied, Yes, O my son; I know my state; and forget not thou my charge.—Then the man began to repeat the two professions of the faith, and to recite [portions of the Ḳur-án], until the known period arrived; when he said to his son, Draw near to me, O my son. So he drew near to him, and his father kissed him, and uttered a groan, whereupon his soul quitted his body, and he was admitted to the mercy of God, whose name be exalted!

His son was affected with extreme grief, a clamour arose in his house, and the companions of his father came together to him. He betook himself to preparing his corpse for burial, and expediting[2] the funeral, and conveyed forth the body in a magnificent manner. They bore the corpse to the place of prayer, and prayed over it; after which they departed with it to the burial-ground, and buried it, and recited over it what was easy of the sublime Ḳur-án. Then they returned to the house, and consoled the son of the deceased, and each of them went his way; and the son of the deceased performed for him the ceremonies of the Fridays, and recitations of the whole of the Ḳur-án, to the end of forty days.[3] He remained in the house, and went not forth save to the place of prayer; and Friday after Friday he visited his father's tomb.

He ceased not to persevere in his prayer, and his recitation [of the Ḳur-án], and his devotion, for a length of time, until his fellows, of the sons of the merchants, came in to him and saluted him, and said to him, How long shall continue this mourning of thine, and the relinquishment of thine occupation and thy traffic, and of thine assembling with thy companions? This conduct will weary thee, and excessive injury will result from it unto thy body.—And when they came in to him, Iblees the accursed was with them, suggesting evil to them. So they proceeded to recommend to him that he should go forth with them to the market, and Iblees seduced him to comply with their request until he consented to go forth with them from the house, in order to the accomplishment of an event which God (whose perfection be extolled, and whose name be exalted!) would bring to pass. They then said to him, Mount thy mule, and repair with us to such a garden, that we may amuse ourselves there, and that thy grief and trouble of mind may be dispelled.

He therefore mounted his mule, took his slave with him, and accompanied them to the garden which they desired to visit. And when they came into the garden, one of them went and prepared for them the dinner, and caused it to be brought thither. So they ate, and enjoyed themselves, and sat conversing until the close of the day, when they mounted and departed, each of them returning to his abode. And they passed the night; and when the morning arrived, they came to him again, and said to him, Arise, and accompany us.—Whither?

he asked. They answered, To such a garden; for it is better than that to which we went first, and more pleasant. And he mounted and went with them to that garden; and when they had arrived there, one of them went and made ready their dinner, and brought it to the garden, together with intoxicating wine; and they ate. Then they brought the wine; and he said to them, What is this? They answered him, This is what dispelleth grief, and manifesteth happiness. And they ceased not to recommend it to him until they overcame him, and he drank with them; and they continued conversing and drinking till the close of the day, when they returned to their abodes. But 'Alee of Cairo was affected with a giddiness from drinking, and he went to his wife in this state: so she said to him, How is it that thou art changed? He answered, We were to-day making merry and enjoying ourselves; but one of our companions brought us some liquor, which my companions drank, and I with them, and this giddiness came upon me. His wife therefore said to him, O my master, hast thou forgotten the charge of thy father, and done that which he forbade thee to do, in associating with people who are objects of suspicion? But he answered her, Verily these are of the sons of the merchants, and are not persons who are objects of suspicion: they are only people of pleasure and enjoyment.

He continued incessantly every day with his companions in this manner. They went from place to place, eating and drinking, until they said to him, Our turns are ended, and the turn is come to thee. And he replied, A friendly and free and an ample welcome to you! And when he arose in the morning, he made ready all that the case required, of food and drink, much more than they had done, and took with him the cooks and the farráshes and the coffee-makers,[4] and they repaired to Er-Róḍah and the Nilometer.[5] There they remained a whole month, eating and drinking, and hearing music, and enjoying themselves; and when the month had passed, 'Alee saw that he had expended a sum of money of large amount; but Iblees the accursed deceived him, and said to him, If thou shouldst expend every day as much as thou hast already, thy wealth would not fail thee. So he cared not for expending his wealth. He continued to do thus for the space of three years; his wife admonishing him, and reminding him of the charge of his father; but he attended not to her words until all the ready money that he had was exhausted. Then he began to take of the jewels, and to sell them, and expend their prices, till he exhausted them also. After this, he betook himself to selling the houses

and other immoveable possessions until none of them remained. And when they were gone, he proceeded to sell the fields and gardens, one after another, till all of them were gone, and there remained nothing in his possession but the house in which he resided. He therefore wrenched out its marbles and its wood-work, and expended of the money which they produced, till he made an end of them all; and he considered in his mind, and found that he had nothing to expend: so he sold the house, and expended its price. Then, after that, the person who had bought of him the house came and said to him, See for thyself a lodging; for I am in want of my house.

He now considered in his mind, and found that he had nothing requiring a house except his wife, who had borne him a son and a daughter; and there remained not with him any servants; but there were only himself and his family. So he took for himself an apartment in one of the Ḥóshes,[6] and there he resided, after grandeur and delicacy, and abundance of servants and wealth; and he became destitute of one day's food. His wife therefore said to him, Of this I used to caution thee, saying to thee, Keep the charge of thy father. But thou wouldst not attend to my words; and there is no strength nor power but in God, the High, the Great! Whence shall the little children obtain food? Arise then, and go round to thy companions, the sons of the merchants. Perhaps they will give thee something wherewith we may sustain ourselves this day.—Accordingly he arose and repaired to his companions, one after another; but every one of them unto whom he went hid his face from him, and made him to hear painful words, such as he abhorred, and not one of them gave him any thing. So he returned to his wife, and said to her, They have not given me any thing. And upon this, she arose and went to her neighbours, to demand of them something wherewith they might sustain themselves that day. She repaired to a woman whom she knew in the former days, and when she went in to her, and her friend saw her state, she arose and received her kindly, weeping, and saying to her, What hath befallen you? She therefore related to her all that her husband had done; and her friend said to her, An ample and a friendly and free welcome to thee! Whatsoever thou requirest, demand it of me, without compensation.—And she replied, May God requite thee well! Then her friend gave her as much provision as would suffice her and her family for a whole month; and she took it, and returned to her abode. And when her husband saw her, he wept, and said to her, Whence obtainedst thou that? She answered him, From such a woman; for when I informed her of that which hath happened, she failed not in aught; but said to me, All that thou requirest, demand of me. And upon this, her husband said to her, Since thou hast this, I will repair to a place that I desire to visit. Perhaps God (whose name be exalted!) will dispel our trouble.

He took leave of her, and kissed his children, and went forth, not knowing whither to go. He walked on without stopping until he arrived at Booláḳ,[7] where he beheld a vessel about to depart to Dimyáṭ;[8] and a man who had been a companion of his father saw him; so he saluted him, and said to him, Whither desirest thou to go? He answered, I desire to go to Dimyáṭ; for I have companions respecting whom I would inquire, and whom I would visit: then I will return. And the man took him to his house, treated him honourably, made

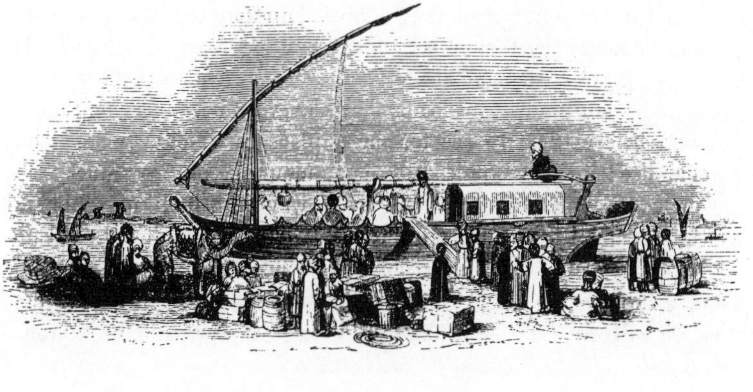

for him provisions for the voyage, and, having given him some pieces of gold, embarked him in the vessel that was going to Dimyáṭ. And when they arrived at that place, he landed, but knew not whither to go. While he was walking, however, a man of the merchants saw him, and was moved with sympathy for him, and he took him with him to his abode. He therefore remained with him some time; after which he said within himself, How long shall I thus reside in other men's houses? Then he went forth from the house of that merchant, and beheld a vessel about to sail to Syria; and the man with whom he was lodging prepared for him provisions for the voyage, and embarked him in that vessel, and it proceeded with its passengers until they arrived at the coast of Syria. 'Alee of Cairo there landed, and he journeyed until he entered Damascus; and as he was walking in its great thoroughfare-streets, a man of the benevolent saw him, and took him to his abode, where he remained some time. And after that, he went forth, and beheld a caravan about to journey to Baghdád; upon which it occurred to his mind that he should journey with it. So he returned to the merchant in whose abode he was residing, took leave of him, and went forth with the caravan; and God (whose perfection be extolled, and whose name be exalted!) moved a man of the merchants with sympathy for him: he therefore took him as his guest, and 'Alee ate and drank with him until there remained between them and Baghdád one day's journey. Then there came upon the caravan a party of robbers who were intercepters of the way, and they took all that was with them, and only a few escaped.

Every person of the caravan went to seek for a place of refuge. But as to 'Alee of Cairo, he repaired to Baghdád, and he arrived there at sunset: he reached not, however, the gate of the city until he beheld the gate-keepers about to close it. So he said to them, Let me come in to you. And they admitted him among them, and said to him, Whence hast thou come, and whither dost thou go? He answered, I am a man of the city of Cairo, and I brought with me merchandise and mules and loads, and slaves and young men, and I came on before them to see for me a place in which to deposit my merchandise; but as I preceded them, mounted on my mule, there met me a party of the intercepters of the way, who took my mule and my things, and I escaped not from them till I was about to yield my last breath. And they treated him with honour, and said to him, Thou art welcome. Pass the night with us until the morning, and then we will see for thee a place suitable to thee.—And he searched in his pocket, and found a piece of gold remaining of those which the merchant at Boolák had given him: so he gave that piece of gold to one of the gate-keepers, saying to him, Take this and change it, and bring us something to eat. He therefore took it, and repaired to the market, where he changed it, and he brought to 'Alee some bread and cooked meat; and he ate with them, and slept with them till the morning.

Then one of the gate-keepers took him and conducted him to a man of the merchants of Baghdád, to whom he related his story; and that man believed him, imagining that he was a merchant, and that he had brought with him loads of goods. So he took him up into his shop, treated him with honour, and sent to his abode, whence he caused to be brought for him a magnificent suit of his own clothing; and he conducted him into the bath.—I went with him, says 'Alee of Cairo, into the bath, and when we came forth, he took me and conducted me to his abode, where dinner was brought to us, and we ate, and enjoyed ourselves. He then said to one of his slaves, O Mes'ood, take thy master, and shew him the two houses that are in such a place, and whichever of them pleaseth him, give him the key of it, and come back. I therefore went with the slave until we came to a by-street wherein were three houses adjacent to each other, new and closed; and he opened the first house, and I looked over it, and we came forth, and went to the second, which he opened, and I looked over it. And he said to me, Of which of the two shall I give thee the key? I said to him, And to whom belongeth this great house? He answered, To us. So I said to him, Open it, that we may look over it. He replied, Thou hast no need of it.—Why so? I asked. He answered, Because it is haunted, and no one lodgeth in it but in the morning he is a corpse; and we open not its door to take forth the dead from it; but go up on the roof of one of the two other houses, and thence take it up; and on that account my master hath abandoned it, and said, I will not henceforth give it to any one.—But I said to him, Open it to me, that I may look over it. And I said within myself, This is what I desire. I will pass the night in it, and in the morning be a corpse, and be relieved from this state in which I now am.—So he opened it, and I entered it, and saw it to be a magnificent house, of which there existed not the like; and I said to the slave, I choose none but this house; therefore give me its key. But he replied, I will not give thee the key until I consult my master. —Then he went to his master, and said to him, The merchant of

Cairo saith, I will not lodge but in the great house.—He therefore arose, and came to 'Alee of Cairo, and said to him, O my master, thou hast no need of this house. 'Alee however replied, I will not lodge in any but it, and I care not for these words. So the man said to him, Write a voucher agreed upon between me and thee, that, if any thing happen to thee, I am not implicated with thee. 'Alee replied, So be it. And the merchant brought a Sháhid[9] from the Ḳáḍee's court, and wrote a voucher testifying against him, and, having taken it into his keeping, gave him the key. He therefore took it, and entered the house; and the merchant sent furniture to him with a slave, who spread it for him upon the maṣṭabah that was behind the door, and returned.

After that, 'Alee of Cairo arose and went within, and he saw a well in the court of the house, with a bucket over it: so he let it down into the well, and filled it, and performed the ablution with its contents, and recited his divinely-ordained prayers. Then he sat a little; and the slave came to him with the supper from the house of his master, bringing for him also a lamp and a candle and candlestick, and a basin and ewer, and a water-bottle; and he left him, and returned to his master's house. So 'Alee lighted the candle, and supped, and enjoyed himself, and performed the prayers of nightfall; after which he said within himself, Arise, go up-stairs, and take the bed, and sleep there, rather than here. Accordingly he arose, and took the bed, and carried it up-stairs; and he beheld a magnificent saloon, the ceiling of which was gilded, and its floor and its walls were cased with coloured marbles. He spread his bed, and sat reciting somewhat of the sublime Ḳur-án; and suddenly a person called to him and said to him, O 'Alee! O son of Ḥasan! shall I send down upon thee the gold?—And where, said 'Alee, is the gold that thou wilt send down? And he had not finished saying so when he poured down upon him gold as from a catapult; and the gold ceased not to pour down until it had filled the saloon. And when it was finished, the person said, Liberate me, that I may go my way; for my service is finished.

Upon this, 'Alee of Cairo said to him, I conjure thee by Allah the Great that thou inform me of the cause of [the descent of] this gold. And he replied, This gold was preserved for thee by a talisman from ancient times, and we used to come to every one who entered this house, and say to him, O 'Alee! O son of Ḥasan! shall we send down the gold? And he would fear at our words, and cry out;

whereupon we would descend to him and break his neck, and depart. But when thou camest, and we called thee by thy name and the name of thy father, and said to thee, Shall we send down the gold?—thou saidst to us, And where is the gold?—so we knew that thou wast its owner, and we sent it down. There remaineth also for thee a treasure in the land of El-Yemen; and if thou wilt journey and take it and bring it hither, it will be better for thee. And I desire of thee that thou liberate me, that I may go my way.—But 'Alee said, By Allah I will not liberate thee until thou shalt have brought hither to me that which is in the land of El-Yemen. He said, If I bring it to thee, wilt thou liberate me, and wilt thou liberate the servant of that treasure?—Yes, answered 'Alee. And he said to him, Swear to me. So he swore to him. And he was about to go; but 'Alee of Cairo said to him, I have yet one thing for thee to perform.—And what is it? he asked. 'Alee answered, I have a wife and children in Cairo, in such a place; and it is requisite that thou bring them to me, easily, without injury. And he replied, I will bring them to thee in a stately procession, and in a litter,[10] and with servants and other attendants, together with the treasure that we will bring thee from the land of El-Yemen, if it be the will of God, whose name be exalted!—Then he obtained permission of him to be absent three days, after which period he promised him that all that treasure should be in his possession; and he departed.

And in the morning, 'Alee searched about the saloon for a place in which to deposit the gold; and he saw a slab of marble at the edge of the leewán of the saloon, in which was a turning-pin. So he turned the pin, and the slab removed, and there appeared to him a door, which he opened, and he entered, and beheld a large treasury, in which were bags of linen, sewed. He therefore proceeded to take the bags and to fill them with the gold and put them into the treasury until he had removed all the gold and put it into the treasury, when he closed the door, and turned the pin; whereupon the slab of marble returned to its place. Then he arose and descended, and seated himself upon the maṣṭabah that was behind the door. And while he was sitting, a person knocked at his door; and he rose and opened it, and saw that this person was the slave of the owner of the house; and when the slave saw him there, he returned quickly to his master, to give him the good tidings. And on his coming to his master, he said to him, O my master, verily the merchant who hath taken up his lodging in the house that is haunted by the Jinn is well, in prosperity, and he is sitting upon the maṣṭabah that is behind the door. So his master arose, full of joy, and repaired to that house, taking with him the breakfast; and when he saw 'Alee of Cairo he embraced him, and kissed him between his eyes, and said to him, What hath God done unto thee? He answered, Well; and I slept not but up-stairs, in the saloon that is cased with marble. And the merchant said to him, Did any thing come to thee, or didst thou see aught?—No, answered 'Alee; I only recited as much as was easy to me of the sublime Ḳur-án, and slept until the morning, when I rose, and performed the ablution, and prayed, and descended and seated myself upon this maṣṭabah. And the merchant said, Praise be to God for thy safety! Then he arose and left him, and sent to him black slaves, and memlooks, and female slaves, and furniture, and they swept the house, above and below, and spread for him magnificent furniture; and there remained with him three memlooks and three male black slaves and four female slaves to serve him: the rest returned to the house of their master. And when the merchants heard of him, they sent to him presents of every precious thing, even of eatables and beverages and clothes, and took him with them into the market, and said to him, When will thy merchandise come? He answered them, After three days it will enter.

Then, when the three days had passed, the servant of the first treasure, who poured down to him the gold from the house, came to him and said to him, Arise, meet the treasure that I have brought thee from El-Yemen, and thy ḥareem, with whom is a portion of the treasure in the form of magnificent merchandise; and all who are with it, of mules and horses and camels, and servants and memlooks, all of them are of the Jánn. Now that servant had repaired to Cairo, where he found that the wife of 'Alee, and his children, during this period had become reduced to excessive nakedness and hunger; and he conveyed them from their place in a litter to the exterior of Cairo, and clad them in magnificent apparel, of the apparel that formed part of the treasure of El-Yemen. And when he came to 'Alee, and informed him of that news, he arose and repaired to the merchants, and said to them, Arise and go forth with us from the city to meet the caravan with which is our merchandise, and honour us by taking with you your ḥareems to meet our ḥareem. So they answered him, We hear and obey. They sent and caused their ḥareems to be brought, went forth all together, and alighted in one of the gardens of the city, where they sat conversing. And while they were thus engaged, lo, a dust rose in the midst of the desert. They therefore arose to see what was the cause of that dust; and it dispersed, and discovered mules and 'akkáms and farráshes and light-bearers,[11] who approached singing and dancing until they drew near; when the chief of the 'akkáms advanced to 'Alee of Cairo, kissed his hand, and said to him, O my master, we have been tardy in the way; for we desired to enter yesterday; but we feared the intercepters of the way; so we remained four days at our station, until God (whose name be exalted!) dispelled them from us. And the merchants arose and mounted their mules, and proceeded with the caravan; the ḥareems remaining behind with the ḥareem of 'Alee of Cairo until they mounted with them; and they entered in magnificent procession. The merchants wondered at the mules loaded with chests, and the women of the merchants wondered at the apparel of the wife of the merchant 'Alee, and at the apparel of her children, saying, Verily the like of this apparel existeth not in

the possession of the King of Baghdád or any other person of all the Kings and great men and merchants.

They ceased not to advance in their stately procession, the men with the merchant 'Alee of Cairo, and the women with his ḥareem, until they entered the house and alighted, and brought the mules with their loads into the midst of the court. Then they put down the loads, and stowed them in the magazines, and the ḥareems went up with the ḥareem of 'Alee to the saloon, and they saw it to be like a garden abounding with trees, spread with magnificent furniture. They sat in joy and happiness, and remained sitting until noon, when dinner was brought up to them, consisting of the best of viands and sweetmeats; and they ate, and drank excellent sherbet, and scented themselves after it with rose-water and perfume.[12] Then they took leave of him, and departed to their abodes, men and women. And when the merchants had returned to their dwellings, they sent to him presents according to their conditions. Their ḥareems also sent gifts to his ḥareem, until there had been brought to them an abundance of female slaves, and male black slaves, and memlooks, and of all kinds of things, such as grains, and sugar, and other goods incalculable. And as to the merchant of Baghdád, the owner of the house in which 'Alee was residing, he remained with him, and quitted him not; and he said to him, Let the slaves and the servants take the mules and other beasts into one of the houses, for the sake of rest. But 'Alee replied, They will set forth on their journey this night to such a place. And he gave them permission to go out from the city, that when the night should come they might set forth on their journey; and they scarcely believed his giving them permission to do so when they took leave of him and departed to the exterior of the city, and soared through the air to their abodes.

The merchant 'Alee sat with the owner of the house in which he resided until the expiration of a third of the night, when they separated, and the owner of the house repaired to his abode. Then the merchant 'Alee went up to his ḥareem, and saluted them, and said to them, What happened unto you after my departure, during this period? So his wife informed him of what they had suffered from hunger and nakedness and fatigue; and he said to her, Praise be to God

for safety! And how came you?—O my master, she answered, I was sleeping with my children last night, and suddenly one raised me from the ground, together with my children, and we soared through the air; but no injury befell us; and we ceased not to soar along until we alighted upon the ground in a place like an encampment of Arabs, where we saw loaded mules, and a litter borne by two great mules, surrounded by servants consisting of pages and men. So I said to them, Who are ye, and what are these loads, and in what place are we? And they answered, We are the servants of the merchant 'Alee of Cairo, the son of the merchant Ḥasan the Jeweller, and he hath sent us to take you and to convey you to him in the city of Baghdád. I said to them, Is the distance between us and Baghdád long or short? And they answered me, Short; for between us and it is no more than the space to be traversed during the darkness of night. Then they placed us in the litter, and the morning came not before we were with you, no injury having befallen us.—And who, said 'Alee, gave you this apparel? She answered, The chief of the caravan opened one of the chests that were upon the mules, took forth from it these garments, and attired me in a suit, and each of thy children in a suit; after which he locked the chest from which he took forth the dresses, and gave me its key, saying to me, Take care of it until thou give it to thy husband:—and here it is, carefully kept in my posses-

sion.—Then she produced it to him; and he said to her, Knowest thou the chest? She answered, Yes, I know it. So he arose and descended with her to the magazines, and shewed her the chests; and she said to him, This is the chest from which he took forth the dresses. He therefore took the key from her, and put it into the lock, and opened the chest; and he saw in it many dresses, together with the keys of all the other chests: so he took them forth, and proceeded to open the chests, one after another, and to amuse himself with a sight of their contents, consisting of treasured jewels and minerals, the like of which existed not in the possession of any of the Kings.

He then locked the chests, took their keys, and went up with his wife to the saloon, saying to her, This is of the bounty of God, whose name be exalted! And after this, he took her and led her to the marble slab in which was the turning pin, and he turned it, and opened the door of the treasury, and, entering with her, shewed her the gold that he had deposited in it; whereupon she said to him, Whence came to thee all this? He answered her, It came to me through the bounty of my Lord. And he related to her what had happened to him from first to last; on hearing which, she said to him, O my master, all this is through the blessing attendant upon the prayer of thy father, when he prayed for thee before his death, and said, I beg God that He cast thee not into affliction without granting thee speedy relief. So praise be to God (whose name be exalted!) for his giving thee relief, and making amends to thee by bestowing on thee more than hath been lost by thee! I conjure thee then by Allah, O my master, that thou return not to thy former ways of associating with those who are objects of suspicion. Be mindful of preserving the fear of God (whose name be exalted!) in private and in public.—She continued to admonish him, and he replied, I accept thine admonition, and beg God (whose name be exalted!) to remove far from us the wicked, and to adapt us to the obedience of Him, and to the compliancé with the precepts of his Prophet; may God bless and save him!

He lived with his wife and children a most comfortable life, and he took for himself a shop in the market of the merchants, placed in it some of the jewels and precious minerals, and sat in it, attended by his children and his memlooks, and became the greatest of the merchants in the city of Baghdád. So the King of Baghdád heard of him, and sent a messenger to him, desiring his presence; and when the messenger came to him, he said to him, Answer the summons of the King; for he desireth thee. And he replied, I hear and obey;—

and prepared a present for the King. He took four trays of red gold, and filled them with jewels and minerals, such as existed not in the possession of the Kings; and he took the trays, and went up with them to the King; and when he went in to him, he kissed the ground before him, and greeted him with a prayer for the continuance of his glory and blessings, addressing him in the best manner he could. The King said to him, O merchant, thou hast cheered our country by thy presence. And he replied, O King of the age, the slave hath brought thee a present, and hopeth that thou wilt in thy favour accept it. Then he placed the four trays before him; and the King uncovered them and examined them, and saw that the contents were jewels such as he possessed not, their value being equal to treasuries of wealth. He therefore said to him, Thy present is accepted, O merchant; and if it be the will of God (whose name be exalted!), we will recompense thee with the like of it. And 'Alee kissed the King's hands, and departed from him.

Then the King summoned his grandees, and said to them, How many of the Kings have demanded my daughter in marriage? They answered him, Many. And he said to them, Hath any one of them presented me with the like of this present? And they all answered, No; for there existeth not in the possession of any of them its like. And the King said, I beg of God (whose name be exalted!) that I may have the happiness of marrying my daughter to this merchant. Then what say ye?—They answered him, The thing should be as thou judgest. And he ordered the eunuchs to carry the four trays with their contents into his palace. He then had an interview with his wife, and put the trays before her; and she uncovered them, and saw in them things like which she possessed not a single piece. So she said to him, From which of the Kings is this? Probably it is from one of the Kings who have demanded my daughter in marriage.—He answered, No: but it is from a merchant of Cairo, who hath come unto us in this city; and when I heard of his coming, I sent to him a messenger to bring him to us that we might become acquainted with him, as we might probably find in his possession some jewels which we might purchase of him to fit out our daughter. He therefore obeyed our command, and brought us these four trays, which he offered us as a present; and I saw him to be a handsome young man, of dignified appearance, and perfect intelligence, and elegant form, almost like one of the sons of the Kings. And on my seeing him, my heart inclined to him, and my bosom became dilated at beholding him, and I desired to marry my daughter to him. I displayed the present to the great men of my kingdom, and said to them, How many of the Kings have demanded my daughter in marriage? And they answered, Many.—And hath any one of them, said I, brought me the like of that? To which they all answered, No, by Allah, O King of the age; for there existeth not in the possession of any one of them the like of that. And I said to them, I beg of God (whose name be exalted!) that I may have the happiness of marrying to him my daughter. What then say ye?—They answered, The thing should be as thou judgest. Now what sayest thou?—She answered him, The affair is for God to decide, and thee, O King of the age; and what God willeth is that which will be. And he replied, If it be the will of God (whose name be exalted!), we will not marry her but to this young man.

He passed the next night, and when the morning came, he went up to his court, and gave orders to bring the merchant 'Alee of Cairo, and all the merchants of Baghdád. So they all came, and when they presented themselves before the King, he commanded them to sit. They therefore seated themselves. He then said, Bring the Ḳáḍee of the court. And he came before him; and the King said to him, O Ḳáḍee, write the contract of my daughter's marriage to the merchant 'Alee of Cairo. But 'Alee of Cairo said, Pardon, O our lord the Sulṭán. It is not fit that a merchant like me be son-in-law of the King.—The King however replied, I have bestowed upon thee that favour, together with the office of Wezeer. Then he invested him with the robe of a Wezeer immediately; whereupon he seated himself on the chair of the Wezeer, and said, O King of the age, thou hast bestowed upon me this favour, and I am honoured by thy beneficence; but hear a word that I would say to thee. He replied, Say, and fear not. And he said, Since thy noble command hath been given to marry thy daughter, it is fit that she be married to my son.—Hast thou a son? asked the King.—Yes, answered 'Alee. And the King said, Send to him immediately. He replied, I hear and obey;—and he sent one of his memlooks to his son, and caused him to be brought; and when he came into the presence of the King, he kissed the ground before him, and stood respectfully. And the King, looking at him, saw him to be more lovely than his daughter, and more beautiful than she in stature, and justness of form, and in elegance and in every charm. He said to him, What is thy name, O my son? And he answered, O our lord the Sulṭán, my name is Ḥasan. And his age at that time was fourteen years. Then the King said to the Ḳáḍee,

Write the contract of the marriage of my daughter Ḥosn-el-Wujood[13] to Ḥasan the son of the merchant 'Alee of Cairo. So he wrote the contract of their marriage, and the affair was finished in the most agreeable manner; after which, every one who was in the court went his way, and the merchants went down behind the Wezeer 'Alee of Cairo until he arrived at his house, instated in the office of Wezeer; and they congratulated him on that event, and went their ways. He then entered the apartment of his wife, who, seeing him clad in the robe of a Wezeer, said to him, What is this? He therefore related to her the case from beginning to end, and said to her, The King hath married his daughter to Ḥasan my son. And she rejoiced at this exceedingly.

Then 'Alee of Cairo passed the night, and when the morning arrived he went up to the court, and the King met him graciously, and seated him by his side, treating him with especial favour, and said to him, O Wezeer, we desire to celebrate the festivity, and to introduce thy son to my daughter. 'Alee replied, O our lord the Sulṭán, what thou judgest to be well is well. And the King gave orders to celebrate the festivity. They decorated the city, and continued the festivity thirty days, in joy and happiness; and after the thirty days were ended, Ḥasan, the son of the Wezeer 'Alee, took the King's daughter as his wife, and was delighted with her beauty and loveliness. The King's wife, too, when she saw her daughter's husband, loved him greatly; and in like manner, she was exceedingly pleased with his mother. Then the King gave orders to build a palace for Ḥasan, the son of the Wezeer; and they built for him quickly a magnificent palace, in which he resided; and his mother used to remain with him some days, and then descend to her house. So the King's wife said to her husband, O King of the age, the mother of Ḥasan cannot reside with her son and leave the Wezeer, nor can she reside with the Wezeer and leave her son. He replied, Thou hast spoken truth. And he gave orders to build a third palace, by that of Ḥasan, the son of the Wezeer; and they built it in a few days; after which the King commanded to remove the goods of the Wezeer to that palace; and they did so; and the Wezeer took up his abode in it. The three palaces communicated, one with another: so when the King desired to speak with the Wezeer, he walked to him in the night, or sent to bring him; and in like manner did Ḥasan and his mother and his father. They ceased not to live together in an agreeable manner, and to pass a pleasant life, for a length of time.

After this, an illness attacked the King, and his malady increased: so he summoned the grandees of his kingdom, and said to them, A violent disease hath attacked me, and perhaps it is that which will occasion my death: I have therefore summoned you to consult you respecting an affair, and do ye give me the advice that ye judge to be good. They said, Respecting what wouldst thou consult us, O King? And he answered, I have become old, and have fallen sick, and am in fear for my kingdom after me, on account of the enemies; wherefore I desire that ye all agree in the choice of one, that I may inaugurate him as King during my life, and that ye may be at ease. To this they all replied, We all approve of the husband of thy daughter, Ḥasan, the son of the Wezeer 'Alee; for we have observed his good sense, and perfection and intelligence, and he knoweth the rank of the great and the small. The King said to them, And do ye approve of that? They answered, Yes. He said to them, Perhaps ye say that before me through a modest respect for me, and behind my back ye will say otherwise. But they all replied, By Allah our words are the same in public and in secret; they change not; and we approve of him with joyful hearts and dilated bosoms. He therefore said to them, If the affair be so, bring the Ḳáḍee of the holy law, and all the chamberlains and lieutenants and chief men of the kingdom, before me to-morrow, and we will finish the affair in the most agreeable manner. And they replied, We hear and obey.

They departed from him, and summoned all the 'Ulamà,[14] and the chief persons among the Emeers, and when the morning came, they went up to the court, and sent to the King, begging permission to come in to him; and he gave them permission. So they entered, and saluted him, and said, We have all come before thee. And the King said to them, O Emeers of Baghdád, whom do ye like to be King over you after me, that I may inaugurate him during my life in the presence of you all? They all answered, We have agreed to accept Ḥasan, the son of the Wezeer 'Alee, and husband of thy daughter. And he said, If the case be so, arise ye all, and bring him before me. So they all arose, and entered his palace, and said to him, Come with us to the King.—For what purpose? said he. And they answered him, For an affair advantageous to us and to thee. He therefore arose and proceeded with them until they went in to the King, when Ḥasan kissed the ground before him; and the King said to him, Sit, O my son. So he sat; and the King said to him, O Ḥasan, all the Emeers have petitioned in thy favour, and agreed to make thee King over them after me, and I desire to inaugurate thee during my life, in order to conclude the affair. But upon this, Ḥasan arose, and kissed the ground before the King, and said to him, O our lord the King, verily among the Emeers is he who is older than I, and of higher dignity: therefore release me from that affair. All the Emeers however said, We do not choose but that thou be King over us. He said to them, My father is older than I, and I and my father are the same, and it is not right to advance me above him. But his father replied, I do not approve of aught but that of which my brethren approve, and they have approved of thee, and agreed to have thee: oppose thou not the command of the King, nor the command of thy brethren. And Ḥasan hung down his head towards the ground, in modest respect for the King, and for his father. So the King said to them, Do ye approve of him? They answered, We do approve of him. And they all recited, in testimony thereof, seven times, the Opening Chapter of the Ḳur-án. Then the King said, O Ḳáḍee, write a legal voucher, testifying of these Emeers, that they have agreed to acknowledge, as Sulṭán, Ḥasan, the husband of my daughter, and that he shall be

King over them. He therefore wrote the voucher to that effect, and signed it, after they had all inaugurated him as King. The King did so likewise, and ordered him to sit upon the throne of the kingdom. After this, all arose, and kissed the hands of the King Ḥasan, the son of the Wezeer, and paid homage to him; and he exercised authority that day in an admirable manner, and conferred magnificent dresses of honour upon the grandees of the kingdom.

Then the court broke up, and Ḥasan went in to the father of his wife, and kissed his hands; and he said to him, O Ḥasan, be mindful to preserve the fear of God in thy conduct towards thy subjects. Ḥasan replied, Through thy prayer for me, O my father, God's guidance will be given me. He then entered his own palace, and his wife met him, with her mother and their dependants, and they kissed his hands, and said to him, May the day be blessed!—and they congratulated him on the dignity to which he had been raised. Then he arose and went from his palace into that of his father; and they rejoiced exceedingly at the favour which God had granted him in conferring upon him the sovereignty; and his father charged him to preserve the fear of God, and to act with clemency to his subjects. He passed the next night in joy and happiness until the morning; when he performed his divinely-ordained prayers, and finished his concluding supplication,[15] and went up to the court. All the troops also went up thither, and the dignitaries; and he judged among the people, commanding to act kindly, and forbidding iniquity, and he invested and displaced, and ceased not to exercise authority until the close of the day; whereupon the court broke up in the most agreeable manner, and the troops dispersed, each person going his way. Then Ḥasan arose and entered the palace; and he saw that the illness of his wife's father had become heavy upon him: so he said to him, No harm betide thee! And the old King opened his eyes, and said to him, O Ḥasan! He replied, At thy service, O my lord. And the old King said to him, Now hath the end of my life drawn near; therefore take care of thy wife and her mother, and preserve the fear of God, and an affectionate obedience to thy parents; stand in awe of the majesty of the Requiting King, and know that God commandeth justice and the doing of good. The King Ḥasan replied, I hear and obey.—Then the old King remained three days after that, and was admitted to the mercy of God, whose name be exalted! So they prepared his body for burial, and shrouded it, and performed for him recitations of portions and of the whole of the Ḳur-án until the end of the forty days;

—and the King Ḥasan, the son of the Wezeer, became absolute monarch. His subjects rejoiced in him, and all his days were happy, and his father ceased not to be chief Wezeer on his right hand, and he took another Wezeer on his left. His affairs were well ordered, and he remained King in Baghdád a long time; he was also blessed with three male children by the daughter of the old King, and they inherited the kingdom after him; and they passed a most comfortable and happy life, until they were visited by the terminator of delights and the separator of companions.—Extolled be the perfection of Him who is eternal, and in whose power it lieth to annul and to confirm![16]

NOTES TO CHAPTER NINETEENTH.

NOTE 1. "EL-MUṢṬAFÀ" is one of the names of Moḥammad, and signifies "the Elect."

NOTE 2. "When any one of you dies," said the Prophet, "you must not keep him in the house; but carry him quickly to his grave:"[1] and again, he said, "Be quick in lifting up a bier; for if the deceased be a good man, it is good to take him up quickly, and carry him to his grave, to cause the good to arrive at happiness; and if the deceased be a bad man, it is a wickedness which ye put from your neck." [2]

NOTE 3.—*Ceremonies observed after a Death.* Towards the eve of the first Friday after the funeral, and, often, early in the morning of the Thursday, the women of the family of the deceased repeat their wailing, in the house, accompanied by some of their female friends: male friends of the deceased also visit the house shortly before or after sunset; and three or four persons are hired to perform a recitation of the whole of the Ḳur-án. On the following morning, some or all of the members of the deceased's family, but chiefly the women, visit the tomb; they or their servants carrying palm-branches, and sometimes sweet basil, to lay upon it. The palm-branch is broken into several pieces, and these, or the leaves only, are placed on the tomb. Often, also, the visiters take with them some kind of food, as bread, pancakes, sweet cakes of different kinds, or dates, to distribute to the poor on this occasion. They recite the Opening Chapter of the Ḳur-án; or, if they can afford it, employ a person to recite first the Thirty-sixth Chapter, or a larger portion of the Ḳur-án; and many persons cause a recitation of the whole of the Ḳur-án to be performed at the tomb, or in the house, by men hired for that purpose.—These ceremonies are repeated on the same days of the next two weeks; and again on the eve and morning of the Friday which completes, or next follows, the first period of forty days[3] after the funeral; whence this Friday is called "El-Arba'een," or "Jum'at el-Arba'een."

NOTE 4. This is one of the instances in which coffee is mentioned in the Thousand and One Nights in a manner not to be mistaken; but perhaps by a copyist. The word

[1] Mishkát el-Maṣábeeḥ, vol. i. p. 387. [2] *Idem*, p. 374. [3] See Genesis, l. 3.

rendered "coffee-makers" is "ḳahwejeeyeh," plural of "ḳahwejee," a compound of Arabic and Turkish, pronounced by the Turks "ḳahvejee." It occurs also in the same passage in the Breslau edition.

NOTE 5. Er-Róḍah is a very pleasant island in the Nile, about two miles and a half in length, near Cairo; lying to the south-west of that city. Its name signifies "The Garden," &c. The Nilometer is at its southern extremity, of which a view is given, from one of my drawings, at page 550.

NOTE 6. The term "ḥósh" generally signifies "the court of a house;" but it is often applied, as in this case, to a court surrounded by mean lodgings, inhabited by persons of the lower orders.

NOTE 7. Booláḳ is the principal port of Cairo. It was founded, and became a considerable town, in the eighth century of the Flight (or the fourteenth of our era). The plain upon which it is situate arose in consequence of a gradual change in the course of the Nile, which formerly flowed very near by the western side of Cairo.

NOTE 8. Dimyáṭ is the town commonly called by us Damietta. Its name is generally pronounced by the modern Egyptians Dumyáṭ.

NOTE 9. See Note 48 to Chapter xi.

NOTE 10. A takhtarawán, described in Note 8 to Chapter viii.

NOTE 11. The terms "'akkám" and "farrásh" have been explained in Note 28 to Chapter xi. and Note 16 to Chapter x. By "light-bearers" are meant men who bear the kind of cresset described in Note 2 to Chapter xiii.

NOTE 12. See Note 8 to Chapter iii.

NOTE 13. "Ḥosn el-Wujood" signifies "the Beauty of the World." See Note 6 to Chapter xviii.

NOTE 14. "'Ulamà" is the plural of "'álim," which signifies a man of science or learning, but is a term more particularly given to a doctor of the law. European writers generally use the plural form of this appellation for the singular.

NOTE 15. See Note 18 to Chapter x.

NOTE 16. This story is followed by an anecdote, of which I here give a translation.

Anecdote of a Townsman and a Bedaweeyeh.

It is related that a man of the pilgrims slept a long sleep, and then awoke, and saw no trace of the other pilgrims. So he arose and walked on; but he wandered from the way, and he proceeded until he saw a tent, and an old woman at its door, and he found by her a dog asleep. He approached the tent, saluted the old woman, and begged of her some food; whereupon she said to him, Go to yon valley, and catch as many serpents as will suffice thee, that I may broil some of them for thee. The man replied, I dare not catch serpents, and I never ate them. The old woman therefore said, I will go with thee, and catch some of them, and fear thou not. Then she went with him, and the dog followed her, and she caught as many of the serpents as would suffice, and proceeded to broil some of them. The pilgrim could not refrain from eating; for he feared hunger and emaciation: so he ate of those serpents. And after this, being thirsty, he demanded of the old woman some water to drink; and she said to him, Go to the spring, and drink of it. Accordingly he went to the spring; but he found its water bitter; yet he could not refrain from drinking of it, notwithstanding

its exceeding bitterness, on account of the violence of his thirst. He therefore drank, and then returned to the old woman, and said to her, I wonder at thee, O thou old woman, and at thy residing in this place, and thy feeding thyself with this food, and thy drinking of this water.—How then, said the old woman, is your country? He answered her, Verily in our country are spacious and ample houses, and ripe and delicious fruits, and abundant sweet waters, and excellent viands, and fat meats, and numerous sheep, and every thing good, and blessings of which the like exist not save in the Paradise that God (whose name be exalted!) hath described to his just servants.—All this, replied the old woman, I have heard; but tell me, have you any Sulṭán who ruleth over you, and oppresseth in his rule while ye are under his authority; and who, if any one of you committeth an offence, taketh his wealth, and destroyeth him; and who, if he desire, turneth you out from your houses, and eradicateth you utterly? The man answered her, That doth sometimes happen. And the old woman rejoined, If so, by Allah, that dainty food and elegant life and those delightful comforts, with oppression and tyranny, are penetrating poison; and our food, with safety, is a salutary antidote. Hast thou not heard that the most excellent of boons, after El-Islám, are safety and health.[4]

Now these may be through the justice of the Sulṭán, the vicegerent of God upon his earth, and through his good policy. The Sulṭán of former times loved to be distinguished by the lowest degree of awfulness; because, when his subjects saw him, they feared him: but the Sulṭán of this age loveth to be distinguished by the most perfect policy and the utmost awfulness; because men now are not like those of former days. This our age is one of a people opprobrious, and greatly calamitous; since they are noted for folly, and for hardness of heart, and are bent upon vehement hatred, and upon enmity. Therefore, if the Sulṭán (in God, whose name be exalted, be our refuge!) should be weak among them, or not characterized by policy and awfulness, no doubt that would be the cause of the ruin of the country. And among the proverbs is this:—The oppression of the Sulṭán for a hundred years, rather than the oppression of the subjects, one over another, for a single year.—And when the subjects oppress, God setteth over them an oppressive Sulṭán and a violent King. Thus it is related in the histories, that there was sent up to El-Ḥajjáj the son of Yoosuf,[5] one day, a petition wherein was written, Fear God, and oppress not God's servants with every kind of oppression. And when he had read the petition, he ascended the pulpit (and he was eloquent), and he said, O ye people, verily God (whose name be exalted!) hath set me over you on account of your actions; and if I die, ye will not be free from oppression with these wicked actions; for God (whose name be exalted!) hath created

---

[4] The following words appear to be the narrator's.

[5] See Note 140 to Chapter x.

many like me; and if I be not, there will be one worse than I, and more severe in oppression, and more violent in impetuosity. As the poet hath said,—

There is no hand but God's hand is above it, nor oppressor that shall not meet with an oppressor.

—Oppression is feared; but justice is the best of all qualities. We beg God to amend our states.

[The above anecdote is followed by the Story of Taweddud, the Learned Slave-girl, ending with part of the four hundred and sixty-second Night. This story almost entirely consists in a display of Taweddud's profound knowledge in religion, &c., in which she surpassed the most eminent professors in an examination before Hároon Er-Rasheed; and as it would not only require a volume of commentary, but be extremely tiresome to most readers of the present work, I omit it.

Next is a series of eighteen anecdotes (or rather fictions related as facts), ending with part of the four hundred and eighty-second Night. From these I have selected for translation only four. Almost all of them relate to saints and miracles. The first of those which I translate is preceded in the original by two of a similar kind.]

A Tyrannical King and the Angel of Death.

A tyrannical King, one of the Kings of the Children of Israel, was one day sitting upon his throne, and he beheld a man who had entered the door of the palace, having an offensive form and a terrible appearance. So the King shuddered at his sudden intrusion upon him, and was terrified at his appearance; and he sprang up in his face, and said, Who art thou, O man, and who gave thee permission to intrude upon me, and who commanded thee to come to my abode? He answered, The Lord of the abode commanded me, and none excludeth me, nor do I require permission to go in unto Kings, neither do I fear the rule of a Sulṭán, nor the multitude of guards: I am he whom no tyrant hindereth, and none can escape from my grasp: I am the terminator of delights and the separator of companions. And when the King heard these words, he fell upon his face, a tremour crept through his body, and he fell down in a fit; and on his recovery he said, Art thou the Angel of Death? He answered, Yes. And the King said, I conjure thee by Allah to give me one day's delay, that I may beg forgiveness of my sin, and seek pardon of my Lord, and restore the wealth that is in my treasuries to its owners, so that I may not suffer the affliction of a reckoning with respect to it, and the misery of punishment on account of it. But the Angel of Death replied, Far, far from thee be that! Thou hast no way of attaining that wish. How can I grant thee a delay when the days of thy life are reckoned, and thy breaths are numbered, and thy moments are fixed and written?—The King said, Grant me an hour's delay. He replied, Verily the hour is included in the account, and it hath past while thou wast heedless, and hath expired while thou wast careless. Thou hast fulfilled the number of thy breaths, save that there remaineth to thee one breath only.—And the King said, Who will be with me when I am removed to my grave? He answered, Nought will be with thee but thy work.[6] The King replied, I have [done] no work. And the Angel of Death said, Without doubt thine abode will be in the fire; and thy destination, to suffer the anger of the Omnipotent.—Then he seized his soul: so he tumbled from his throne, and fell to the ground; and a clamour arose among the people of his kingdom; their voices were raised, and their cries and weeping were loud; and had they known the indignation that he had gone to endure from his Lord, their weeping for him had been greater, and their lamentation had been more violent and more abundant.

---

[6] See foot-note in page 456 of this volume.

Advantages of Piety and Industry.

There was, among the Children of Israel, a good man, who applied himself diligently to the worship of God, and abstained from worldly enjoyments, discarding them from his heart; and he had a wife who aided him in his pursuit, and who always obeyed him. They lived by making trays and fans,[7] working all the day; and at the close of the day, the man went forth with the things that he had made in his hand, and walked with them along the streets and roads, seeking a purchaser, to whom to sell them; and they fasted continually.[8] Now one day[9] the man went forth as usual, and an event befell him which constrained him to throw himself from the top of a lofty house, in order to avoid an act of disobedience unto his Lord; but God sent to him an angel, who bore him upon his wings, and set him down upon the ground in safety, without any injury happening to him. And when he rested upon the ground, he praised God (to whom be ascribed might and glory!) for the protection which He had afforded him, and the mercy that He had granted him, and returned without any obstacle to his wife. He had been long absent from her, and entered bringing nothing with him; so she asked him respecting the cause of his tardiness, and respecting the things which he had taken forth in his hand, and as to what he had done with them, and how he had returned without any thing. He therefore informed her of the temptation that had happened to him, and that he had thrown himself down from that place, and God had saved him. And his wife said, Praise be to God who hath averted from thee the temptation, and interposed between thee and the calamity! Then she said, O man, verily the neighbours have been accustomed to observe that we light our oven every night, and if they see us this night without fire, they will know that we are destitute. Thankfulness to God requireth the concealment of our poverty, and the conjoining of the fast of this night with that of the past day, and spending it in the service of God, whose name be exalted!—Accordingly she arose and went to the oven, filled it with firewood, and set light to it to delude the women who were her neighbours; and she recited these verses:—

I will conceal the desire and the griefs that I suffer, and will light my fire to delude my neighbours.
I approve of that which my Lord hath decreed: perhaps He will see my submission, and approve me.

After this, she and her husband arose, and performed the ablution, and began to pray. But, lo, one of her female neighbours begged permission to light from their oven. They therefore said to her, Go to the oven, and do as thou desirest. And when the woman drew near to the oven to take the fire, she called out, O such-a-one! (mentioning the name of the woman of the place) come to thy bread before it burneth. So she said to her husband, Heardest thou what this woman said? And he replied, Arise and see. She arose, therefore, and went to the oven, and, lo, it was filled with fine white bread; and she took the cakes of bread and went in to her husband, thanking God (to whom be ascribed might and glory!) for the abundant good, and great favour, which He had bestowed. They ate of the bread, and drank some water, and praised God, whose name be exalted! Then the woman said to her husband, Come, let us supplicate God (whose name be exalted!): perhaps He will favour us with something that will render us independent of the trouble necessary to obtain our livelihood, and of the fatigue of working, and will aid us to employ ourselves in his worship and to occupy

---

7 The former are made of rushes, &c.: the latter, of palm-leaves or of feathers.

8 That is, every day; eating only in the night. I remember a man in Cairo who did so, except on the "Two Festivals," when fasting is unlawful; and other instances are mentioned by historians.

9 A portion of my original I here omit.

ourselves with his service. He replied, Well. So the man supplicated his Lord, and the woman said Amen to his supplication; and, lo, the roof clove asunder; and there descended a ruby, which illuminated the chamber by its lustre; whereupon they increased in their thanksgiving and praise. They were greatly rejoiced with that ruby, nd said as many prayers as God (whose name be exalted!) willed.[10] Then, at the close of the night, they slept; and the woman saw in her sleep as though she entered Paradise, and beheld many pulpits ranged in order, and chairs set; whereupon she said, What are these pulpits, and what are these chairs? She was answered, These are the pulpits of the prophets, and these are the chairs of the just and the good.—And where, said she, is the chair of my husband, such-a-one? She was answered, It is this. And she looked at it, and, lo, in its side was a hole. She therefore said, What is this hole? And she was answered, It is the hole of the ruby that descended upon you from the roof of your house.—So she awoke weeping and mourning for the defect of the chair of her husband among the chairs of the just; and she said, O man, supplicate thy Lord to restore this ruby to its place; for the endurance of hunger and poverty during the days that are few will be a lighter matter than the hole in thy chair among the people of excellencies. And the man supplicated his Lord, and, lo, the ruby flew up to the roof, while they looked at it; and they ceased not to live in their poverty and devotion until they met God, to whom be ascribed might and glory

Anecdote of a Muslim *Warriour and a Christian Maiden.*

The Prince of the Faithful, 'Omar the son of El-Khaṭṭáb, sent an army of the Muslims against the enemy, in Syria, and they besieged vehemently one of their fortresses; and there were among the Muslims two men, brothers, to whom God had given impetuosity and boldness against the enemy, so that the lord of that fortress said to his auxiliaries, and to his heroes who were before him, If these two Muslims were made prisoners, or slain, I should suffice you against the rest of the Muslims. They ceased not to set snares for these two men, and to employ stratagems against them, laying ambushes, and increasing the number of the men in the lurking-places, until one of the two Muslims was taken prisoner, and the other was slain a martyr. So the captive Muslim was carried to the lord of that fortress; and when the latter saw him, he said, Verily the slaughter of this man would be an evil, and his return to the Muslims would be a calamity. I wish that he would embrace the Christian faith, to be an auxiliary and a helper to us. And one of his Baṭreeḳs[11] said, O Emeer, I will seduce him so that he shall apostatize from his religion; for the Arabs are exceedingly fond of women, and I have a daughter endowed with loveliness and perfect beauty: so, if he see her, he will be seduced by her. The Emeer therefore said, He is committed unto thee: then convey him away.

Accordingly he conveyed him to his abode, and clad the damsel in attire which increased her beauty and loveliness; after which, he took the man into the house, and caused the food to be brought; and the Christian damsel stood before him as a maid serving her master and waiting for him to give her some command which she should perform. And when the Muslim saw what had befallen him, he kept himself from sin by seeking refuge with God (whose name be exalted!); he closed his eyes, and occupied himself with the worship of his Lord, and reciting the Ḳur-án. Now he had an excellent voice, and an effective talent in the use of it; and the Christian damsel was affected with a violent love for him, and became greatly enamoured of him; and this

---

[10] That is, very many.

[11] "Baṭreeḳ," or "Biṭreeḳ," (from "patricius") is a title which was formerly given by the Arabs to a Christian general; according to the Ḳámoos, to one who commanded ten thousand men. It should not be confounded with "Baṭreek" or "Baṭrak," which signify a "Patriarch."

state of affairs continued seven days, until the damsel said, Would that he may consent to my embracing El-Islám! And when her patience failed, and her heart was contracted, she threw herself down before him, and said, I conjure thee by thy religion that thou hear my words! He replied, And what wouldst thou say? She answered, Propose to me El-Islám. So he proposed it to her, and she became a Muslimeh. Then she purified herself, and he taught her how to pray; and when she had done so, she said, O my brother, verily my embracing El-Islám was on thine account, and from my wish to have thee near unto me. He replied, El-Islám forbiddeth marriage unless there be two legal witnesses, and a dowry, and a guardian;[12] and I find not the two witnesses, nor the guardian, nor the dowry; but if thou contrive means of our going forth from this place, I may hope to arrive in the abode of the Muslims, and I will make a covenant with thee that I will have no wife among the Muslimehs but thee. So she said, I will contrive a stratagem to accomplish that. She then called her father and her mother, and said to them, Verily the heart of this Muslim hath become softened, and he desireth to embrace the faith; and I will grant him the accomplishment of that which he desireth of me. He hath said, however, This shall not happen unto me in a town where my brother was killed; but if I go forth from it, that my heart may be diverted, I will do as thou desirest. No harm will ensue if ye send me forth with him to another town; for I am a surety to you and to the King for the accomplishment of that which ye desire.

So her father went to their Emeer, and informed him; and he was greatly rejoiced at that, and gave orders to send her forth with him to the town that she had mentioned. Accordingly they went forth, and when they had arrived at the town, and remained the rest of the day, and the darkness of night overshadowed them, they departed, and pursued their way, like as one of the poets hath said,—

They said, The time of our departure hath drawn near. I replied, How oft shall I be threatened with departure?
I have nothing to do but to cross the waste, and to traverse the earth, mile after mile.
If the beloved journey towards another land, I travel thither, a son of the road:
I make my desire my director to her, and it sheweth me the way without other guide.

And they proceeded throughout that night. The young man had mounted a swift horse, and placed her behind him; and he ceased not to traverse the earth until morning was near, when he turned with her from the road, and set her down; and they performed the ablution, and recited the morning-prayers. But while they were thus engaged, they heard the clashing of weapons, and the clinking of bits and bridles, and the voices of men, and the sounds of the hoofs of horses. So he said to her, O such-a-one (mentioning her name), this is a troop of the Christians in pursuit, which hath overtaken us: what then shall be our resource, when the horse hath become wearied and jaded so that he cannot stir a step? But she replied, Wo to thee! Art thou alarmed and afraid?—He said, Yes.—Where then, she rejoined, is the power of thy Lord, of which thou toldest me, and his succour to those who seek it? Come, let us humble ourselves before Him, and supplicate Him: perhaps He will grant us his succour, and make us to participate in his gracious protection: extolled be his perfection, and exalted be his name!—And he replied, Excellent, by Allah, is that which thou hast said! Accordingly they began to humble themselves before God (whose name be exalted!), and he recited these verses:—

Verily I am hourly in need of thine assistance, and should be though a crown were placed upon my head.
Thou art my greatest want, and if my hand obtained what I desire, I should have no wants remaining.

---

[12] See Note 39 to Chapter iv. (vol. i. pp. 285 and 286).

Thou hast not any thing that Thou withholdest; for the flood of thy munificence floweth copiously and in torrents;
But I am excluded by my transgression: yet resplendent is the light of thy pardon, O Clement!
O Dispeller of anxiety, remove my affliction! for who but Thyself can dispel this anxiety?

And while he was supplicating, and the damsel was saying Amen to his supplication, and the trampling of the horses was approaching them, the young man heard the voice of his brother the martyr, saying, O my brother, fear not nor grieve; for the approaching troop is the troop of God, and it is his Angels, whom He hath sent unto you to witness your marriage. Verily God hath gloried in you before his Angels, and given you the recompense of the blessed and the martyrs, and contracted for you the earth, so that in the morning thou wilt be among the mountains of El-Medeeneh. And when thou meetest 'Omar the son of El-Khaṭṭáb (may God be well pleased with him!), greet him with salutation from me, and say to him, May God recompense thee well for the Muslims; for thou hast given good counsel, and laboured with diligence.—Then the Angels raised their voices, saluting him and his wife, and said, Verily God (whose name be exalted!) decreed her in marriage to thee before the creation of your father Adam (on whom be peace!) by two thousand years. And upon this they experienced joy and happiness, and security and gladness: confidence was increased, and the guidance of the pious was confirmed: and when daybreak came, they performed the morning-prayers.

Now 'Omar the son of El-Khaṭṭáb (may God be well pleased with him!) used to perform the morning-prayers in the darkness before dawn; and sometimes he entered the place of prayer in the mosque, followed by two men, and began with the Chapter of Cattle,[13] or the Chapter of Women;[14] whereupon the sleeper awoke, and he who would perform the ablution performed it, and he who was at a distance came so that the first rek'ah was not completed before the mosque was filled with people. Then he

[13] The sixth Chapter of the Ḳur-án.

[14] The fourth Chapter of the same.

performed the second rek'ah with the recitation of a light chapter, and doing it quickly. But on that day, he recited in the first rek'ah a light chapter, doing it quickly, and in like manner in the second; and when he had pronounced the salutations,[15] he looked towards his companions, and said, Come forth with us that we may meet the bride-groom and bride. So his companions wondered, and understood not his words; and he advanced, with them following him, until he went forth to the gate of the city.

The young man, as soon as the light appeared to him, and he beheld the standards of El-Medeeneh, advanced towards the gate, with his wife behind him; and 'Omar and the Muslims his companions met him and saluted him. And when they entered the city, 'Omar (may God be well pleased with him!) gave orders that a feast should be prepared; and the Muslims came and ate. The young man entered with his bride; and God (whose name be exalted!) blessed him by her with children who fought in the way of God,[16] and kept their genealogies, because they gloried in them; and they ceased not to pass a most comfortable life, and to enjoy the most perfect happiness, until they were visited by the terminator of delights and the separator of companions.

The Justice of Providence.

A certain prophet employed himself in devotion upon a lofty mountain, beneath which ran a spring of water; and during the day he used to sit upon the summit of the mountain, so that people saw him not. There he repeated the praises of God (whose name be exalted!), and saw such persons as came to drink at the spring. And as he was one day sitting looking towards the spring, he beheld a horseman, who approached, and alighted from his horse, put down a leathern bag that was slung to his neck, and rested, and drank of the water; after which he departed, leaving the leathern bag, in which were pieces of gold. And, lo, a man came to drink of the water, and he took the leathern bag with the money, and drank of the water, and departed in safety. Then there came after him a man who was a wood-cutter, bearing a heavy bundle of firewood upon his back, and he seated himself by the spring, to drink of the water. But, lo, the horseman first mentioned approached in a state of distress, and he said to the wood-cutter, Where is the leathern bag that was here? He answered, I know nothing of it. And the horseman drew his sword, struck the wood-cutter, and slew him; and he searched in his clothes, and found nothing: so he left him, and went his way.

And that prophet said, O Lord, one person took a thousand pieces of gold, and another hath been slain unjustly. But God said to him by revelation, Occupy thyself with thy devotion; for the government of the kingdom is not thine affair. Verily the father of this horseman had taken by force a thousand pieces of gold of the property of the father of this man; so I have put the son in possession of his father's property: and verily the wood-cutter had slain the father of this horseman; wherefore I have enabled the son to take retaliation.—And thereupon that prophet said, There is no deity but Thou! Extolled be thy perfection! Thou art all-knowing with respect to secret things![17]

[Next to the series of anecdotes from which the above are selected, follows the Story of Ḥásib Kereem-ed-Deen,[18] or rather, a combination of the stories of Ḥásib, Bulooḳiyà, and Jánsháh, ending with the five hundred and thirty-sixth Night. It is

---

[15] At the end of his prayers. See Note 8 to Chapter xii.

[16] That is, for the defence of religion.

[17] This prophet was Moses. The story is also related by El-Ḳazweenee, in the preface to his 'Ajáïb el-Makhlooḳát. For a better one of the same kind, more agreeing with Parnell's "Hermit," see the Ḳur-án, ch. xviii. vv. 64 *et seqq.*, commencing, "And [coming to the rock] they found one of our servants."

[18] In the translations derived (through the medium of the German) from Von Hammer's called "Jamasp."

mainly a compound of the most extravagant absurdities, and would, I think, be extremely tedious to many readers of the present translation, with the exception of the portion relating to Jánsháh; but this is similar in its general character, and in the incidents upon which it is chiefly founded, to the Story of Ḥasan of El-Baṣrah, which is one that I purpose to include in this work. I therefore pass on to the five hundred and thirty-seventh Night, with which commences the Story of Es-Sindibád of the Sea (the famous Voyager) and Es-Sindibád of the Land.

The stories which I omit in these volumes I do not consider destitute of interest or value, nor should I regard them, with the exception of a few, as unworthy of being presented to English readers, if some were abridged, and considerable *alterations* were made in others, when the *omission* of gross passages would render them incoherent; but even if they were thus abridged and altered, I should not think it advisable to introduce them in this collection, which is designed to comprise no tales that are greatly inferior in interest to those in the old version.]

END OF THE SECOND VOLUME.